The Complete Book of

MOTHERCRAFT

The Complete Book of

MOTHERCRAFT

*A Collection of Expert Advice
for Successful Parenthood*

With Contributions From
TWENTY-FIVE LEADING SPECIALISTS

**Physicians, Pediatricians, Psychologists,
Psychiatrists, Educators, Gynecologists,
and Obstetricians — Experts in Every
Branch of the Care of Child and Mother**

PUBLISHED FOR PARENTS' INSTITUTE
by Greystone Press

COPYRIGHT 1952 BY

THE GREYSTONE PRESS

100 SIXTH AVENUE

NEW YORK 13, N. Y.

Acknowledgments

A volume so wide in scope as *The Complete Book of Mothercraft* would never have been possible without the active assistance and cooperation of scores of persons and organizations, both public and private, that take a special interest in the welfare of mother and child. For making available valuable explanatory photographs, the Publishers wish to salute in particular the United States Children's Bureau, the Play Schools Association of New York City, the National Safety Council, the New York City Board of Education, the New York Maternity Center Association, the American Dental Association, the Blue Cross Hospital Service Plan, the Cleveland Health Museum, the Cleanliness Bureau, the Carnation Company, the Davol Rubber Company, the Dennison Manufacturing Company, the Eastman Kodak Company, the Children's Record Guild, the Evaporated Milk Association, Gerber's Baby Foods and Miss Lucille Shearwood, General Foods (Baker's Cocoa), the Michigan Department of Health, the National Board of Fire Underwriters, the National Foundation for Infantile Paralysis, the National Film Board of Canada (and the Board's Miss Janet Scellen), the Scott Paper Company, E. R. Squibb and Sons and the Standard Oil Company (N.J.). The value of this work has been considerably enhanced through the gracious consent of the following publishers, organizations, and/or authors to the use in these pages of the copyright selections listed: American Medical Association: "Painless Childbirth" by Abraham Tamis; "The Facts About Adoption" by Frank Howard Richardson; "A Cure For Dawdlers," "Let Your Child Have His Say," "Naughtiness is Preventable," and "A Summer Camp," by Elizabeth B. Hurlock, from *Today's Health (Hygeia)*; copyright 1949, 1950, 1951, by American Medical Association. Appleton-Century-Crofts, Inc. and McIntosh and Otis: "Indoor Fun for Mother and Child," pages 673-693 from *Things to Make from Odds and Ends* by Jessie Robinson copyright 1945 by Jessie Robinson. Child Study Association of America: Excerpts from *Aggressiveness in Children* by Edith Atkin, copyright 1950; *Discipline Through Affection* by Aline B. Auerbach and *What Makes A Good Home* by Anna W. M. Wolf, copyright, 1951; all three copyright by the Child Study Association of America, 132 E. 74 St., New York 21, N. Y., from which these writings are individually available in pamphlet form. *Family Circle:* "Start Your Child's Art Experience Early" by Victor D'Amico, copyright 1950. Harper & Brothers: "Natural Childbirth" from *Childbirth Without Fear* by Grantly Dick Read, copyright 1944 by Grantly Dick Read; "Learning the Uses of Money" from *We the Parents* by Sidonie Matsner Gruenberg, copyright 1930, 1948, by Sidonie Matsner Gruenberg. Houghton Mifflin Company: "The First Against the Second Child" from *Father of the Man* by W. Allison Davis and Robert J. Havighurst, copyright 1947 by W. Allison Davis and Robert J. Havighurst. The John Day Company: "The Priceless Privilege of Parenthood" from *Home Guidance for Young Children* by Grace Langdon, copyright 1931, 1946, by Grace Langdon Ackerman. New York *Sunday Times* and Dr. Arnold Gesell: "What We Do and Don't Know About Children" by Dr. Arnold Gesell, from New York *Sunday Times Magazine*, May 26, 1946. Public Affairs Committee, Inc.: Excerpts from *Comics, Radio, Movies and Children* by Josette Frank, copyright 1949 by the Public Affairs Committee, Inc. Science Research Associates: Excerpts from *Self-Understanding: A First Step to Understanding Children*, a Better Living Booklet by William C. Menninger, copyright 1951 by Science Research Associates. Simon and Schuster, Inc.: "Weaning or Taking the Baby Off the Breast" from *The Baby Manual* by Herman N. Bundesen, copyright 1944 by Herman N. Bundesen. The Viking Press: "The Nursery School" and "When Your Child Does Not Go to Nursery School" from *How to Help Your Child in School* by Mary and Lawrence K. Frank, copyright 1950 by Mary and Lawrence K. Frank. The National Association for Mental Health: "When a Child Still Sucks His Thumb," "When a Child Still Wets," "When a Child Masturbates," from *Some Special Problems of Children* by Nina Ridenour, in collaboration with Isabel Johnson, copyright 1947 by New York Committee on Mental Hygiene of the State Charities Aid Association. Beatrice Landeck: "How Can I Help My Child be Musical" from *Children and Music* by Beatrice Landeck, published by William Sloane Associates, copyright 1952. The Indiana State Department of Public Instruction: "The Handicapped, Exceptional or 'Different' Child," from "Is Your Child Exceptional . . . Different from Other Children?" by Verna S. Carlisle, published 1951. The Greystone Press: "Teaching Your Child About Sex" by George Gardner and "Preparing Your Daughter for Womanhood" by Phyllis Blanchard, from *Every Woman's Standard Medical Guide*, copyright 1948, 1949, 1951, by The Greystone Press; "Diseases of Childhood" from *The Family Physician*, by Drs. Herman Pomeranz and Irvin S. Koll, copyright 1951 by The Greystone Press. The Children's Record Guild: "Music's Place in the Child's Life," from *Your Child Is Musical*. The New York Committee on Mental Health and the New York State Charities Aid Association: *Avoiding Behavior Problems* by Benjamin Spock, M.D., prepared by Bureau of Child Hygiene of the City of New York Department of Health, and reprinted in part from the *Journal of Pediatrics*, October 1945. The superb work done by the various agencies of the United States Government—in particular, the Children's Bureau and the Department of Agriculture—has been drawn upon, too, and to them and their experts acknowledgment is made. Chester Lawrence, distinguished specialist in the field of literature for parents, teachers, and children, performed the vast task of planning, preparing and coordinating the manuscript of *The Complete Book of Mothercraft*. It was developed in editorial consultation with Frederick Drimmer, and manufactured under the supervision of Mort Dorchin. Many others not individually named also gave generously of their time and effort, and their contribution is gratefully remembered.

Manufactured in The United States of America

About This Book

IN THE demands they make upon your body and soul, few careers are more exacting than that of the parent. At every stage in your children's development—almost from the day they are conceived until they have reached adulthood—perplexing problems are certain to confront you. Often they are small, worrisome ones, but every now and then they overwhelm you with their implications. To help you solve these problems quickly, pleasantly, and competently is the purpose of this anthology. A guide to successful parenthood, it has been planned to show you how to make your children healthy, happy, and secure, with a minimum of the emotional wear-and-tear, the drudgery, and the doubts that are the lot of most mothers and fathers. It is dedicated to the principle that parenthood can and should be fun, and that happy parents make happy children.

This book will prove valuable to you for many reasons. Here are just a few of them:

It is authoritative. The specialists whose advice is presented to you in this book include distinguished physicians, pediatricians, psychologists, psychiatrists, educators, and gynecologists—experts in every branch of the care of child and mother. Among them are Dr. Arnold Gesell, founder of the Yale School of Medicine's famous Clinic of Child Development; Dr. Herman N. Bundesen, Director of the Chicago Board of Health; Dr. Benjamin Spock, of the Mayo Foundation; Sir Grantly Dick Read, eminent developer of the modern method of natural childbirth; Dr. William C. Menninger, of the Menninger Foundation; Lawrence K. Frank, of the Caroline Zachry Institute for Human Development, and many others equally distinguished, whose names appear at the ends of the chapters in this volume. Wherever a chapter is unsigned, in general it is a composite work, written by a group of experts.

It is complete and comprehensive. This book will be of help to you whether your child is still unborn or is of high-school age. It takes you through the entire range of Mothercraft, from prenatal care right through infancy, the preschool years, the school years, and adolescence. To each of these subjects a complete section is devoted. A sixth section takes up in detail a multitude of special problems of interest to parents, such as

5

aggressiveness, exceptional children, art and music for the child, sex education of children, first aid, and medical care. The medical chapters of this volume, although unusually detailed, are not intended to supplant your physician, but rather to give you the factual background you need so that you can co-operate with him to your fullest advantage.

It is up-to-date. Here you will find the most modern approved methods taught by child-care experts, incorporating the latest findings in medicine, psychology, nutrition, education, and other fields. How to judge television programs and comic books, choosing a baby sitter, how to select a nursery school, new ways of toilet training, discipline through affection, how to deal with children's fears—these and other subjects you have been reading about recently in newspapers and magazines are explained here in full.

It is easy to understand. This is a book for mothers and fathers. It is written in clear, simple language, and in an interesting, human way. Where medical and other scientific terms cannot be avoided, they are explained in words that anyone can understand. Photographs and drawings further make the authors' meaning unmistakable.

It is easy to use. As already mentioned, the vast amount of advice brought together for parents in this one comprehensive volume is organized in five parts, each pertaining to a particular age group; the sixth part includes subjects that, in general, may concern children of various ages. For a well-rounded picture of your child's development at a given age, and how to give him the best care, read through the part devoted to his age. Or else, for specific information, turn to the end, where there is a comprehensive ready-reference index of over two thousand important subjects that will enable you to find any particular one in an instant.

It has many special features. Study the table of contents and you will discover many features of unusual interest and usefulness that go far beyond the scope of the average book on child care. For example, in Part One there is a chapter called "Choosing a Name for the Baby," giving hundreds of boys' and girls' names, with their origins and meanings. In Part Four there is a chapter called "The School Lunch Box" which not only tells you what is required for a wholesome lunch, but also explains how to make lunches appetizing and gives you attractive menus for children of different ages. In Part Six you will find a thirty-two-page chapter called "Indoor Fun for Mother and Child" which gives you dozens of ideas for things the child of preschool and school age will enjoy making under your guidance when he must stay indoors. There are many other helpful features like these, all designed to make your job as a parent simpler and more certain of success.

Among The Authors

EDITH LESSER ATKIN, M.S.
Psychiatric Social Worker; Member, Council of Child Development Centre. Formerly Member of the Staff of the United States Children's Bureau.

ALINE B. AUERBACH
Coordinator of Leadership Training and Parent Group Work, Child Study Association of America.

PHYLLIS BLANCHARD, PH.D.
Psychologist, Philadelphia Child Guidance Clinic; Instructor, Pennsylvania School of Social Work; Guest Lecturer, Philadelphia Psychoanalytic Institute, Philadelphia.

HERMAN N. BUNDESEN, M.D.
President, Chicago Board of Health; Professorial Lecturer on Public Health Administration, University of Chicago; Senior Surgeon, United States Public Health Service; Honorary Vice-President, Child Conservation League of America; Noted Author.

VERNA S. CARLISLE
Consultant, National Society For Crippled Children and Adults.

VICTOR D'AMICO, B.S., M.A.
Director, Department of Education, Museum of Modern Art, New York City. Formerly Head of Fine Arts Department, Fieldston School, Fieldston, N. Y.

W. ALLISON DAVIS, PH.D.
Professor, Department of Education, University of Chicago.

JOSETTE FRANK
Noted Author; Educational Associate, Child Study Association of America.

LAWRENCE K. FRANK
Chairman of the Advisory Committee, Division of World Affairs, National Committee on Mental Hygiene; Member of the Inter-Professional Advisory Committee of the World Federation for Mental Health; Recipient of the Lasker Award in Mental Health. Formerly Director of the Caroline Zachry Institute of Human Development. Noted Author, and Co-Author with Mary Frank.

GEORGE E. GARDNER, M.D., PH.D.
Co-Director of Judge Baker Child Guidance Center; Associate Professor of Psychiatry, Boston University School of Medicine.

ARNOLD GESELL, M.D., PH.D., SC.D.
Founder and Director, Clinic of Child Development, Yale University. Formerly Professor of Child Hygiene, Yale School of Medicine; Attending Pediatrician, New Haven Hospital. Noted Author and Educator.

SIDONIE MATSNER GRUENBERG
Director, Child Study Association of America; Member, Editorial Boards, *Parents' Magazine* and the Junior Literary Guild. Formerly Lecturer in Parent Education, Teachers College, Columbia University, New York University, University of Colorado; Formerly Chairman of National Council for Parent Education. Noted Author; Lecturer before Women's Clubs, Parents and Teachers Associations, and Social Workers.

ROBERT J. HAVIGHURST, PH.D.
Professor, Department of Education, University of Chicago; Chairman, Committee on Human Development, University of Chicago.

7

ELIZABETH B. HURLOCK, PH.D.
> Associate Professor in Child Psychology, University of Pennsylvania. Formerly Associate Professor in Psychology, Columbia University, New York City; Noted Author.

IRVIN S. KOLL, M.D.
> Director, Department of Health, Western Illinois State College. Formerly Head of Genito-Urinary Department, Chicago Post-Graduate School of Medicine; Chief of Urology, Valley Forge Hospital. Co-Author of *The Family Physician* and Numerous Other Medical Works.

BEATRICE LANDECK
> Instructor, Mills College of Education; Author of *Children and Music* and Other Works.

GRACE LANGDON, PH.D.
> Noted Author and Child-Care Consultant; Lecturer, New York University and Child Education Foundation, New York.

WILLIAM C. MENNINGER, M.D., M.A.
> Professor of Psychiatry, Menninger Foundation School of Psychiatry; Member, Attending Staff, Christ's Hospital, Topeka, Kansas; Consultant in Psychiatry, Winter Veterans Administration Hospital; Consultant in Neuropsychiatry, Veterans Administration, Washington, D. C.; Consultant in Neuropsychiatry to the Surgeon General of the United States Army; Member, Medical Advisory Committee to the Secretary of War.

HERMAN POMERANZ, M.D.
> Visiting Physician, Manhattan General Hospital, New York City; Co-Author of *The Family Physician;* Author of Numerous Other Medical Works.

SIR GRANTLY DICK READ, M.D., M.A.
> Member, Royal College of Surgeons of England, Royal Society of Medicine; Fellow, Royal Institute of Public Health; Honorary Consulting Physician to the Southern Railway Orphanages, England; Noted Author and Lecturer.

FRANK HOWARD RICHARDSON, M.D.
> Member of the Staff of the Children's Clinic at Black Mountain, North Carolina; Author of Scientific and Popular Articles on the Physical and Emotional Phases of Child Health.

NINA RIDENOUR, PH.D.
> Director, Division of Education, National Association For Mental Health. Formerly Chief Psychologist, Children's Center, Detroit; Consultant, New York City Bureau of Child Hygiene, and Welfare Department Division of Day Care; Executive Officer, International Committee for Mental Hygiene; Instructor, School of Education, New York University.

BENJAMIN SPOCK, M.D.
> Associate Professor in Psychiatry, Mayo Foundation, University of Minnesota; Consultant in Psychiatry, Mayo Clinic. Formerly Instructor in Pediatrics, Cornell Medical College; Assistant Attending Pediatrician, New York Hospital; Consultant in Pediatric Psychiatry, New York City Health Department. Noted Author.

ABRAHAM B. TAMIS, M.D.
> Associate Clinical Professor of Obstetrics and Gynecology, New York Medical College.

ANNA W. M. WOLF
> Member, Professional Staff, Child Study Association of America; Noted Author and Editor.

Contents

Part One: THE EXPECTANT MOTHER

Guiding your child toward a full, happy life — the difference between indulgence and love—the danger of concealing parental affection—how to let your child know he is loved—the surest basis for your child's security —enjoying your child—sharing pleasures with your child.

The full meaning of pregnancy—the first signs of pregnancy and how to recognize them — choosing the right doctor — pregnancy tests and their accuracy—how to plan for your care—how to meet the problem of expense —the examination—what the doctor will do—the internal examination—age and its bearing on pregnancy—chart for figuring probable date of birth.

How the physical changes affect a woman's emotions—common fears and doubts and how to handle them—talk about your fears to another person— how to keep yourself looking well-groomed—why you should keep up your interests—the "baby blues"—how to avoid family upsets—the emotional aftermath of pregnancy and how to meet it.

A baby is a family affair—changes in the husband's life and how he can prepare for them—talking it over with the doctor—how the husband can help the expectant mother through periods of emotional distress—the husband's doubts and how to resolve them—if the husband feels neglected.

When to tell your children about the new baby—forestalling jealousy—how to draw children into plans for the newcomer—the children's care while you are away—introducing the new baby—how to reassure the older child.

The menstrual cycle—conception—how fertilization takes place—the first week of life after conception—the development of the embryo from the third to the seventh week—growth of the fetus from the third to the ninth month —when the baby is ready for birth—the placenta and bag of waters—factors that determine the baby's sex—how to find out whether you will have twins —how to tell whether the baby is developing normally—birthmarks.

How the baby is nourished—eating for two—how diet affects labor—the most important foods for the expectant mother—how a poor diet affects the baby —underfeeding and overweight—the balanced diet—mineral requirements—

vitamin requirements—foods the expectant mother needs every day—fluids—
sample menu for pregnancy diet—rest and sleep—how to exercise—comfort
in clothing—what to do about smoking and drinking—care of the teeth—care
of breasts—traveling—marital relations during pregnancy—working mother.

Part Two: THE FIRST YEAR OF LIFE

quantity of milk needed by the baby from the first day of life through his ninth month—after the baby is nine months old—amounts of sugar and water—how to make the evaporated milk formula—feeding schedule for the bottle-fed baby—utensils for preparing the formula—caring for the equipment—preparing a day's formula—sample milk mixtures for well babies.

Part Three: ONE TO SIX YEARS OLD

average gain in height and weight in a year—differences in growth between boys and girls—learning to walk—learning to talk—your child's growth and development at one year—at two years—at three years—from four to six.

together—time for listening—the movies—too young for movies—parental responsibility for what the child sees—television—why television sessions for children should be time-scheduled.

Why it is difficult to teach a child the uses of money—spending before earning—the inevitability of the young child's contact with money—the allowance—how much allowance to give—learning to save—pay for work done in the home—sharing in family councils about money.

Part Five: *APPROACHING ADULTHOOD*

The period of adolescence—problems of adolescence—how youngsters grow and develop—sudden increases in height and weight—the reproductive organs mature—signs of approaching sexual maturity—the fundamentals of physical hygiene—adolescent behavior—when the child becomes self-conscious about his physical changes—the bad complexion and how to treat it.

When girls begin to menstruate—how menstruation varies in different girls —preparing the girl for menstruation—why the girl is self-conscious—why some girls have an aversion to menstruation—why irregular menstruation occurs—psychological preparation for womanhood—when the girl is curious about boys—understanding the girl's sex longings—how parents influence the girl's emotional life—why some girls are attracted to older men—how the possessive mother harms her child—social preparation for womanhood— why girls have conflicts with their parents—beginning to date—why girls smoke and use cosmetics—how early love affairs affect the girl.

Guiding your son's sex education—when the father discusses sex with the boy—why the young boy uses obscene language and tells smutty jokes— what the parents' attitude and corrective approach should be—adolescent masturbation: why parents should not be alarmed by it—how to help the adolescent break the habit—the danger of prying into his sex behavior.

Adolescent friendships are important—why some adolescents are unable to make friends—how children reflect their homes—teen-age "crushes"—what the family's attitude toward the "crush" should be—how the teacher is able to help—boy-and-girl relations—petting—too many prohibitions.

Measuring intelligence—the intelligence quotient—what intelligence tests mean—planning the education of the child with a slow mind—the youngster with an average mind—when the child has a superior mind—providing adequate stimulation for the superior child without pushing him ahead— special aptitudes, talents, and disabilities, and how to deal with them.

The problems of educational progress—causes of failure in school—lack of ability is not always the reason for failure—when your child requires a broader type of instruction to meet his needs—how inadequate preparation in early grades can lead to serious difficulties—if schooling is interrupted— why children cannot concentrate—when there are too many diversions at school—when the child is uninterested in his studies—how emotional attitudes cause failure—when parents set impossible standards for the child.

Contents

Part Six:

SPECIAL PROBLEMS OF PARENTS AND CHILDREN

Part One

THE EXPECTANT MOTHER

Parents' Pledge to Their Children

In every home where this pledge is made and kept, children will have a greater opportunity to grow into healthy, intelligent, and useful members of society.

FROM YOUR EARLIEST INFANCY we will give you our love, so that you may grow with trust in yourself and in others.

WE WILL RECOGNIZE your worth as a person and we will help you to strengthen your sense of belonging.

WE WILL RESPECT your right to be yourself and at the same time help you to understand the rights of others, so that you may experience cooperative living.

WE WILL HELP you to develop initiative and imagination, so that you may have the opportunity freely to create.

WE WILL ENCOURAGE your curiosity and your pride in workmanship, so that you may have the satisfaction that comes from achievement.

WE WILL PROVIDE the conditions for wholesome play that will add to your learning, to your social experience, and to your happiness.

WE WILL ILLUSTRATE by precept and example the value of integrity and the importance of moral courage.

WE WILL ENCOURAGE you always to seek the truth.

WE WILL PROVIDE you with all opportunities possible to develop your own faith in God.

23

WE WILL OPEN the way for you to enjoy the arts and to use them for deepening your understanding of life.

WE WILL WORK to rid ourselves of prejudice and discrimination, so that together we may achieve a truly democratic society.

WE WILL WORK to lift the standard of living and to improve our economic practices, so that you may have the material basis for a full life.

WE WILL PROVIDE you with rewarding educational opportunities, so that you may develop your talents and contribute to a better world.

WE WILL PROTECT you against exploitation and undue hazards and help you grow in health and strength.

WE WILL WORK to conserve and improve family life and, as needed, to provide foster care according to your inherent rights.

WE WILL INTENSIFY our search for new knowledge in order to guide you more effectively as you develop your potentialities.

As YOU GROW from child to youth to adult, establishing a family life of your own and accepting larger social responsibilities, we will work with you to improve conditions for all children and youth.

Aware that these promises to you cannot be fully met in a world at war, we ask you to join us in a firm dedication to the building of a world society based on freedom, justice and mutual respect.

So may you grow in joy, in faith in God and in man, and in those qualities of vision and of the spirit that will sustain us all and give us new hope for the future.

---

* *This pledge to children was unanimously adopted by 6000 delegates at the Midcentury White House Conference on Children and Youth, held in Washington, D. C., December 3-7, 1950.*

The Priceless Privilege
of Parenthood

FROM the moment the baby first turns his eyes to the light, or shows that he has noticed a sound; from the time he first reaches out for his rattle or for the finger held invitingly near or toward the face smiling above him; from the moment he kicks and coos with delight as someone who loves him comes near; from the moment that he responds with evident joy to some light, some color, some sound; in short, from tiniest babyhood on, a child is reaching out with eagerness to take the world in his grasp. He reaches out to feel, to taste, to touch, to hold. He reaches out for color and light and sound. He searches for meanings. Even before he can talk one hears the questioning in his tones and sees it in his actions. When words begin to come he questions why, why, why of anyone who will answer him. He revels in new understandings as they unfold to his searching thought. He shows his delight in beauty as it is revealed to him in word, in rhythm, in sound, in color, in the love of the people around him. He glories in his ability to do, in his accomplishments, in his achievements. He has his ups and downs, his babyhood problems, the trials of childhood, but they are all a part of understanding the mysteries of living, of finding his place in the universe and his relationships to the beings who people his world. Daily new meanings unfold in his thought, new understandings are imparted to him, new abilities are revealed—and with what joy he accepts them all! To parents is given the priceless privilege of giving guidance that will ensure that all the meanings are rich and fine, that all the understandings are true, that all the abilities find their expression in useful, loving actions. With such guidance every day of the child's living can be a thing of joyous activity, of rich meaning, of deep and abiding contentment.

LOVE THE CHILD AND LET HIM KNOW IT

No child was probably ever loved too much. Many are indulged too much; some are spoiled in the name of love; but no child ever could have too much real genuine love, that deep and abiding affection which makes him feel wanted and secure and content. A child needs a great deal of this kind of love. He needs to know that he has it. There was a time when parents were advised to be very casual and matter-of-fact with their children, and not to make much display of affection. They were urged to be coolly unemotional when any difficulty occurred. Fortunately that time is past and one hears little now of such advice. Children need loving. They need a great deal of it. Different parents have different ways of showing their love for their child. No one can tell another how to do it. If one feels a surge of deep affection toward the child, it is best just to let it come out in its own natural form of expression. Sometimes parents seem to feel that they must bottle it up. Maybe in their own home there was never any outward show of affection and so they feel that they should hide what they feel. Or perhaps they would like to show it more but just don't know how. Deep and genuine and abiding love can find many ways of expressing itself—in the look, the gesture, the tone, the words, the things that are done for one, the way they are done, the hug here, the kiss there, the pat on the shoulder, the squeeze of the hand, the doing of things together. One will not need anyone to tell him *how* to do it if he will just let down whatever barriers there are and love the child and let him know it. That is what the child needs. It is a companionship of spirit, an expression of the finest feeling one can have toward a child, the richest thing in his whole experience, the surest basis for his security. With that in his life, difficulties may come and go. It matters little, for he is ready for them all. He knows that he is loved, that he is wanted, and he is secure.

ENJOY THE CHILD

Along with this deep and abiding love for the child one hopes there is an enjoyment of him. If one tries to get acquainted with him day by day, if one sees him as an individual, if one respects his individuality, and if one loves him deeply, then one is likely to enjoy him. Sometimes, though, parents get beset by so many other concerns that they do not let themselves enjoy their child. Perhaps they are intent on having everything just exactly right for him and lose much of the fun of the doing in their anxiety lest all is not just as it should be. Or sometimes there are financial worries which seem to take all the thought that might be otherwise turned to enjoyment of the child. Or it may just not have occurred to them that here is someone from whom they might get a great deal of pleasure. Some people have had little to do with children until they have their own, and then are overwhelmed with a sense of the great responsibility; they take it so seriously that they miss the fun they might have. Others may find all of the work connected with the child so irksome that they do not see any fun in it.

Many parents get great enjoyment with a child as he goes exploring, experimenting, questioning, investigating, enjoying through his days. He himself gets such a thrill of enjoyment out of each new thing he discovers, out of each new bit of understanding that comes to him, out of every new-found ability, out of every bit of doing and accomplishment, out of the difficulties, too, that the parent with a seeing eye and an understanding heart can get real pleasure in sharing that enjoyment.

It is very important for a child to have his parents enjoy him, enjoy the things he does, enjoy things with him—it is the beginning of a companionship that can make living richer for both parents and child. It can begin in early babyhood and last all through the years. And how it can grow with a little nourishing and cherishing!

Parents who set out thoughtfully in search of the wisdom and understanding to guide a child toward ever wider meanings and understandings and appreciations, and toward ever more useful ways of living, and toward ever deepening and more enriching values, have embarked on a great adventure. The search will not end when the child is six. It will have only begun. And what a joyous search it can be! It will have its up and downs, many of them. There will doubtless be moments when one wonders which way to turn now, what next move to make. Even as one wonders, the child will have changed. Often one will wish for greater wisdom, for more understanding. But always there can be joy in giving the best one has to give. A child responds so readily to guidance when it is lovingly given—he catches a thought or suggestion so quickly, he weaves it into the fabric of his living so eagerly, he turns so trustingly to those who have seen and understood and helped, he shows so surely his confidence and security in their understanding, that one rejoices in doing all one can to help him find the ways that make living a thing of joy and beauty and usefulness.

GRACE LANGDON, PH.D.

The Expectant Mother

THE moment a woman learns she is to become a mother should be one of the happiest in her life. Childbearing is woman's priceless privilege. When a woman conceives and bears a child, she is truly fulfilling the role for which she was born.

There is a sense of accomplishment which comes with the mission of passing on life to another tiny human being, who will embody not only your own qualities and those of your husband, but those of your ancestors as well. Bearing a child is an achievement which is infinitely greater than being the most successful business or professional woman in your community. Ask any mother, and she will tell you it is true.

Every woman should have an intelligent grasp of what pregnancy means to her. First of all, there are adjustments to be made, of course. The care of a competent physician is essential, and, if possible, the facilities of a modern hospital when the time comes for delivery. It is important to be guided by your doctor, and follow explicitly what he tells you to do. This will make the road much easier to travel, and you will reap the reward in a happy pregnancy that will progress in time to a triumphant conclusion.

As soon as you suspect you are pregnant, lose no time in consulting your doctor. Occasionally the usual signs of pregnancy do not appear at once, and two or three months may pass before either you or your doctor can be certain. Medical advice is a must, for if you are pregnant, then you will be assured of excellent care during the months you are carrying your child in your uterus (womb), and will be able to give him the best opportunity for health. If you are not pregnant, nothing is lost.

The first thing most women notice when they think they might be pregnant is that the regular menstrual period does not appear. This is not always a sure sign, for most women do not menstruate exactly on time every month. But if you skip a second period, the chances are much greater that a baby is really on the way. A few women do have brief menstrual periods during the first two or three months of pregnancy. These periods are not so long nor the flow so much as usual. Some women notice vague cramps when their first and second periods are due, but without any show of blood. These are the reasons the doctor will ask you when your last "normal" period began.

If you really are pregnant, you may begin to notice some other things after the first missed period. You may be more sleepy than usual. Your breasts will probably begin to grow larger and feel tender. You may need to pass your urine more often. Sometimes you may feel nervous and easily upset. You may or may not have morning sickness, a feeling of nausea that may come in the morning or at times when you are very tired or hungry.

Few women go through the first three months of pregnancy without having some of these feelings. You and your husband need not be disturbed by them. They are simply reactions of your body as it adjusts to the developing baby's needs. The enlarging breasts mean they are getting ready for their later job of producing milk. The need to pass urine so often results from changes in the position of the uterus and the bladder as the uterus begins to grow larger.

Some women notice only one or two of these changes. Many women never have morning sickness. It used to be considered a necessary part of pregnancy for all women. Even now some of your friends may not believe you *are* pregnant if you don't become nauseated. However, with the right food and a cheerful outlook on life, many women are not troubled with vomiting. If you do get a sickish feeling, ask your doctor what to do. Many little things help. We will talk about some of these later on.

When you choose a doctor, make certain that he has had good training and experience in caring for pregnant women. You may already have a family doctor who knows a lot about pregnancy. Or you may want to go to an obstetrician (a doctor who has had several extra years of special training in the care of pregnant women). Or you may have a good hospital clinic or public health clinic nearby.

Perhaps you are worried about the expense. Many doctors and clinics now charge a lump sum which covers all your care during pregnancy, at delivery, and for a period after the baby's birth. Discuss the cost frankly when you first see your doctor. It is best to have a clear understanding from the beginning. Most doctors consider your pocketbook in deciding how much to charge, so don't put off going because you think it might cost too much. Delay may cost you much more. So choose early and go to see the doctor as soon as you can. There are several reasons for this—all important. First of all, he can find out if you really are pregnant. Then he will give you a complete physical examination—perhaps the most complete you've ever had. And he will give you care and guidance throughout your pregnancy, labor, and the period following your baby's birth.

PREGNANCY TESTS. These are special laboratory tests used at times to help the doctor know whether or not a woman is pregnant. Such a test may be advisable for some women because of health problems. Unless such problems exist, however, all that is needed is a little patience, for time will soon tell whether a baby is on the way. Your doctor may not think it is necessary to do a pregnancy test on you—and if he doesn't, don't urge him. They are expensive and usually have to be done in a special laboratory.

Most pregnancy tests are based on the fact that a pregnant woman passes certain chemical substances out in her urine. If a little of the pregnant woman's urine is injected into certain female animals, such as a mouse, rabbit, or frog, these substances cause changes in the animal's reproductive organs.

These pregnancy tests can only be used during a certain period of time. If too early, they may be called "negative" when the woman really is pregnant, and after three months they are seldom needed. Most doctors use them only in addition to their own observations.

PLANNING YOUR CARE

Many communities have various kinds of resources for expectant parents who want help in working out plans for care or in answering some of their questions. Large cities have most of them; small towns or rural communities may have only a few. Some of them are listed in telephone directories, or your doctor may know about them.

What are these resources? They are hospital clinics, public health departments, social agencies, visiting nurse associations, and other organizations that are interested in the care of mothers and babies.

Do you want help in finding a good doctor? Several places can give you a list of doctors who specialize in the care of mothers and babies. Ask at the local or state public health agency, the local or state medical society, or at the medical school if there is one in your community.

Is expense a problem? Many large hospitals have free or special rate clinics, and some health departments have free clinics which provide care for you before your baby's birth, and, sometimes, delivery of your baby and care for a period of time after birth. Many of these clinics have medical social workers who can help you work out problems of budgeting and financial arrangements.

Are you wondering who will care for the rest of the family when the baby comes? The medical social worker at the clinic or hospital can often help you work out a practical plan.

Do you know about public health nurses? Many clinics have visiting nurses or public health nurses. They not only help the doctor but also conduct classes in maternity and baby care, make home visits before and after the baby comes, and help the mother with plans for her own care and care of the baby. The services of a public health nurse are available to anybody in the community.

Are there other problems or questions which bother you? Many public health and hospital clinics, as well as social agencies, have trained social workers who understand a lot about economic and emotional problems and can help to work them out. Your doctor or the public health nurse can help you find out about them.

THE EXAMINATION

Many women dread going to the doctor, most of them because they have never had a complete examination and don't know what it includes. If you've been examined before you became pregnant, you may know more what to expect. Anyway, everything your doctor does in examining you has real plan and purpose to it. He or she will make every effort to see that the examination is as free from embarrassment as possible.

Every doctor has a different way of making his first examination. but many of them follow a plan something like this:

First of all, your doctor or the nurse will talk with you. They want to know about your past health, your parents' and grandparents' health, your husband's health, what sort of work you do, how you and your husband get along, whether you have had any miscarriages, what happened in other pregnancies you may have had—and all sorts of things you may have almost forgotten. You will be asked about your menstruation, your age when it began, how regular it is, when you had your last normal period. All of this information is put down on your record, which your doctor will keep and add to during your entire pregnancy. Try to remember all the kinds of sickness you have had. Even such apparently minor illnesses as measles or flu may give the doctor information he needs to give you good care.

After this history-taking, you undress completely. The nurse will give you a sheet or robe to wrap yourself in. You will probably be told to pass your urine into a special pan, from which a small amount will be taken for examination. The doctor will examine it for albumin and sugar, and look at it under the microscope. Most people think of urine as a waste. To doctors, however, it tells many things about how our bodies are acting. If the kidneys are not working well, or if we have some other kind of illness, something may

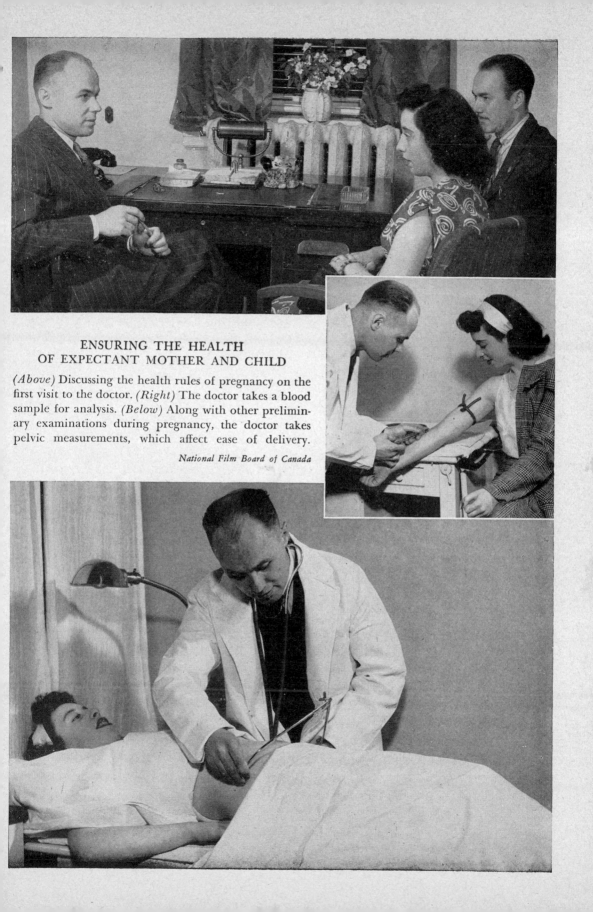

ENSURING THE HEALTH
OF EXPECTANT MOTHER AND CHILD

(Above) Discussing the health rules of pregnancy on the first visit to the doctor. *(Right)* The doctor takes a blood sample for analysis. *(Below)* Along with other preliminary examinations during pregnancy, the doctor takes pelvic measurements, which affect ease of delivery.

National Film Board of Canada

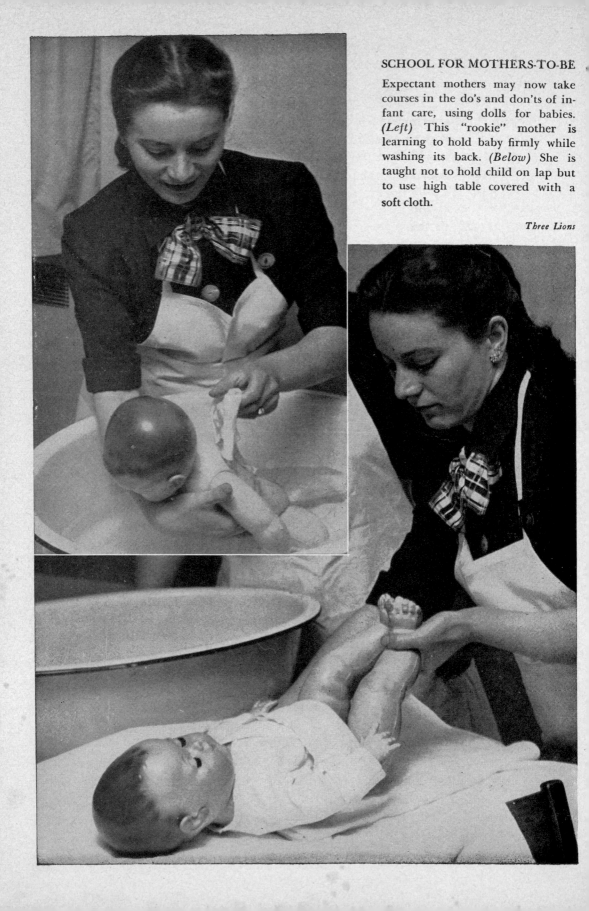

SCHOOL FOR MOTHERS-TO-BE

Expectant mothers may now take courses in the do's and don'ts of infant care, using dolls for babies. *(Left)* This "rookie" mother is learning to hold baby firmly while washing its back. *(Below)* She is taught not to hold child on lap but to use high table covered with a soft cloth.

Three Lions

appear in the urine which does not normally belong there. Your doctor will want to examine a sample of your urine at every visit.

Your weight will be taken sometime during the examination.

During the physical examination your doctor will do a number of things. He will take your blood pressure. He will check your eyes, ears, nose, and throat for any sign of infection. He will examine your breasts. Is there any secretion? Are they tender? Most women begin to have a thin watery secretion from their breasts about the third or fourth month of pregnancy. This secretion is perfectly normal but may sometimes cause a little irritation of the nipples. He will thump your chest and listen to your heart and lungs with a stethoscope. Then he will examine your abdomen.

Your doctor will also make an internal examination, at which time he may take certain measurements, which tell him whether the birth canal is large enough for a normal birth. Most women have a normal birth canal, but the doctor always measures to be sure. Some doctors prefer to wait until a later visit to take these measurements, but they will be done sometime during your pregnancy.

During your first visit, the doctor will take a small amount of blood (about one to two teaspoonfuls) from one of your arm veins with a small needle. This is no more painful than an ordinary pin-prick. He will use the blood for several tests. One test will tell him if you are anemic. Also he will do a blood test for syphilis, find out what type your blood is, determine the Rh factor, and do any other tests that are necessary.

When the examination is over, the doctor or nurse will talk with you again. They will tell you about what to eat, how much sleep and exercise to get, what sort of clothing you will need, and when to make your next visit to the doctor.

Ordinarily a pregnant woman should see her doctor once a month for the first six months, then at more frequent intervals. On later visits he may not need to examine you so completely. He may ask you a few questions, take your weight and blood pressure, examine your abdomen to see how much the baby has grown, test the urine, and occasionally prick your finger for a drop of blood to be sure you do not become anemic. Some doctors will want a chest X ray taken.

You may want to keep notes on questions that come up in between your visits to help you remember what you wanted to ask on the next visit to the doctor.

WHEN WILL THE BABY ARRIVE?

If someone could discover how to tell just when a baby is due, he would earn the gratitude of the doctor and mother alike. But this is one of the secrets nature still holds. All we can do is figure roughly.

In the human being the average time from conception to birth is about 266 days. Since it is difficult to tell the exact day on which conception occurred, doctors have hit on a convenient scheme, which is fairly reliable, to estimate when the baby is due. The scheme is based on the observation that many babies are born about 280 days after the last normal menstrual period occurred. To figure about when the baby is due, count back three months from the first day of your last normal menstrual period and add seven days. For example, if your last period began June 10, count back to March 10, add seven days, and the baby will be due about March 17.

You notice we say "about" then. Very few mothers will have their babies on the exact day. It is better to prepare yourself to expect the important arrival anywhere from one to four weeks before or after the chosen date. It may be a help to know, however, that most babies arrive within a week of the expected time.

WHAT ABOUT MOTHER'S AGE?

The talk about the advantages of having children early has made some women afraid of having babies after they reach the age of thirty-five or so. Many doctors do feel that a woman in her early twenties is a little more likely to have an easy pregnancy and labor than if she has her first child at forty. But a number of women over forty have had their first babies without any difficulty, and go on to have more. No woman needs to be afraid of pregnancy just because she is over thirty-five. With good medical care and guidance, she probably will have very little more discomfort than her younger and more "elastic" sister. Some older women who have kept them-

CHART FOR FIGURING THE PROBABLE DATE OF THE BABY'S BIRTH

Directions for Using the Chart

In the column of light type and figures, find the date of the first day of the last menstrual period.

The probable date of the baby's birth will be found to the right—in heavy type and figures.

Jan	Oct	Feb	Nov	Mar	Dec	Apr	Jan	May	Feb	Jun	Mar	July	Apr	Aug	May	Sept	Jun	Oct	July	Nov	Aug	Dec	Sept
1	8	1	8	1	6	1	6	1	5	1	8	1	7	1	8	1	8	1	8	1	8	1	7
2	9	2	9	2	7	2	7	2	6	2	9	2	8	2	9	2	9	2	9	2	9	2	8
3	10	3	10	3	8	3	8	3	7	3	10	3	9	3	10	3	10	3	10	3	10	3	9
4	11	4	11	4	9	4	9	4	8	4	11	4	10	4	11	4	11	4	11	4	11	4	10
5	12	5	12	5	10	5	10	5	9	5	12	5	11	5	12	5	12	5	12	5	12	5	11
6	13	6	13	6	11	6	11	6	10	6	13	6	12	6	13	6	13	6	13	6	13	6	12
7	14	7	14	7	12	7	12	7	11	7	14	7	13	7	14	7	14	7	14	7	14	7	13
8	15	8	15	8	13	8	13	8	12	8	15	8	14	8	15	8	15	8	15	8	15	8	14
9	16	9	16	9	14	9	14	9	13	9	16	9	15	9	16	9	16	9	16	9	16	9	15
10	17	10	17	10	15	10	15	10	14	10	17	10	16	10	17	10	17	10	17	10	17	10	16
11	18	11	18	11	16	11	16	11	15	11	18	11	17	11	18	11	18	11	18	11	18	11	17
12	19	12	19	12	17	12	17	12	16	12	19	12	18	12	19	12	19	12	19	12	19	12	18
13	20	13	20	13	18	13	18	13	17	13	20	13	19	13	20	13	20	13	20	13	20	13	19
14	21	14	21	14	19	14	19	14	18	14	21	14	20	14	21	14	21	14	21	14	21	14	20
15	22	15	22	15	20	15	20	15	19	15	22	15	21	15	22	15	22	15	22	15	22	15	21
16	23	16	23	16	21	16	21	16	20	16	23	16	22	16	23	16	23	16	23	16	23	16	22
17	24	17	24	17	22	17	22	17	21	17	24	17	23	17	24	17	24	17	24	17	24	17	23
18	25	18	25	18	23	18	23	18	22	18	25	18	24	18	25	18	25	18	25	18	25	18	24
19	26	19	26	19	24	19	24	19	23	19	26	19	25	19	26	19	26	19	26	19	26	19	25
20	27	20	27	20	25	20	25	20	24	20	27	20	26	20	27	20	27	20	27	20	27	20	26
21	28	21	28	21	26	21	26	21	25	21	28	21	27	21	28	21	28	21	28	21	28	21	27
22	29	22	29	22	27	22	27	22	26	22	29	22	28	22	29	22	29	22	29	22	29	22	28
23	30	23	30	23	28	23	28	23	27	23	30	23	29	23	30	23	30	23	30	23	30	23	29
24	31	—Dec.		24	29	24	29	24	28	24	31	24	30	24	31	—July		24	31	24	31	24	30
—Nov.		24	1	25	30	25	30	—Mar.		—Apr.		—May		—June		24	1	—Aug.		—Sept.		—Oct.	
25	1	25	2	26	31	26	31	25	1	25	1	25	1	25	1	25	2	25	1	25	1	25	1
26	2	26	3	—Jan.		—Feb.		26	2	26	2	26	2	26	2	26	3	26	2	26	2	26	2
27	3	27	4	27	1	27	1	27	3	27	3	27	3	27	3	27	4	27	3	27	3	27	3
28	4	28	5	28	2	28	2	28	4	28	4	28	4	28	4	28	5	28	4	28	4	28	4
29	5	29	6	29	3	29	3	29	5	29	5	29	5	29	5	29	6	29	5	29	5	29	5
30	6			30	4	30	4	30	6	30	6	30	6	30	6	30	7	30	6	30	6	30	6
31	7			31	5			31	7			31	7	31	7			31	7			31	7

This chart was compiled by Dr. Herman N. Bundesen, President, Chicago Board of Health.

selves youthful with proper food, good exercise, and a happy outlook on life may find their pregnancy and labor actually very easy.

SOME FALLACIES REGARDING PREGNANCY

There are many popular fallacies or mistaken beliefs regarding
pregnancy. For example, it is still widely held that a seven-month
baby is more likely to live than an eight-month baby. The fact is
that the nearer the term of delivery, the better the chance of survival for the fetus.

It is equally untrue that the wearing of high-heeled shoes during
pregnancy may cause the child to be cross-eyed, or that three Cae-
sarean babies are the most any woman can have. Contrary to popular
opinion, too, a woman can become pregnant while she is nursing
her first child.

Many people believe that maternal impression—looking at an ugly
person, or a mouse, for example—will leave its birthmark on the
offspring. This contradicts the medical facts. What a woman thinks
or sees cannot imprint itself physically on the child she is bearing.

Making the Emotional Adjust-
ments to Pregnancy

THE changes a woman's body undergoes during pregnancy usually
cause her to experience many kinds of emotions. And, indeed,
pregnancy requires an emotional adjustment as well as a physical
one. Perhaps you will be able to maintain an even disposition, but
do not be surprised if your spirits suddenly sag, and for no apparent
reason. One moment you may feel happy and excited, the next,
disturbed and depressed.

All kinds of questions may fill your mind at the most unexpected
times. You will find yourself worrying about your baby's birth.

Will he be normal? Will I be able to endure the labor pains? How will I get everything ready on time? Will I soon look as ungainly and awkward as some of my friends? At such times, you will find small comfort in the thought that almost every child is born normal, and that the destiny of women is to be mothers.

While more common during the first pregnancy, these times of doubt and uncertainty, mixed with pleasurable anticipation, may also be experienced with succeeding pregnancies. There is much more to having a baby than the physical changes in the body. The experience means assuming new responsibilities, making additional sacrifices, and the loss of personal freedom. There is also the matter of money, and perhaps planning for a new place to live.

Your state of mind and feelings will depend a good deal on whether you really want the baby and are ready for the responsibilities of being a parent. Babies don't always come at just the right moment. Many people find they have to grow up a lot themselves when they have children. If you have always had your own way, or if your husband is used to having all your attention, or if you find it hard to make ends meet even before the baby comes, you may have to make a lot of changes in your way of life. Babies are demanding, too, and it may be necessary for you and your husband to learn how to share each other with the baby.

Even if you want the baby very much and have been hoping and planning for one, you may have doubts at times about whether you can carry out all the demands a family puts upon you. This is a perfectly natural feeling. It is natural, too, to hide away many of such doubts and feelings. Most women have been brought up to think that of course all mothers want and love their babies and are ready and able to take good care of them. They feel ashamed and guilty if they wonder at times whether they really want a baby and can make a go of it. But it is no reflection on you to have such doubts. There is no need to feel ashamed. Most mothers have these questions, both before and after the baby comes.

It is important to face these doubts and fears frankly. Get them out in the open and talk them over with an understanding person. Some women find it easier to talk to someone outside the family, such as the doctor, the nurse, or the social worker. If you can look at these worries clearly, you may find they are not so alarming, after all.

KEEPING UP APPEARANCES

It is a mistake to take advantage of your condition by slopping around the house in old slippers and a messy housecoat, with your hair uncombed. If you can keep yourself neat and well groomed, you may be surprised to find how much the bluest feelings improve. Some women find they feel their best both physically and mentally when they are pregnant and many of them are prettier than ever, too.

Pregnancy isn't a synonym for dowdiness any more. A lot can be done by cleverly cut clothes, and a lot more by careful grooming. Take extra pains with your hair, your nails, and your makeup, and you'll draw attention away from the temporary bulge. Have at least one good, but not necessarily expensive, dress, for wear when you go out. If it's a becoming color, and has some eye-catching, fresh, frilly accessories, you'll feel well-dressed even though you wear it often.

KEEPING UP YOUR INTERESTS

One of the best ways to help yourself feel happy and confident is to keep up an active interest in all sorts of things. Visits to relatives and friends, movies, bridge games, walks, and other social activities, reading, and keeping up with the news—all these will help to keep you feeling your best.

Knitting or sewing for the baby can be lots of fun. Many young mothers-to-be have found it very helpful to spend some time with friends who have small children—helping to bathe and feed the baby, or taking him for a walk, and finding out some of the practical ins-and-outs of being a mother.

Some communities have mothers' classes where expectant mothers can learn about and discuss their own care and the care of the baby. These classes are usually sponsored by public or private health centers, hospitals, visiting nurse associations, or other community groups. You might want to find out about such classes in your own community.

A great deal of family upset and disappointment can be avoided if you and your husband make up your minds early to accept a boy or a girl with equal love and pleasure. Even little children can sense disappointment and disapproval very early, no matter how hard you try to hide it. And it can put real stumbling blocks in the way of a child's normal growth and development, when he does not have the feeling of love and security that is so important in the development of his own self-confidence.

Doubts and questions may come up again after the baby is born. With so much excitement right at first, and so many things to do and learn, you and your husband will be carried along for a while with the wonders of the new baby. But often, when the baby is a week or two old, is gaining weight well, and his feeding has been going along fine, you may suddenly feel pretty tired and blue. Some mothers have spells of weeping and just don't know what is wrong. Others feel all worn out. Some doctors call this reaction the "baby blues." It isn't anything to worry about. It seems to be a way your body takes to relieve the tension and anxiety that all mothers feel at times. This feeling really isn't a problem unless you just can't seem to climb out of the dumps. In that case, your doctor ought to know about it and may be able to help clear things up. It is normal to feel tired at this time, and you may feel better if you can talk it over with someone who understands.

Another feeling may come up at times with a woman who has been actively and happily working outside the home. After the busy office days and friendly contact with coworkers, these young mothers sometimes find the day-to-day routine of the home and the care of the baby a lonely experience. You do not need to feel guilty about such feelings. Talk it over with your husband. See if you two can work out a plan to give you a chance to get away occasionally from the day-to-day routine. You won't be neglecting the baby if you go out once in a while. In fact he will get along better if you are relaxed and happy.

Most young fathers and mothers need to realize too that their personalities will not change completely when they become parents. They need to go out together at times, to have friends in, and to continue some of their previously shared outside interests. You will be happier, and the baby will get along better too if he is a part of a normal family group.

A Word to Expectant Fathers

A BABY is a family affair. Yet too often the father-to-be stands on the sidelines, an indifferent or neglected spectator. A husband should know what labor and childbirth are like, and how the baby grows, before and after birth. He should take an interest in what his wife is doing to preserve her good health and spirits.

While you, as the father, will be spared the emotional conflicts and discomforts of pregnancy, and the pangs of labor, you will not remain untouched during the ordeal. There are many changes in your way of life to be faced. Whether this is your first or fifth baby, children mean added responsibility in time and money, as well as the thoughtful planning that must go into good parenthood.

The support and encouragement you give your wife from the very beginning is most important to her. Plan to see her doctor sometimes during the early months of her pregnancy. He can help you understand a lot of the things you and your wife need to know about parenthood. At times your wife will need a special word of encouragement — perhaps about her diet, or how she looks, or whether she is getting enough rest. No one can give her quite the same feeling of confidence that you can give. It is very common for the most even-tempered woman to feel depressed at times during pregnancy. If you can understand this and give her that needed boost at just the right moment, both of you will grow in your understanding and love for each other.

IT'S YOUR BABY TOO!

Some communities have fathers' classes, where expectant fathers can go to learn how to take care of a baby, and have a chance to talk over with a doctor or a nurse some of the things that have puzzled them. Most men who have been to these classes think them very helpful. Some of these classes are sponsored by health departments, some by the Y.M.C.A., or other community agencies. Many of the puzzling things about pregnancy and babies are cleared up when young fathers get together with someone who can answer their questions.

If you are handy with tools and like to make things, you might want to make a crib, play pen, or cabinets for the baby. Plans for baby furniture are sometimes published in magazines, or can be found in books on furniture-making or woodworking. Ask your public library to help you find some good plans, if you want to try your hand at this. Or you may be lucky enough to get some hand-me-down furniture, or some secondhand pieces that need only a little refinishing to make them as good as new.

Many husbands help with housework, whether their wives are pregnant or not. Some men, however, are used to being waited on. They forget that certain tasks are hard for their wives to do during pregnancy. Plan together to arrange the housework so your wife will not get too tired. If you can get used to changes in the household routine before the baby comes, it is going to be easier to adjust to the other changes after the baby is here.

If this is your first baby, you may have doubts, too, about whether you are going to be a good father, and whether you can carry all the responsibilities as well as you'd like. Many young parents have these questions. Talk them over with your wife, or with her doctor, or with some of your friends who are young fathers. The hurdles aren't really so big, and the enjoyment and pride you will feel in your child will more than offset them.

If you catch yourself feeling neglected because the household routine is changed, or because things seem different now that your wife is pregnant, stop a minute and figure it out. You won't have such feelings long if you remember that you are just as important to your wife as ever, and that you will be a very important person to the baby. The good comradeship that you and your wife shared in other things can be carried over into your thinking and planning for the baby. The necessary adjustments that come with parenthood won't seem very hard to make if you and your wife understand each other, and can share in both the fun and work.

After the baby comes, there will be many new demands on your wife. The whole process of parenthood will be new and strange to you both. Don't think you can't change a diaper. You can, and your wife will certainly appreciate it. She was probably just as awkward the first time or two she tried. You needn't be afraid to pick up the baby. You will find it is lots of fun to get acquainted. He needs your love as much as he needs his mother's. Pitch in and help her get things done. You will all feel rewarded in the long run.

Preparing Other Children for the New Arrival

WHEN should you tell the other children about the new baby? You don't need to tell them as soon as you know you are pregnant. Seven or eight months is a long time to a child. If they ask about it, tell them when they ask. If they haven't asked, tell them two or three months before the baby is due. Most children notice changes in the mother's figure in the later months, and may overhear scraps of conversation. Or they may see the mother getting together the baby clothes and furniture. They will probably wonder and worry if they are not told about the baby. It is a mistake to wait until the baby has arrived, or until the mother leaves home for the hospital, and then expect the new baby to be a happy experience for the other children. They need to know ahead of time that a baby is on the way, and that their mother may be away for a while.

If they do, the natural jealousy that any child feels at times toward a new brother or sister is less likely to become a problem.

Many times, children can be drawn into the plans for the new baby—where he will sleep, helping mother to get the baby's clothes ready, and perhaps going with mother to see a friend's new baby. Many children are quite enthusiastic in helping to plan for the baby. Don't be surprised, though, if your child thinks new babies look funny, or if he announces he doesn't want a new baby brother or sister. Some children need time to get used to the idea. Parents need to understand that even the best adjusted child will have many moments after the baby comes, too, of wishing the baby was not there. He will need continuing reassurance both before and after the baby comes that you still love him too.

Some parents have found it helps a lot to ease the mother's absence if the child could see the hospital building before mother goes there, and know that is where mother will be. To many children, a big unknown hospital is a frightening place, especially if it keeps mother away from home. They may not feel so upset, however, if they have a chance to see the building and are told about the nurses and doctors who help mother get ready to come home quickly.

If you plan to have a relative or friend, or someone else, come in to take care of the children while you are in the hospital, try to have her come while you are still at home. In that way, the children can get used to her while you are still there, and the separation and strangeness will not be so upsetting to them.

Other parents, particularly those with toddlers, have found it a good plan to have the friend or relative or nurse take over responsibility for the new baby when the mother and baby first get home. The mother can then spend much of her time with the older child, since the new baby sleeps a lot and does not need her personal attention as much as he will later.

A new baby often is the center of much attention and interest, and an older child may feel completely left out in all the stir and bustle. If his father can give him some extra attention too, during these early weeks, it will help to keep the older child from feeling displaced.

Most parents have to think out for themselves how best to handle these early weeks of adjustment. The most important thing to remember is to be as natural and loving with the older child or children as you have always been—never to be afraid or apologetic.

How a Baby Grows—from Conception to Birth

THE MENSTRUAL CYCLE. Lying deep in the lower part of a woman's abdomen are the organs of menstruation and childbearing; the uterus, or womb, the two ovaries and Fallopian tubes, and the vagina or birth canal. These organs are protected by the bony walls of the pelvis.

The pear-shaped uterus is about three inches long and located directly above the vagina, with a small opening leading into it. The walls of the uterus are composed of thick muscle, the lower ends being called the cervix. Branching to left and right from the upper corners of the uterus, are the Fallopian tubes. These are also about three inches long and one-eighth to one-quarter of an inch in diameter. The outer end of each tube lies near an ovary. Each ovary is about the size and shape of an unshelled almond. The Fallopian tubes form a passage leading into the uterus, which in turn opens into the vagina.

Within the ovaries are many tiny white specks, visible only under a microscope, which are capable of developing into mature female sex cells. About every twenty-eight days, midway between two menstrual periods, one of these female cells is released by an ovary and enters into a branch of the Fallopian tube.

This activity of the ovaries is related to the menstruation process, or the monthly flow of blood. The female cell is released from the ovary at a fairly regular time each month. In most women this is about fourteen days before a menstrual period is due. However, this is not a hard and fast rule. The time varies in different women.

As the ovary prepares itself to release the cell, changes are taking place in the lining of the uterus to get it ready for a possible pregnancy. As soon as a menstrual period is finished, the lining of the uterus begins to grow. Tiny glands form in the outer layer of the lining. Many little blood vessels grow up into this layer, and the whole lining becomes soft and velvety.

If the female cell is fertilized by a male cell and pregnancy begins, the lining of the uterus will be ready for the newly forming baby. If pregnancy does not occur, the female cell dies in about three days, and the growth of the lining of the uterus slows up.

The monthly flow occurs when the top layer of the lining stops growing and begins to come loose. The top layer contains the newly formed glands and many of the little blood vessels. As it loosens, a flow of blood results, which carries out most of the lining with it. The flow is heavy at first, but slows up as the lining becomes thinner and the little blood vessels disappear. At the end of the menstrual period, the lining is almost completely gone. Now it begins to grow again, as we have described, and the whole process is repeated. About twenty-eight days from the beginning of the last menstrual period, a new menstrual period begins.

If pregnancy does occur, menstruation will stop. The lining grows thicker, and it will not be shed, for it is now in use. No more female cells will be released by the ovary during pregnancy, and menstruation will not begin again until several weeks or months after the baby is born.

THE START OF A NEW LIFE

CONCEPTION. A baby grows from the union of a male cell and a female cell. Male cells (called spermatozoa) form in the testes (sex glands) of a man. Female cells, or ova, form in the ovaries of a woman. The union of a spermatozoon with an ovum is called conception, or fertilization, and is the beginning of pregnancy.

The female cell is about one two-hundredths of an inch in diameter. In shape, it is round. It is surrounded by a protective outer

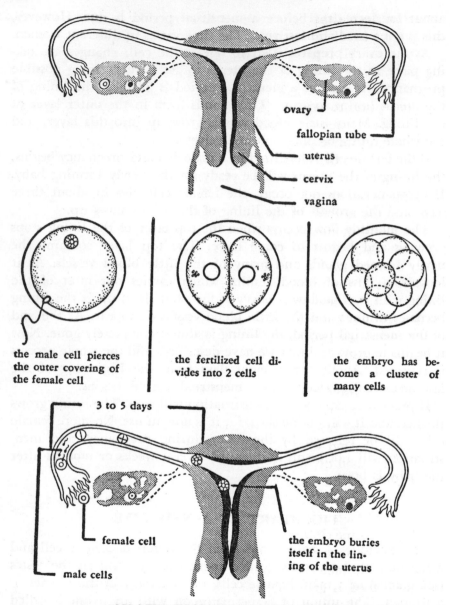

ovary

fallopian tube

uterus

cervix

vagina

the male cell pierces
the outer covering of
the female cell

the fertilized cell di-
vides into 2 cells

the embryo has be-
come a cluster of
many cells

3 to 5 days

female cell

male cells

the embryo buries
itself in the lin-
ing of the uterus

HOW FERTILIZATION TAKES PLACE

(Top) The child-bearing organs. *(Center)* Process of fertilization as male and
female cells meet. *(Bottom)* Showing the movement of the fertilized embryo
through the tube into the uterus. The same ovum is shown in different positions
as it moves down tube into the uterus.

covering. Inside this is a layer of food material, and deep in the middle is a small inner circle called a nucleus.

The male cell is many times smaller. It moves by lashing its long, slender tail. The female cell, however, cannot move by its own power. The male cell must find its way to the female cell in order for conception to take place.

Millions of male cells, or spermatozoa, are passed into the vagina at each intercourse. Some of these cells pass up through the uterus and into the tube. They can move fast enough to reach the end of the tube within an hour after intercourse. If one of them finds a living ovum there, conception can take place. If not, the male cell will die within a few days. Those remaining in or near the vagina probably die within twenty-four hours.

When a male cell reaches a female cell, it pierces the protective outer covering and its tail drops off. It passes through the layer of food material and unites with the nucleus of the female cell. This is fertilization. A new life has started.

You will not know when conception takes place. In fact, the baby will develop for two weeks or longer before you even suspect you are pregnant.

THE FIRST WEEK OF LIFE. Neither the male nor female cell is complete in itself, but upon their union they form a cell that is complete, that can begin to grow. This newly formed cell contains all the material from which the baby gets his inheritance: what he will look like, and what his basic capacities will be.

This cell soon divides into two cells, and the two into four, and so on. This process of cell division will continue on throughout life. During these early days, however, cell division is more rapid than it will ever be again.

The increasing cluster of cells is called an embryo.

During the first few days after conception, the embryo gets its food from the material in the middle layer of the original female cell. This food is gradually exhausted as the embryo moves down the tube into the uterus. It probably takes about three to five days to make this journey.

At the end of six days, the embryo has become a mass of many tiny cells. It sinks into the thick soft lining of the uterus. The lining contains many glands and tiny blood vessels. As the embryo settles into this lining, it finds a bed and food for itself.

SECOND WEEK AFTER CONCEPTION.   About the ninth or tenth day, the protective outer layer has disappeared, and a shaggy growth with many little finger-like structures takes its place. These little finger-like structures fasten the embryo to the inner lining of the uterus, and are the beginnings of the placenta.

During the second week after conception the original cluster is beginning to form into three different groups of cells. Some of these cells will develop into the baby himself. Some will form the attachment to the uterus—the placenta—which will be joined to the baby by the umbilical cord. Some will develop into the membranes that will surround and protect the baby.

THIRD WEEK AFTER CONCEPTION *(about the time your first period is missed)*.   In this week the group of cells which develop into the baby looks like a flat grooved, or ridged, oblong. It is just barely large enough to be seen by the naked eye. Many beginnings of organs are present. The area which will develop into the head and brain is growing very, very fast. There are shallow depressions where the eyes will form.

THE BABY'S 4TH WEEK OF LIFE.   The embryo is growing very rapidly. At the end of four weeks it measures about one-sixth of an inch in length. During this important week, all the internal organs (such as the heart, liver, digestive tract, brain, and lungs) are really beginning to take form. The heart begins to beat, although it cannot be heard for many more weeks yet. You are probably beginning to think now that you might be pregnant.

THE BABY'S 5TH WEEK OF LIFE.   The embryo is bent in an arch, and looks like a little fat semicircle. The backbone begins to form. The head is developing much faster than the rest of the body, as it will continue to do until after the baby is born. Tiny limb-buds, the beginnings of the arms and legs, have appeared.

THE BABY'S 6TH WEEK OF LIFE.   The embryo is now almost one-half an inch long. The four limb-buds have grown into arms and legs with tiny webbed fingers and toes. The embryo has a well-

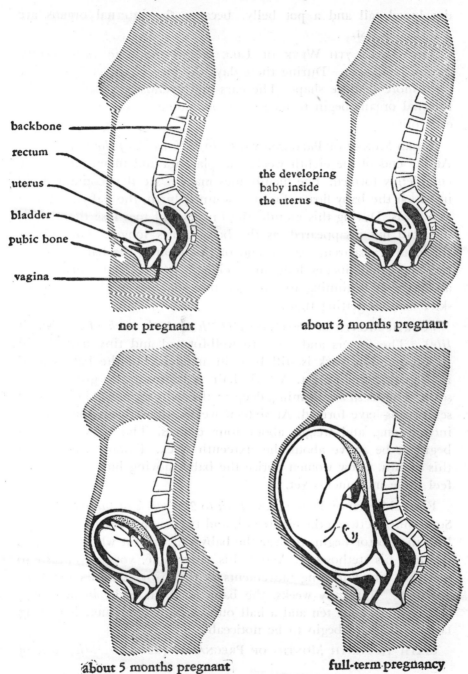

backbone

rectum

uterus

bladder

pubic bone

vagina

not pregnant

the developing
baby inside
the uterus

about 3 months pregnant

about 5 months pregnant

full-term pregnancy

HOW THE BABY DEVELOPS

developed tail and a pot belly, because the internal organs are growing so fast.

THE BABY'S 7TH WEEK OF LIFE *(about the time your second period is missed).* During these days the face of the embryo takes on a more definite shape. The ears and eyelids are forming. The internal organs begin to take their permanent place in relation to each other.

THIRD MONTH OF PREGNANCY *(8th to 12th week of the baby's life).* At the end of the eighth week, the placenta and membranes have completely formed. The membranes make a sac that contains fluid in which the baby floats. From now until birth, the baby is known as a fetus. During this month, the fingers and toes lose their webs. The tail has disappeared, as the body grows longer. The skin is thin and transparent. At the end of this month, the baby is about two and a half inches long and weighs about half an ounce. Your abdomen is beginning to enlarge, and you may notice that your skirt band is getting tight.

FOURTH MONTH OF PREGNANCY *(12th to 16th week of the baby's life).* The fingers and toes are well-formed and tiny nails begin to appear. The back is still bent in an arch, but the baby's head is becoming more erect. A little hair is beginning to grow on the scalp. The teeth are forming, deep in the baby's gums. The external sex organs have formed. At sixteen weeks, the baby is four to five inches long, and weighs about four ounces. The baby's muscles begin to be active about the sixteenth week. Toward the end of this month, a few women notice the baby moving but most do not feel these movements yet.

FIFTH MONTH OF PREGNANCY *(17th to 21st week of the baby's life).* Sometimes between the eighteenth and twentieth week of the baby's life, the doctor begins to hear the baby's heart beat when he listens through his stethoscope. About this same time, you may begin to feel the aint fluttering movements as the baby stretches his arms and legs. At twenty weeks, the baby is about eight inches long, and weighs about ten and a half ounces. Your abdomen is getting large enough to begin to be noticeable.

SIXTH TO NINTH MONTHS OF PREGNANCY *(22nd to 38th week of*

the baby's life). From now on, you will notice your abdomen enlarging more rapidly. The baby's body grows very fast in length. Until about the eighth month, his skin is wrinkled and red, and he looks somewhat like a little old man. During the last two months, his body fat is formed, and he becomes more rounded and filled out. From the sixth month until shortly before birth, his skin is covered with soft downy fuzz. A soft white creamy secretion called vernix begins to collect on his body.

His movements become real thumps by the sixth month. The baby may change his position many times. Sometimes he lies on one side, sometimes on another, sometimes with his head down and sometimes with it up. Usually by the seventh month, the baby will take one position, either with his head up or down, and will probably keep this position until he is born.

There may be times when you do not feel any movements. Some doctors think the baby has periods of waking and sleeping, just as he will later on after birth.

A few babies born before their twenty-eighth week of development have lived, but this is very rare. Before this time, the baby's internal organs have not developed enough for him to be able to live in the outside world. After the twenty-eighth week, or roughly about six and a half calendar months of pregnancy, his chances of living, if prematurely born, increase with each month. A seven-months baby has a fair chance of surviving premature birth; an eight-months baby even better chances, if he is given the special care that all premature babies need.

WHEN THE BABY IS READY FOR BIRTH *(full-term).* At the ninth month, the tiny fuzz covering the skin has largely disappeared. The baby's skin has more natural color and is thickly covered with the soft, creamy vernix secretion. His head is covered with fine hair, and his eyes are a dark slate color. As soon as he is born, he will cry vigorously and move his arms and legs energetically.

The average weight of a full-term baby is about seven and a half pounds, and the average length about twenty inches. But normal full-term babies vary all the way from five and a half to ten or eleven pounds, and from nineteen to twenty-two inches. Boy babies usually weigh a few ounces more than girl babies.

THE PLACENTA AND BAG OF WATERS

Most mothers want to know how the baby is attached to them; just what is the connection between their bodies? Actually there is no connection except through the placenta. This important structure provides a way for the baby to get nourishment. It is often called the afterbirth, because it passes out of the uterus after the baby is born.

As the embryo settles into the lining of the uterus, in the second week after conception, its outer covering spreads many little finger-like structures out into the lining. These fingerlike structures, together with the region of the lining where they are fastened, form the placenta. As the uterus and the baby grow, the placenta grows, too. The little fingers going down into the lining of the uterus lie near many of the blood vessels in the wall of the uterus. Blood vessels from the baby's body run through the umbilical cord out into the placenta, where they can pass close to the mother's blood vessels.

Although these blood vessels lie close together, there is no direct connection between the mother's and baby's blood streams. Food materials from the mother and waste products from the baby must pass to and fro through the blood vessel walls in the placenta. The food material is carried to the baby by the blood vessels in the umbilical cord. In addition to supplying food to the baby, the mother's blood stream carries away all the waste from the baby's body.

The "bag of waters" is a sac formed from thin membranes which grow from the edges of the placenta and completely surround the baby. This sac is filled with a thin watery fluid.

One might ask, "But why doesn't the baby drown if he is floating in fluid?" There is no danger of that, because the baby does not use his lungs to get oxygen as he will after birth. He gets all the oxygen he needs from your blood. His lungs will not fill with air until after he is born. There are good reasons for the fluid. It keeps him at an even temperature. It also acts as a cushion or shock-absorber to protect him from the jolts and bumps he might get from your ordinary activity.

WHAT DETERMINES THE BABY'S SEX?

How does it come about that the baby will be a boy or a girl? It is apparently a matter of chance. Scientific studies seem to show that the male cells determine whether the baby will be a boy or a girl. There are two kinds of male cells, one which will cause a girl baby, the other a boy baby. The two kinds of male cells are probably produced in about equal numbers. As far as we know now, it is chance that decides which kind of male cell fertilizes the female cell.

There is no way known at present of telling definitely before birth whether the baby is a boy or girl. X ray will not help, as it merely shows the baby's bony structure.

TWINS. Twins are born about once in eighty-six pregnancies on the average. About 25 per cent of all twins are identical. Triplets and quadruplets are born so seldom that they usually rate a story in the newspapers.

Nowadays, twins usually do not come as a surprise. The doctor can often tell by hearing two separate heart beats or feeling two separate babies as he examines your abdomen. If he has any question, an X ray after the fourth month will show whether there is one baby or more.

There are two types of twins, those called fraternal and those called identical. Fraternal twins are entirely separate babies from the very first. They come from two separate female cells, each of which was fertilized by a separate male cell. Each baby has its own placenta and bag of waters. This type of twin probably develops because both ovaries release a female cell at the same time, or because one ovary happens to release two cells at once. These babies are no more alike in looks and disposition than any other brothers and sisters. Boy-and-girl twins are always of this type, although fraternal twins may also be two boys or two girls.

Identical twins form in a different way. They come from the union of one female cell and one male cell. When this new life begins to grow, something apparently causes it to separate entirely into two parts, which develop independently. No one knows why this happens. These babies usually have separate umbilical cords and bags of waters, but are attached to one placenta. They are always of the same sex, and look so alike that even their mothers have trouble at times in telling them apart.

Triplets and quadruplets can be either identical, fraternal, or both.

WILL MY BABY BE NORMAL?

Many a mother wonders at times whether her baby is developing normally. It is comforting to know that only a very few babies are born with any sort of defect. The reason for this is that defects are often the result of a flaw in the cell material of either the male or female sex cell from which the baby was formed. When the defect is there from the beginning, the baby cannot develop normally and is often miscarried very early.

Many people used to think that marking the baby came about because of something the mother thought, or saw, during pregnancy. This superstition, however, is not true. There is no direct connection between your nerves or your blood stream and the baby's at all. Your thoughts and the things you see cannot have any direct effect on the way the baby's body is formed. If a baby is born with a deformity, it is not the result of any action or fright or thoughts the mother may have experienced.

Doctors know some of the causes for deformities, but not all. Some defects may result when the mother has certain illnesses, such as German measles, early in pregnancy. Some rare conditons—certain types of eye deformity or extra fingers and toes—are inherited. Some deformities may result from an extreme lack of certain essential foods in the mother's diet. Others, as we have mentioned, are the result of defects in the original cells from which the baby grew.

Birthmarks usually come about because of some small flaws in the early development of the baby. These marks often fade away as the baby grows older. Often newborn babies have small purple discolorations on their foreheads or the back of their necks. These are not true birthmarks and usually begin to fade in a few days or weeks. Their cause is not known.

What to Do to Keep Well During Pregnancy

SINCE the baby gets his food through your body, the food you eat is most important. However, it is the *kind* of food rather than the amount you eat that is important. Actually, a pregnant woman needs only slightly more food than she would normally eat. To be sure, some women need a larger amount of food than others, during pregnancy, but there are usually reasons for this. Much depends on what your weight was before you became pregnant.

EATING FOR TWO. If your weight has been normal for your height and build (as determined by your doctor) you should not gain more than twenty to twenty-five pounds during your entire pregnancy. It may be desirable to add a few pounds if you have always been underweight, but if you are inclined to overweight, don't gain that much. The safe course is always to follow your doctor's advice in the matter of weight. "Eating for two" merely calls for a well-balanced diet that will supply your baby with all he needs without harming your own health or figure.

The food you eat is absorbed into your blood stream, where it can be used by your own body tissues or by the baby. When the proper building materials are in the mother's blood stream, the baby can get exactly what he needs for proper growth. If the mother's food does not contain all these necessary substances, her blood will try to supply them to the baby from her own body tissues. This can only be done when the mother's body contains these needed substances. You can see for yourself what might happen if the mother does not eat the right foods. Her body and her blood stream might not contain enough of what her baby needs. And the draining of the important materials from her own body may make her ill. A woman who does not eat the essential foods can do real harm to herself and the baby. Recent studies have shown that mothers with adequate diets during pregnancy tend to have better labor and are less likely to have premature or sickly babies.

55

The most important foods that a mother's diet must contain are those rich in protein, calcium, iron, and all the vitamins. In some regions, extra iodine must be supplied. Calcium and protein are the bone- and body-building substances, and iron is needed for good rich blood. Vitamins are needed for normal activities of all the body cells. There are other materials in everyday foods, such as sugars, starches, and fats, which everyone needs to provide enough calories (another name for energy). But these materials are not so necessary for the baby's growth as those mentioned above, and this type of food can be cut down to a minimum if a mother is gaining too much weight.

THE NEED FOR INCREASED NUTRITION

The complex mechanisms behind the formation of the eggs in ovaries and fertilization with the sperm undoubtedly require a nicety of adjustment. The accurate timing of these momentous details are particularly dependent upon the environment in which they occur. Many investigators in the role of nutrition in pregnancy have stressed the importance of nutritional balance when trying to become pregnant, as well as in pregnancy. One group of investigators were able to show, by X ray, bony changes in the hand and foot in the development of the embryo in relationship to the calcium and protein intake of the mother. Various other workers have shown that the deciduous teeth development is dependent upon the prenatal diet of the mother. It is obvious that a patient's tissues on borderline of adequacy will become deficient when she becomes pregnant if her eating habits remain unchanged.

MORTALITY AMONG THE NEWBORN. The main causes of the frequency of mortality among the newborn are prematurity and congenital debility, or weakness at birth. A baby born to a mother who is in a run-down condition will start life without reserves. The diets of many of our American women have too frequently deteriorated to coffee and a sweet roll for breakfast and a cup of soup and a sandwich for lunch. The National Research Council, analyzing the diets of a large group of women, found that only 10 per cent met all requirements and could be termed good, 40 per cent were fair, and 50 per cent were poor.

It is logical to suppose that large reserves might protect the embryo during the first and most critical periods of its development when the mother's reserves may be depleted by the loss of appetite and vomiting. Many patients during this period have difficulty in taking food or even retaining it. This too may happen to the supplemental vitamins prescribed for them.

Underfeeding and Overweight

The pregnant woman's meals must be carefully planned, then, so that all essentials of a balanced diet are retained. It is too often taken for granted that an overweight patient must of necessity be well nourished. This, of course, is far from true. Life insurance and medical statistics show that overweight persons may be more poorly nourished on account of their unbalanced diet and that their overloaded machine breaks down, years before it needs to, with "burned-out bearings" of heart and kidney disease.

The amount of weight a patient should gain during pregnancy will depend on the degree of nausea during the first three months and the weight level when pregnancy began. The average patient loses from twenty to twenty-five pounds in the six weeks following delivery.

PSYCHIATRY AND PREGNANCY. It is now claimed by some physicians that psychiatry may be helpful in controlling some of these difficult problems. A psychiatrist may be helpful in coping with some of the appetites of pregnancy or distaste for food. A combination of methods may be necessary just as it is in the control of overindulgence of alcohol. The psychiatric approach may find its place just as it is now doing in the care of children. After all, many of the problems are just grown-up feeding problems of childhood.

DIET IN PREGNANCY

We see, then, that not only is the well-being of the mother preserved and improved by good nutrition, but the child's chances of survival and health are greatly increased. The diet should be simple, nourishing and easily digestible.

Studies of the diets of nursing mothers have indicated that when the diet of the mother falls below a certain minimum, her milk will be inadequate in quality and especially in quantity. Yet a word of caution is necessary with regard to the not uncommon practice of overfeeding patients in an effort to stimulate milk production. Many examples of obesity in women during pregnancy are attributable to such ill-advised attempts at overfeeding.

The Balanced Diet

A balanced diet is extremely important, as ever. The pregnant woman should have a full quota of proteins, fats, carbohydrates and minerals. The heightened bodily processes of the pregnant woman and the demands of the growing fetus render her dietary requirements different from, and on the whole greater than, those of other adults. The diet must be rich in fruits and vegetables, but even this does not insure a proper intake of vitamins and minerals, since during pregnancy the requirements for protein, minerals, and vitamins may be increased 100 per cent or more.

The fetus acquires two thirds of its total birth weight in the last three months of pregnancy, two thirds of its calcium, four fifths of its iron, three fourths of its protein, and over 90 per cent of its fat. It is during this period that the serious effects of malnutrition are most likely to appear in the mother if she does not eat properly.

MINERAL REQUIREMENTS. To be healthy, the mature human body must be richer in calcium than in any other mineral element; yet every child is born calcium-poor and iron-rich. The calcium poverty facilitates birth in that the bones are then soft. On the other hand, pregnancy usually results in a depletion of the mother's body calcium.

Pregnancy, then, considerably increases the requirement of calcium. Enough must be supplied to meet both normal adult needs and the demand of the growing fetus. If the dietary supply is inadequate, the skeleton of the fetus will develop at the expense of the mineral content of the mother's bones and teeth. Deficiency may

lead to mild or latent tetany in the mother. The main reliance
should be placed on green vegetables and milk. Plenty of sunlight
or vitamin D (or both) is necessary to insure the greatest possible
use of calcium in the diet.

Phosphorus is as essential a dietary element as calcium, but the
danger of deficiency is less. A normal intake of meat, fish, eggs and
dairy products should insure a good supply. The iodine needs are
also higher, and can be met by the use of iodized salt. This is particularly important in areas where the soil lacks iodine, even in the
small amount that is necessary for man. Iron is an essential con-
stituent of the human body, and should be available in sufficient
quantity in a good diet. The salt and fluid intake should be watched
in pregnancy. Extreme salt restriction is ordinarily unnecessary,
but sodium intake should be only moderate, since excess leads to
fluid retention and swelling.

OVERALL VITAMIN REQUIREMENTS.   The requirements for all the
known vitamins and particularly those of the B complex are increased during pregnancy.

VITAMIN A.   Vitamin A is essential for normal reproduction and
milk production, as well as for resistance to infection. The required
amounts may be obtained by the daily consumption of a quart of
milk, one egg, one ounce of cheese, one or two servings of green leafy
vegetables, and a teaspoonful of cod-liver oil. Carrots and butter are
other good sources. In women deficient in vitamin A, maternal
deaths have been found to be more than four times as great as in
those on a vitamin-A-rich diet.

VITAMIN B COMPLEX.   The members of the B family of vitamins
are all-important in the proper functioning of the human body. The
need for the B complex as a whole is much increased in pregnancy.
Its importance in this condition is shown by the scientific evidence
that animals completely deprived of it during the first half of pregnancy invariably have abortions.

THIAMINE.   Thiamine, found in almost all plants, is essential for
metabolism and growth. Pork and dried brewer's yeast are good
sources. To be sure of an adequate supply of thiamine, include
whole-grain breads and cereals, milk, dried beans and peas in the

daily diet. Symptoms frequently noted in pregnancy which may indicate a relative lack of vitamins are fatigue, poor appetite, indigestion, nausea or vomiting, disturbed bowel function, palpitation, frequency of urination, shortness of breath, headache, or backache. Proper diet will improve these conditions if they are nutritional in origin.

FOLIC ACID. The average diet is unlikely to be lacking in folic acid if salads and raw fruits are included. This member of the B complex is best known for its curative effects in certain anemias. It has a maturing effect on the cells of the bone marrow, and plays an essential role in body activity.

VITAMIN C. The need for vitamin C is considerably increased during pregnancy, the fetus acting, so to say, as a parasite in this regard. An adequate amount of vitamin C can be supplied by five ounces of unstrained orange juice, or by generous amounts of foods rich in this vitamin (tomatoes, grapefruit, raw cabbage, leafy green vegetables, and potatoes cooked in their skins).

VITAMIN D. The need for vitamin D is greater in pregnancy and milk production (lactation) than in any other period after the first year of life. An adequate intake of this vitamin is necessary for the proper absorption of calcium and phosphorus, and for their proper utilization by the bones and other tissues. Because vitamin D is contained in only a few of the foods in the average diet, and only in small quantities, the requisite daily allowance must be provided by some form of vitamin supplement.

VITAMIN E. There is a great deal of scientific evidence that a vitamin E deficiency may be one factor in recurrent abortion.

VITAMIN K. A vitamin which assumes great importance as pregnancy draws to its close is vitamin K, the antihemorrhagic vitamin. Its value is less to the mother (whose diet will usually be high enough in K for her own needs, due to its extensive distribution in natural foods) than to the child, which possesses virtually no vitamin K during the first weeks of life. Hemorrhagic disease of the newborn is associated with this vitamin lack, and it is now common practice to guard against it by administering vitamin K (about two milligrams daily) during the last weeks of pregnancy, or just before or during delivery.

An expectant mother needs the following foods every day:

MILK. One quart of whole or skim milk a day. Part of this can be used as cream soups, custards, puddings, or creamed foods. Cheese may be used at times. Yellow cheese supplies most of the important materials found in milk. One-eighth of a pound is about equal to one pint of milk. Skim milk can be used if you are overweight, if you are getting vitamin A from other foods. Milk is an important source of protein, and supplies nearly all the calcium that is so necessary to insure good teeth and bones in your baby. In fact, there is no food that can take the place of milk in providing this important mineral. Milk is also the richest source of the vitamin riboflavin.

Some women who do not like milk think that they can take calcium tablets instead. Calcium tablets are not a complete substitute for milk because they do not supply protein or riboflavin.

FRUITS AND VEGETABLES. You will need five to seven servings of fruits and vegetables a day, and at least one serving of each should be raw. Include a serving of oranges, grapefruit, or other citrus fruits, or tomatoes, berries, or melon, and one or more leafy green vegetables. Choose other fruits and vegetables as you wish. Eating plenty of these fruits and vegetables will give you vitamins and iron, and also some of the calcium and energy you need.

LEAN MEAT, POULTRY, FISH. At least one quarter of a pound a day of meat or fish, in one or two servings, is desirable. All meats are good foods, but the lean parts supply the building materials for muscles and blood. Liver, kidney, and sweetbreads are especially good; tripe, brains, and heart may also be used. All kinds of seafood may be used in place of meat.

EGGS. At least one egg a day. Eggs are a good source of iron, which helps to build good blood for both you and the baby.

CEREALS AND BREAD. Three servings a day of cereals and bread are needed to supply certain vitamins. These are good energy foods, too. Use only the whole-grain, restored, or enriched cereals, breads, and flour. In the white or refined products, much of the important minerals and vitamins have been lost or removed. When these foods are labeled "restored" or "enriched," vitamins and minerals have been added to replace some of those that were lost.

BUTTER AND FORTIFIED MARGARINE. These contain vitamin A, but they are fatty foods and should be used sparingly, if you are watching your weight. You can get vitamin A from other foods that are less likely to be fattening, such as liver, carrots, yellow squash, and leafy green vegetables.

FLUIDS. Plenty of water and other fluids are needed to keep your kidneys working well. Soups, milk, and fruit juices are good sources of fluid, but most expectant mothers need to drink several glasses of water a day in addition. However, you need not carry this to an extreme—four to six glasses of water are enough unless your doctor tells you to drink an extra amount. Tea and coffee in moderation do no harm, but ask your doctor about these.

Liberal amounts of the important foods that have been listed should satisfy your appetite. If you are still hungry, and the doctor does not think you are gaining too much weight, you may eat other foods as you wish, but beware of stuffing yourself with cakes, candy, jelly, pastries, soft drinks, and other goodies. These will send your weight sky-high, take away your appetite for the necessary foods, and play havoc with your health if you are not careful.

Some doctors think pregnant women should not eat much salt. If your doctor has told you to cut out salt, do not add it in cooking, but let the rest of the family season their food later. A little pepper or a very small amount of sugar will help make the food appetizing, and you will not miss the salt after a few days. Remember, too, if your doctor has told you to stop eating salt, omit any foods which contain extra salt. These are such foods as bacon, ham, chipped beef, corned beef, salted and smoked fish, salted nuts, pretzels, salted crackers, popcorn, or potato chips.

You will find that your doctor watches carefully how much weight you gain during pregnancy and how fast you gain it. Most doctors find that women who weighed about the right amount before they became pregnant do best when they gain only twenty to twenty-five pounds. They tend to feel much better, may have easier labor, and regain their figures more quickly after the baby comes. Consider what makes up the added weight. The average full-term baby weighs about seven and a half pounds. The placenta and membranes are about one and a quarter pounds, the enlarged uterus about two pounds, and the fluid inside the bag of waters about two pounds. This adds up to nearly thirteen pounds. The increased size of your breasts adds a little more. Your body tissues absorb and keep more water during pregnancy and this adds a little to your weight, too. If you gain a lot more, you only add to your body fat, and may have a hard time getting rid of the extra weight after the baby comes.

The amount of food you eat will not have much effect on the size of the baby. So it won't help much, and may actually harm the baby, if you try to starve yourself in order to have a small baby.

SAMPLE MENU FOR PREGNANCY DIET

Breakfast. Fruit, two eggs, one-half piece toast, beverage.

Midmorning. One-half cup oatmeal, one-half glass milk, prunes.

Lunch. Three ounces cooked meat, fish, poultry; one cup of two vegetables; one-half cup of salad greens; one-half glass milk.

Midafternoon. Two ounces cheese—cottage or cheddar variety; one-half piece bread, one-half glass milk.

Dinner. Three ounces cooked meat, one cup of two vegetables, one-half cup salad greens, simple dessert, one glass milk.

Before Bedtime. One egg, one glass milk, one-half slice bread.

Remember, there is as great danger in overweight as there is in underweight.

REST AND SLEEP

Every pregnant woman needs at least eight hours of sleep at night, and a rest period at least once during the day. This daytime rest may be nothing more than taking off your dress and lying down for ten or fifteen minutes. Even if you do not go to sleep, the relaxation will do you a great deal of good. Doctors are stressing more and more the importance of learning to relax, especially if you are inclined to be tense.

If you are employed, try to rest with your feet up, for a few minutes after lunch or when you get home from work. Some businesses or industries provide extra rest periods for pregnant women.

Frequent stops during the day when you are doing your housework will help to refresh you. Sit down several times a day for a few minutes with your feet up—you will be surprised how much better you feel at the end of the day. The slang phrase "take the load off your feet" expresses it pretty well.

HOW MUCH EXERCISE?

A moderate amount of exercise is good for anyone, and this is particularly true for a pregnant woman. Unless you have been ill or unless there is some other complication, you can continue your housework, gardening, daily walks, and even swim occasionally. Your doctor will probably tell you to keep on with most of the things you have been doing, but to avoid very heavy housework and heavy lifting. He may also tell you to stop strenuous exercise like horseback riding, basketball, or diving. He will probably tell you to work more slowly and to rest a few minutes several times a day. Most women can keep up much of their normal activity until the baby is due, although the awkwardness late in pregnancy makes it harder to be active then.

Plan to spend some time out of doors every day. If you have a garden, it will give you a good excuse to get some fresh air as you work. If not, you may enjoy taking a walk every day. Try to walk to the store or to your friend's house instead of riding—but do not get too tired. And on the day you have a heavy bag of groceries, you had better ride.

If your indoor work involves much exercise, it may be better to make the outdoor time a rest period, especially in nice weather when it is pleasant to sit outdoors.

To sum it up, don't consider yourself an invalid. The old idea of being "in a delicate condition" is not popular any more. Many women find they feel better during pregnancy than at any other time.

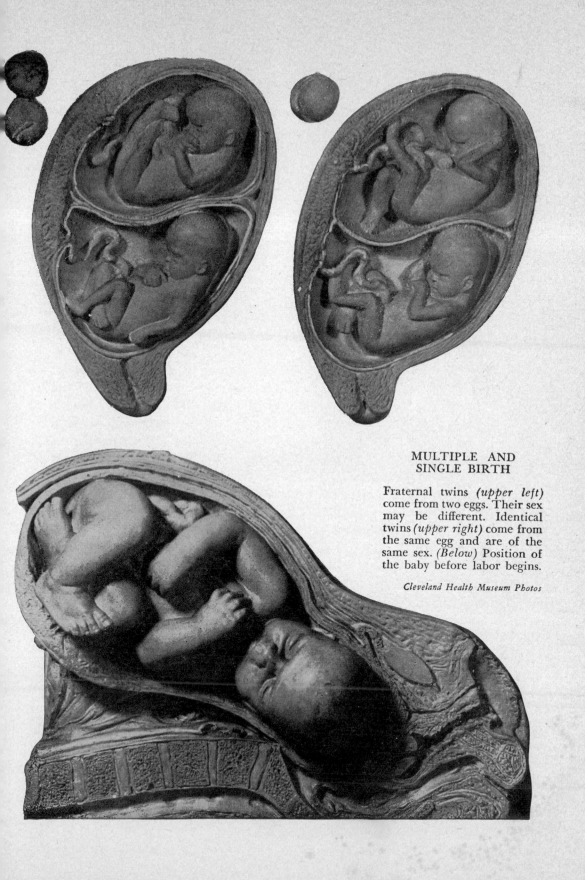

MULTIPLE AND SINGLE BIRTH

Fraternal twins *(upper left)* come from two eggs. Their sex may be different. Identical twins *(upper right)* come from the same egg and are of the same sex. *(Below)* Position of the baby before labor begins.

Cleveland Health Museum Photos

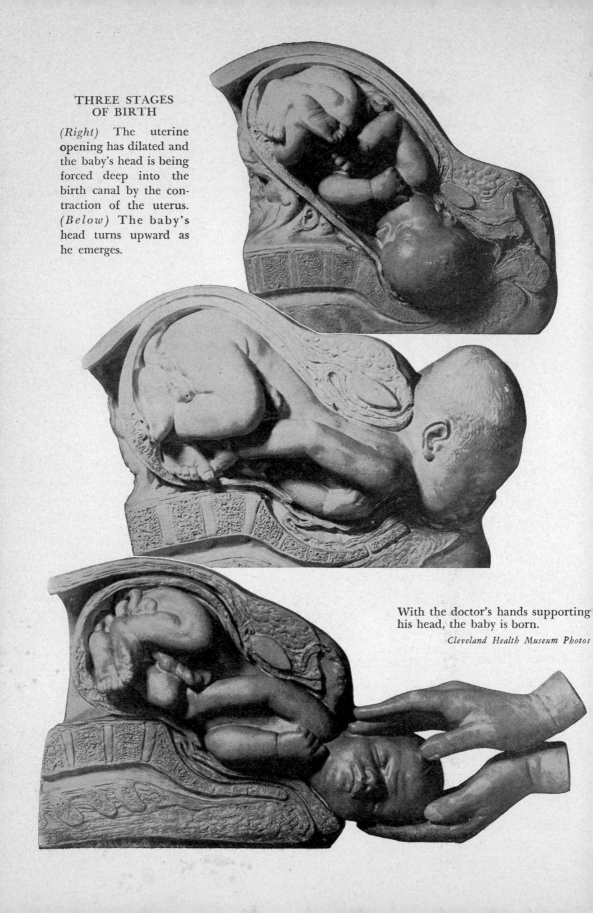

THREE STAGES OF BIRTH

(Right) The uterine opening has dilated and the baby's head is being forced deep into the birth canal by the contraction of the uterus. *(Below)* The baby's head turns upward as he emerges.

With the doctor's hands supporting his head, the baby is born.

Cleveland Health Museum Photos

COMFORT IN CLOTHING

Wear clothing that is attractive, comfortable, and loose. Today, it is fairly easy to find clothes, including underwear, that are especially made for the pregnant woman. You can find many attractive patterns, too, if you make your clothes. Most important is to avoid anything tight or binding about the waist. If dresses, skirts, and slips hang from the shoulders and have adjustable waistlines they will not put pressure on the abdomen. Panties are more comfortable if they are loose enough to be adjusted easily as your waistline expands.

You probably will not need maternity dresses until the fourth or fifth month. Most women cannot afford to buy several maternity dresses and you may get very tired of them if you start to wear them too early.

Select a brassiere that gives good support to the breasts, but is not too tight. The best type has a full cup, wide shoulder straps, and pulls each breast up and in toward the opposite shoulder. By the fifth month, your breasts will probably be as large as they are going to become during pregnancy. You may not need to buy any larger brassieres after that until you get your nursing brassieres. Some women wear nursing brassieres during pregnancy with tucks that can be let out after the baby comes.

One of the definite "don'ts" refers to round garters. Discard these during pregnancy, and don't roll your stockings into a tight band at the top. Any tight band may slow up the normal blood flow in the legs, and might add to the discomfort of muscle cramps or varicose veins. Many pregnant women find it easier to wear socks or to go without stockings altogether. If you wear stockings, but not a girdle, you can buy or make an adjustable garter belt with straps over the shoulders to support it. These "suspenders" sound bulky, but are really comfortable.

The question of whether or not to wear a corset is one your doctor can help you decide. If you have always worn a girdle or corset, you will probably need one during pregnancy. During the first two or three months, it is all right to wear an ordinary elastic girdle without bones, but after that, you will need a special maternity corset, with adjustable sides and back fitted to your measure. Your doctor or clinic can probably tell you where to get this. A maternity corset is put on in a different way. You will find it more comfortable to lie on your back, with a pillow under your hips if needed. Then pull the corset up over your legs into position and start fastening with the bottom hooks. Or put it on in the usual way without hooking it. Then lie down on your back to fasten it. The first time you try this may be awkward, but you will find it supports the uterus better. And later in pregnancy it is easier than struggling into the corset while standing up.

If you have never worn a girdle or corset, you may not need one during pregnancy. Ask your doctor about this if you have any question.

An abdominal support can be made at home with a wide band of soft muslin or similar material. Pin this firmly around the abdomen, as you lie on your back, starting at the bottom. This will pull the abdomen up into normal position. You may find it hard to put on this type of support properly without help and it is not as satisfactory as a maternity corset. However, it can be used if you cannot get a corset.

Flat-heeled or low-heeled shoes which fit you comfortably will help your posture as well as your disposition by keeping you from getting too tired. It is important that shoes give you good support, for a flat, shapeless moccasin may tire you just as much as high heels. The increased weight in your abdomen changes your usual posture, and badly fitting or high-heeled shoes will throw you even farther off balance. There is more danger of falling, too, if you wear high heels. You may find a pair of medium heeled shoes a good transition from high heels to low, if you have always worn high-heeled shoes.

WHAT TO DO ABOUT—

SMOKING AND DRINKING.　Doctors differ in their opinions regarding smoking and drinking during pregnancy. Ask your doctor about these questions.

BATHING.　You may perspire more during pregnancy than you did before. Perspiration is one way of throwing off waste products.

Since the baby's waste must be cast out, too, the amount of perspiration may increase. A daily bath during pregnancy will help keep you fresh and is the best care you can give your skin. During most of your pregnancy, it may be a tub bath, a shower, or a sponge bath, as you choose.

Late in pregnancy, take only a shower or sponge bath. It is important not to take tub baths at this time.

CARE OF TEETH. Good dental care is important during pregnancy, just as it is at all times. Go to your dentist early and see him regularly. He will tell you how often. If you have cavities, he will see that they are filled. This prevents further decay which might mean the loss of a tooth. Infection of the gums needs prompt treatment. A tooth that has become badly infected or is dead can be pulled during pregnancy. It is better to have the tooth out and the infection cured as quickly as possible. Pulling teeth will not cause a miscarriage or harm the baby.

On the other hand, it is better not to plan on a lot of complicated dental work during pregnancy. You need to be able to eat regularly, so most dentists prefer to leave very complicated repairs until later.

CARE OF THE BREASTS. The best thing you can do to care for your breasts is to wear a good brassiere that supports but does not bind.

Keep the breasts and nipples clean. The colorless secretion that begins to ooze from the nipples about the fourth month may be a little irritating. If so, wash them with mild soap and water and rub on a little cold cream, lanolin, or cocoa butter. Some doctors used to recommend rubbing the nipples with alcohol to toughen them. This idea has been discarded, for it may actually make the nipple sore. You will probably not need anything on them except a little cold cream.

If your nipples are inverted, ask your doctor if he thinks any treatment is necessary.

If your breast or nipple becomes sore or inflamed, or if you notice any lumps in your breast, let the doctor know at once.

TRAVELING. If you are likely to get carsick easily during the fist two or three months of pregnancy, it is a good idea to limit any traveling to short trips. If you are not easily upset, a trip of a hundred or a hundred and fifty miles in a car will probably not cause you discomfort. Many women continue to drive a car during pregnancy, although most doctors advise against driving alone during the last month.

Long trips by car or train may be be very tiring. This is particularly true in traveling by automobile. Trips are less tiring if you can plan to have stretching periods, when you can stand up and walk around a while.

There is not much evidence that traveling during early pregnancy, causes miscarriage. Late in pregnancy, however, the jolting and jarring of a long trip by auto might start you into labor at a most inconvenient time. If you must make a long trip after the sixth month, it is better to go by train or plane. Talk to your doctor about it and get his advice before you set out.

The question often comes up about moving. If you are planning to move into a bigger house before the baby comes, try to arrange, if possible, to move before the seventh month of pregnancy. Or, let your husband, family, or friends move the household while you are in the hospital. Even if you do not do any lifting, moving requires an endless amount of packing, sorting, and stooping, and is a very tiring procedure.

MARITAL RELATIONS

Most doctors advise that you avoid intercouse during the time your second and third menstrual periods would have taken place. At these times miscarriage is thought to be a little more likely. Doctors also advise that you discontinue intercourse entirely during the last few weeks of pregnancy. It should not be resumed until several weeks after the baby's birth.

The germs which are always present on the skin and in the vagina may be carried up near the uterus during intercourse. These germs usually do no harm, but they may during labor, if intercourse has taken place shortly before labor begins. Since it is not possible to know just when labor is likely to begin, doctors advise that you discontinue intercourse for the last few weeks before the baby is due. The danger of infection is present for several weeks after the baby's birth, for the uterus and vagina take about six weeks to return to normal after the baby arrives.

THE WORKING MOTHER

Fashion no longer demands that pregnant women remain shut up at home, seeing only their husbands and a few intimate friends. Many women are employed outside the home nowadays and keep on working during part of their pregnancies.

If you are employed, you may wonder how long it is safe to continue. It depends a lot on how you feel and what kind of work you do. A job that requires a great deal of standing or continuous motion of the feet is likely to be too tiring. Desk work, on the other hand, may not tire you at all. Occasionally employers are willing to arrange work during pregnancy that allows you to sit down most of the time. Some women keep their employment until the eighth month, while others find it necessary to stop earlier.

If you have tiring work that requires long standing, or much bending or lifting, and your employer cannot change it, you should plan to stop after the fourth or fifth month. But if you can get enough sleep and rest, are eating the right kinds of food, and do not have a tiring job, there is no reason why you should not work up to about six weeks before the baby is due. Take your doctor's advice about this.

Discomforts That May Go With Pregnancy

DURING pregnancy women often experience discomfort in one form or another. While these discomforts are not serious, they can prove bothersome and annoying. To recognize them for what they are and understand their causes is to be spared needless worry. Some of them appear during the early months of pregnancy, others toward the end, and these are the natural result of bodily changes. Or again you may be overdoing and rest is the answer. In most instances they respond to simple treatment and the exercising of common sense.

MORNING SICKNESS. Many women are not bothered with this sickish feeling and occasional vomiting. Don't worry if you do have these feelings. Some women seem to have more sensitive digestive systems than others. This seems to be more common in women who find it hard to relax. As your body gets used to the changes of pregnancy, morning sickness should disappear. It seldom lasts longer than the third month.

You can do several things to help overcome it. Rest is important. If you are feeling a little nauseated, don't try to jump out of bed in the morning and do all your work at once. Take it easy. Move more slowly. Wait to brush your teeth until after breakfast, and do it gently. Let your husband get the breakfast, and leave the dishes and bedmaking until a little later. But don't make the mistake of lying in bed all day. And don't feel sorry for yourself. You will find, as the day goes along, that you feel better and better.

The best thing to do, strangely enough, is to eat something before you get out of bed in the morning. Try leaving a few crackers on the bedside table, and eat them when you first wake up. Then relax about fifteen minutes before getting up. Or have your husband bring you some toast or cereal before you get up. It may not be wise to drink much liquid with this early snack. Liquids often make matters worse. Sweet foods, like cookies, are not good either. The best foods are dry crackers, toast, or a soft food like cereal with a little milk and very little sugar, if any.

After you have been up a while, you may be able to eat your usual breakfast with no difficulty. If you feel like vomiting during the day, lie down and rest a while. Don't starve yourself, though. You will find that morning sickness is not like the usual kind of stomach upset, for eating helps. You might try eating six small meals instead of three big ones. Or take crackers or soft foods of some sort every two hours between meals until the period of nausea is over. Do something interesting, or read a good book to take your attention away from your stomach.

THE MYTH OF FOOD CRAVINGS. Some of the older generation of women like to tell of the things they just *had* to eat during pregnancy. These tales range all the way from dill pickles to ice cream. We know now that such cravings are not a necessary part of pregnancy at all. They may be the result of poor food habits. Or they may happen if a woman becomes so excited or upset by becoming pregnant that she wants special attention. On the other hand, every woman, pregnant or not, has times when she particularly wants a certain food.

At times, craving a certain kind of food (for example, oranges or lemons) means that the food really is needed. But if you are used to eating irregularly and have not paid attention to a good diet, you may crave things you do not need. If you find yourself wanting to eat certain things more than usual, talk to your doctor about it. If these foods are necessary parts of your diet and will not upset your weight gain, he may tell you to go ahead. On the other hand, if they will do you harm, it is better for you to use a little self-control. Most women who have had an adequate diet before they become pregnant, and who can arrange to eat the proper foods during pregnancy, find they do not have any cravings.

FREQUENCY OF URINATION. You will notice that you have to empty your bladder more often during early pregnancy. Most women first notice this when they find they have to get up at night to urinate. During the middle months of pregnancy this frequency often disappears; then toward the ends of pregnancy you will notice it again.

The bladder is normally located just in front of the uterus. In the early months of pregnancy, when the uterus begins to grow, it pulls on the lower end of the bladder, and you feel the need to urinate more often. This position changes after about the fourth month.

In the last month of pregnancy, the baby moves down, getting in position to be born. This brings him down against the bladder, and the resulting pressure will make you need to pass urine often. Some women notice leaking of urine when they cough or laugh heartily, or if they happen to step down hard.

SLEEPINESS. Sleepiness is quite usual during the early part of pregnancy. By the time you are three or four months pregnant, however, you may not notice it. Sleep and rest are nature's way of helping us feel refreshed. During early pregnancy your body is getting accustomed to the changes of pregnancy, and you probably do need extra sleep. As pregnancy goes along, however, your body adjusts more easily, and the sleepiness should disappear. You can help by getting regular hours of sleep at night and taking a rest period during the day.

MOUTH WATERING. A few women find their mouths watering a great deal during pregnancy. We do not know why this happens, and it will usually stop by itself after a while. It is an unpleasant feeling because it may cause vomiting at times. Eating several small meals rather than three big ones has sometimes helped. Some women find that chewing gum helps. If you are troubled with mouth watering, talk it over with your doctor.

HEARTBURN. Heartburn is a kind of indigestion. It has nothing to do with the heart, but gets its name because the pain seems to be up in the chest near the heart. Heartburn is noticed more during the last three months of pregnancy. At this time, the growing baby presses upward against the stomach and may interfere with the normal movements of the stomach during digestion. There are medicines which help, so ask your doctor which he would suggest. Baking soda should never be taken unless your doctor prescribes it.

CONSTIPATION. Constipation is fairly common in pregnancy, even with women who have had normal bowel habits before. You can help to prevent it by eating plenty of fruits and vegetables and drinking plenty of water. Try to have a regular time each day to move your bowels. After breakfast is usually a good habit. Some people normally have bowel movements only every two or three days. If this is your usual habit, you should not expect them to move every day. Taking large amounts of laxatives all the time is harmful rather than helpful. It keeps the bowel lining irritated and may keep you from forming good habits. Prune juice, or raw or stewed prunes eaten once a day, may help to keep your bowels moving regularly. Some doctors recommend drinking two glasses of water before breakfast. Your doctor may have some other suggestion.

If you do become constipated, avoid harsh laxatives, such as castor oil. You are likely to upset your stomach with strong laxatives during pregnancy. And they usually cause severe cramps in your lower abdomen. Strong laxatives seldom cause miscarriage, but will cause trouble by irritating the bowel. If you feel you need a laxative, talk this over with your doctor. He may tell you to take a tablespoonful of mineral oil or milk of magnesia before going to bed if you continue to have trouble.

HEMORRHOIDS. Hemorrhoids are groups of enlarged blood vessels located at the lower end of the bowel, just inside the small muscle which controls the emptying of the bowel. They are often called piles. Many people who are not pregnant have hemorrhoids, but these enlarged veins are more common during pregnancy. Hemorrhoids are nearly always the result of constipation, because of straining. When there is pressure in the lower abdomen, as in pregnancy, hemorrhoids develop more frequently. A little petroleum jelly placed just inside the rectum before a bowel movement may make it unnecessary to strain.

Hemorrhoids may become very painful, especially if straining has squeezed them outside. If this happens, your doctor can show you how to wrap a piece of cotton around your finger and push them back. Lie down on your side, with your hips on a pillow, and use mineral oil or petroleum jelly to lubricate your finger. Sometimes a compress made of a few folds of clean gauze soaked in ice-cold witch hazel or a solution of Epsom salt will relieve the discomfort. Hemorrhoids may also bleed. If this happens, let your doctor know.

BACKACHE. As your abdomen grows bigger your general posture changes. The muscles of your back are pulled into different positions. Some women notice backache during the latter part of pregnancy, usually at the end of the day. You can avoid backache to some extent by wearing low-heeled shoes, which give you better balance. An abominal support or corset may also help. If you notice backache often, rest as much as possible.

MUSCULAR CRAMPS. Muscle cramps are noticed by some women during the latter part of pregnancy. They may be leg cramps, or cramps in the muscles of the abdominal wall. Leg cramps are due to slowing up of the circulation of the blood in the legs, because of the pressure of the baby and uterus on the large blood vessels in the lower part of the abdomen. Most women seem to notice these cramps more at night after they go to bed. You can relieve the cramps by rubbing the legs gently, by bending your foot forward with your hands, or by putting a hot-water bottle against the cramped muscles.

Cramps in the muscles of the abdominal wall are not very frequent. They are due to stretching of the abdominal muscles as the baby grows. This type of cramp may pass away without any treatment. It can often be helped by resting. If you have these cramps often, you may need an abdominal support or corset.

VARICOSE VEINS. Varicose veins are enlargements of the leg veins which lie just beneath the skin. Some people develop varicose veins more easily than others, and they seem to be a family tendency. The leg veins empty into the large blood vessels in the lower part of the abdomen. If something slows up the circulation of blood in the legs, such as the pressure of the baby in the lower abdomen during pregnancy, varicose veins may develop, or may get worse if you already have them. Varicose veins can become quite painful, or may break open, so it is important to take proper care of your legs.

Varicose veins cannot be prevented entirely, but your doctor may suggest ways to make you more comfortable. Resting with your feet up as much as possible helps. You may need to wear an elastic bandage or stocking during the day, which should be removed at night. Attractive elastic stockings are now available that hardly show under fairly thin stockings. Your doctor or the nurse in the clinic can show you how to wear them properly. Put on the bandage or stocking before you get up in the morning, before the veins have a chance to fill. In putting on the elastic bandage, be sure you wrap a turn or two around the instep of the foot. This will anchor the bandage and keep your foot from swelling. The elastic bandage can be washed often, and some doctors prefer it to a stocking.

If the varicose veins are very troublesome, your doctor may suggest that you have them treated. Some doctors feel, however, that it is better not to treat them during pregnancy, since the condition may improve after the baby is born.

Some women notice enlargement of the veins around the vaginal entrance. Enlargement of these veins is more common after you have had several babies. This enlargment also is due to the pressure of the baby in the lower abdomen. It will probably disappear after the baby is born. No treatment is necessary, but it is wise to avoid having anything rub against this region.

VAGINAL DISCHARGE. During pregnancy, the tissues of the vagina are changing and getting ready for the baby's birth. The lining of the vagina becomes softer and thicker and more elastic, so the vagina can stretch easily during birth. The glands in the cervix form a sticky solution called mucus all the time, even when you are not pregnant. Normally, the amount of secretion is so small that it is not noticed. In pregnancy, however, much more mucus is formed. Most pregnant women notice a slight whitish, sticky discharge, which merely means that the vaginal passage is becoming lubricated.

This softening process, however, also makes the vagina and cervix more likely to become infected during pregnancy. Germs which are always present on the skin or in the vagina and usually do no harm may begin to grow in the softening mucous membrane. If you notice that you are having more vaginal discharge than usual, or if the discharge becomes yellow, greenish, or frothy, let your doctor know. These infections can usually be cleared up if treated early. If you wait too long, they may cause enough irritation to be painful and are harder to cure. You should never take a vaginal douche during pregnancy unless your doctor orders it.

CHANGES IN THE SKIN. Some women worry about the little red streaks that may appear on the skin of the abdomen or breasts. These little streaks are due to stretching of the skin, and are not serious. They will fade into thin white lines after the baby is born, but will probably not disappear entirely. Some doctors believe that proper support of the abdomen and breasts during pregnancy will keep these streaks from forming.

SHORTNESS OF BREATH. In the last month or two of pregnancy, some women find they are a little short of breath when they climb stairs, or are very active. When the baby has grown so large, he is taking up a lot of space in your abdomen and you cannot breathe as deeply as you ordinarily would. If you notice this often, mention it to your doctor.

Signs That Warn of Complications

GOOD care all through pregnancy is the best safeguard against the relatively rare complications that sometimes develop. To be on the safe side, you should be prepared to recognize certain warning signals as they appear. These are not the imaginary ills or magnified discomforts that some women seize upon to gain sympathy and attention but are the forewarnings of trouble that tell you to see your doctor at once. Many difficulties may thus be avoided by receiving immediate treatment.

These are the most important signs of trouble:

Bleeding from the vagina.

Severe or continuing nausea and vomiting.

Continuing or severe headache.

Swelling or puffiness of the face or hands, or marked swelling of
the feet or ankles.

Blurring of vision or spots before the eyes.

A marked decrease in the amount of urine passed.

Pain or burning on passing urine.

Chills and fever.

Sharp or continuous abdominal pain.

Sudden gush of water from the vagina before the baby is due.

If you notice one or more of these signs, let your doctor know at
once.

MISCARRIAGE. This refers to the birth of the baby at a time
before it has developed enough to live in the outside world. This
usually means before the sixth month. After the sixth month, birth
of the baby before it is due is called premature labor. About two
thirds of all miscarriages occur in the first three months of pregnancy, and these early miscarriages are fairly common.

The earliest signs of a threatened miscarriage are bleeding from
the vagina and pain in the lower abdomen. The bleeding may be
only a slight spotting or it may be a gush of blood with clots.

*It is important to remember that bleeding from the vagina at any
time during pregnancy is abnormal.*

Slight spotting may mean that a miscarriage is only threatening;
more severe bleeding usually means that a miscarriage is actually
happening. If a miscarriage is only threatening, proper rest in bed
may be enough to prevent it. Try to save any blood clots or tissue
in the bedpan or in a small pan for the doctor to examine.

If you notice bleeding at any time during pregnancy, go to bed
at once and notify the doctor. Plan to stay there until your doctor
tells you it is safe to get up. Have your meals in bed and use a bedpan unless your doctor tells you otherwise. The doctor will want
to know when the bleeding began, how much bleeding there is,
whether you have passed any clots, and whether you have had any
pain or cramps in your lower abdomen.

The cause of a miscarriage is often hard to discover. Miscarriage
used to be blamed on a fall, a blow on the abdomen, overwork,

severe mental shock, or some similar strain. Doctors know now that such things seldom cause miscarriage. A normal baby that has become properly settled in the uterus at the time of conception cannot be dislodged so easily. Some pregnant women have even had serious injuries and still carried their babies to normal, full-term delivery. A few women miscarry with no apparent reason. Many miscarriages happen because the baby is not developing normally, because the mother may have had a prolonged or serious illness during pregnancy, or because there is some lack in the normal activities of the many glands in the mother's body.

In many instances, early miscarriage seems to be nature's way of stopping pregnancy when an abnormal baby is developing. This type of miscarriage usually happens early in pregnancy, and nothing you or the doctor can do will stop it.

Any woman who has had more than two miscarriages, and cannot seem to carry a baby to full term, should have a complete medical examination before she becomes pregnant again to see if any health problems or glandular lacks exist.

A miscarriage which comes about naturally is usually not dangerous to the mother's health, and recovery may be very rapid. The only dangers to your health occur if you keep on bleeding for a period of several weeks or if infection sets in. Neither is likely to happen if you are under the care of a doctor. At times he may need to remove bits of tissue which did not come out, since they might cause continued bleeding.

ABORTIONS.   Doctors often refer to early miscarriage as abortion. However, to most people the word abortion means deliberate miscarriage, brought about by illegal means. Occasionally there are times when it may seem necessary for medical reasons to stop a pregnancy. If this decision is made, the operation must be done by a qualified doctor with the advice and consultation of several other doctors. Any other type of deliberate miscarriage is forbidden by law.

CRIMINAL ABORTION.   There is no drug or other means known to the medical profession by which it is possible for a woman to bring on a miscarriage without greatly endangering her life. This is entirely apart from the ethical and legal aspects. Even if the patient is but a week pregnant, there is the same difficulty in causing a harmless abortion, the same danger to the patient's life, and the same degree of crime. Persons who perform abortions are usually as incompetent as they are criminal. All too frequently blood poisoning and death of the patient result. The very secrecy required is, of itself, sufficient to prevent the abortionist from giving the patient proper care, even if he were competent to give it.

UNUSUAL COMPLICATIONS

PROLONGED VOMITING. Here is an unusual complication. It comes on after the third month of pregnancy and is more severe than morning sickness. This type of vomiting may not be helped by eating, but often gets worse. It seems to develop more often in women who are highly nervous, who are subject to glandular disorders, or who have had a very poor diet. Serious family problems or other overwhelming worries may also be connected with this illness.

Few women have this difficulty. Talk to your doctor if anything is worrying you extremely. He may be able to help straighten things out, or arrange for you to talk to someone who can give you the kind of help you need.

KIDNEY INFECTION. A pregnant woman is a little more likely to develop a kidney infection (pyelitis) than a woman who is not pregnant. Certain changes in the capacity of the bladder and the tubes leading from it to the kidneys apparently make it easier for the kidneys to become infected. Kidney infection is especially serious in a pregnant woman, since her kidneys have to work for both her and the baby.

Pyelitis usually begins with a sharp chill, fever, and pain in the back near the waistline. These symptoms are often accompanied by pain or burning during urination. If you notice such symptoms at any time, call the doctor, go to bed, and drink plenty of water. Certain medicines help to clear up kidney infection, but they must be prescribed by your doctor.

ANEMIA.   This is a condition of the blood resulting from a reduction either in the number of red blood cells or in the amount of hemoglobin. Hemoglobin is the colored substance in the red blood cells which carries oxygen to the body tisues. If the amount of hemoglobin is below normal, or if there are too few red blood cells, not enough oxygen will get to the tissues. In pregnancy, it is particularly important to prevent anemia since both the mother's body and the baby need a good supply of oxygen.

Anemia may develop from loss of blood or from a lack of sufficient iron in the diet. Iron and protein are important materials for forming hemoglobin. Lean meats, especially liver, and eggs, are good sources of iron and protein. A pregnant woman may more easily become anemic because it is often difficult for her to get enough iron from food alone to take care of her needs and the needs of the baby. Often some kind of iron compound, in the form of pills or capsules, will help supply the extra needs during pregnancy. Your doctor can decide about this by checking the amount of hemoglobin in your blood from time to time.

Some types of anemia in pregnancy are due to more complicated causes and may be harder to treat.

PREMATURE BIRTH.   A sudden gush of water from the vagina several weeks before the baby is due usually means that premature birth of the baby is likely. The gush of water results from breaking of the bag of waters and is often the first sign of premature labor. If the bag of waters breaks, let your doctor know at once. Premature labor may be very short, because a premature baby is smaller than a full-term baby and can pass through the birth canal more quickly. Also a premature baby is not as strong as a full-term baby, and must be given special care immediately after birth in order to live.

Some of the causes of premature labor are toxemia, syphilis, or a very inadequate diet. However, most cases cannot be explained. Women who have had good care during pregnancy are less likely to have premature babies than those who do not get good prenatal care.

TOXEMIA OF PREGNANCY.   Toxemia is a complex disorder which used to be more common than it is nowadays. A woman who has toxemia with one pregnancy is more likely than not to develop it again during another pregnancy. This is one of the reasons why good prenatal care is important with every pregnancy.

Not much is known about the cause of toxemia. It is a condition in pregnancy in which there is some interference with the normal activity or condition of the mother's kidneys, heart, or circulation of the blood. It usually develops gradually, during the second half of pregnancy. One of the first signs the doctor may notice is a rise in blood pressure above normal limits. This rise may happen before you realize that anything is wrong, and is the reason why the doctor checks your blood pressure on each visit. The doctor may find you have gained a lot of weight in a short time. Such rapid gain is usually due to an over-accumulation of water in your body tissues. The signs you may notice yourself are marked swelling or puffiness of the face, hands, or feet, blurring of vision, or sometimes severe headache. Another serious sign is a sharp decrease in the amount of urine passed.

Two dangers in toxemia are death of the baby before birth, and the possibility of the mother's developing convulsions or eclampsia.

Eclampsia usually develops from untreated toxemia and is a very serious illness. It is becoming much less common as more women receive good prenatal care. Eclampsia can be prevented by intelligent cooperation between the pregnant woman and her doctor, and no woman need fear this complication if she takes proper care of herself and follows her doctor's advice.

Treatment of mild or early toxemia consists primarily of rest in bed and cutting out all salt in the diet. The doctor may prescribe certain medicines. Usually, rest in bed and strict attention to the doctor's orders will be enough to stop the trouble from developing any farther. Sometimes, however, rest and treatment in the hospital are necessary.

After the birth of the baby, the mother's circulation and kidney activity usually return to normal.

THE RH FACTOR. This is a substance present in the red blood cells of a large proportion of people. If you have the Rh factor in your red blood cells, you are called Rh positive; if you do not, you are Rh negative. Both conditions are natural and normal and cannot be changed. Inheritance determines whether you are Rh positive or Rh negative. A special blood test can show whether or not your blood contains the Rh factor.

The Rh factor has only recently been discovered. Many scientific studies are being carried on and a great deal of publicity resulted about the problem of being Rh negative.

Actually, being Rh negative is only a problem under certain and rare circumstances. A woman who is Rh negative and whose husband is Rh positive may sometimes develop certain conditions during pregnancy which affect the baby who has inherited Rh positive blood. These conditions usually happen only if she has had previous transfusions with Rh positive blood, or if she has had more than one pregnancy with Rh positive babies. Under such circumstances a few Rh negative women may form substances called antibodies in their blood which can get through the placenta into the baby's blood stream. These antibodies are not a danger to the mother herself (unless she happens to be transfused with Rh positive blood) but they may produce erythroblastosis in an Rh positive baby. In this disease, the baby's Rh positive red blood cells are destroyed by the antibody, and severe anemia results.

Fortunately only a few Rh negative women form antibodies, and most Rh negative women have normal babies. And a baby who has inherited Rh negative blood would not have this complication.

Your doctor will probably want to test your blood to see whether you are Rh positive or Rh negative. If you are Rh negative, he will also want to test your husband's blood. This knowledge may help to avoid trouble. Most doctors follow the progress during pregnancy of Rh negative women whose husbands are Rh positive by doing repeated blood tests. These tests show whether the antibodies are forming that might give rise to complications. If antibodies have not appeared by the end of the seventh month, the baby will not have erythroblastosis.

Recent studies of erythroblastosis have taught doctors a great deal, both about the cause and the treatment of this condition in the baby. Immediate treatment after birth has saved a number of babies who would have died without this care. With frequent blood tests on an Rh negative woman during her pregnancy, the doctor can be prepared to give both the mother and the baby the benefit of all that has been and is being learned about the Rh factor.

You need not be alarmed if you are Rh negative. Most such women have had several babies with no difficulty whatever from the Rh factor.

CHRONIC DISEASES.   If you have had certain chronic illnesses or disorders before you became pregnant, you may have some difficulty during pregnancy because of them. Such illnesses as diabetes, rheumatic heart disease, chronic kidney disease, tuberculosis and syphilis may cause special problems.

For a woman with any of these diseases, good care and continuing medical supervision are absolutely necessary during pregnancy. If you have ever had one of these illnesses, you must pay particularly close attention to your doctor's advice and recommendations.

Diabetes, heart disease, and chronic kidney disease may interfere with normal functioning of the mother's internal organs.

Tuberculosis is not inherited by the baby, but after birth a baby may catch this disease from contact with his mother. It is necessary to keep the baby of a mother with active tuberculosis away from her until she is well.

The germ of syphilis can get through the placenta and infect the baby before birth.

Many states now have laws that require a test for syphilis on every pregnant woman. Such tests are important because it is possible for a woman to become infected with syphilis without knowing it. Her unborn child may become badly infected if the mother does not receive proper treatment. With early and adequate treatment the chances of having a normal baby are almost 100 per cent, but untreated syphilis can cause the death of a baby either before or after birth. If an infected baby lives it may be physically and sometimes mentally damaged.

Even if the mother has been previously treated for syphilis, the baby can sometimes become infected before birth. Syphilis is a complex disease, and relapse can happen. A woman who has, or has had syphilis, must follow a careful treatment plan with frequent blood tests during her pregnancy. This treatment should begin as early as possible for the baby to have the best chances.

Preparing for the Baby's Coming

MOST parents-to-be prefer to have all the necessary baby needs in readiness well in advance of the home-coming. If you are wise, you will get only the absolute essentials beforehand. By so doing, you will avoid duplicating any gifts the baby may receive and, by waiting, you can fill in later whatever is lacking. Then, too, after you see how fast he grows you can add things later as they are needed.

HIS CLOTHING

A very simple layette will meet all of a newborn baby's needs. The more simple the garments, the better for both baby and mother. Clothes should be comfortable, easy to wash and easy to put on. Garments that tie are far easier to handle than those having buttons. If buttons are used, they should be large enough to fasten easily. Necklines should be smooth and without collars and trimming. The neck openings and armholes should be large enough to put the head and arms through easily.

A baby's clothes are for the baby's comfort and should be planned with that in mind and not to satisfy the mother's longing for frills.

Clothing planned for a newborn baby will be suitable for only about half the first year. At the end of that time the baby will have outgrown many of the clothes he wore soon after birth. He will be much more active than he was when he was very young and will therefore need clothing of a somewhat different type. Besides, in most parts of the United States the temperature changes considerably, and by the time he is six months old the baby usually needs clothes that are warmer or cooler than those he needed at birth.

The average baby needs the following for about the first six months:

84

Diapers	(dozen)	3-4
Shirts (long or short sleevs, or sleeveless, according to climate		3-4
Abdominal bands		3
Nightgowns (or wrappers)		5-6
Sweaters		2
Flannel squares or baby blankets		2-3
Warm hood (if climate is cold)		1

Other garments, such as dresses, additional sweaters, and a bunting or other wrap for cold weather, may be good to have but are not essential. It is better to have plenty of diapers, shirts, and night-gowns so that the baby can always have plenty of clean ones.

All of these can be bought or made quite inexpensively. Do not get the smallest size shirts and wrappers. The baby will outgrow them so quickly that they will be an additional expense. Infant size two allows for growing, yet is not much too big for the average baby at first. Cotton is the best material for the shirts, since wool may irritate the baby's skin and is likely to shrink. Nightgowns may be made with a drawstring around the bottom, but they should be long enough to allow for the baby's growth. The best kind of night-gown is made of soft cotton or knitted material. If they open down the back, you will find them easier to put on. Drawstrings should not be used around the neck of a baby's garment because this might cause the baby to choke.

Sweaters are easier to put on if they open down the front. A bunting to wear in cold weather is nice to have but is not essential, for a small baby can be wrapped in a flannel square or a blanket when taken outdoors. If you do not have a bunting, the baby needs a warm hood or a cap when taken outdoors in cold weather.

The newer material for diapers, such as gauze or the so-called Curity-layette cloth, are more satisfactory than the old-fashioned birdseye cotton because they dry more quickly and are less clumsy when wet.

In most cities nowadaws, there are diaper services which launder baby diapers. These services usually supply the diapers as well as wash them.

Many babies can wear a waterproof protection over the diaper quite satisfactorily and thus save the mother considerable laundry. Some babies break out with a diaper rash if such pants are worn. Obviously, if the pants produce a rash, they must not be used. Rubber pants that are loose and have air holes for ventilation are less likely to cause trouble than very snug pants. Sometimes knit "soakers" can be used even though rubber pants cause trouble.

BABY'S FIRST FURNISHINGS

BASSINET. The first bed for the baby may be a bassinet, a large flat clothesbasket, or even a wooden box. Such a bed should not be left on the floor when the baby is in it, because the floor is apt to be drafty. It may be convenient to have legs on the bassinet or to have a large sturdy table on which to place it.

The bassinet will be outgrown in a few months, but during the early period of life, when the baby sleeps most of the time, it will be convenent to be able to move him, bed and all, from place to place to give him sunshine and fresh air.

CRIB. A larger bed will be needed by the time the baby is three to five months old, and many mothers prefer to start with the crib. If a crib is bought it is wise to get one large enough to accommodate the child for the first two or even three years of life. It should be sturdy, with the bars close enough together to prevent the baby from getting his head caught between them and with no sharp posts on which he can hurt himself.

If the crib is painted, the paint should be of a kind that the manufacturer says is harmless to babies. Some babies develop a habit of biting the railing of the crib; if the paint contains lead, the baby may be poisoned.

BEDDING. *For the bassinet* several thicknesses of quilted cotton padding or a folded cotton blanket may be used as a mattress; it should be flat and smooth.

A soft pillow should not be used as a mattress, for a baby might bury his face in it and be smothered. No pillow of any kind should be put under the baby's head. It is better for his back if his head is not propped up.

Bassinet sheets can usually be made by cutting up a partly worn-out sheet from the household supply. A pillowcase can be used as a bassinet sheet.

For the crib a firm mattress and a spring that does not sag are needed.

Unless the mattress has waterproof ticking it should have a rubber covering. The rubber sheet can be tied under the mattress with strong tapes sewed to each corner, or it can be made like a pillowcase to cover the whole mattress.

A pad between the waterproof material and the sheet will help to keep the baby from becoming too warm. This may be of quilted cotton or of more rapidly drying gauze.

Lightweight wool blankets will be needed except during very warm weather. Cotton blankets, which wash easily, are desirable for use in mild weather. It is better to have several light blankets than one or two heavy ones.

A clean cloth may be placed under the baby's head and tucked around the mattress. If the baby should spit up, the cloth can be changed easily; this is easier than changing the sheet.

A folded diaper or a square of quilted cotton under the buttocks, with a square of rubber sheeting under it, likewise will save fre-changed easily; this is easier than changing the sheet.

You will need the following articles of bedding. Much of it can be made at home—particularly the sheets and blankets which might be made from partly worn household sheets or blankets.

- 1 rubber sheet—big enough to tuck under the mattress on both sides.
- 5-6 quilted cotton pads about eighteen inches square to put under the baby.
- 3-6 crib-size sheets (a pillowcase makes a good bassinet sheet).
- 2-3 lightweight crib-size wool or cotton blankets, depending on the season.

TABLE FOR DRESSING. A table of a convenient height on which to change the baby's diaper and to dress him is a great help. If the table is made with a heavy canvas top it will help to keep him from rolling off. A table with a canvas top can be made readily at home.

If a table with a solid top is used it should be covered with a soft pad firmly fastened to the table.

PAIL FOR SOILED DIAPERS.   Any covered pail that will not rust is satisfactory for holding soiled diapers until they are washed.

Covered enamelware pails made especially for this purpose are on the market. These can be used for boiling diapers as well as for holding soiled ones.

An ordinary galvanized-iron scrub pail or an earthenware crock may be used to hold diapers, and a heavy piece of planking may be used as a cover.

CHAIR FOR THE MOTHER.   The chair that the mother sits in when she feeds the baby should be low enough to permit her to have a good lap on which to hold him. Some mothers would rather sit in an ordinary chair and use a footstood than sit in a low chair.

An armchair may be convenient, for it is easier for the mother to hold the baby if her elbow rests on the arm of a chair. A rocking chair may be used.

Bath Supplies

    1 bathtub—enamelware or rubber.
    2-4 soft towels.
    3 soft washcloths.
    1-2 bath towels to use in covering the bath table.
    1 cotton bath blanket.
    Sterilized absorbent cotton.
    Covered jars for pieces of cotton.
    Rustproof safety pins.
    Plain mineral oil (and a small flat dish to hold a day's supply
        of oil)
    Soap and soap dish (any bland unmedicated soap will do).

You can buy a fitted tray for the bath supplies such as soap, cotton, oil, and safety pins, or you can make your own by using a flat baking pan and screw-topped jars, of the kind various foods come in. You can use jars you already have. Wash and boil them at frequent intervals.

BATHTUB.   The family tub may be used for bathing the baby, but a small tub for this purpose is a great help to the mother as it saves her much stooping. Enamelware tubs and folding rubber ones are on the market.

Unless the tub has legs it should be placed on a sturdy table. The table should be of such a height that the mother can bathe the baby comfortably.

It may be convenient to put the table, with the baby's tub on it, near, or even in, the family tub, where it will be convenient to the hot- and cold-water faucets. The baby's tub can then be filled by means of a rubber hose, which saves carrying water. If rubber cups are placed on the feet of the table, it will stand more firmly and it will not scratch the surface of the large tub.

If an enamelware tub is selected, it is desirable to get one that is long enough (twenty-eight inches) to permit the baby to splash and play a little as he gets older.

Folding rubber tubs usually have legs and a canvas top on which to dress the baby.

BABY CARRIAGE. If a baby carriage is used, it should be large enough to permit the baby, with whatever wraps are necessary, to lie full length or to sit up, and it should have a firm, full-length mattress that lies flat.

During the fly and mosquito season, a piece of mosquito netting should be used to cover the carriage when necessary.

Be Prepared in Advance for Delivery

IF you want to be spared last-minute confusion and worry, to say nothing of forgetting some important item that is always left out when you are rushed, have your preparations for the delivery completed at least two months before the baby is due. There is always the possibility that the baby may arrive ahead of time, so this is none too early to have everything in readiness.

Of course the ideal place to have your baby is in a well-equipped hospital where you can receive the best of care should any complications arise. On the other hand, there may be reasons why it is desirable to remain at home. This is something your doctor should help you decide. Your local hospital may lack the facilities for the proper care of mothers and babies, or there may be other factors that favor having the baby born at home. Whatever the final decision, your preparations will vary depending on where the delivery is to take place.

HOSPITAL DELIVERY

If you decide on hospital delivery, your doctor may make the arrangements for you, or he may expect you to handle them. Some hospitals have different types of accommodations, such as private, semiprivate, or ward beds which differ considerably in cost. You will want to find out about hospital charges. Some hospitals make separate charges for delivery room, anesthetics, and nursing care for yourself and the baby. In other hospitals a lump sum is charged for the entire cost. If you happen to have hospital insurance, or belong to some group for hospitalization, find out how much of the hospital expense this will cover.

If there is a medical social worker at the hospital or clinic, she may be able to help you arrange for hospital care to suit your income. She might also have suggestions in planning the care of the rest of your family while you are in the hospital.

Pack a suitcase with the things you will need in the hospital for yourself, and have it in a handy place all ready to go. Then pack for the baby, putting his things into a separate suitcase or bundle. Leave this bundle in a safe spot for your husband to bring to the hospital later on when you are ready to take the baby home.

Many hospitals supply hospital gowns for the mother's use during the early days after delivery, but you may want a nightgown or two of your own. Some hospitals do not supply baby clothes for the time the baby is in the hospital, but most do. If they do, you will not need clothes for the baby until you are ready to go home.

You will not need many things for yourself. However, you will be happier if you have your own toilet articles and a pretty bed jacket. The following list is about what you will want:

Bathrobe.
Bedroom slippers.
Two or three nightgowns or pajama tops (some women like these better).
Bed jacket.
One or two nursing brassieres.
Sanitary belt (hospital will furnish pads).
Comb, brush, and hand mirror.
Toothbrush and toothpaste.
Cosmetics.
Talcum powder or cologne for yourself.
Box of paper handkerchiefs (sometimes the hospital supplies these).
A book or magazine to read (a book on child care might be a good idea).
Fountain pen or pencil, stationery, and stamps.

In the baby's bundle for home-coming you will need:

Two or three diapers.
Shirt.
Four large safety pins.
Wrapper (or dress and petticoat).
Sweater.
Cap.
Blanket or bunting.

The amount of outer covering for the baby will depend, of course, on the weather. On a warm summer day the sweater would not be needed and the outer blanket could be a flannel square. On a winter day the baby needs both a sweater and a heavy outer wrap—a bunting, for example, or a warm wool blanket.

HOME DELIVERY

A delivery at home involves much more preparation.

If you have public health nurses in your community, you will find they know a lot about home deliveries. They will be glad to help you in planning and preparing the necessary supplies. Often the doctor or nurse will bring many of the supplies at the time of delivery. So it is a good idea to sit down with your doctor or the public health nurse at least three months before the baby is expected and make a list of exactly what you need and how to prepare the supplies. Certain equipment must be sterilized. It may be possible to buy it already sterilized. Or the public health nurse may be able to arrange for its sterilization.

Select a room for the delivery that is quiet, well-lighted, and as near the bathroom or a source of running water as possible. See that the bed is placed so it can be approached from either side. When the time comes for delivery, have the extra furniture moved out, leaving only the bed, several straight chairs and two or three small tables. Remove rugs and protect the floor with newspapers. If the bed is low, have the casters removed and have blocks six or seven inches high placed under the legs of the bed. These blocks will bring the mattress up to about thirty inches from the floor, which will be more comfortable for you at delivery and make the doctor's and nurse's care easier. Keep the mattress from sagging by putting a firm board, such as a table leaf or ironing board across the bed, between the mattress and spring.

In making up the bed for delivery, cover the mattress with water-proof sheeting, or heavy brown paper, or several layers of news-paper. Over this spread a clean bed sheet and tuck it in tightly. Place two delivery pads (described below) in the center of the bed, where the mother's hips will be. One pad should be in the center, the other overlapping it a little, and extending to one side of the bed. Cover the pillow with a clean pillowcase, and fold the top sheet and blanket lengthwise along the side of the bed opposite to the delivery pads. The top sheet and cover should not be tucked in at the foot of the bed.

SUPPLIES AND STERILIZING

Following is a complete list of supplies needed. How much you have to prepare will depend on what you, the doctor, and the nurse decide.

One and one-half yards of waterproof sheeting at least thirty-six inches wide, or 1½ yards of white table oilcloth to protect the mattress. Heavy brown paper can be used instead.

Four clean sheets and four clean pillowcases.

Receiving blanket for the baby (a piece of old, clean blanket or cotton flannel about a yard square, or a very soft bath towel).

Four delivery pads. To make, take twelve open-out sheets of newspaper and cover them with old muslin or clean white cotton material. Wash and iron the material, using a hot iron, or iron the pads after they are made. Fold the pads and put them away in a clean pillowcase.

Plenty of newspapers.

One-quarter pound absorbent cotton (new package).

One pail with cover.

Bedpan.

One covered stewpan with handle (two-quart size).

Two small enamel wash basins.

Mild soap.

Tube of plain white petroleum jelly.

Two-quart fountain syringe or enema can with rectal tip.

Hot-water bottle.

One dozen safety pins, size o.

One dozen safety pins, size 4.

One new nail brush, stiff and cheap.

Four washcloths.

Four bath towels.

Three nightgowns (either low enough in the neck to allow for nursing or open down the front) or pajama tops.

One pair of white cotton stockings, or clean tan cotton stockings.

One dozen gauze sponges, four inches square. These can be bought. They may be a few cents more expensive to buy than to make, but the saving of your time and effort is worth it.

Two dozen sanitary pads.

Five dozen cotton pledgets. These can be bought already sterilized or can be made from absorbent cotton. To make one take a piece of absorbent cotton the size of an egg, make it into a ball, twist the loose end. Put pledgets into five small muslin bags, and tie the bags shut with string.

One yard of umbilical tape, or bobbin (narrow cotton) tape, or strong cotton string to tie the baby's cord.

One roll of toilet paper.

Put away unopened the packages of gauze sponges, absorbent cotton, sanitary pads, and toilet paper. If you buy the cotton pledgets they also should not be opened. If you make them at home they must be sterilized. Your doctor may bring the umbilical tape to tie the baby's cord, but if he does not, this, too, will have to be sterilized. Cut the tape into four pieces, each nine inches long.

The simplest method of home sterilization is to place the materials into small muslin bags, or white cotton bags, and place the bags in an old pillowcase. Pin the pillowcase shut. Bake the pillowcase in a moderate oven (350° to 375°) for an hour. If you do not have an oven thermometer, place a large white potato in the oven. When it is done, the pillowcase has been in the oven long enough.

The pillowcase should not be opened until the time of delivery. If the articles are not used within a month, they must be sterilized again.

The Miracle of Childbirth

As you draw closer to your period of confinement, or, as the doctors say, "labor and delivery," your body is experiencing a final series of important changes. Sometime during the ninth month the baby has gradually settled down in your abdomen and is now resting in the bony canal of your pelvis, so he will be ready when labor starts. This is called "lightening" and is more likely to occur with a first baby than with later ones.

Your baby has now developed sufficiently to be ready to take his place in the outside world.

Just what happens to start the process of birth is still a mystery. When the uterus is ready, nature decides that it is time for the baby to be born, and the strong muscles begin their work. Contracting regularly, these muscles push the baby from the uterus, through the birth canal, and out into the world.

FALSE LABOR PAINS

All during pregnancy, the muscles of the uterus are getting ready for the labor of helping the baby to be born. From time to time they tighten and release. This process of growing tight and then relaxing is called a contraction. These contractions ordinarily cause no discomfort, and you may not even feel them. However, they sometimes become stronger late in pregnancy. If so, you may have episodes of what the doctors call "false labor." In false labor the contractions are strong enough so that you can feel them, but they are irregular, which makes them different from real labor. They may come and go, off and on, over a period of several hours. You need not worry about them, for they are not a sign of any trouble. Sometimes, however, these contractions are hard to tell from real labor, so let your doctor know whenever you feel any strong contractions.

Occasionally, even after one reaches the hospital, the labor pains may stop. It is usually safer to go home and wait for the onset of genuine labor pains, rather than to insist that your doctor bring them on at this particular time. False labor pains are no indication that there is anything wrong with your pregnancy or baby. They may precede actual labor by twenty-four hours to two weeks. Follow your doctor's advice and his interpretation of these false labor pains.

WHEN TRUE LABOR STARTS

The woman whose first baby is coming into the world entertains many misconceptions about labor pains, the use and effects of anesthesia, and other proceedings that may or may not occur during the entire process of labor. She should realize, first of all, that childbirth is a normal process. If she has been under a physician's care during her pregnancy, has followed his advice faithfully, and her pregnancy has run a normal course, she has nothing to fear.

At the beginning of labor, the location of the pains is usually vague and more or less resembles a mild intestinal colic, or gas in the bowel. If it is the calculated time for delivery, before calling the doctor, she should watch the clock in order to get the exact frequency of the pains. If the pains gradually extend toward the back and resemble a real backache, they are more likely to be from the womb than from any intestinal cause. At first the true labor pains usually occur about every half hour, gradually increasing in frequency.

If the abdomen is not too fat, a good test for true womb contractions is to place the palm of the hand over the most dependent part of the abdomen and wait for a pain to come. The uterine contractions can then be felt as a sort of hardening of the muscles. This may be misleading, as a bowel contraction may give a similar sensation, but it is worth noting before calling the doctor. If you now call your doctor he will probably tell you to go to the hospital when the pains occur every five to ten minutes.

HOSPITAL DELIVERY

So you now go to the hospital promptly. You are shown to your room. Here is what follows in a well-regulated hospital. You are put to bed, your temperature is taken, a specimen of urine is sent to the laboratory and you are shaved. It is curious that this procedure should disturb most women. Maybe it is the extensive paraphernalia, brought in on a large tray, that you might mistake for a sign of some emergency that is being kept from you. But, for aseptic precautions, all the hair of the external sexual organs must be removed. Next, you get an enema, which is also necessary.

THE EXAMINATION. You are now taken to the examining room. You may walk if you prefer, but do not become frightened if a cart is brought to roll you in. If your doctor has not yet arrived, you may be examined by the resident obstetrician. You are first prepared by thorough cleansing of the genitals with soap and water, then some

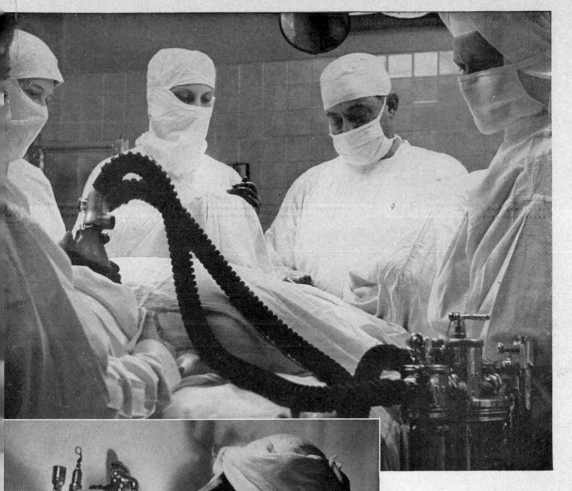

IN THE DELIVERY ROOM

The modern baby is born in the gleaming whiteness of a sterile operating room. Robed and masked, the obstetrician, surrounded by attending nurses, assists the mother in her labor, while the use of a merciful anesthesia eases her birth pangs.

Three Lions

JUST ARRIVED!

A gentle slap and baby utters a wail of protest as he draws his first breath after being severed from his mother upon delivery.

Roy Pinney (Monkmeyer)

GREETING THE NEW BABY

(Right) Here Father is permitted his first view of his young heir through the nursery window. (Below) The newly delivered baby's umbilicus is tied, silver nitrate is dropped in his eyes and he is rubbed down with an antiseptic oil to prevent irritation. An identification tape is wound around his wrist and he is soon ready to leave the delivery room for a little nap in the nursery.

Right: Blue Cross Photo
Below: Three Lions Photo

VISITING HOURS
WARD
TUES. & FRI. 7·30-8 P.M.
SUNDAY 3·30-4 P.M.
SEMI-PRIVATE
EVENINGS 8-9 P.M.
SUNDAY 3·30-4·30 P.M.

mild antiseptic solution. The examiner wears sterile rubber gloves. The examination is for the purpose of learning just how far labor has progressed. This is determined by the extent of the dilation of the mouth of the womb, also by whether or not the "bag of waters" has ruptured, which you may or may not have noted.

After this examination there is seldom another. Depending upon the degree of dilation, and the frequency and severity of the pains, you may be taken back to your bed or taken into the delivery room. If the latter, then you are further prepared locally and sterile leggings are put on.

RELAXING FOR DELIVERY. As the pains increase in severity you are told to put into use the relaxation procedures in which you should have been instructed. If you have had no such instruction, then you are given enough anesthetic to take off the edge of the pain. If you have become proficient in relaxing, then you will need little or no anesthetic, but in any case you are not allowed to suffer unduly. Remember that muscular tension has an undesirable effect on the accomplishment of natural spontaneous childbirth.

When the bearing-down stage is reached, you are told when and when not to bring into play the voluntary muscles. Again, you will probably be given a light anesthesia, just enough to relieve the pain, but rarely enough to produce unconsciousness. Above all, have confidence in your physician and in all those around you.

Your cooperation with your obstetrician will make deep anesthesia unnecessary and you will then be able to get that glorious thrill of your baby's first cry. You will be kept upon the delivery table until the afterbirth (placenta) is delivered. This usually takes place in about twenty minutes. Do not worry about this as it is quite painless.

LENGTH OF LABOR. You may ask, "How long will labor last?" And your doctor will answer that he cannot tell you exactly. The length of labor differs in every woman and in every pregnancy. The labor time does not necessarily depend on whether you are tall or short, fat or thin. The first baby usually takes a little longer to be born than later babies, because your body has never had this experience before. Recent studies have shown that women who have had a good diet and good care during pregnancy tend to have shorter labors. Your mental attitude has a lot to do with it, too. If you are not afraid, you will find it easier to relax and get some rest between your contractions, and the time will seem shorter.

THE THREE STAGES OF LABOR

Labor is usually described as being divided into three periods, or stages. In the first stage, the contractions of the uterus cause the opening at the lower end of the uterus, the cervix, to be stretched so the baby can pass out of the uterus into the birth canal. In the second stage, the baby passes down through the birth canal and out through the vaginal opening, which stretches to allow him to be born. In the third stage, the placenta and membranes (the after-birth) are loosened from the uterus and passed out. At the end of labor, the uterus is entirely empty, except for the remains of its thick lining.

The first stage of labor is by far the longest. During pregnancy, the cervix softens and relaxes, so that when labor begins it is thin and has opened to about a half inch. There is usually a small amount of mucus present, as a sort of plug. During the first stage of labor, the cervix must open to a diameter of about four inches in order to let the baby's head pass through. The cervix, as well as the lining of vagina, have all been softened in pregnancy so they can stretch as much as is needed. As the baby is pushed against the cervix by the strong contractions of the uterus, the opening gradually gets bigger and bigger, until finally the baby can pass through. As the cervix opens, the mucous plug becomes loosened and passes out, often with a small amount of blood. This is called the "show."

In this first stage, the doctor may make several rectal examinations. The mother cannot tell how fast the cervix is opening; the doctor must determine this. This examination tells him how much the cervix is opening. A rectal examination is easier than a vaginal examination, although at times a vaginal examination is necessary.

The second stage of labor is much shorter, usually only one-half hour to two hours long. The strong abdominal muscles begin to help the muscles of the uterus push the baby out, and you will have what are called bearing-down feelings. You will have a strong urge to push with each contraction and your doctor may tell you to hold your breath and push hard. Pushing at this time helps, but if you try to bear down before your body tells you it is ready, you will just tire yourself needlessly.

After the baby is born, the doctor clamps the umbilical cord and cuts it. The placenta begins to separate from its attachment to the lining of the uterus. In a short time—usually ten to fifteen minutes —the muscles of the uterus contract once more and the placenta and membranes are pushed out. This is the third stage of labor. A moderate amount of bleeding, from the area where the placenta was attached, accompanies the afterbirth but this bleeding soon becomes slight.

Shortly after the placenta passes out some women have a brief shivering chill which lasts only a minute or two. This chill is thought to be a normal release of muscular or nervous tension.

BABY'S POSITION WHEN BORN.   Most babies are born head first. This is the easiest way, for the baby's head, which is the largest part of its body, can help to stretch the cervix more quickly. Sometimes the baby is born feet or buttocks first. A baby in this position is called a breech baby. If the baby comes as a breech, labor may be a little longer.

EASING CHILDBIRTH.   Many women have been needlessly frightened by tales of the pain of labor. Yes, the contractions can be painful. The muscles of the uterus are working hard. It takes some force to push the baby down the birth canal. Much depends, however, on your reaction to pain and discomfort, and whether or not you are afraid. Fear and anxiety help to make muscles tense, and can in this way add to the discomfort of labor. Women who know how to relax should experience little discomfort.

Doctors differ in opinion as to whether any medicines to relieve pain are advisable or necessary during labor. If given too early, some medicines slow up the birth of the baby. Late in labor, certain medicines can be given to reduce discomfort without interfering with the progress of labor. Not all medicines work in the same way for all women, and too much medicine makes some babies groggy.

Your doctor can decide what is best for you as he watches your progress.

Every doctor who takes care of women during childbirth has his own preference for medicines. This preference is based on his experience and his knowledge of each patient's particular needs. It is best to let the doctor decide which medicine, if any, is best for your individual care. Do not try to persuade him to use something new that you have heard or read about. Some of these methods prove to be suitable only for certain types of patients.

During the second stage of labor, when the contractions are coming close together and when the bearing-down sensations begin, some doctors give an anesthetic—such as gas—with each contraction. Then as the time comes for the baby to be born, a local injection or an anesthetic which puts you to sleep may be used.

WHEN FORCEPS ARE USED. Not too many years ago forceps, or "instruments," were used only for complicated births when the baby could not be born naturally. So, many women dreaded the idea of a forceps delivery, for they were afraid it would do real harm to them or to the baby. Nowadays in normal deliveries forceps may be used at times simply to lift the baby's head out. Forceps are used only after the mother has been put to sleep or the pelvic region is made numb by local anesthetics. They sometimes cause a small bruise on the baby's cheek, but this will disappear within a few days.

CESAREAN SECTION. Cesarean section is a major abdominal operation and is done when there is some reason why normal birth is not possible, or if normal birth through the vagina would be dangerous to the mother.

The period of convalescence after a Cesarean section is longer than that after normal labor, since the abdominal wound must heal. Aside from this, it is not much different. There is no reason why you cannot breast-feed your baby and take as much care of him as you feel able to do after a section.

Painless Childbirth

A n entirely new approach to the problem of making childbirth painless was recently introduced into this country by an English obstetrician, Sir Grantly Dick Read. In essence, the point he makes is that pain is the result of fear; fear of labor itself and the dread of possible birth of an abnormal baby, of a prolonged labor and a thousand and one imaginative things that may come to mind in the nine months it takes to develop a fully mature infant. With this in mind, he reassures the expectant mother during the prenatal course, stressing the concept that nature never intended a normal process, such as giving birth, to be painful, any more than eating should cause indigestion or elimination should cause cramps.

This is a new concept and there is much evidence to confirm its effectiveness. The womb is a hollow muscular organ, like the stomach and intestines. The muscles of the stomach and intestines are in constant action to aid in the digestion of food and to eliminate the residue. This function goes on without any pain unless abused, as we become immediately aware whenever we overeat or partake of poisonous foods. The early pains of labor are mild indeed and are the result of the muscular contractions of the womb attempting to open it up in order for the baby to pass through and advance into the birth canal. These early pains are felt as a pressure low down in the back where they then encircle the pelvic girdle. The entire pain may last from thirty to sixty seconds and then disappear until the next uterine contraction which may not return for thirty minutes to one hour. As time passes, the interval between the labor pains generally reduces and the pain itself becomes more noticeable. Few patients complain of these contractions until the interval between pains is about every five minutes. Where the Read method is practiced, the patient will lie quietly in bed, relax all her muscles, and breathe slowly and deeply in and out. The natural pain response is exactly the opposite, for the patient will get tense all over, clench her fists, purse her lips tightly together and squirm about. This increased tension serves to exaggerate the pain and add to the fear of labor. Read makes his patients practice relaxing for weeks before they go into labor.. Knowing the why and the wherefore of labor, his patients try to follow the relaxing measures during labor itself and find themselves agreeably comfortable. Highly neurotic women may require the assistance of a pain-relieving drug; in these cases the physician generally uses a new synthetic which has replaced morphine to a considerable extent. By relaxing, deep breathing and occasionally the aid of the drug, Read is able to carry the patient comfortably to the stage of active delivery at which time a light anesthetic, such as gas-oxygen, is given to those who wish it. The babies are born naturally for the most part, as nature intended them to be, and the mothers do not find labor to be an ordeal.

Read's patients get the benefit of considerable personal care of their physician during labor and that is a factor whose importance should not be underestimated. One great fear of the woman in labor is that her doctor may not be at her bedside in time. No matter how much the pain, the moment a woman sees her doctor she no longer seems to suffer. Her mind is more at ease and so are the labor pains. Kindness too, is important. A little consideration on the part of the delivery room nurse and the intern staff does much to allay the fear that comes from being in a strange environment. These factors, and the principles of relaxation and confidence, none of which are entirely new, have gained new impetus, and it seems possible that in this way the Read method may influence most obstetric practice, whatever the choice of anesthetic.

ABRAHAM B. TAMIS, M.D.

NATURAL CHILDBIRTH

In his book, *Childbirth Without Fear,* Dr. Read reports that some of his patients became so adept in relaxing that they appeared to be lying in a trance from the beginning of labor until the end. The relaxation of these patients was so complete that they became almost oblivious to the fact that they were giving birth. Between contractions during the second stage of labor they continued to lie completely relaxed but woke up to participate fully in the expulsion effort. Then as soon as a contraction wore off they again sank into an amnesic, almost anesthetic, state.

Here is Dr. Read's approach, in his own words:

The idea of anesthetic and pain to these completely relaxed women is quite absurd; it does not enter their minds; they have no demand for it; they do not have pain, but they are conscious of muscular effort, particularly during the second stage. They can understand what is said to them, they listen, and they carry out instructions. After the baby is born and they awake once more to the full floodlight of motherhood, their physical freshness, the complete absence of shock, and their inability to recall the incidents of their labor are most marked.

But in the average labor we have slightly different circumstances to meet. A woman is perhaps willing to try and relax during her first-stage contractions. I do not advise that during the first stage of the average labor a woman should be asked to relax the whole time unless she wishes it, and unless she has overcome all the difficulties of progressive relaxation and is adept at the art. In the ordinary labor, I prefer the woman to be awake to her general condition; I prefer her to be able to listen to instruction and to learn what is going on, and to be able to recognize the encouragement given her by those in attendance. Immediately there is a sign of a uterine contraction, she must at once apply herself to the task, and relax to the very best of her ability. During the first stage of labor, relaxation must be practiced during the uterine contractions; between them I do not ask for continual relaxation; a quiet restfulness is sufficient. I disagree with those who advocate certain definite positions during the first stage of labor. I have seen them in many books, and I regret that I cannot agree with those who teach the hanging on to the bottom of the bed, standing on tiptoe, stretching the pelvis, the opening of the pelvic brim, and a variety of other suggestions of those who put more stress upon athletics and exercises than upon the neuro-muscular relaxation. Undisturbed peace should characterize the first stage of labor without mental or physical tension, with every happiness that a woman can be given, with every urge to confidence in the right outcome of her parturition.

Relaxation during the first-stage contractions has the most astonishing effect. Very often, quite at the beginning, after the laughter and merriment that so many girls start their labors with has worn off, and as the mental attitude becomes more serious, it is necessary to maintain control, both physically and mentally. Relaxation is of the greatest aid at this time. If she has been sympathetically treated and well instructed, she should have no difficulty whatever in avoiding all pain during the first stage of normal labor. It may be, as I said before, that it is not easy for her, during the last part of the first stage, to avoid discomfort, but we must remember that the calmer she is, the more relaxed she will become. It is difficult to relax when under the influence of strong emotional disturbance.

During the second stage the whole picture alters. You do not require, nor could you obtain if you wished, physical relaxation during the second stage of expulsive contractions. The idea of Nature here is that the door being widely open, and the birth canal being fit to pass the baby through, the muscles that can assist in that purpose are brought into play, and brought into play very vigorously. This entails real physical exertion, and after each second-stage contraction you can see plainly that the woman is out of breath; deep breaths are drawn, and the effort is just as great as any other muscular exercise of rather a violent nature. Therefore, it is between the contractions that we wish to have complete relaxation, for that is the most effective manner of reconstituting the muscular power. There is very little, if any, discomfort in the average second stage of labor that has been properly conducted. Many women who have felt it a hardship that they are unable to help, who have accepted the teaching that they can do nothing during the first stage and have relaxed and allowed the uterus to do its own work, have become bored and not a little tired at the feeling that they have done nothing. When the second stage begins, they are told they can help; a tremendous sense of relief very often fills a woman's mind as she realizes that not only can she help, but the greater effort she applies to it within reason, so much the greater sense of comfort she gets. There is no pain with a good honest second-stage expulsive effort until the first sense of dilatation of the perineum is appreciated. I am not, of course, speaking of those abnormal cases where there are large masses of piles which come down as the head stretches the anterior wall of the rectum, but of the normal, unimpeded case where there is no pathological condition present at all.

When the head gets down on to the perineum a woman often finds it difficult to relax, because she gets that sense of bursting. There is no doubt at all that if a woman does endeavor to resist when the head arrives on the perineum and contracts her pelvic floor and squeezes up the vulva and the rectum, she runs a very good chance of having not only acute pain but also, by increasing that tension, of a torn perineum. If a woman can relax well at that stage, if she can be told that that sensation of bursting is a myth and that the head will not tear the perineum if she is relaxed, it is astonishing how large a baby will pass through what appears to be a small vulva without any tear to the perineum at all. If, between the final second-stage contractions, after the head has adequately crowned, you can persuade the woman to remain relaxed, the complete absence of difficulty with which the head can be produced is surprising. I am sure that a large number of torn perineums are due to the effort of the woman to resist the oncoming head by violently contracting the muscles at the outlet. When a baby arrives under these conditions the woman, being conscious and not filled with anesthetic, realizes only when she hears her baby cry that it is born. A child passes through a relaxed vulva with almost complete absence of sensation to the mother. There is no doubt that with relaxation of the vulva there is also a temporary anesthesia of its sensory nerves. Should a tear be unavoidable, one or even two stitches can be put in carefully and without any feeling whatever. The woman is again asked to relax while they are being inserted. I have mentioned this before; it must be done at once because that anesthesia of the vulva disappears in a few minutes.

After the baby is born, in the third stage, there is no need for relaxation. Here we get the beautiful tension of satisfaction. The sympathetic nervous system sweeps in with all its joys and its pleasing emotions, and so there is no desire for relaxation and no need for it. There is no necessity to relax during the third stage because the sound of the baby and the consciousness of the mother, the absence of hemorrhage and the general sense of delight, seem to be all that is required to make the uterus get rid of the after-birth as quickly as possible. Not infrequently a mother will expel the after-birth without any assistance from the physician, and this, I think, is possible particularly when there is an absence of shock in cases which have been carried out under good general relaxation.

I do not wish to encourage anyone to feel that relaxation is the whole secret of natural childbirth. It is a most important adjuvant, but without education and without an understanding of the phenomena of labor, relaxation by itself is really not effective. I have heard natural childbirth spoken of as "labor under the influence of relaxation." That is quite untrue; this is an adjuvant to labor, and is one of the means by which we are enabled to relieve the natural woman of the contrary influences to which she has been subjected by culture, civilization and ignorance.

How To Relax

1. Stand with the feet eighteen inches apart, with the hands on the hips; stretch the body to its full height; inspire deeply through the nose to full capacity, and expire, allowing the shoulders to drop and the head to come forward as the lungs empty. Repeat this breathing exercise six or eight times.

2. Either on a sofa, a rug on the floor, a hard bed or in an upright chair with arms, sprawl in the most comfortable position.

3. If lying down, place the feet six inches apart, hands by the sides of the trunk, head lying on one side on a pillow.

4. Take five or six more deep breaths, close the eyes and remain perfectly still.

5. Concentrate on each arm in turn to be sure it is not being held stiffly in any part, that the muscles are not twitching, or the fingers fidgeting.

6. Do the same with the legs, buttocks and back. Note carefully the muscles of the back; if they are loose you should have the

sensation of pressure upon the bed or chair of your body weight.

7. Let the abdominal muscles go and allow the respiration to be easy and quiet.

8. Finally, relax the muscles of the face, the brow, eyelids, cheeks (which will allow the jaw to drop slightly), and the muscles around the mouth. Lie in this condition for twenty minutes to half an hour. Sleep in a relaxed condition is satisfactory, and many patients will go to sleep soon after they attain a state of relaxation.

Further Hints On Relaxation

POSITION. Supine, on wide couch or fairly hard bed with a small bolster under the head and shoulders, and a smaller pillow or cushion under the knees. Arms by the side, elbows half bent, hands half closed, knees slightly separated, *i.e.,* all joints so far as possible in semi-flexion.

DIRECTIONS TO PATIENT. Relax the:

Shoulders by thinking of them "opening outwards."
Arms by imagining them falling out of shoulder girdle, "as though they did not belong to you."
Back—sinking through couch on to the floor.
Legs, knees and feet—falling outwards by their **own weight**.
Head—making a dent in the pillow.
Eyelids—half closing by their own weight.
Face—as though hanging from the cheek bones.
Jaw—hanging loose.

Give about two minutes to each group, and take them in the same order each time.

BREATHING. Let the chest wall collapse with its own weight on expiration, and pause for two seconds (or until you want a new breath) at the end of expiration. Get a feeling of general relaxation, letting all the joints give a little more with each outgoing breath. Do this six times.

Note the train of sensations in the limbs—usually heaviness followed by lightness or "floating"; faint, transient pins and needles in the hands; feeling of warmth passing up from the extremities.

A pleasant, torpid, day-dreaming state generally ensues (as in sunbathing) and any tendency to directed thinking should be deliberately diverted into a day-dream.

DURATION. Half to one hour. (The sense of the passage of time is often lost or blunted.)

Sleep is not aimed at and, for most patients, muscular relaxation seems to be more refreshing. But many insomniacs can put themselves to sleep during the day by relaxation, and the ability to do so gives them confidence at night.

The patient should get up slowly at the end of relaxation and stretch. Jumping up suddenly is sometimes followed by faintness.

AN ACTUAL CASE RECORD

This morning, Mrs. ——, aged forty-two, had her second child, the first one having been born some eight years ago. An intelligent, sensible woman who had accepted all the teaching she instinctively knew to be right, who had practiced her relaxation to the best of her ability, who had taken a great interest in all the information I had given her upon the mechanism of labor, she reaped her reward.

Her labor commenced at about seven-thirty in the morning in the normal manner—rhythmical contractions which she felt in the groin first of all. Her relaxation destroyed all unpleasant sensations; she was able to doze, and, as she herself told me, felt in only a semi-conscious condition during the first stage, so completely did she relax. At nine-thirty she was roused and walked into the labor ward, still entirely free from discomfort. So little had appeared to be going on that I was not sent for until shortly after she had arrived in the labor ward. I found her lying on her side, semi-conscious, quiet and quite contented except, as she explained to me, that there was considerable aching in her back. It was not a pain, she said, but a dull ache; it extended through to the front, and she felt it quite definitely along the bone and above the bone in front. When this occurs, I always do the same thing—turn the patient over on to her back with a pillow under the shoulders and the head well up, and during the next contraction bring the knees upwards and outwards as far as possible; this almost invariably moves the pain in the front and relieves the discomfort in the back. I then explained to her the use of the gas apparatus, having placed it, as usual, in her hand, so that she could use it when necessary. She said there was no need for it, but it lay on the bed beside her so that she could use it if she wanted.

She told me that the pain in front disappeared after one or two contractions in that position, but that there was still a considerable ache in the back. She thought, possibly, that being forty-two her bones were a little stiffer than they should be; otherwise she felt quite convinced that there was no need even for the ache that she felt over the lower sacrum. She had not, up to that time, been using contractions very well, so I explained to her the best method of using them. "Wait," I told her, "until the contraction is at the top—you will understand what I mean; then draw a long breath and hold it; do not push violently, but just lean on it." She did this and told me it was very much more comfortable.

Her contractions came at about six-seven minute intervals; in between them she slept. She was quite comfortable and controlled. When she awakened for a contraction, she said, "Now it is coming," and we lifted up her knees and let her push her feet against our hands. She hung on to her knees once or twice, but managed to do very well without exertion, and I told her not to press violently as the baby would come easily.

And so we went on. At eleven-thirty the head crowned. Then it was interesting again that she said to me, "I feel quite sure that, having been so badly torn with my last child, I can never get this baby without rupturing again, and last time I remember so clearly, although I was partially anesthetised, feeling that dreadful sensation of splitting." I assured her that there was very little reason why she should tear this time if she allowed her baby to come in a quiet and controlled manner. She decided, however, at this point, that since the baby was so near she would prefer to take gas. I asked her if it was hurting; she said it did not hurt, but that she felt so definitely that she could not have this baby without splitting, and that she remembered so vividly the horrible feeling of that "rip," that she would have some gas if I did not mind. For the next four or five contractions she took three or four breaths of gas—certainly not enough to anesthetise her. Then the baby crowned, and I asked her whether she felt that same sensation now? She replied that strangely enough it did not feel so tight now as it did at first.

That is a point upon which I should like once again to lay emphasis. Many women will have that distinct fear of splitting at the beginning of dilatation of the vulva, but many of them, too, will lose that sensation after the vulva is practically fully dilated. This is, of course, not an invariable rule, but it has made me wonder sometimes whether the dilatation of the vulva in some way or other does paralyse certain sensory nerves. There is no doubt about the relative anesthesia of the perineum during the late second stage and for some minutes after the child has been born.

I have already drawn attention to the fact that stitches may be inserted immediately the baby is born with practically no discomfort to the mother.

This baby was born quite perfectly. Mrs. —— had put away her gas apparatus, and assured me there was no discomfort. The baby weighed seven pounds seven ounces, and passed through the vulva easily without any injury. The rest of the body followed after about a minute, and was found to be a girl. I held the baby up for her to see, and she presented that same beautiful picture of happiness that I am never tired of describing. She reached over and took its hand and called it all those things which a mother calls a child she has waited and longed for. The cord was rapidly anemic; the child cried and stretched as she held it; I separated it, and the uterus was immediately hard. After five to seven minutes, the uterus started contracting again; she told me there was a certain amount of tightness about her abdomen, and very soon the cord lengthened some four inches. I put my hand flat on her abdomen, and told her with the next tightening to bear down as she had done before, and her placenta appeared at the vulva, turned inside out, and the placental blood, enclosed in the membrances, came away. There was not one ounce of bleeding after the placenta had left the vagina. She then told me that she understood now what she had never understood before; how the Egyptian women had their babies and walked home so soon afterwards (she had lived in Egypt). She told me she felt she could have done the same with comfort, and with no distress; she knew she was strong enough, and I agreed. Her pulse had remained at 70-72, she was in no way tired or exhausted, and she felt the whole thing had been a glorious experience.

If this is possible with the old bones of a woman of forty-two, how much more possible should it be with the relatively elastic bones of girls.

Two women medical students were present at this labor. They had asked to see how natural childbirth was conducted. I was as much interested in the expressions upon their faces as I was in the normal, natural childbirth that I was conducting. Their mouths opened, and in silence their eyes opened wide and wider; they looked at the woman as though she were mad or demented; they failed to understand that she was speaking the truth. They had, each of them, seen and conducted many labors; they did not realize the importance of certain simple phenomena of labor. As I came away from the theater, having explained just how and why this thing had occurred, one of them made a remark which I think most people will make when they first see a natural childbirth. She said, "It's perfectly simple to have a baby like that. If that is what obstetrics means, there is nothing in it." I replied, "Exactly. There is nothing in normal, natural obstetrics except that which is put into it by the scientific and misunderstanding minds. Obstetricians are essential to deal with the abnormal; they should not complicate the normal."

So Mrs. —— went back to her room. She was perfectly happy and felt she had been through an experience which she would willingly undergo again. But the greatest concentration of her happiness was upon the delightful child for whom she had waited so long, who she had feared many times would not arrive because of her advancing years. She became again a young woman and felt, as she told me, that war or no war, she still had much to live for.

For my own part, I felt most grateful for those experiences which had made it possible for me to instruct her in this thing, because it is satisfying to be able to bring this joy to women of mature years who have thought about it, considered it and finally disbelieved it, until experience has proven that after all Nature is the greatest obstetrician.

Sir Grantly Dick Read, M.D.

When Your Baby Is Born

WHILE the baby is in the uterus, there is no need for him to breathe. He gets his oxygen from the mother's blood, supplied through the placenta. However, nature started well in advance to prepare for the moment when the baby would begin to use his own lungs for breathing. With his first cry, the baby's lungs begin to fill with air and start supplying his body tissues with the oxygen they now need. With his first breath, his body begins to adjust to his new environment.

As soon as the umbilical cord is clamped and cut, the baby is wrapped in a warm clean cotton blanket. A new baby loses body heat very fast and must be kept warm. The cord is tied with tape, and the clamp is then removed. Some doctors put a dressing over the cord stump, but others consider this unnecessary. The small piece of cord still attached to the baby's navel will dry up within a few days, and drops off after seven to fifteen days.

Next, the doctor will put drops in each of the baby's eyes. This precaution is required by law in nearly every state and is a means of preventing eye infection.

If your baby is born at home he will not need any mark of identification. In a hospital, however, he will be tagged, perhaps with adhesive tape or a bead necklace bearing your name. Sometimes his footprints and your fingerprints are put on the same piece of paper in the hospital record. This identification is done right after birth.

No doubt you have heard tales of some mothers' surprise when they first see their newborn babies. Some babies are pink and white and plump; others are long and red and scrawny. But even if your baby does not look just as you expected, he will change a lot in the first few days.

At birth, your baby may weigh anywhere from five and a half to ten or eleven pounds—the average being seven and a half pounds. He is usually about nineteen to twenty-two inches long. His skin is covered with a white substance called vernix. His scalp has a lot of fine, soft baby hair. His head is big in proportion to his body, and may be a little lopsided from being squeezed a bit as he came down through the narrow, bony canal of your pelvis. The bones of the baby's head are flexible and any lopsidedness will disappear in a few days. The bones of the baby's head will not grow together for several months. The soft spot right on top of his head, called the fontanel, is the last place to close.

His tiny arms and legs are so bowed that they do not look at all like an adult's. They wave about and kick aimlessly. His eyelashes and eyebrows are so fine you can hardly see them. When he opens his eyes, they roll about in a startling manner, for he has not learned how to focus them. It may take him six weeks or longer to learn this. When he cries, there are no tears, for the tear glands are not quite ready to function. He sleeps a lot. He does not yet know how to smile or to respond.

Most little babies cry when they are hungry. Some cry when they are wet or uncomfortable; some do not. Some cry more than others.

Rooming-in. These little "newborns" get a great deal of satisfaction and comfort from being held and cuddled and sung to. This attention won't spoil them. Instead, they need it to make them feel warm and loved and secure. Some hospitals are recognizing the importance of this by making it possible for the baby to spend a great deal of time in his mother's room. The baby's crib might be brought in and left in the room, or a few hospitals have small individual nurseries connected with the mother's room. This second plan is called rooming-in. By either of these arrangements the mother can see her baby as often as she wishes. She also has a chance to find out what some of the baby noises mean and learn something of how to take care of him. Then she won't be completely lost when she goes home and has the entire responsibility on her hands.

REGISTERING THE BABY'S BIRTH. All states now have laws requiring that a baby's birth be registered. Births are usually reported by the doctor or midwife in attendance. After the information has been sent in to the State Bureau of Vital Statistics, the mother receives a notification that the birth has been registered. When you give the doctor or midwife the necessary information, be sure the date of birth, the name, and the sex of the child are entered correctly. Then check the record you receive. Few mistakes are made, and they can be easily corrected if caught early.

BREAST FEEDING

BENEFITS OF BREAST FEEDING. Most healthy women are able to breast feed their babies. Breast feeding takes a little time and patience for both the mother and baby to learn, but once learned it is easier than making formulas and can be a very satisfying experience.

Unless there is a medical reason why breast feeding is unwise, give it a fair trial. That means keeping at it for more than just a few days. The baby will learn to suck better if he is hungry. For this reason many doctors have stopped the practice of giving the baby bottle feedings during these early days when the baby is learning how to get milk from the breast. A healthy, normal infant will probably learn to suck effectively from the breast within the first few days after birth, although he may be very lazy at first.

Breast milk is a natural food containing most of the necessary food elements in the easiest form for the newborn baby to use, and it is always at the right temperature. The close relationship between a mother and her baby during breast feeding is important for them both. Even during pregnancy a mother cannot have that same feeling of closeness and joy in her baby that she gets while nursing him. Breast feeding is one of the first ways a baby can feel the security and love of his mother. Babies need this feeling of closeness to the mother. It helps them to grow into healthy, happy, well-adjusted children.

Successful breast feeding depends to a large extent on a desire to breast feed the baby. This desire helps to promote a good supply of milk. The calm, placid, well-adjusted mother finds it easiest to breast feed her baby, for many so-called nervous factors can influence the supply of milk. Getting too excited, too tired, or overanxious can slow up your milk supply. So it is important for you to talk out your worries, and to have some help when you go home, so you will be less likely to get tired out and feel upset.

The baby may not be brought to you for breast feeding until twelve to twenty-four hours after birth. After this first feeding, the time between feedings may depend upon several things: the size and weight of the baby, how often he seems to need feeding, and whether or not you and your doctor want to try a self-regulating feeding plan. Some doctors recommend a three- or four-hour interval between feedings. Others feel that it is better for a baby to make his own schedule and be fed whenever he is hungry. The doctors who recommend this latter method call it the self-regulating or self-demand plan of feeding. A self-regulating schedule may not work for all mothers and babies. But many mothers who have tried it like it, and their babies thrive on it. Talk to your doctor if you want to try this plan.

During these early feedings, the nurse will help you in teaching the baby how to get milk from your breast. Even though babies are born knowing how to suck, some of them have trouble in learning to take the nipple in their mouths and get results. They may get tired at first and become fussy and fretful. This is particularly true in the days before the milk is formed. During this time let your baby suck for a short time on each breast—about five to ten minutes. Let his cheek touch your breast. Then he will root around and find the nipple. See that he gets the nipple well into his mouth. After the milk begins to come, on the third day or so, he will suck longer, and often can get all he wants from one breast at that feeding.

In teaching the baby to suck, hold the top of your breast away from his nose so he can breathe easily. If the breast presses against his nose, he may stop sucking because he cannot breathe. In trying to breathe, he may swallow air, which fills up his stomach and makes him fretful. After the feeding, hold him up against your shoulder, or have the nurse do so. Pat his back gently so he can belch up any air he may have swallowed.

Keep your nipples clean, and they will be less likely to crack or become sore. If you bathe them completely once a day and wear a clean nursing brassiere, you may not need to wash the nipples between feedings. However, it is best to wipe off any milk remaining on the nipples with a clean cloth. If your nipples are unusually tender, the doctor may advise you to put a little clean cold cream on them between feedings. Wash this off, though, before the baby is fed. Also, the doctor may recommend that you put a clean pad of gauze or soft cotton cloth over the nipples to protect them between feedings.

After the milk has started, it will continue to form as the baby sucks. But if he does not learn to suck well, your milk supply will gradually dry up.

THE BOTTLE-FED BABY. Some mothers are not able to breast feed their babies, or for other reasons breast feeding seems inadvisable. In these instances, the doctor will probably suggest that bottle feedings be given. These mothers should not feel guilty about their inability to breast feed. It does not mean they cannot be good mothers. Bottle feedings will not deprive the baby of a good start in life if they are properly given.

As we have mentioned before, one of the important reasons for breast feeding is the contact with the mother's arms and body and the feeling of closeness and security a baby gets from being held during feedings. A bottle-fed baby can be given this same security if the mother holds the baby in her arms to feed him, just as she would at her breast. This can be done in the hospital as well as at home, and is strongly recommended by doctors who know that the close contact between mother and baby during feeding is important.

THE FIRST BATHS. Some hospitals still give sponge baths with soap and water to new babies, but many doctors believe this is not important. Your baby may be given an oil bath on the first day after birth, or he may not be bathed at all for several days. Many doctors feel that the vernix on the baby's skin helps to prevent skin infections in the early days of life, so they leave it on to wear off by itself.

Most of it disappears in a few hours. Most babies get their first real baths on the seventh or eighth day after birth. Tub baths are delayed until the cord stump has fallen off and the navel is healed.

During the early days, a little oil may be placed in the folds of the skin. Whenever the diaper is changed the region around the genitals and buttocks should be carefully cleaned with oil. A new baby's skin often becomes dry and scaly, but this is nothing to worry about and will correct itself as the baby gets older.

THE FIRST FEW DAYS. The biggest danger to tiny babies is infection. Good hospitals take care to keep them away from people with colds, sore throats, intestinal upsets, or skin infections. If the baby is born at home, follow this same plan. Some hospitals have the nurses wear masks in caring for the babies, and the mothers wear a mask while breast feeding. Others do not require this. There is no real need for masks if the persons caring for the baby are free from infection.

Most new babies lose weight for the first few days, and may not begin to regain their birth weight until they are five to seven days old. This weight loss is due largely to loss of water and the passage of intestinal material which accumulated in the baby's bowel before birth. It is a perfectly normal adjustment and is nothing to worry about unless the baby does not begin to gain by the end of the first week.

In the first few days the breasts of some babies seem to grow bigger and get a little reddened. A few drops of milk may even ooze out of the baby's nipple. This can happen with either a boy or a girl baby, but it is not very common. It simply means that some of the internal substances which were getting your breasts ready for feeding also passed into the baby's body before birth. Your internal secretions got into the baby's body in the same way that food materials and oxygen went across the placenta from your body into his. This swelling of the baby's breasts will disappear gradually. It is important not to press or rub the baby's breasts during this time.

Some little girl babies may also have a few drops of blood appear from the vagina during the early days after birth. This bleeding is caused in somewhat the same way as the breast enlargement. It is nothing to worry about and will disappear shortly.

Convalescing from Childbirth

THE ordeal through which a mother passes in bringing her baby into the world will make her perfectly willing to rest and relax for the first day. No matter how normal and relatively easy the labor, the organs of birth have performed their functions at the expense of her entire body. Sleep and rest is nature's way of quickly restoring the energy expended and of rebuilding her strength.

The length of time you stay in bed will vary, depending on the length of your labor or the need for stitches. It will also depend on your doctor or the hospital. Some doctors will get you out of bed for a while the next day, others will keep you there for a week. In many hospitals today, the mother gets out of bed on the third day and is sent home on the fifth. But whatever the length of time, she is advised not to take up her household duties immediately and to get plenty of rest at home.

To put a sudden strain on the overstretched organs may cause a descent of the uterus. Therefore, it is most desirable to go back to a regular routine gradually.

Your doctor will tell you when it is safe to take tub baths. One of the important things is to keep the area around the vaginal opening as free from infection as possible. Avoid touching this area. While you are in bed the nurse will cleanse the region. She will show you how to give yourself this care after you get up.

Most doctors will let you eat a regular diet as soon as you feel like it. You may be given a light diet of soup and soft foods the first day, but after that you will probably find yourself eating heartily. You need to eat the same foods that you ate during pregnancy, plus an extra pint of milk a day, and another serving of oranges, grapefruit, or tomatoes, if you are breast feeding.

As you begin to work about the house you will need more protein food in order to keep up your supply of breast milk. Another serving each day of lean meat, eggs, dried beans, or dried peas will supply the extra protein you need.

CHANGES THAT TAKE PLACE IN THE BREASTS. True milk does not

appear in the breast for at least three days after the birth of the baby. It seems to take that long for the various internal substances which control the beginning of milk secretion to get under way. The coming of milk into the breasts is called lactation.

During the time before the true milk is secreted, the breast secretes a thin, watery fluid called colostrum, which is rich in protein and nourishes the baby until the milk is formed. This period before the milk comes in also gives you a chance to help the baby learn how to suck.

About the third day after the baby's birth, you will notice that your breasts are becoming tense and firm, with the veins standing out clearly. This firmness of the breasts means that the secretion of milk is ready to begin. Your breasts may be a little painful at this time, but the discomfort can often be relieved by wearing a good nursing brassiere.

If for any reason you cannot or should not nurse your baby, the doctor will give instructions on how to dry up the breasts.

It is important to have your breasts supported properly during these early days after the baby's birth. Even while you are in bed, you should wear a firm, well-fitting brassiere. A good nursing brassiere is best. Sagging breasts are not a result of breast feedings, but may be caused by poor support during pregnancy and the nursing period.

WHAT CAUSES AFTERPAINS? During the first week after the baby's birth, you may notice occasional cramplike contractions in your abdomen. These cramps are called afterpains and are very much like the cramps of a menstrual period. They happen more often with a second or third baby than with a first baby. The afterpains are contractions of the uterus as it pushes out clots of blood and tissue which collect in the uterine cavity. They will probably stop in a few days. You may notice them more when you are breast feeding the baby, since the sucking of the baby at the breast seems to stimulate these contractions.

SHRINKING OF THE UTERUS. During the first six weeks after the baby's birth, the uterus shrinks from its large size of about two pounds down to about 2 ounces. This process is called involution, which means "turning in" or becoming smaller. No one knows exactly how this change takes place, but it is just as amazing and perfect a process as is the growth of the uterus during pregnancy. A part of this extra material is absorbed into the blood stream as the uterus grows smaller, but some of it is passed out of the body.

This discharge from the vagina after the birth of the baby is often called menstruation, but it really is not the same. The remains of the thick lining of the uterus are passed out in this way after the baby's birth, so the uterus can shrink. At first the discharge comes quite freely and is very bloody, but it gradually becomes less in amount and finally is colorless. It will probably disappear in three to four weeks after the baby is born. If bleeding continues after the second week, notify your doctor.

Use sanitary pads during this time. It is not safe to use any sort of tampon or to put anything into the vagina to absorb the discharge. A serious infection might result.

URINATION. You will pass a large amount of urine during the first day or two after the baby's birth because of certain chemical readjustments in your body. It is important not to let the bladder get too full. One of the first things the nurse will suggest when you are settled in your room after the baby's birth is that you try to empty your bladder. You should empty it every six hours at least.

Most women have no trouble in passing urine after delivery. But sometimes the urethra is pressed so tightly against the pubic bone during the baby's birth that it becomes numb. This numbness makes it dfficult to pass urine normally. If you have this trouble, it may be necessary for the doctor or nurse to pass a small tube called a catheter into the bladder to draw off the urine. Catheterization is not painful, only a little uncomfortable. It may not be necessary more than once or twice, since the numbness usually passes away in a few hours.

CONSTIPATION. This is very common in the first week or two after the baby's birth. It is partly because you are spending so much time in bed and partly because the pressure against the rectum during labor may have made it a little numb. Your doctor may prescribe a mild laxative or changes in your diet. Avoid strong laxatives. In addition to their cramping tendencies, they may get into your milk and give the baby loose bowel movements.

THE VALUE OF EXERCISES

While you are in bed, move about as much as possible, even to sleeping on your stomach. Moving about will help you get your strength back more quickly. Your doctor may recommend certain exercises, both while you are in bed and later on. If your doctor has you get up within the first few days after the baby's birth, you may not need to do exercises.

Each doctor has his own preference for exercises he recommends. Some doctors today feel special exercises are no longer needed if a woman is getting up and about actively within a few days after the baby's birth. Others may have certain exercises they feel are particularly helpful.

The simplest exercises are done lying flat on your back in bed, with arms at your sides, and without a pillow. One exercise is to raise your head from a flat position and try to touch your chin to your chest several times. After a few days, try to sit up without bracing yourself or moving your legs. This exercise is hard to do at first, so try it once the first time, twice the next day, and so on.

Another good exercise is to lie on your back and raise one leg at a time, trying to bring it as far up as possible without bending your knees or raising your head. Try to keep your back flat. Or you can bend your knee and pull your leg in as close to your body as you can. Try these two exercises first with one leg, then the other. Each day try to do them one more time. You will gradually be able to bring both legs up together, but this may take several weeks.

You will probably be discouraged to find how hard it is to do these exercises at first. But take it easy and do each one slowly until you can repeat it several times without getting tired. You will soon find you can do more and more. It will take several months, though, to get your full strength and your old figure back again, so don't try to hurry it too much.

Many hospitals limit the number of visitors a new mother may have, and it is a good plan to do this at home, too. You need rest and quiet for the first few days after the baby's birth. It is very tiring to have to be polite and talkative when all you want to do is have some time to yourself. If the baby is in the room with you, it is even more important to limit the number of people who come in. All hospitals keep visitors out of the room when the baby is nursing. Both you and the baby need to devote all your energies to learning this new experience, and it is easier to do this without distractions.

RETURNING HOME

Some hospitals give instruction about baby care to new mothers just before the mother and baby go home. This is helpful even if you have had such instruction during pregnancy. It is easier to see the reason for doing certain things now that the baby is here.

If it is possible at all, plan to have someone help you when you first return from the hospital. You probably will not feel like doing much toward running the house for several weeks. You can probably take care of the baby yourself without much trouble, but try to have someone else take over the responsibility for the housework. If you cannot afford to hire someone, perhaps a friend or relative would come. Even if she only comes in every day to cook the dinner or clean the house, it will help a great deal. Many communities have public-health nurses or visiting nurses, who can visit your home during these early days and show you how to care for the baby. Your husband can help, too, during this time in doing many little things to make it easier for you. Many men have fun cooking and cleaning and taking care of the children, even of the baby.

Before you go home, or sometime during the second or third week, your doctor may examine you to see if your pelvic organs are returning to normal. This examination is called a postpartum examination.

YOUR EXAMINATIONS AFTER CHILDBIRTH

When your baby is six weeks old, be certain to return to your doctor for a final examination. At that time if there is any correction or treatment to be given to your internal sexual organs, it can be done easily and quickly. Any neglect at this time may result in inflammation of your tubes and ovaries at a later date. You might take the opportunity at this time to discuss the planning and spacing of the rest of your family.

It is also wise to make a regular visit every twelve to fifteen months for an internal examination. Only by this method will it be possible for you to avoid the danger of some serious change taking place in your sexual organs unknown to you. This is one way to prevent and control the spread of cancer among women.

GETTING BACK TO NORMAL. Avoid intercourse during the time your organs are returning to normal. Most doctors advise that you wait six weeks after the baby is born before resuming sexual relations.

Your doctor will tell you when you can begin to do other things— for example, how soon you can go up and down stairs, and when to drive a car. Except for the special points we have talked about, you can begin to do more things as soon as you feel equal to them.

Some women have trouble with backache after the baby's birth. Mothers do not remember that they bend over a thousand times a day. If you can plan your work to eliminate all extra bending, you may not be troubled with backache. Sit down as much as possible when taking care of the baby. You will find this helps a lot. Some doctors advise wearing a well-fitting corset for a period after the baby's birth, but this depends a lot on your posture and how much support your back seems to need.

RETURN OF MENSTRUATION. The time when menstruation returns varies. A woman who does not breast feed her baby will usually menstruate within five to six weeks after the baby's birth. A woman who is breast feeding may not have a period during the entire time she is feeding the baby. However, some women do begin to menstruate during this time, and most of them have a period by five to six months after the baby's birth.

Absence of menstruation during the nursing period does not mean that you cannot become pregnant then. During this time the ovaries begin to function again even before you begin to menstruate.

Menstruation need not interfere with breast feeding, and the baby does not need to be weaned if menstrual periods begin. A nursing baby may be fussy during your menstrual period, but this does not mean the milk is harmful. During menstruation the milk supply is often decreased, which is probably why the baby complains.

The first menstrual period is likely to be abnormal. It may be longer or shorter than usual, or may stop and start again. Later periods, however, should become more regular.

Emergency Measures

What to Do If the Baby Comes Before Medical Help Arrives

Sometimes a baby is born before the doctor arrives, or before the mother can leave home to get to the hospital. This emergency is unusual, and is not as likely with a first baby as it is with later babies.

When a baby is born so quickly that you cannot get the doctor in time, it nearly always means the birth is normal. You would probably have had time to get the doctor, or to get to the hospital if the birth was going to be difficult.

Certain things can be done which will make it easier for both you and the baby. You cannot do these yourself. So get someone to stay with you until the doctor comes.

INSTRUCTIONS TO THE HELPER

1. Be sure the doctor or ambulance has been called.
2. See that the mother is comfortably lying down.
3. Wash your hands thoroughly.
4. Do not touch the area around the vaginal entrance.
5. Place a clean towel under the mother's hips for the baby to come on to. If you have time, protect the bed with newspapers.

6. Let the baby come naturally.

7. If the bag of waters has not broken, and the baby is born still inside the sac, puncture the sac with a pin or tip of scissors. Wipe the sac and fluid away from his face and head with the inside of a clean handkerchief.

8. As soon as he is born, wipe the baby's mouth, nose, and face with the inside of a clean handkerchief. Do not use cotton or paper tissues.

9. Move him carefully to a clean spot between the mother's legs, with his head elevated a little and away from any fluid or secretions. *Do not stretch the cord.* Let it remain a little slack.

10. If the doctor has been called and is on his way, you do not need to tie the baby's cord. Leave it attached. Leave the baby in a clean spot between the mother's legs, but cover his body with a blanket or towel to prevent chilling. Leave his head uncovered so he can breathe.

11. If you have not been able to reach the doctor, or if he can‑ not get there within an hour, the cord should be tied.

    (*a*) Tie the cord *tightly* in two places about two inches apart with clean pieces of tape or strong twine. The tie nearest the baby should be about six inches from his navel.

    (*b*) Cut the cord *between* the two ties with a clean pair of scissors.

    (*c*) Wrap the baby in a clean flannel square or blanket, with his face uncovered, and lay him on his side in a warm place.

12. Let the afterbirth come by itself. *Do not pull on the cord to make it come out.* Save the afterbirth in a basin or news‑ paper for the doctor to examine.

13. As soon as the afterbirth has passed out, place your hands over the mother's uterus (a firm lump just below the mother's navel) .

14. Cup your hands around the mother's uterus and massage the

uterus several times to keep it firm. If it does not stay firm, hold your hands around it until it does.

15. Clean the mother's buttocks and lower thighs, but do not touch the area around the vaginal entrance.

16. Make the mother comfortable and see that the baby is warm and breathing. Give the mother a hot drink, such as tea, if she wishes.

17. Do not leave the mother until the doctor comes.

The Premature Baby and His Care

A PREMATURE baby is a baby that is born more than two weeks before the expected time. Because it is difficult to determine the exact time a baby is due, all babies weighing less than five and a half pounds are considered premature. Even if the baby is full-term according to the mother's reckoning, if he weighs less than five and a half pounds he needs special care and should be treated as premature.

Premature babies may need to live in an incubator for a while, where there is carefully regulated temperature and humidity and where they can have extra oxygen. If they are very tiny they should not be handled any more than is absolutely necessary. This restriction may make it impossible for a mother to care for her premature baby during these early days. It may mean that she cannot see him except through the windows of the incubator. She may not be able to take him home from the hospital when she goes, or perhaps cannot keep him at home if he was born there. The length of his stay in the hospital depends to some extent on whether he is very tiny or is just under five and a half pounds. Most premature babies are not sent home until they weigh five and a half to six pounds.

Probably the mother will not be able to breast feed the baby at first, although the doctor may want her to learn how to express her milk by hand or with a breast pump so it can be fed to the baby. Some mothers learn to do this skillfully, and can even keep up their milk supply well enough to begin breast feeding the baby when he is big enough to come home.

A premature baby should be born in a hospital, if possible, where there are good facilities to take care of him. If he is born at home, and is quite small, every effort should be made to get him to a hospital which has special equipment and staff for the care of premature babies.

Caring for a small, premature baby at home is a big and difficult undertaking, and should not be tried unless there is absolutely no way to get good hospital care for him. A larger premature baby, such as one weighing four pounds or over, may be cared for at home, if he is born there. The public-health nurse can help you a lot in caring for a premature baby.

The successful rearing of a premature baby requires not only the advice of a doctor and the assistance and guidance of a nurse, but also intelligent and earnest cooperation by the mother, the father, and all the other members of the family.

The doctor's directions will be aimed at keeping the baby warm, properly nourished, and protected from infection, and they should be carried out carefully. The instructions given here are intended to help the mother care for her baby in whatever way her own doctor directs. If these instructions differ from those of her doctor, the mother should realize that her doctor's instructions should be followed. His examination of her baby and his observation of that baby's behaviour, growth, and development, are planned to meet her baby's individual needs.

It is well for the mother of a premature baby to realize that if her baby keeps well he has as good a chance as a full-term baby to develop normally. After he grows up he is likely to be as strong as if he had been born at the normal time.

A mother who, during pregnancy, places herself under a physician's care will be more likely to have a full-term baby than one who goes without such care. Some causes of premature birth are unavoidable, however, and, in spite of every effort, a certain number of babies are born prematurely.

Most premature babies are born unexpectedly, and it is wise for every expectant mother to have all equipment ready about two months before the baby is due.

The earlier a baby is born, the more difficult it is to care for him. A baby born two or three weeks before the expected date of his birth may be quite strong and little different from a full-term baby, but a baby born four or more weeks early may be very small and difficult to save. Occasionally a baby born at full term is exceptionally small and feeble and must be cared for like a premature baby. *All babies weighing less than five and a half pounds at birth should be treated as if premature.*

It is of the utmost importance to give a premature baby proper medical care during and *immediately after* birth.

Gaining Weight

The premature baby, like the full-term baby, usually loses some weight in the first two or three days after birth. He begins to take food when he is about eighteen hours old, and when he is four or five days old he will usually be able to take enough food to prevent further loss of weight. Premature babies, usually regain the birth weight by the second or third week.

The baby should be weighed at least twice a week. The weighings should be at about the same time of day, and the weight should be written down and shown to the doctor. Great care should be taken not to chill the baby during the weighing. He can be weighed in his jacket or gown or wrapped in a warmed blanket. Then the covering can be weighed separately and its weight subtracted from the total weight of the baby and the covering.

The baby may not gain weight every day, and some days he may lose weight, but week by week he should gain steadily if he is well and properly fed.

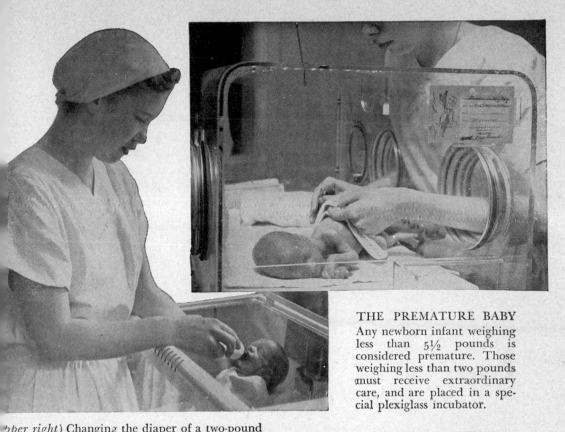

THE PREMATURE BABY

Any newborn infant weighing less than 5½ pounds is considered premature. Those weighing less than two pounds must receive extraordinary care, and are placed in a special plexiglass incubator.

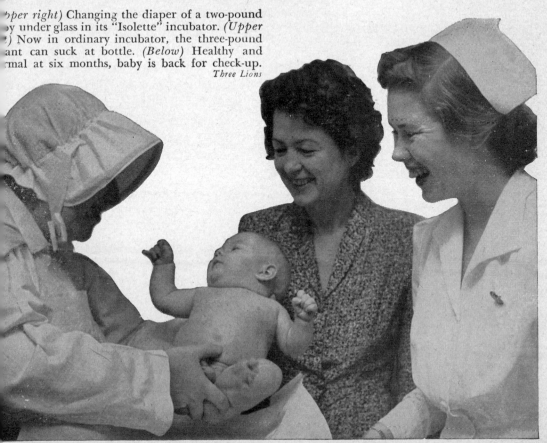

(Upper right) Changing the diaper of a two-pound baby under glass in its "Isolette" incubator. *(Upper left)* Now in ordinary incubator, the three-pound infant can suck at bottle. *(Below)* Healthy and normal at six months, baby is back for check-up.

Three Lions

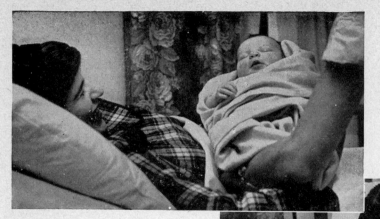

ROOMING IN

In many maternity hospitals day the newborn baby stays the same room with his moth instead of in the hospital nurse

(Right) Close by mother's bedside, baby gets attention and loving affection from the time he is born. As mother regains her strength, she is taught the techniques of baby care. *(Below)* Here, too, father immediately becomes part of the family and shares in learning to care for baby.

Photos by Three Lions

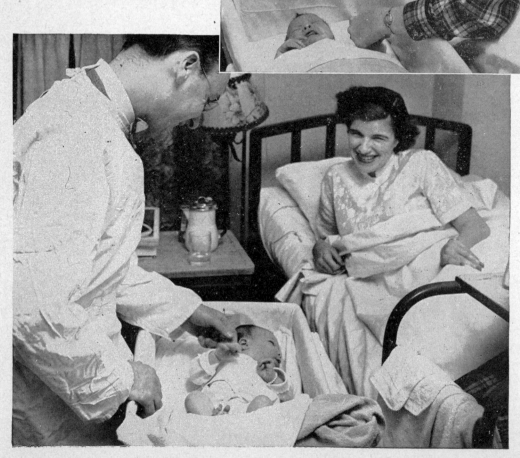

Choosing a Name for the Baby

IT's fun to know what your friends' or children's names really mean. Most people are so used to thinking of names entirely as personal identification tags that they give little thought to their original meanings. However, practically all names, with the exception of those coined by novelists, actresses, or others seeking the unusual, are derived from words and phrases of ancient languages. These can be traced to their origins and defined just like any other word.

In ancient times each person was called by but one name, and that name was usually "hand-tailored" to fit—just as nicknames such as "Slim," "Red" or "Blondie" today are picked to fit their possessors. This choice of names was by no means limited to personal characteristics, but might have been related to some circumstance of birth, some quality of character, or some outstanding achievement in later life. Thus we find such names as *Adam,* meaning "formed of red earth"; *Abigail,* meaning "her father's joy"; *Andrew,* meaning "manly"; and *Conrad,* meaning "wise counselor."

But not everybody was given a brand-new name—for it eventually became the custom to name people after Biblical, historical and legendary characters. The growing use of certain names then made it necessary to devise some further means of individual identification to distinguish one James from another, one Joseph from another, and one Mary from another. So people began adding surnames or family names to their given names—a custom generally followed throughout England by the middle of the fourteenth century.

Family names were usually derived from such sources as local surroundings, trades and occupations, ancestral homes and nicknames. Thus John, the son of John, became John Johnson. John who hailed from Scotland was called John Scott. John who was a cook by trade became John Cook. And John who was strong and robust was likely to be called John Strong.

Since the history and meaning of family names is a tremendous study in itself, this chapter is concerned only with the meanings and probable origins of given names. Even the given names listed on the following pages are limited to those most commonly in use.

The derivations and definitions given have been carefully checked, but authorities often disagree as to origins and meanings. As in any study where there are no absolute mathematical facts to guide us, there are bound to be differences of opinion. For instance, occasionally it is not certain from which language a name has been derived. The name *Alfred* is a good example of this. It might easily have come from the Teutonic, meaning "elf-counseled." Or it might have been derived from the Saxon, meaning "all peace." In such situations the compilers of this chapter have either chosen the meaning which seems to be backed by the weight of opinion or included both meanings in the listing.

The point is that while the study of names is a fascinating one, it cannot be considered an exact science. Therefore, if you do not agree with or like the meaning ascribed to your name—don't feel upset about it. For, after all, the interpretation of your name by etymologists is not nearly so important as the meaning your own personality has given it. Your name means to you and the people around you what you yourself make it mean. It doesn't matter what this or any other book says, so long as *your* name means "okay" or "grand person" to your friends.

It is usually not a bad idea to look into the meaning of names before you pin one on your son or daughter. Since a child usually lives with his name for the rest of his life, it's just as well to select a fitting one. For example, you wouldn't choose a name which means "dark of complexion" for a child that's likely to be a towhead. Nor would you pick one meaning "small, gentle" for a son whose ancestry indicates he'll grow up to be six feet six. And why pick names that have unpleasant or ridiculous meanings?

Of all the things you may be called upon to do, there is probably none more difficult than "naming the baby." Your child will bless you for choosing a pleasing name—but remember that your selection isn't necessarily final. A person can always legally change his name by appearing before the proper court.

Abbreviations

Arab.—Arabic	*Gr.*—Greek	*Phoe.*—Phoenician
Aràm.—Aramaic	*Heb.*—Hebrew	*Russ.*—Russian
Celt.—Celtic	*Ir.*—Irish	*Sax.*—Saxon
Dut.—Dutch	*Ital.*—Italian	*Scot.*—Scotch
Eng.—English	*Lat.*—Latin	*Slav.*—Slavonic
Fr—French	*Nor.*—Norman	*Sp.*—Spanish
Gael.—Gaelic	*O.F.*—Old French	*Teut.*—Teutonic
	Pers.—Persian	

GIVEN NAMES OF MEN AND THEIR MEANINGS

Aaron (*Heb.*) A mountain of strength; he who is exalted.

Abbott (*Heb.*) Father; ruler of an abbey.

Abel (*Heb.*) Vanity; ephemeral.

Abelard (*Teut.*) Noble firmness.

Abner (*Heb.*) Father of light.

Abraham (*Heb.*) Father of a multitude.

Abram (*Heb.*) High father; exalted.

Absalom (*Heb.*) Father of peace.

Achilles (*Gr.*) Without lips. (Among the Greeks, Achilles was the ideal of strength and valor.)

Adair (*Celt.*) The place of oaks.

Adam (*Heb.*) Formed of red earth.

Addison (*Scot.*) Son of Adam.

Adelbert (*Teut.*) Nobly bright.

Adolph (*Teut.*) Noble wolf; noble helper.

Adrian (*Gr.*) Manly; brave.

Alan (*Gael.*) He who is fast, majestic and graceful; a hunting dog.

Alban (*Lat.*) Of fair complexion; white.

Albert (*Teut.*) Noble; bright; famous.

Alexander, Alexis (*Gr.*) Helper of men.

Alfonso See Alphonse

Alfred (*Sax.*) All peace. (*Teut.*) Elf-counseled.

Algernon (*Fr.*) With whiskers. (*Teut.*) Noble; brave.

Allan, Allen (*Lat.*) Cheerful. Also see Alan.

Alonso, Alonzo Forms of Alphonse.

Aloysius (*Lat.*) Grace.

Alphonse, Alphonso (*Teut.*) Eager for battle; a helper of many.

Alvin (*Sax.*) Completely successful. (*Teut.*) Beloved by all.

Ambrose (*Gr.*) Like a god; immortal.

Amos (*Heb.*) Burden bearer; strong; vigorous.

Anatole (*Gr.*) Rising of the sun; the East.

André (*Fr.*) Form of Andrew.

Andrew (*Gr.*) Manly; brave.

Angelo (*Gr.*) Angelic.

Angus (*Celt.*) Excellent virtue.

Anthony (*Lat.*) Flourishing; graceful.

Archibald (*Teut.*) Bold; valiant; daring.

Armand (*Teut.*) Commander of an army.

Arnold (*Teut.*) Eagle power. (*Sax.*) Faithful to his honor.

Arthur (*Welsh*) Strong as a bear. (*Gael.*) Noble; exalted.

Asa (*Heb.*) Physician.

Asher (*Heb.*) Happy; blessed.

Ashley (*Sax.*) A field abounding in ash trees.

Aubrey (*Teut.*) Fair-haired chief. (*Sax.*) Rich and mighty.

August, Augustin, Augustine, Augustus *(Lat.)* Noble; royal; imperial.

Austin *(Lat.)* Imperial; renowned; royal.

Axel *(Teut.)* Divine reward.

Bailey *(Scot., Lat.)* A bailiff.

Balderic *(Teut.)* Prince ruler.

Baldwin *(Teut.)* Prince friend; speedy conqueror.

Barnabas, Barnaby *(Heb.)* Son of consolation or prophecy.

Barnard See Bernard.

Barron *(Celt.)* A valiant, respectable man.

Barry *(Uncertain)* Son of Harry.

Bartholomew *(Heb.)* Son of furrows; he who prevents affliction.

Barton *(Sax.)* A homestead.

Baruch *(Heb.)* Blessed.

Basil *(Gr.)* Kingly; royal.

Baxter *(Sax.)* A baker.

Bayard *(Sax.)* Good intellect.

Benedict *(Lat.)* Blessed; wishing all good.

Benjamin *(Heb.)* Son of the right hand.

Bennett See Benedict.

Berkeley *(Teut.)* Birch field.

Bernard *(Teut.)* Bold as a bear. *(Sax.)* Childlike; innocent.

Berthold *(Teut.)* Bright; firm. *(Sax.)* A ruler.

Bertram *(Sax.)* Fair and pure. *(Teut.)* Bright raven.

Bertrand *(Teut.)* Bright raven; shield.

Boniface *(Lat.)* Favored by fortune.

Booth *(Celt.)* A dwelling place.

Boris *(Russ.)* Fight.

Boyd *(Gael.)* Yellow-haired.

Bradford *(Eng.)* Broad ford (of a stream.)

Brian *(Celt.)* Strong. *(Gael.)* Well-born. *(Fr.)* Having a thundering voice.

Bruce *(Scot.)* Happy conqueror. *(Fr.)* From Bruys, a place in Normandy.

Bruno *(Teut.)* Brown.

Byron *(Eng.)* Clear discerner.

Cadwallader *(Celt.)* Battle arranger; valiant in war.

Caesar *(Lat.)* Having much hair.

Caleb *(Heb.)* Faithful as a dog.

Calvin *(Lat.)* Bald.

Cameron *(Gael.)* Crooked nose.

Campbell *(Celt.)* Crooked mouth.

Carew *(Welsh)* Castle by the water.

Carl *(Teut.)* Strong; manly.

Carrol *(Teut.)* Man. *(Lat.)* Praise.

Carter *(Gael.)* A man who drives a cart.

Casimir *(Slav.)* Looking peaceful; prince of the chief house.

Caspar *(Pers.)* A horseman; treasure master.

Cecil *(Lat.)* Blind; dim-sighted.

Cedric *(Teut.)* War chief.

Chad *(Celt.)* War. *(Sax.)* Abbr. of Chadwick, cottage by the harbor.

Chandler *(Lat.)* A candlemaker.

Charles *(Teut.)* Of great strength; manly.

Chauncey *(Sax.)* Silent praise.

Chester *(Lat.)* A camp.

Christian *(Gr.)* A follower of Christ.

Christopher *(Gr.)* Christ-bearer.

Cicero *(Lat.)* Vetch planter.

Clare, Clarence *(Lat.)* Famous; bright; noble.

Clark *(Eng.)* Clerk; clergyman; scholar.

Claude *(Lat.)* From Claudius (lame).

Clayton *(Eng.)* A town built upon clay or marl.

Clement *(Lat.)* Mild-tempered; gentle; merciful.

Clifford *(Eng.)* The ford by the cliff.

Clinton *(Eng.)* Town on the brow of a hill.

Clive *(Sax.)* A cliff.

Clyde *(Meaning uncertain).*

Colin *(Gr.)* Victory of the people.

Conan *(Celt.)* Wisdom.

Conrad *(Teut.)* Wise counselor.

Constantine *(Lat.)* Unyielding; resolute.

Cooper *(Eng.)* A barrelmaker.

Cornelius *(Lat.)* Horn, symbol of kingship.

Craig *(Gael.)* A rock or stone.

Crispin *(Lat.)* He who has curly hair.

Cuthbert *(Teut.)* Famous for knowledge.

Cyril *(Teut.)* Splendor. Also see Cyrus.

Cyrus *(Gr.)* Lordly. *(Pers.)* The sun; illustrious.

Dale *(Sax.)* A small valley.

Daniel *(Heb.)* Judge of God; God is my judge.

Darius *(Pers.)* King; brave; preserver.

David *(Heb.)* Beloved.

Dean *(Lat.)* An officer of the Church.

Demetrius, Dmitri *(Gr.)* Consecrated to Demeter, the earth mother.

Denis, Dennis *(Gr.)* From Dionysos, god of wine and drama.

Derrick *(Sax.)* Powerful among the people.

Desmond *(Meaning uncertain)*

Dexter *(Lat.)* The right.

Dietrich *(Teut.)* People's ruler.

Dion, Dionysius See Denis.

Dominic, Dominick *(Lat.)* Born on Sunday.

Donald *(Celt.)* Proud chief.

Douglas *(Gael.)* Dark; swarthy.

Drummond *(Gael.)* Back of the mountain.

Dudley *(Meaning uncertain)*

Dugald *(Celt.)* Black-haired; dark stranger.

Duncan *(Celt.)* Powerful chieftain; brown-haired warrior.

Dunstan *(Sax.)* Stone hill; strong fortress. *(Teut.)* Supremely high or dignified.

Durand *(Lat.)* Lasting; enduring; used to hardships.

Earl *(Eng.)* A title of nobility.

Ebenezer *(Heb.)* Stone of help.

Edgar *(Teut.)* Good spearman; successful in war. *(Sax.)* Honored; he who fulfills his promise.

Edmund *(Sax.)* Blessed peace; defender of happiness.

Edward *(Teut.)* Happy guard; guardian of happiness.

Edwin *(Sax.)* Happy conqueror. *(Teut.)* Rich friend.

Egbert *(Teut.)* Eminent for wisdom. *(Sax.)* Always bright; famous.

Einar *(Teut.)* Chief warrior.

Eli, Elias, Elihu, Elijah, Ellis *(Heb.)* God is the Lord; God is exalted.

Elliott See Eli. *(Welsh)* A huntsman.

Elmer *(Sax.)* Noble; bright.

Emanuel, Emmanuel *(Heb.)* God with us.

Emerson *(Sax.)* Son of the noble.

Emery *(Teut.)* Foreman; work ruler. *(Sax.)* Ever rich or mighty.

Emmet *(Sax.)* An ant (possibly implying industry).

Ennis *(Gr.)* He who is praised. *(Celt.)* An island or peninsula.

Enoch *(Heb.)* Dedicated; devoted; educated.

Enrico *(Ital.)* Form of Henry.

Ephraim *(Heb.)* Fruitful; prosperous.

Erasmus *(Gr.)* Amiable; worthy to be loved.

Eric *(Teut.)* Mighty lord; hero. *(Sax.)* Brave; powerful.

Ernest *(Sax.)* Zealous; serious. *(Teut.)* Eagle king.

Errol *(Meaning uncertain)*

Erwin *(Sax.)* A victorious lord, master or soldier. *(Welsh)* Very fair; white.

Esteban *(Sp.)* Form of Stephen.

Ethan *(Heb.)* Strength; power.

Ethelbert *(Teut.)* Noble; bright. *(Sax.)* He who shines by acts of humanity.

Eugene *(Gr.)* Well born.

Eustace *(Gr.)* Steadfast; resolute.

Evan *(Celt.)* Young warrior. *(Welsh)* Form of John.

Everard, Everett *(Teut.)* Strong as a wild boar. *(Sax.)* Ever honored.

Ezekiel *(Heb.)* God is my strength.

Ezra *(Heb.)* A helper.

Fabian *(Lat.)* Bean grower; cultivator.

Fairfax *(Sax.)* Fair-haired.

Felix *(Lat.)* Happy.

Ferdinand *(Teut.)* Daring; valiant; quick of comprehension.

Fergus *(Gael.)* Strong man; fierce chieftain.

Fernando See Ferdinand.

Fletcher *(Fr.)* Maker of arrows.

Florian *(Lat.)* Flowery; all blooming.

Floyd *(Welsh)* Brown; gray; hoary.

Francis *(Teut.)* Free; indomitable courage and strength.

Frank See Francis.

Franklin *(Teut.)* A freehold farmer.

Fraser *(Fr.)* A hairdresser.

Frederick *(Teut.)* Peaceful ruler.

Gabriel *(Heb.)* Strength or hero of God.

Gamaliel *(Heb.)* Recompense of God; gift of God.

Garret *(Teut.)* He who is honored. *(Sax.)* Learned; skillful.

Gaspard *(Pers.)* Treasure master; a horseman.

Geoffrey *(Teut.)* Joyful peace. *(Sax.)* He who delights in peace.

George *(Gr.)* A farmer; husbandman.

Gerald, Gerard *(Teut.)* Powerful spearman.

Gervais *(Gr.)* Honored. *(Teut.)* Eager for war.

Gideon *(Heb.)* A warrior; who breaks courage and strength; a cutter-down, i.e., brave soldier.

Gifford *(Sax.)* Kind and generous disposition.

Gilbert *(Teut.)* Bright pledge.

Giles *(Gr.)* A shield; a goatskin or little goat. *(Teut.)* A companion.

Giordano *(Heb.)* The river Jordan.

Glenn *(Gael.)* A small valley.

Godfrey *(Teut.)* God's peace.

Godwin *(Sax.)* Beloved of God; a conqueror for God. *(Eng.)* Divine friend.

Gordon *(Gael.)* A fine man. *(Welsh)* A strong man.

Graham *(Gael.)* Stern, morose, gloomy; a man with a frowning visage.

Grant *(Fr.)* Great; brave; valorous.

Granville *(Fr.)* Great town or city.

Gregory *(Gr.)* Watchman; vigilant.

Griffith *(Welsh)* Strong in faith. *(Lat.)* Ruddy.

Grover *(Sax.)* Dweller in a grove.

Gustave *(Teut.)* Staff of war; Goth's staff.

Guy *(Fr.)* The mistletoe. Also: guide; leader; director.

Halbert *(Scot., Teut.)* Bright stone.

Hans *(Sax.)* A free market or hall. *(Teut.)* Form of John.

Harold *(Teut.)* Leader of the army.

Harrison Son of Henry.

Harry See Henry.

Harvey *(Celt.)* Bitter. *(Teut.)* Noble soldier.

Hector *(Gr.)* A stout defender; an anchor.

Heinrich *(Teut.)* Form of Henry.

Henry *(Teut.)* Home ruler. *(Sax.)* A brave, powerful lord; ever wealthy.

Herbert *(Sax.)* Glory of the army. *(Teut.)* Illustrious ruler.

Herman *(Sax.)* Soldier; army man.

Hezekiah *(Heb.)* Strength of the Lord.

Hilary *(Lat.)* Cheerful; merry; gay.

Hiram *(Heb.)* High-souled.

Holmes *(Teut.)* Meadow land near a stream.

Homer *(Gr.)* A pledge; a hostage.

Horace, Horatio *(Lat.)* Light of the sun; keen-eyed.

Howard *(Teut.)* Keeper of a hall; keeper of a stronghold.

Hubert *(Teut.)* Bright mind; clear thinker. *(Sax.)* Of clear, bright color.

Hugh, Hugo *(Teut.)* Mighty; thoughtful; wise. *(Celt.)* Fire. *(Dut.)* High; lofty.

Humphrey *(Sax.)* Protector of the home.

Iago *(Sp., Heb.)* Supplanter; beguiling.

Ian *(Gael.)* Form of John.

Ignatius *(Gr.)* Fiery; a kindled flame.

Ingram *(Sax.)* Pure as an angel. *(Teut.)* Raven.

Ira *(Heb.)* City watch; watchful.

Irwin See Erwin.

Isaac *(Heb.)* Laughter.

Isadore, Isidor *(Gr.)* Strong gift; gift of Isis.

Isaiah *(Heb.)* Salvation of the Lord.

Israel *(Heb.)* The prince of God; prevailing in the Lord.

Ivan *(Russ., Welsh)* Form of John.

Jack See John.

Jacob *(Heb.)* Supplanter.

Jacques *(Fr.)* Form of Jacob.

James *(Eng.)* Form of Jacob.

Jan *(Dut.)* Form of John.

Jason *(Gr.)* A healer.

Jasper *(Gr., Heb.)* A precious stone. *(Pers.)* Treasure master.

Jay *(Meaning uncertain)*

Jeffrey *(Sax.)* Joyful peace.

Jeremiah, Jeremy, Jerry *(Heb.)* Exalted of the Lord.

Jerome *(Gr.)* Holy name.

Jesse *(Heb.)* Wealthy. Also, the Lord exists.

Job *(Heb.)* One who mourns; persecuted man.

Joel *(Heb.)* He who wills or commands; Jehovah is God.

John *(Heb.)* The Lord's grace.

Jonah *(Heb.)* A dove.

Jonathan *(Heb.)* Gift of the Lord.

Joseph *(Heb.)* He who shall increase.

Joshua *(Heb.)* A saviour or deliverer; the Lord is salvation.

Josiah *(Heb.)* The fire of the Lord; whom the Lord gives.

Juan *(Sp.)* Form of John.

Judah *(Heb.)* One who is praised, praise the Lord.

Jules, Julian, Julius *(Lat.)* Soft-haired; downy-bearded.

Justin *(Lat.)* Just; righteous; upright.

Karl See Carl.

Kean *(Ir.)* Vast. *(Gael.)* A chief; a commander.

Keith *(Gael.)* A windy place. *(Welsh)* An enclosed place; deep hollow.

Kemp *(Sax.)* A soldier; a champion at arms.

Kenneth *(Celt.)* Comely. *(Gael.)* Chieftain; commander.

Kevin *(Celt.)* Comely; a noble, kind and friendly man.

Lambert *(Sax.)* Fair lamb; innocence. *(Teut.)* Distinguished among his people.

Lance, Lancelot *(Lat.)* Servant — so called from carrying a lance or pike. *(Sp.)* Little lance; warrior.

Lawrence *(Lat.)* Laurel-crowned.

Leander *(Gr.)* Man of renown.

Lee, Leigh *(Teut.)* A pasture; meadow; sheltered place. *(Welsh)* A stream.

Lemuel *(Heb.)* Consecrated to God.

Lennox *(Gael.)* Field on the river. *(Welsh)* Placid stream. *(Scot.)* Chieftain.

Leo, Leon, Leonard *(Lat.)* A lion; lionhearted.

Leopold *(Teut.)* Beloved and brave; defender of the people.

Leroy *(Fr.)* The king.

Leslie *(Teut.)* Low meadow. *(Sax.)* A lessee.

Lester *(Sax.)* Lustrous. Possibly from Leicester, meaning meadow camp.

Levi *(Heb.)* Joined.

Lewis *(Sax.)* Safeguard of the people. *(Teut.)* Illustrious warrior.

Lincoln *(Gael., Welsh)* A steep place in a river.

Lionel *(Lat.)* Little lion. See Leo.

Llewellyn *(Welsh)* Form of Lionel.

Lloyd *(Welsh)* Brown; gray.

Lorenzo *(Ital., Sp.)* Form of Lawrence.

Louis *(Fr.)* Form of Lewis.

Lucian, Lucius *(Lat.)* Light; born at daybreak.

Ludwig *(Teut.)* Safeguard of the people; a good leader.

Luke See Lucian.

Luther *(Teut.)* Famous warrior.

Lyman *(Meaning uncertain)*

Lynn *(Gael.)* A pool or lake.

Magnus *(Lat.)* Great.

Malcolm *(Gael.)* The brow of a rock; a bald head; a monk. *(Celt.)* A servant of Columbia.

Manuel *(Heb.)* God with us.

Mark *(Lat.)* Polite; polished; brilliant; born in the month of March.

Marshall *(Teut.)* Commander; master of the house.

Martin *(Lat.)* Martial; warlike.

Marvin *(Gael.)* A ridge of very high hills.

Matthew *(Heb.)* Reward; recompense; gift of the Lord.

Maurice *(Lat.)* Dark of complexion; Moorish.

Maximilian *(Lat.)* Compounded of Maximus (greatest) and the name Aemilianus.

Maxwell *(Gael.)* Little son.

Melvin *(Meaning uncertain)*

Meredith *(Welsh)* Admiral; protector of the sea.

Michael *(Heb.)* Who is like God.

Miles *(Lat.)* A soldier. Other interpretations: a crusher; a kind of grain; a champion; a contraction of Michael.

Millard *(Sax.)* A grinder.

Milton *(Sax.)* Mill-town or Middletown.

Mitchell *(Sax.)* A big man. Possibly a variation of Michael.

Monroe *(Celt.)* From a mount on the River Roe in Ireland; or a mossy place on the Roe.

Montague *(Fr.)* From the steep mountain.

Morgan *(Welsh, Celt.)* A seaman; sea-dweller; born on the sea or by the seaside.

Morris See Maurice.

Mortimer *(Nor.)* Norman place name.

Morton *(Gael.)* Great hill.

Moses *(Heb.)* Drawn from the water.

Murray *(Gael.)* Great water.

Myron *(Gr.)* Myrrh.

Napoleon *(Gr.)* A lion of the forest; or, of the new city.

Nathan, Nathaniel *(Heb.)* Gift of God.

Neil *(Celt.)* Champion. *(Gael.)* Of a dark or swarthy complexion.

Nelson Son of Neil.

Nestor *(Gr.)* A man of experience; one who remembers.

Nicholas *(Gr.)* Conqueror of the people.

Nigel *(Lat.)* Black-haired.

Noah *(Heb.)* Rest; consolation; peace.

Noël *(Fr.)* Christmas; born on Christmas Day.

Norman *(Teut.)* Man of the North; native of Normandy.

Octavius *(Lat.)* The eighth-born.

Ogden *(Sax.)* Oak valley. *(Gael.)* Young man.

Oliver *(Lat.)* Olive tree, emblem of peace.

Orlando *(Ital.)* Form of Roland.

Orville *(Fr.)* Town of gold.

Oscar *(Celt.)* Bounding warrior; he who leaps to the fight.

Osmund *(Sax.)* Domestic peacemaker. *(Teut.)* Protected by the gods.

Oswald *(Sax.)* Ruler of a house; steward. *(Teut.)* Chief appointed by the gods.

Otis *(Gr.)* Quick of hearing.

Otto *(Teut.)* A mountain; wealthy.

Owen *(Welsh)* Of distinguished birth; a lamb; a form of John.

Parker *(Teut.)* Keeper of a park.

Patrick *(Lat.)* Noble; a senator.

Paul *(Gr.)* Small; gentle.

Pedro *(Sp.)* Form of Peter.

Percival *(Lat.)* Very courteous. *(Celt.)* Companion of the chalice.

Percy See Percival.

Perry Possibly a form of Peter.

Peter *(Gr.)* A stone; rock.

Philbert *(Teut.)* Very distinguished.

Philip *(Gr.)* Lover of horses.

Phineas *(Sax.)* An open and trusty countenance.

Pierre *(Fr.)* Form of Peter.

Quentin, Quintus *(Lat.)* The fifth-born.

Ralph *(Teut.)* Form of Randolph.

Randall See Randolph.

Randolph *(Teut.)* Shielded by the wolf-god. *(Sax.)* pure, disinterested help.

Raphael *(Heb.)* Healing of God.

Raymond *(Teut.)* Wise protection; quiet, peaceful. *(Teut.)* Strong man.

Reginald *(Teut.)* Powerful judgment; chief ruler. *(Sax.)* Sincere love; strong.

René *(Lat.)* Reborn.

Reuben *(Heb.)* Behold, a son!

Rex *(Lat.)* King.

Reynold See Reginald.

Richard *(Teut.)* Stern king. *(Sax.)* Generous; benevolent; liberal.

Robert, Robin *(Teut.)* Bright in counsel.

Roderick *(Sax.)* Rich in advice; generous counselor. *(Teut.)* Famous king.

Rodney *(Teut.)* Famous in counsel.

Rodolph See Randolph.

Roger *(Teut.)* Speak of fame; strong in counsel.

Roland *(Teut.)* The country's glory. *(Sax.)* Counselor to his country.

Rolf, Rolfe See Randolph.

Romeo *(Lat.)* A fair Roman.

Ronald See Reginald.

Roscoe *(Meaning uncertain)*

Ross *(Teut.)* A horseman; knight; chevalier.

Roy *(Fr.)* A king. *(Celt.)* Red.

Rudolph See Randolph.

Rufus *(Lat.)* Red-haired.

Rupert See Robert.

Russell *(Fr.)* Red-haired.

Salvador, Salvatore *(Lat.)* Saviour.

Samson *(Heb.)* Brilliant sun.

Samuel *(Heb.)* Asked of God.

Saul *(Heb.)* Asked of the Lord.

Schuyler *(Teut.)* A scholar. *(Dut.)* A shelter; hiding-place.

Sebastian *(Gr.)* Reverenced; venerable; honorable.

Seth *(Heb.)* Appointed.

Seymour *(Eng.)* From St. Maur. *(Sax.)* A tailor.

Sherwood *(Sax.)* A clearing in the woods.

Sidney Derived from St. Denis.

Siegfried *(Teut.)* Conquering peace.

Sigismund *(Teut.)* Victorious peace; man of victory. *(Sax.)* He who fights for peace.

Silas *(Lat.)* A forester; woodsman.

Silvanus *(Lat.)* Living in a wood; the god of forests.

Simeon See Simon.

Simon *(Heb.)* Hearing and obeying; attentive.

Solomon *(Heb.)* Peaceful.

Spencer *(Fr.)* A steward; dispenser to a large household.

Stanislaus *(Slav.)* Glory of the camp or state.

Stanley See Stanislaus.

Stephen *(Gr.)* A crown.

Stewart See Stuart.

Stuart *(Teut.)* A steward; waiter; one who has charge of a place.

Sylvester See Silvanus.

Talbot *(Sax.)* A term in heraldry for a hunting dog.

Terence *(Lat.)* Tender; soft.

Thaddeus *(Aram.)* Praise.

Theodore *(Gr.)* Divine gift.

Thomas *(Aram., Heb.)* A twin.

Timothy *(Gr.)* Who honors God.

Tobias *(Heb.)* Goodness of God.

Tristram *(Lat.)* Grave; pensive; sad. *(Celt.)* Herald; venturesome knight.

Ulrich *(Teut.)* Noble ruler. *(Sax.)* A powerful or rich helper.

Ulysses *(Gr.)* Angry.

Valentine *(Lat.)* Powerful; healthy.

Vaughn *(Welsh)* Small in stature.

Vernon *(Fr.)* A place name from Normandy.

Victor *(Lat.)* A conqueror.

Vincent *(Lat.)* A conqueror; invincible.

Virgil *(Lat.)* Flourishing; good fortune; a garland of laurel.

Vladimir *(Slav.)* Ruling the world.

Wade *(Dut.)* A meadow or pasture.

Waldemar *(Teut.)* Powerful fame.

Waldo *(Teut.)* Mighty; powerful.

Wallace *(Gael.)* From Wales.

Walter *(Teut.)* Chief of an army; woodmaster.

Ward *(Teut.)* A keeper; defender.

Warner *(Teut.)* Protecting warrior.

Warren *(Teut.)* Protecting friend.

Webster *(Teut.)* Maker of webs; a weaver.

Wendell *(Dut.)* A walker or traveler. *(Teut.)* Wandering.

Wilbur *(Sax.)* Wild boar.

Wilfred *(Sax.)* Peaceful.

William, Willard, Willis *(Teut.)* Defender; protector of many; shield.

Winfred *(Teut.)* Friend or winner of peace.

Xavier *(Arab.)* Bright; glorious.

Xerxes *(Pers.)* Fighting king; lion king.

Zachary *(Heb.)* Whom the Lord remembers.

GIVEN NAMES OF WOMEN AND THEIR MEANINGS

Abby *(Sax.)* Sweet refuge; also a form of Abigail.

Abigail *(Heb.)* Her father's joy.

Ada *(Teut.)* Happy. *(Heb.)* Ornament, significant of great beauty.

Adelaide See Adele.

Adele *(Teut.)* Noble maiden.

Adeline *(Teut.)* Noble. *(Sax.)* Descending from nobles.

Adria, Adrienne *(Lat.)* Black earth; peat soil.

Agatha *(Gr.)* Good.

Agnes *(Gr.)* Pure; chaste; honorable.

Aïda *(Ital.)* The first.

Aileen See Helen.

Aimée *(Lat., Fr.)* Beloved.

Alberta *(Teut.)* Noble; bright.

Alda *(Teut.)* Rich.

Alethea *(Gr.)* Truth.

Alexandra, Alexia *(Gr.)* Helper of mankind.

Alfreda *(Sax.)* All peace. *(Teut.)* Elf-counseled.

Alice *(Sax.)* Noble; illustrious.

Aline *(Teut.)* Noble.

Alison *(Teut.)* Holy fame. *(Fr.)* Form of Alice.

Allegra *(Lat.)* Lively, merry.

Alma *(Lat.)* Fair.

Althea *(Gr.)* Wholesome.

Alvina *(Fr.)* Bright; joyous.

Alwin *(Teut.)* Elf friend; loved by all.

Amabel, Amabelle *(Lat.)* Lovable; amiable.

Amanda *(Lat.)* Beloved.

Amaryllis *(Gr.)* A refreshing stream.

Amelia *(Gr.)* Busy; energetic; a worker.

Amy *(Fr., Lat.)* Beloved.

Anastasia *(Gr.)* Easter born; resurrection.

Andrea Feminine form of Andrew: brave, noble.

Angela, Angelica, Angelina *(Gr.)* Angelic; exquisite; beautiful.

Anita *(Sp.)* Form of Ann.

Ann, Anna, Anne, Annie *(Heb.)* Grace; gracious; merciful.

Annabel *(Heb., Lat.)* Beautiful Ann.

Annette *(Heb., Fr.)* Little, charming Ann.

Antoinette, Antonia *(Lat.)* Inestimable. *(Gr.)* Blooming; graceful; perfect.

April *(Lat.)* The fourth month; open.

Arabella *(Lat.)* Fair altar; sweet refuge. *(Teut.)* Eagle heroine.
Arbutus *(Lat.)* The Mayflower.
Ariadne *(Gr.)* Sweet singer.
Arleen, Arlene, Arline *(Meaning uncertain)*
Astrid *(Teut.)* Impulse of love.
Audrey *(Eng.)* Noble threatener; illustrious; august.
Augusta *(Lat.)* Noble; royal; imperial.
Aurelia *(Lat.)* Golden-haired.
Aurora *(Lat.)* Dawn; the golden hour.
Avis *(Lat.)* A bird. *(Teut.)* War refuge.

Barbara, Babette *(Gr.)* A stranger; foreign.
Beatrice *(Lat.)* Blessed; happy.
Belinda *(Ital.)* Serpent; graceful in motion.
Belle *(Fr.)* Fair. *(Phoe.)* Oath of Baal.
Bernadette, Bernadine *(Teut.)* Bold as a bear. *(Sax.)* Childlike; innocent.
Bernice *(Gr.)* She who brings victory.
Bertha, Berta, Bertina *(Sax.)* Bright; famous.
Beryl *(Gr.)* A gem.
Bessie, Bettina, Betty From Elizabeth *(Lat.)* Blessed. *(Heb.)* Oath of God.
Beulah *(Heb.)* Married.
Beverley *(Sax.)* Beaver meadow.
Bianca *(Ital.)* White; pale; very fair.
Blanche *(Fr.)* White; fair; beautiful.
Blossom *(Eng.)* A flower.
Bona, Bonita, Bonnie *(Lat.)* Good; fair.
Brenda *(Teut.)* A sword. *(Celt.)* Dark-haired; dark-eyed.
Bridget *(Celt.)* Strength. *(Gael.)* Fiery dart.

Camilla, Camille, Camellia *(Lat.)* Servant of the temple.
Carla *(Teut.)* Strong.
Carlotta *(Sp., Teut.)* Strong; valiant.
Carmen *(Lat.)* Song; also signifies a charm.
Carmine *(Ital., Heb.)* Vineyard; a vine-dresser.
Carol, Caroline, Carrie *(Teut.)* Strong; valiant.

Cassandra *(Gr.)* She who inspires love.
Catherine *(Gr.)* Pure; virtuous.
Cecilia *(Lat.)* Gray-eyed; blind.
Celeste, Celestine *(Lat.)* Heavenly.
Celia, Celine *(Gr.)* One who commands.
Charis, Charissa *(Gr.)* Loving or loved; graceful.
Charity *(Lat.)* Beloved of the poor; kindness.
Charlene, Charlotte *(Teut.)* Strong; valiant.
Chloë *(Gr.)* Fresh; youthful; blooming.
Christine *(Gr.)* Follower of Christ.
Claire *(Fr.)* Form of Clara.
Clara, Clare *(Lat.)* Shining; glorious; brilliant.
Claribel *(Lat.)* Brightly fair.
Clarice, Clarissa *(Lat.)* Rendering famous; fair; pure.
Claudette, Claudia *(Lat.)* From Claudius, meaning lame.
Clementine *(Lat.)* Mild in temper and disposition; merciful.
Cleopatra *(Gr.)* Glory of her father or her country.
Clotilde *(Teut.)* Famous battle maid.
Cobina Possibly from Jacobina.
Colette *(Gr.)* Victorious over the people.
Colleen *(Ir.)* A maid; girl.
Columbine *(Lat.)* A dove.
Constance *(Lat.)* Steadfast; firm; unyielding.
Consuelo *(Meaning uncertain)*
Cora *(Gr.)* A maiden.
Coral *(Gr.)* Coral.
Cordelia *(Celt.)* Jewel of the sea.
Corrine *(Gr.)* A maiden.
Cornelia *(Lat.)* Horn, the symbol of kingship.
Crystal *(Gr.)* Clear; frost.
Cynthia *(Gr.)* Another name for Diana; from Mt. Cynthus.

Dagmar *(Teut.)* Glory of the Danes; the dawn.
Daisy *(Sax.)* The eye of day. The daisy is a symbol of innocence.

Dale *(Sax.)* A small valley.

Daphne *(Gr.)* A laurel or bay tree.

Dawn *(Sax.)* Daybreak; the beginning or unfolding.

Deborah *(Heb.)* A bee; industrious; active.

Delia *(Gr.)* Shining; bright.

Delilah *(Heb.)* Delicate.

Della See Adele.

Delphine *(Gr.)* Of Delphi; a loving sister.

Denise *(Gr.)* From Dionysos, god of wine and drama.

Desirée *(Fr., Lat.)* Beloved.

Diana *(Lat.)* The moon; clear; bright. The goddess of hunting.

Dinah *(Heb.)* She who is judged; vindicated.

Dolly See Dorothy.

Dolores *(Sp., Lat.)* Sorrow; in allusion to the seven sorrows of Mary.

Donna *(Lat.)* A lady.

Dora See Dorothy.

Dorcas *(Gr.)* A gazelle; she who has beautiful eyes.

Dorinda *(Gr.)* A gift.

Doris See Dorothy.

Dorothy *(Gr.)* Gift of God.

Drusilla *(Gr.)* Dewy eyes.

Dulce *(Lat.)* Sweet.

Edith *(Teut.)* Rich gift; happiness; prosperity.

Edna *(Heb.)* Pleasure.

Edwina Feminine form of Edwin

Effie See Euphemia.

Eileen *(Ir.)* Form of Helen.

Elaine See Helen.

Elberta *(Teut.)* Noble; bright; famous.

Eleanor, Elinor See Helen.

Elise See Elizabeth.

Elizabeth, Eliza *(Heb.)* Oath of God.

Ella *(Teut.)* Elf friend. Also see Helen.

Ellen See Helen.

Eloise *(Teut.)* Famous holiness.

Elsa, Elsie *(Teut.)* Noble cheer. Also a form of Alice or Elizabeth.

Elvira *(Lat.)* White; courage.

Emanuela *(Heb.)* God with us.

Emily *(Lat.)* A worker; busy; energetic. *(Gr.)* Of winning manners. *(Sax.)* A nurse.

Emma *(Teut.)* Grandmother; a nurse.

Enid *(Celt.)* Soul.

Erica Feminine form of Eric.

Ernestine *(Sax.)* Serious; zealous. *(Teut.)* An eagle.

Esmeralda *(Sp., Gr.)* Beautiful as the emerald.

Estelle *(Fr., Lat.)* A star.

Esther *(Pers.)* A star.

Ethel *(Teut.)* Noble.

Etta *(Teut.)* Home ruler.

Eudora *(Gr.)* A beautiful gift.

Eugenia, Eugenie *(Gr.)* Well born.

Eulalie *(Gr.)* Fair speech; one who speaks sweetly.

Eunice *(Gr.)* Happy victory; she who makes fortunate conquests.

Euphemia *(Gr.)* Fair speech; well spoken of.

Eustacia *(Gr.)* Steadfast; resolute.

Eva, Eve *(Heb.)* A mother; life-giving.

Evangeline *(Gr.)* Happy messenger; bringer of good news.

Evelina *(Celt.)* Pleasant.

Evelyn *(Lat.)* Hazel nut. *(Celt.)* Pleasant.

Faith *(Lat.)* A firm believer.

Fanchette *(Fr., Teut.)* Free.

Fanny See Frances.

Faustina *(Ital., Lat.)* Lucky; happy.

Fay *(Sp.)* Faith.

Felice, Felicia *(Lat.)* Happy; fortunate.

Fern *(Sax.)* The fern is a symbol of sincerity.

Fidelia *(Lat.)* Faithful.

Filippa *(Ital., Gr.)* Lover of horses.

Flavia *(Lat.)* Yellow-haired, blonde.

Flora, Florette *(Lat.)* A flower.

Florabel *(Lat.)* A beautiful flower.

Florence *(Lat.)* Flourishing, prosperous.

Frances, Francine *(Teut.)* Free; indomitable courage and strength.

Frederica *(Teut.)* Peaceful ruler.

Frieda *(Teut.)* Peaceful.

Gabriella, Gabrielle (*Heb.*) Strength of God.

Gail See Abigail.

Gay (*O.F.*) Loving pleasure; merry.

Genevieve (*Celt.*) White as sea foam.

Georgette, Georgia, Georgina Feminine forms of George: of the farm.

Geraldine (*Teut.*) Spear power.

Gerda (*Nor., Teut.*) Enclosed cornfield, an emblem of peace.

Gertrude (*Teut.*) Spear maiden.

Gladys (*Welsh*) Lame.

Gloria (*Lat.*) Glory.

Grace, Gratia (*Lat.*) Grace; kindness; patience.

Greta, Gretchen See Margaret.

Griselda (*Teut.*) Gray-eyed lady; heroine.

Guinevere (*Celt.*) White; fair.

Gwendolyn (*Celt.*) White-browed.

Haidee (*Gr.*) Modest.

Hannah (*Heb.*) Gracious; merciful; benign.

Harriet, Hattie (*Teut.*) Home rule. (*Sax.*) Ever rich and powerful.

Hazel (*Heb.*) One that sees God.

Heather (*Scot.*) A bell-like flower, symbol of loneliness.

Hedda, Hedwig, Hedy (*Teut.*) Lady of defense; war refuge.

Helen (*Gr.*) Light; bright as the dawn.

Helga (*Nor.*) Holy.

Heloise (*Gr.*) Bright as the sun. (*Teut.*) Famous holiness.

Henrietta (*Teut.*) Home ruler. (*Sax.*) Ever rich or mighty.

Hephzibah (*Heb.*) My delight is in her.

Hermione (*Gr.*) Maiden of high degree.

Hester See Esther.

Hilaria (*Lat.*) Cheerful; gay; mirthful.

Hilda (*Teut.*) Battle maid.

Hildegard, Hildegarde (*Teut.*) Battle maid; protection.

Holly (*Sax.*) The holly is emblematic of friendship and happiness.

Honoria (*Lat.*) Honorable.

Hope (*Sax.*) Trust in the future.

Hortense (*Lat.*) A gardener.

Huldah (*Heb.*) A weasel, in the sense of being quick and sprightly.

Ida (*Teut.*) Happy. (*Celt.*) Thirsty.

Imogene (*Gr.*) Beloved child; last-born.

Ina (*Meaning uncertain*)

Inez (*Sp., Gr.*) Pure; a maid.

Irene (*Gr.*) Messenger of peace; peaceable.

Iris (*Gr.*) A link of beauty uniting earth and sky; the rainbow.

Irma (*Teut.*) Maiden of high degree.

Isabel (*Sp.*) Form of Elizabeth.

Isadora (*Gr.*) Gift of Isis.

Isolde (*Celt.*) Fair; my only one.

Ivy (*Sax.*) Friendship; fidelity.

Jacobina Feminine form of Jacob.

Jacqueline (*Heb.*) Supplanter; beguiling.

Jamesina Feminine form of James.

Jane, Janet, Janice Derived from John. (*Heb.*) The Lord's grace.

Jean, Jeanne, Jeanette, Jennie, Jenny See Jane.

Jemina (*Heb.*) A dove; handsome as the day.

Jennifer (*Celt.*) White wave.

Jerusha (*Heb.*) Possession.

Jessica, Jessie (*Heb.*) Wealthy.

Jewel (*Heb.*) Life. (*O.F.*) Joy.

Jill (*Lat.*) Soft-haired.

Joan, Joanna, Johanna See Jane.

Jocelyn (*Lat.*) Sportive; just; virtuous.

Josephine (*Heb.*) She who shall increase.

Joy (*Lat.*) Gladness; cheerful, merry.

Joyce (*Lat.*) Sportive; vivacious.

Juanita (*Sp.*) From John, meaning the Lord's grace.

Judith (*Heb.*) She who praises.

Julia, Juliana, Juliet (*Lat.*) Soft-haired.

June (*Lat.*) Youthful.

Justine (*Lat.*) Just; righteous.

Karen *(Teut.)* Pure.

Karla See Carla.

Katherine, Kathryn See Catherine.

Kathleen *(Celt., Gr.)* Little darling; pure; beautiful-eyed.

Keturah *(Heb.)* Incense; perfume; winsomeness.

Kezia *(Heb.)* Cassia, a bark similar to cinnamon.

Lala *(Slav.)* A tulip.

Laura, Laurel, Laurette *(Lat.)* Laurel. The laurel is an emblem of fame.

Lavinia *(Lat.)* Left-handed.

Leah *(Heb.)* Weary; exhausted.

Leatrice *(Meaning uncertain)*

Leila *(Arab.)* A dark beauty.

Lena *(Gr.)* Light. *(Lat.)* Peace; gentleness.

Leona *(Lat.)* A lion.

Leonore *(Gr.)* Light. *(Lat.)* Lionlike strength and courage.

Leslie *(Teut.)* Low meadow.

Letitia *(Lat.)* Joy; gladness; good fortune.

Lida *(Slav.)* People's love.

Lillian, Lily *(Lat.)* The lily is a symbol of purity.

Linda *(Teut.)* Lovely maid. Also see Belinda.

Lisette, Lizette See Elizabeth.

Lois *(Gr.)* Desirable; virtue.

Lola *(Meaning uncertain)*

Loretta See Laura.

Lorna *(Meaning uncertain)*

Lorraine *(Meaning uncertain)*

Lottie See Charlotte.

Louella Probably a combination of Louise and Ella.

Louise *(Fr., Sax.)* Protectress of the people.

Lucretia *(Lat.)* She who gains in money or goods; a good housewife.

Lucia, Lucille, Lucinda, Lucy *(Lat.)* Light; born at daybreak.

Ludmilla *(Slav.)* People's love.

Lydia *(Gr.)* She who is from Lydia.

Lynn *(Gael.)* A pool or lake.

Mabel *(Lat.)* Beloved; beautiful. *(Fr.)* My belle, or fair one.

Madeline, Madelon See Magdalene.

Madge See Margaret.

Mae Possibly a form of Mary. Also see May.

Magdalene *(Heb.)* A watchtower; elevated; magnificient.

Maisie A form of either Mary or Margaret.

Malvina *(Celt.)* Handmaid. *(Fr.)* Smooth-browed.

Marcella, Marcelle See Marcia.

Marcia *(Lat.)* Martial; fearless; brave.

Margaret, Margot, Marguerite *(Gr.)* A pearl; precious; beautiful.

Maria, Marie, Marietta See Mary.

Marian, Marianna, Marianne Combinations of Mary and Ann.

Marigold *(Heb., Sax.)* A golden flower. The marigold is symbolic of sympathy.

Marilyn, Marlene Derived from Mary.

Marion See Mary.

Marjorie See Margaret.

Marsha See Marcia.

Martha *(Heb.)* Becoming bitter. *(Syriac)* Teacher.

Mary *(Heb.)* Distressed; tearful.

Matilda *(Teut.)* Mighty battle maid; a noble lady.

Maude Form of Matilda or possibly Magdalene.

Maureen, Maurya *(Ir.)* Forms of Mary.

Maxine *(Lat.)* Possibly from Maximus, meaning greatest.

May *(Heb.)* Bitter. *(Gr.)* Pearl. *(Lat.)* Beloved. *(Eng.)* Born in May.

Maybelle Possibly a form of Mabel.

Melanie *(Gr.)* Black.

Melicent *(Gr.)* Sweet as honey. *(Teut.)* Work strength.

Melinda *(Gr.)* Sweet as honey.

Melissa *(Gr.)* Honey bee.

Mercedes *(Lat.)* A favor; a gift.

Merle *(Fr.)* A blackbird.

Merry *(Sax.)* Mirthful.

Meta *(Gr.)* A pearl; life.

Mildred *(Teut.)* Mild of speech; gentle.

Millicent See Melicent.

Mina *(Teut.)* Memory; beloved. Also a form of Wilhelmina.

Minerva *(Lat.)* Goddess of wisdom, war and the liberal arts.

Minnie *(Teut.)* Borne in memory; beloved. Also a form of Wilhelmina.

Miranda *(Lat.)* To be admired.

Miriam See Mary.

Molly See Mary.

Mona *(Teut.)* The moon. *(Gr.)* Solitary.

Monica *(Gr.)* One dwelling alone. *(Lat.)* Adviser.

Muriel *(Gr.)* Myrrh; perfume.

Myra *(Gr.)* She who weeps; myrrh.

Myrna *(Meaning uncertain)*

Myrtle *(Gr.)* The myrtle, sacred to Venus; beauty's crown.

Nada, Nadine *(Slav.)* Hope.

Nancy, Nanette See Ann.

Naomi *(Heb.)* Good to look at; agreeable; pleasant.

Natalie *(Lat.)* Christmas child.

Nellie See Helen.

Nicolette *(Gr.)* Conqueror of the people.

Nina *(Sp.)* Little darling. Also see Ann.

Ninette See Ann and Nina.

Nola *(Ir.)* White shoulders.

Nona *(Lat.)* The ninth-born.

Nora *(Lat.)* Honor. Also see Leonore.

Norma *(Lat.)* A rule, model, standard.

Octavia *(Lat.)* The eighth-born.

Olga *(Russ., Teut.)* Holy.

Olive, Olivia *(Lat.)* The olive tree, emblem of peace.

Opal *(Gr.)* The opal is a token of hope.

Ophelia *(Gr.)* Serpent; help-giver; useful.

Ottilie *(Teut.)* Happy battle maid.

Palma *(Lat.)* Palm tree, signifying victory.

Pamela, Pamella *(Gr.)* All sweetness; a brunette; a song or melody.

Pansy *(Fr.)* Pensive flower.

Patience *(Lat.)* Bearing up; enduring affliction without complaint.

Patricia *(Lat.)* Of noble birth.

Paula, Pauline *(Lat., Gr.)* Small, gentle.

Pearl *(Lat.)* The pearl is a token of health and long life.

Peggy See Margaret.

Penelope *(Gr.)* A weaver; industrious; a good wife.

Perpetua *(Lat.)* Lasting.

Philomena *(Gr.)* Music lover.

Phoebe *(Gr.)* Radiant; splendid; the moon.

Phyllis *(Gr.)* A green bough; a reed.

Polly *(Heb.)* Bitter.

Poppy *(Lat.)* The poppy is a symbol of peaceful sleep.

Portia *(Lat.)* A harbor; safety.

Primrose *(Lat.)* The primrose signifies childhood, youth.

Priscilla *(Lat.)* Little; quaint; old-fashioned.

Prudence *(Lat.)* Wisdom; discretion; knowledge.

Rachel *(Heb.)* A sheep or lamb; innocence.

Rebecca *(Heb.)* A rope with a noose; a snare; a girl who ensnares men by her beauty.

Regina *(Lat.)* A queen.

Renée *(Teut.)* Warrior of judgment. *(Lat.)* Renewed.

Rhoda *(Gr.)* A rose.

Rita See Margaret.

Roberta *(Teut.)* Bright in counsel.

Rosabel *(Lat.)* Fair rose.

Rosalind, Rosalie, Roselyn *(Lat.)* Fair as a rose.

Rosamond *(Lat.)* Rose of the world. *(Teut.)* Famed protection.

Rose *(Lat.)* The rose is a symbol of love.

Rosemary *(Lat.)* Rose of the sea; or, a compound of Rose and Mary. The rosemary is a token of remembrance.

Rowena *(Celt.)* White skirt. *(Sax.)* To acquire peace.

Roxana *(Pers.)* Dawn of day.
Ruby *(Lat.)* Red. The ruby betokens a contented mind.
Ruth *(Heb.)* A vision of beauty.

abina *(Lat.)* Chaste; religious.
Sadie, Sally See Sara.
Salome *(Heb.)* Peaceful.
Sandra From Alexandra or Cassandra.
Sara, Sarah *(Heb.)* A princess or noble lady.
Selina *(Gr.)* Fair as the moon.
Selma *(Celt.)* Fair.
Sheila See Cecilia.
Shirley *(Meaning uncertain)*
Sibyl *(Gr.)* A prophetess; divinely inspired; wise woman.
Sigrid *(Teut.)* Conquering council.
Silvia *(Lat.)* Of the forest.
Sonia *(Meaning uncertain)*
Sophia *(Gr.)* Wise woman.
Stella *(Lat.)* A star.
Stephanie *(Gr.)* A crown.
Susan, Susette *(Heb.)* A lily.
Sybil See Sibyl.
Sylvia See Silvia.

Tabitha *(Heb.)* A gazelle; timid; animated; with charming eyes.
Tallulah *(Meaning uncertain)*
Teresa See Theresa.
Thalia *(Gr.)* Flourishing; blooming.
Thecla *(Gr.)* Divine fame.
Thelma *(Meaning uncertain)*
Theodora *(Gr.)* Divine gift.
Theresa *(Gr.)* Carrying ears of corn; a harvester. *(Heb.)* Beautiful.
Thomasena, Thomasina, Thomasine Feminine forms of Thomas.
Thora *(Teut.)* Thunder; consecrated to Thor.
Thyrza *(Heb.)* Pleasant; agreeable.
Tilda, Tillie See Matilda.
Tracy A form of Theresa.

Uda *(Teut.)* Rich.
Ulrica *(Teut.)* Noble ruler. *(Sax.)* Rich in help.
Una *(Celt.)* Born in famine. *(Lat.)* The figure one.
Undine *(Lat.)* Of the waves; sea-born.
Ursula *(Lat.)* A little bear.

Valerie *(Lat.)* Healthy; robust; valiant.
Vera *(Lat.)* Truth. *(Slav.)* Faith.
Verna, Verne *(Lat.)* Springlike; youthful.
Veronica *(Lat.)* True image.
Victoria *(Lat.)* Successful in contests; conqueror.
Vida *(Lat.)* Life. *(Heb.)* Beloved.
Viola, Violet *(Lat.)* A violet; pretty and modest.
Virginia *(Lat.)* A virgin; chaste.
Vivian *(Lat.)* Lively; merry. *(Welsh)* The small water.

Wanda *(Meaning uncertain)*
Wilhelmina *(Teut.)* Protector of many; shield; defense.
Winifred *(Teut.)* Friend or winner of peace.

Xenia *(Gr.)* Hospitality.

Yolanda, Yolette *(Lat.)* Violet. *(Teut.)* Fairest in the land.
Yseulte, Ysolt *(Celt.)* A vision of beauty.
Yvette *(Meaning uncertain)*
Yvonne *(Teut.)* Archer. *(Heb.)* God's grace or gift.

Zenobia *(Arab.)* Her father's ornament. *(Gr.)* Everlasting life.
Zoë *(Gr.)* Life.
Zora *(Slav.)* Dawn.

Part Two

THE FIRST YEAR OF LIFE

A Home for Your Child

Young couples starting a family usually give much thought to the kind of home they want in which to bring up children. They wisely prefer to live by themselves and build their own home life, rather than live with parents.

No doubt they will fully explore the possibilities of owning their own home and, if this is not immediately feasible, will compromise on the kind of house to rent. But whether owning or renting, there will be many things that will have to be considered.

If possible, foremost in their planning will be two bedrooms, one for themselves and a nursery, because both baby and parents rest better when separated at sleeping time.

The matter of choosing a location is usually a major problem but if there is a choice, equal consideration should be given to the child's needs as well as to those of the adults.

The proximity of a shopping center, church and transportation should be weighed against the nearness of a school, indoor and outdoor play facilities and safety of location. Then there are the advantages of living in a neighborhood with parents having children of a similar age, where you have congenial interests and can all make allowances for the noise and confusion in a neighborhood of children.

But however desirable the neighborhood environment, it is the atmosphere within the home that counts most. No matter how modest the home, the baby who can grow up in a happy and well-ordered home atmosphere will carry with him throughout life the feeling of peace and security he absorbed from his parents and his home.

147

HEALTH CONDITIONS AND THE HOME

THE CITY HOME.   Living in congested city areas always presents many problems, with its noise, heavy traffic and absence of yards. In addition, there may be the heavy smoke and fumes from industrial plants. If there is any choice, parents will try to select a neighborhood where the air is not polluted and where there is some place nearby for a child to get the benefits of sunshine and safe outdoor play.

IN THE COUNTRY.   Prime considerations here are to avoid living near a swampy region where mosquitoes breed and to locate where the water is safe. If the water comes from a well or spring, this should be located where it cannot be polluted by drainage from barns, stables, cesspools, or privies. It is a good plan to have the drinking water tested once a year. Write to your state department of health to have your water tested.

Cesspools, septic tanks, and privies should be so built that the health of the family is protected.

Garbage, unless fed to livestock, must be burned or buried. If burned, it must be completely destroyed so that no moist parts remain to bring flies; if buried, it must be buried so deep that animals cannot dig it up.

Any stagnant water (water that is not flowing) can become a breeding place for mosquitoes, and every effort should be made to avoid having any such water near the house. One way to prevent mosquitoes from breeding in a rain barrel is to screen the top of it with a tightly fitting cover made of window screening.

The house should have good drainage and good heating and lighting arrangements, and some of the rooms should have plenty of sunshine. The cellar should be dry. A sunny porch, where young children can play when the ground is damp, is a great advantage.

Every window and every outside door should be screened. It is a good idea to have porches screened too.

Flies carry disease germs, especially those of typhoid fever and dysentery. The flies get their feet covered with disease germs when walking over manure piles, unscreened privies, open garbage cans, or any other place where filth accumulates. Then, unless the house is well screened, the flies enter the house and walk over the family's food. To protect food, especially the baby's, from diseases carried by flies, not only the whole house but outdoor privies should be screened, and manure and other filth should be kept at a distance from the house.

THE NURSERY

If it is not possible for the baby to have a room to himself, it would be well at least to have him sleep at night in some place other than his parents' bedroom—a place that is near enough for them to get to him easily.

HEATING AND VENTILATING. A very young baby needs a warmer room than an older baby or an adult. For the first weeks of a baby's life the temperature of his room should be kept between 70° and 75° F. night and day. For older babies the day temperature may be from 68° to 70° F. and the night temperature from 55° to 60° F.

In order to make sure that the baby's room is neither too warm nor too cold it is necessary to measure the temperature. The thermometer should be hung on an inside wall at about the level of the crib, not near a heater nor where the sun can shine on it.

The baby's room needs fresh air. If there are windows on two sides of the room, and one is opened at the top and the other at the bottom, fresh air will circulate through the room. Fresh air is especially needed when a gas stove is burning in a room.

The baby must be protected from too much breeze. One way of doing this and still letting fresh air into the room is to use a window board.

A window board is a piece of glass or a board, as long as the width of the window and about ten or twelve inches wide. It is held in place at the bottom of the window opening by a triangular support fastened to each end of the window frame. The bottom of the board rests on the window sill, slanting toward the inside of the room. When the window board is in place the window may be opened at the bottom about eight inches, and the board will keep out direct drafts.

A screen may also be used to keep drafts from the baby's head.

If the room is too cold, a small movable stove or heater may be used if it is placed and handled with great care. Any heater must be placed so that the baby will not be able to touch it and so that no one will be likely to stumble against it. An oil heater especially must be placed so that it will not be knocked over, for any oil spilled might cause a serious fire.

A gas heater must be inspected often to see that no gas leaks out. It should be connected to the gas inlet by metal pipes with solid connections, never by rubber tubing. A gas heater should have a pipe leading to a chimney or directly to the outside.

Gas in the air will make a baby sick, and the least smell of gas means that there is some leak and that the heater should be repaired.

At least one window should be open when a gas heater is burning, and a screen should be used to keep wind from blowing out the flame.

An electric heater must be protected from getting wet, and it must never be touched with wet hands. People have been killed by turning off an electric switch with wet hands.

A fire screen is necessary for safety if an open fire is used.

In parts of the country where there is much hot weather the baby's room should be one in which he can be kept as cool as possible on hot days. Shades, shutters, or awnings that can be adjusted to keep out the hot sun help to keep the room comfortable. It is often a good plan to close the windows during the middle of the day to keep out the hot outdoor air.

The baby can be made more comfortable in hot weather if the air is kept in circulation with an electric fan. The fan should be tilted so that the current of air is directed toward the ceiling, not toward the baby.

CLEANLINESS. The baby's room and everything in it should be kept clean. Walls that can be cleaned and window curtains that are thin and easily laundered are desirable. If a room is freshly papered and painted it is easier to keep clean. A bare floor or a floor covered with linoleum is easier to keep clean than a carpeted one. A washable rug may be used to add warmth and brightness to the room.

DECORATIONS. A very young baby does not, of course, notice the things about him, but as he gets older and begins to notice them, he may enjoy a few decorations in bright clear colors.

Walls and floors in solid colors or with small patterns are better than those with elaborate nursery designs.

A few sharply outlined pictures of the things with which the baby soon becomes familiar—children, animals, characters in stories—can be cut out and put in places where he can see them easily. An attractive yellow chicken, for example, pasted on the front of the bottom drawer of the dresser will get many an affectionate pat and gurgle from the baby as he creeps about his room.

Ornaments that collect dust or are easily upset or broken do not belong in a baby's room.

AS BABY GROWS

BABY CARRIAGE. If a baby carriage is used, it should be large enough to permit the baby, with whatever wraps are necessary, to lie full length or to sit up, and it should have a firm, full-length mattress that lies flat.

During the fly and mosquito season, a piece of mosquito netting should be at hand to cover the carriage when necessary.

When the baby is old enough to sit up he needs a small firm cushion at his back. He needs also to be fastened into the carriage by a strap. A strap that is attached to the carriage and that fastens about his waist is safer than one that is fastened to the carriage only.

PLAY PEN OR PLAY YARD. A play pen or play yard can be bought ready-made or built at home.

A play pen that is kept always in the same place, such as a corner of the porch or a part of the yard, may easily be built at home, as it need consist only of a low fence to keep the baby in the enclosure.

A play pen to be used indoors is, as a rule, one that can be moved about and put away when the baby is not using it.

If a movable play pen is to be used in the house in cold weather, it should be raised from the floor in order to avoid floor drafts. Some pens are built with legs or casters that raise the pen some distance from the floor.

If the pen is not raised above the floor a blanket fastened with tapes or safetypins to the side of the pen will help to keep a draft away from the baby.

When the baby is so young that he lies down a good deal of the time, the floor of the pen should be covered with a soft, washable pad tied to the corners by strong tapes. Later, when the baby sits or stands most of the time he is in the play pen, no covering on the floor of the pen is necessary unless the floor of the room is chilly.

LOW TABLE AND CHAIR. A low table for the toddler should be made in such a way that the child can get his knees under it. Legs and braces for the table should be at the center or the corners and not along the edges. A child gives his table hard wear, and it should be so sturdy that it will not become wobbly.

The chair to be used with the table should be low enough for him to put both feet on the floor when he sits in it.

See that the height of the table and that of the chair are suited to each other, so that when the child sits in the chair he is at the right height to use the table.

A discarded table or one bought secondhand makes a fine play or mealtime table if the legs are cut so that the table top is twenty inches from the floor.

HIGH CHAIR. If a high chair is used be sure to get one that has legs spread wide apart and weighted at the bottom, so that the chair will not tip over. It should have a footrest, and a safety strap to keep the baby from falling out of the chair. A high chair with a tray to hold the baby's dishes is more convenient than one without.

BATHTUB. The family tub may be used for bathing the baby, but a small tub for this purpose is a great help to the mother as it saves her much stooping. Enamelware tubs and folding rubber ones are on the market.

Unless the tub has legs it should be placed on a sturdy table. The table should be of such a height that the mother can bathe the baby comfortably.

It may be convenient to put the table, with the baby's tub on it, near, or even in, the family tub, where it will be convenient to the hot- and cold-water faucets. The baby's tub can then be filled by means of a rubber hose, which saves the mother from carrying water. If rubber cups are placed on the feet of the table, it will stand more firmly and it will not scratch the surface of the large tub.

If an enamelware tub is selected, it is desirable to get one that is long enough (twenty-eight inches) to permit the baby to splash and play a little as he gets older.

Folding rubber tubs usually have legs and a canvas top on which to dress the baby, and with this kind of tub a table is not needed. These tubs can stand on the floor or inside the family tub. A rubber tub should not be used if it becomes rough on the inside, because it may scratch the baby.

TOILET SEAT OR CHAIR. By the time the baby is old enough to be trained in toilet habits he needs a small toilet; the family toilet is too large for him. The simplest thing to do is to fit onto the family toilet a thin board with a hole cut in it to fit the baby's buttocks. Such a board may be made at home or it may be bought. The commercially made ones usually have a clip for fastening the board securely onto the toilet. Toilet seats that fasten on the regular toilet may be bought. They are made with back and armrests and have a safety strap. Some of them have also a footrest, which makes the baby more comfortable.

A low toilet chair, with a chamber under it, may be used instead of a toilet seat. Such a chair can be made at home.

If the family bathroom is upstairs or if the family has an outside toilet, it is sometimes convenient to have a nursery chair to use downstairs.

THE GROWING BABY'S CLOTHES

To keep the baby comfortably warm, but not too warm, his clothing should be selected to suit the climate, the season, the temperature of the house, and the baby's age and condition.

In hot climates and those in which the range in temperature is nearly constant, night and day, for most of the year, it is easy to dress a baby so that he will not be too cold nor too warm. In parts of the country where seasonal and even daily variations in temperature are considerable and sudden—conditions found over the greater part of the United States—keeping a baby comfortably warm requires considerable thought and judgment.

When the baby is outdoors in cold weather be sure that his clothing is warm enough and especially that his hands, feet, and ears are warmly covered. Care should be taken, however, that he is not dressed too warmly, whether he is indoors or outdoors. If he is dressed too warmly he will perspire, and his body will become damp. If this happens while he is wearing outdoor wraps the dampness may cause him to be chilled when he comes indoors and his outdoor wraps are removed.

Very young babies and feeble ones lie still most of the time, and they need warmer clothing than older and more robust babies, who are active.

All About Diapers

Diapers should be soft, absorbent, light in weight, and not bulky. (Bulky diapers may interfere with good posture when the baby begins to stand or walk.) They should be made of material that absorbs moisture quickly, is easy to wash, and dries quickly. Diapers of cotton birdseye cloth are satisfactory; also those made of two layers of soft, fine-meshed, gauzelike cotton material, finished without hems and woven together at all the edges.

Many mothers put pieces of old cotton goods or absorbent paper tissues inside the diaper to catch the stool. Disposable diapers and also disposable diaper linings are on the market.

The shape of the diaper depends largely upon the mother's preference. Some choose square diapers, some oblong. The size depends partly upon the size of the baby; a diaper that is too large for the baby is bunchy and uncomfortable. Many square diapers are twenty-seven inches each way (after shrinking); others are smaller. Oblong diapers are usually twenty by forty inches.

PUTTING ON THE DIAPER. *If the diaper is square,* fold it triple thickness.

Then fold one end back about one-third, so as to make a pad of six layers of cloth. For a girl baby this six-layer pad is to go behind the baby; for a boy baby, in front. The part that is to pass between the legs is only three layers thick.

Lay the baby on the folded diaper (the turned-back flap may be either on the inside or on the outside).

Draw the other end up between the baby's legs, over the abdomen, and pin the front and back of the diaper together at each side at the waistline with safetypins, keeping your hand between the baby's body and the point of the pin.

The pins should be placed crosswise and should pass through both shirt and diaper. The back fold of the diaper should overlap the front.

Pin the front and back of the diaper together at each knee.

A square diaper may also be folded into kite shape (see illustrations). Fold two corners to center line, making a V. Fold top down, making a triangle. Bring point up to top edge.

If the diaper is oblong, it may be folded to form a center panel of extra thickness. (See illustrations.)

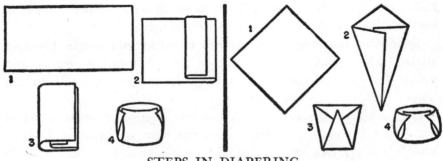

STEPS IN DIAPERING
(Left) Oblong Diaper.   (Right) Square Diaper.

To form this panel, using a twenty- by forty-inch diaper (1), fold the diaper crosswise, bringing one end to about eight inches from the other (2). The folded diaper will then be twenty by twenty-four inches.

Turn back the short end to about three inches from the fold (3).

Bring the other end of the diaper over to the first fold. The diaper will then be twelve by twenty inches, with a panel about six inches wide in the center (4).

It may then be pinned on like a square diaper, except that there is no flap.

Care should be taken not to hamper the free movements of the baby's body or legs by pinning the diaper too tight.

HOME CARE OF DIAPERS. The diaper should be changed as often as it is wet or soiled. At night it should be changed when the baby is taken up to be fed. No diaper should be used a second time before being washed. Used diapers should never be left lying about the room nor dried on radiators.

Wet diapers should be placed at once in a covered pail and left until they can be washed.

Diapers soiled with stool should be held over the toilet and shaken, brushed, or scraped so that as much stool as possible may be removed before they are put into the pail.

All the diapers should be washed in very hot water with plenty of mild, unmedicated soap, with no washing powder or strong soap. They should be rinsed through four waters so that all the soap is rinsed out. Diapers should be dried in sunshine and open air whenever possible. It is not necessary to iron diapers.

Sometimes the skin of the baby's buttocks and thighs becomes chafed. This chafing is often due to soap left in the diaper and means that greater care in rinsing the diapers must be used. Boiling diapers helps to remove soap.

Occasionally, with some babies, there is an odor of ammonia when the diaper is changed. In some cases the odor is noticed only after a night's sleep. Not only is the odor unpleasant, but the ammonia in such diapers frequently causes an irritation of the baby's buttocks and sometimes, in boys, of the end of the penis.

When ammonia diaper occurs it can be remedied by caring for the diapers as follows:

After washing and rinsing the diapers, wring them as dry as possible and place them in a solution made by dissolving four level tablespoonfuls of boric acid to one quart of warm water. Wet the diapers thoroughly with the solution. Then wring them lightly and dry them, preferably in the open air.

If the baby has diarrhea the diapers should be boiled after they are washed and rinsed. The boiling should be done every day until the diarrhea is gone.

It is unwise to put an unboiled diaper under a baby's head, or to use it near any part of the body other than the genital region.

BABY PANTS.   Pants over the baby's diaper to protect his clothes or bedding should be used only on special occasions when such protection is particularly important. Ordinarily it is better to provide extra protection by placing a rubber square and a folded diaper or a square of quilted cotton on the bed under his buttocks.

Occasionally, when it seems especially important to protect the baby's clothes or surroundings, as during a journey, pants over the diaper are very helpful.

Knit wool pants for this purpose are better than waterproof ones, as they permit more evaporation. If waterproof pants are worn they should not be so tight at the waist or knee as to leave marks on the baby's skin, and they should be made with air holes to allow for evaporation. Pants that are cut to fit the waist and thigh permit better ventilation and are therefore less heating than those in which elastic is used at these places.

When a baby wears waterproof or absorbent pants over the diaper the mother should be especially careful to change the diaper as soon as it is wet or soiled.

ABDOMINAL BANDS.   A baby's first band is usually a strip of gauze or soft flannel four to five inches wide and eighteen to twenty inches long, which holds the navel dressing in place. It should never be tight enough to bind. As soon as the navel has healed the baby no longer needs an abdominal band.

SHIRTS.   Under most circumstances cotton is the best material for the baby's shirts. In cold climates, if it is hard to keep the room warm, it is usually better to keep the baby warm with sweaters or other garments rather than with a wool shirt. Wool may irritate the baby's skin, and all-wool shirts shrink considerably.

Before buying a shirt that goes on over the head, see whether the neck will stretch enough to go over the baby's head easily and yet be firm enough to stay in place on the shoulders. Shirts should have large armholes so that the baby's arms can be put into the sleeves easily.

A hem or a facing at the bottom of the shirt to which the diaper can be pinned will make a shirt last longer.

STOCKINGS AND SOCKS. In warm weather or in a well-heated house a baby who has not yet begun to creep will be most comfortable barelegged and barefooted; he will not need any kind of stockings nor shoes—not even bootees. In cold weather outdoors or in a house that is not well heated, his legs and feet will need to be covered. If long stockings are worn they should be fastened to the diaper in such a way that they will not bind the baby and restrict his activity. Short socks or bootees are not very satisfactory as they can be kicked off easily. One way to keep the baby's legs warm is to put a pair of long pants on him, like overalls, pajama pants, or the pants of "sleepers." These may be made with feet.

Later, when the baby needs some kind of stockings to wear with his shoes, short socks are better than long stockings since they do not need to be fastened up and so cannot pull on the other clothing. Overalls will keep his legs warm.

Socks and stockings, after washing, should be at least half an inch longer than the baby's foot. A baby's feet grow quickly, and the mother needs to watch the size of the stockings she puts on the baby to see that they are not cramping his feet.

SHOES. Shoes for the baby before he walks are for protection only, not for support. When he is creeping, especially if the floors are rough, shoes will protect his feet from being scratched. At this time soft-soled shoes such as moccasins, which permit free movement of the feet, are satisfactory.

When the baby begins to walk the sole of his shoe should be shaped like the natural outline of his foot, straight along the inner line. It should be made of rough leather so as not to be slippery. It should be firm, but should not have a stiff metal shank. Heels are not advisable.

The uppers should be made of soft, pliable material, such as kid. They should not be made of patent leather, as such leather is finished with a varnish that keeps perspiration from evaporating.

The shoe should fit snugly at the heel, and it is best if it is made with a stiff counter around the heel to keep the foot firmly in place.

Shoes should always be long enough, wide enough, and deep enough (at the toe) not to crowd the baby's toes. Shoes should be about a half inch longer than the baby's foot and at least one-fourth inch wider at the toes. Notice the thickness of the baby's toes and see that the shoes provide ample space for them up and down. This is very important; sometimes shoes are correct in the shape of the sole and in length and width, but are not high enough at the toe. Check the fit of the shoe carefully and often to see that the toes are not crowded as the feet grow. As soon as the baby's toes come within one-fourth inch of the end of the shoe, longer shoes should be bought.

When the doctor gives the baby a health examination ask him whether the baby's shoes are the right style and size.

NIGHTGOWNS. During the first few months of life, when a baby sleeps almost all the time, he may wear nightgowns both day and night. A nightgown may be embroidered or otherwise made dainty and pretty, but it should wash easily. It should be easy to put on and take off, and be the right weight for the time of year.

Any soft material may be used for nightgowns, such as cotton or part-wool flannel, or, in warm weather, thin white-cotton goods such as batiste.

Winter nightgowns for a very young baby may be made with a drawstring through the hem at the bottom. Such a nightgown must be long enough to come well below the baby's feet so as to permit him to kick.

In hot weather a nightgown is unnecessary.

Many mothers like to use wrappers for the baby. A wrapper is easy to put on the baby when the mother wants to remove a dress or nightgown that is wet or soiled but when she is not ready to dress the baby again; or it may be used instead of a dress or nightgown. Wrappers are usually made of knitted material or outing flannel.

FOR THE CREEPER. When the baby is at the creeping age he needs the greatest possible freedom for reaching, trying first steps, and getting around on hands and knees. If he is to have this freedom his garments should be designed, cut, and fitted so that there is extra room exactly where it is needed.

Creepers, overalls, or sun suits are less apt to get in the baby's way than dresses. Such garments should be made so that they are easy to put on and take off and so that the diaper can be changed easily. They should be made of fabrics that will stand hard wear, such as cotton broadcloth, cotton poplin, and gingham. The colors should stand much washing.

Overalls or long pants like sleeper pants will protect the baby's legs when he is creeping over rough surfaces.

Outer Garments. In parts of the country where the weather may be cold one day and mild the next, the baby's outer clothes should be changed accordingly. It is wise to have a sweater for a light extra wrap to be worn indoors or outdoors, as it can be taken off and put on easily.

For a very young baby a square of blanketing may be used as an outdoor wrap.

An older baby may wear a woolen play suit in cold weather. A knitted suit gives more freedom for activity than a suit made of woven material; but it is not very warm, and there may be times when an extra sweater and pants are needed.

The baby may need a winter wrap, such as a bunting, of warm woolen material, with or without a thick interlining of wool.

A warm woolen cap or hood will be needed in cold weather. In mild weather no head covering is needed for warmth, but a soft muslin or silk cap may be worn if the mother wishes. On hot days the baby's head should be protected from the sun by a sunbonnet or cap.

Bibs. Toward the end of the first year, when the baby begins to help feed himself, a bib will be needed to protect his clothes. A bib should be large, for a baby just learning to eat spills food all over himself.

The baby's bib may be merely an oblong piece of cloth, fastening around his neck by means of short tapes; or it may be made something like a pinafore, tying around the waist as well as the neck.

Bibs can be bought or made of any absorbent goods, such as absorbent gauze, or old turkish towels. Oilcloth is sometimes used.

PUTTING BABY IN THE TUB

Place your left arm and hand under his head and shoulders, grasping his left arm at the shoulder to hold him securely. Hold his leg firmly with your right hand as you lower him into the tub.

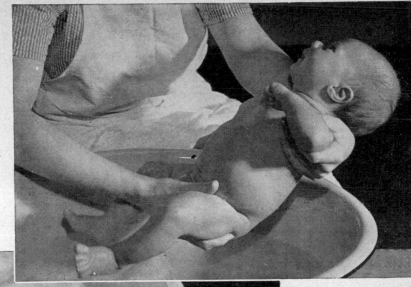

AFTER BABY IS IN THE TUB

Hold him with your left hand, your arm resting against the edge of the tub, right hand free for washing and rinsing.

WASHING HIS BACK

With your right hand grasp him under his left arm, your arm supporting his chin and chest and your left hand free for washing or rinsing.

Maternity Center Ass'n.

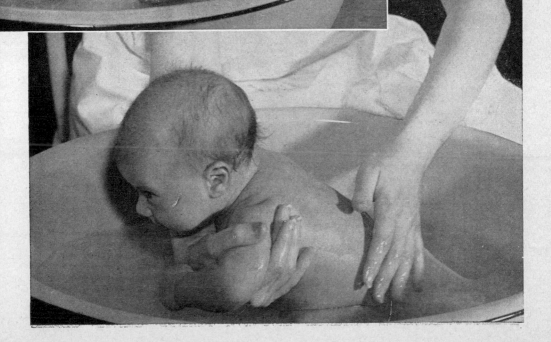

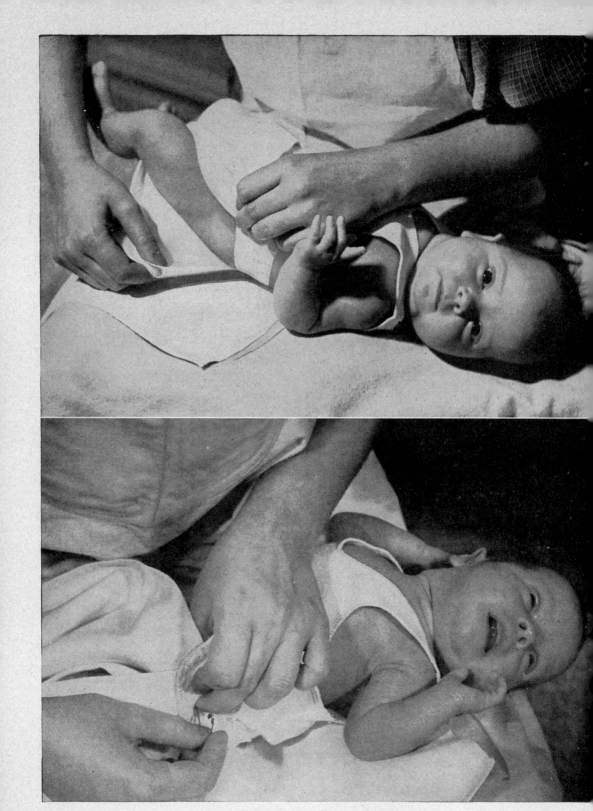

PUTTING ON THE DIAPER

Diapers should be soft, absorbent, light in weight and not bulky. The pins should be placed sidewise, passing through both shirt and diaper, with your hand between the baby's body and point of pin. Check to make certain that pin has closed securely.

Maternity Center Assn.

Planning Your Baby's Day

FOR the first few weeks a baby sleeps most of the time, waking only when he is hungry. During the first few days, if he is offered the breast (or bottle) at regular times he is more likely to form the habit of waking up and wanting food at these times.

Though most babies fit easily into a plan of feeding every four hours—for example, at six, ten, and two o'clock (until the 2:00 A.M. feeding is given up)—some babies will need a different schedule. For some, feedings every three hours are better. Occasionally, as a baby gets a little older and is awake more of the time, a mother will find that at one of the feeding times the baby is usually too sleepy to eat. By shifting the hours of feeding to a time a little earlier or a little later, she can adjust the schedule so as not to interfere with his hours of sleep.

There are no fixed hours at which every baby should be fed. If your baby does not fit into the routine you plan for him, try to change the plan to suit his needs. After you find the best routine for him, however, try to keep to the same plan each day. Babies thrive on doing the same thing at the same time, day after day.

The majority of babies will fit themselves easily into the plan that you make for them, as long as it provides for regular feedings and regular hours of sleep. It is usually possible, therefore, for the mother to consider her own convenience in planning the baby's day.

There is nothing rigid, therefore, about the feeding hours that are shown in the following schedules. It is usually best for the mother to take such a plan, shift the hours a bit one way or the other if this is more convenient for her and the household, and then follow the plan until the baby shows that some other plan would suit him better. He may show this by crying regularly half an hour or more before feeding time or by sleeping through feeding time. If the baby cries before it is time for him to waken for his feedings, it may be that he needs more food rather than a change in his schedule, and the doctor should be consulted regarding a change in his feeding.

161

First Four Months

6:00 A. M. . . . . *Feeding.* Breast or bottle feeding.

Sleep or play, alone in crib.

9:30 A. M. . . . . Cod-liver oil or other source of vitamin D, and orange juice.

Bath. Undress baby in time to allow for exercise and play before bath.

10:00 A. M. . . . . *Feeding.* Breast or bottle feeding.

Nap, out of doors if weather permits.

Drink of water after nap. Put baby where he can play safely.

Sun bath if weather permits. (In very hot weather give sun bath before morning bath or after afternoon nap.)

2:00 P. M. . . . . *Feeding.* Breast or bottle feeding.

Nap, out of doors if weather permits.

Cod-liver oil or other source of vitamin D, and orange juice, when the baby wakens from nap. Put baby where he can play safely. Offer water at some time during afternoon.

5:45 P. M. . . . . Prepare for night. Allow time for exercise and play.

6:00 P. M. . . . . *Feeding.* Breast or bottle feeding.

Bed, lights out, windows adjusted for night, door shut.

10:00 P.M. . . . . *Feeding.* Breast or bottle feeding.

2:00 A. M. . . . . *Feeding.* (Before end of second month most babies give up this feeding. Some give it up soon after birth.)

Beginning about the second or third month most babies will have a waking period in the late afternoon. This will develop into a playtime as the baby gets older. It is wise to let the baby spend part of this time by himself so that he may get used to being alone.

Fifth and Sixth Months

6:00 A. M. . . . . *Feeding.* Breast or bottle feeding.

Sleep or play, alone in crib.

9:30 A. M. . . . . Cod-liver oil or other source of vitamin D, and orange juice.

Bath. Undress baby in time to allow for exercise and play before bath.

10:00 A. M. . . . . *Feeding.* Cereal and breast or bottle feeding.

Nap, out of doors if weather permits.

Drink of water after nap. Put baby where he can play safely.

Sun bath if weather permits. (In very hot weather give sun bath before morning bath or after the afternoon nap.)

2:00 P. M. . . *Feeding.* Egg yolk, vegetable (after baby is five months old), and breast or bottle feeding.

Nap, out of doors if weather permits.

Cod-liver oil or other source of vitamin D, and orange juice, when baby wakens from nap. Put baby where he can play safely. Offer water at some time during afternoon.

5:45 P. M. . . . . Prepare for night. Allow time for exercise and play.

6:00 P. M. . . . . *Feeding.* Cereal and breast or bottle feeding.

Bed, lights out, windows adjusted for night, door shut.

10:00 P. M. . . . . *Feeding.* Breast or bottle feeding. (If baby does not waken, this feeding may be omitted.)

During these months the baby usually has longer and longer periods when he is awake, especially before the 2:00 and 6:00 P. M. feedings. If he is wakeful at night it may be well to waken him a little earlier from his afternoon nap.

The baby should spend part of the time he is awake alone with a toy or two, in a place where he can play safely—in his crib or play pen, or on a pad on the floor—but part can be a playtime with the mother or father or other children.

Seventh, Eighth, and Ninth Months

6:00 A. M. . . . . Feeding. Breast or bottle feeding.

Sleep or play alone in crib.

9:30 A. M. . . . . Cod-liver oil or other source of vitamin D, and orange juice.

Bath. Undress baby in time to allow for exercise and play before bath.

10:00 A. M. . . . *Feeding*. Cereal and breast or bottle feeding.

Nap, out of doors if weather permits.

Drink of water after nap. Put baby where he can play safely.

Sun bath if weather permits. (In very hot weather give sun bath before morning bath or after the afternoon nap.)

2:00 P. M. . . . *Feeding*. Egg yolk or meat, vegetable, and breast or bottle feeding.

Nap, out of doors if weather permits.

Cod-liver oil or other source of vitamin D, and orange juice, when baby wakens from nap.

Put baby where he can play safely. Offer water at some time during afternoon.

5:45 P. M. . . . Prepare for night. Allow time for exercise and play.

6:00 P. M. . . . *Feeding*. Cereal, fruit, and breast or bottle feeding.

Bed, lights out, windows adjusted for night, door shut.

When the baby is seven months old consult the doctor about weaning him.

The baby can now begin to learn to take some of his milk from a cup.

Most babies at this age will begin to shorten either the morning or the afternoon nap.

Tenth, Eleventh, and Twelfth Months

About the tenth month some babies are ready for a schedule of three meals a day. Many babies are not ready for this schedule until two or three months later; these may continue on four-hour schedules.

The three-meal-a-day plan that will best suit your baby and yourself will depend partly on the habits he has already formed, such as the time when he takes his nap, and partly on what fits into your day. One such schedule follows.

6:00 A. M. . . . . (or a little later, depending upon when the baby wakens).

Orange juice.

Sleep or play, alone in crib.

Wash and dress baby before breakfast.

7:30 A. M. .... *Breakfast.* Cereal, toast, milk, cod-liver oil.

Play, out of doors when the weather is suitable. Let baby have some water to drink during morning.

Sun bath, if weather permits.

11:30 A. M. .... *Dinner.* Egg or meat, vegetables, toast, milk.

Nap. Undress baby for nap. When he wakens from nap give him a cup of milk.

Play. Offer some water during this time.

5:00 P. M. .... Bath.

5:30 P. M. .... *Supper.* Cereal or potato, fruit, toast, milk, cod-liver oil.

6:00 P. M. .... Bed, lights out, windows adjusted for night, door shut.

If the baby takes a long nap in the morning undress him for his nap at a regular time (usually about 10:30 or 11:00 A. M.) and give him a cup of milk. Give him his dinner at 1:00 or 1:30.

Many babies continue to take two naps at this age. The time of the noon meal for such babies will depend upon whether the long nap is taken in the morning or in the afternoon.

In some families it is more convenient to give the baby his breakfast at 6:30 or 7:00 and his orange juice at 9:00 or 9:30.

The bath may be given at any hour of the day (except shortly after meals). It is best to have a regular time for it.

A Few Suggestions for Baby Care

UNTIL a baby's back and neck muscles have had time to strengthen they have to be supported. He should always be picked up with one hand supporting his back and the other under his head. When you rest him over your shoulder, tip his body forward to prevent his head bobbing backward. In putting him down, be careful that he does not slump over.

He will need support for his head until he is about three months old, either when lying or being held. Even after he is able to lift his head his back will need support.

WHEN HE CRIES

This is a signal that something needs to be done. He may need to be turned over, to have his diaper changed, to be given a drink of water, or to have companionship.

Frequently the small amount of attention that goes with satisfying his wants will give him all the companionship he needs, and he will become peaceful. Sometimes, however, a baby will continue to cry. It is true that short periods of crying will not harm even a young baby and that crying is good exercise if it does not last too long. If the crying lasts for more than fifteen minutes, however, after the baby has apparently been made comfortable, he probably needs further attention.

If it is near his feeding time the mother may pick him up, hold him, and sing to him a little until the time for feeding.

If it is not near feeding time, the baby may need a little extra food; if so, he should have it.

If the little baby frequently wakes and cries when it is not his feeding time, he is probably not getting enough food or the right kind of food, or he is not being fed at the right intervals, or something else is the matter. The doctor should be consulted.

If you get in the habit of picking your baby up every time he whimpers, you may do more harm than good. An inexperienced mother, who isn't quite sure of herself, may find her baby getting more and more demanding, and not a bit happier. In her eagerness to give good care she is too conscientious, and tires both herself and the baby out with her attentions.

A baby quickly learns to take advantage of his mother's uncertainty. By the age of six weeks or so babies are becoming aware enough of their surroundings so that if their crying means they're taken back where there are lights and people, they may be smart enough to try it pretty insistently.

Carrying a baby around a lot or rocking him by the hour may only stimulate him to stay awake. As he gets more tired, he becomes increasingly demanding. Both parents and baby get worn out, and the sleep of all three is disturbed.

Don't let anyone persuade you to give your baby any kind of medicine to make him sleep. All soothing sirups and other preparations of that sort contain drugs that are bad for a baby. Many of them are extremely dangerous. If there are times when it is necessary to help the baby get sleep, your doctor will be the one to prescribe something that he considers safe.

It should be remembered that if a baby cries for no apparent reason he may be sick. If you suspect that he is sick, take his temperature.

CLEANLINESS IS IMPORTANT

The mother should always wash her hands before she picks up the young baby, and the father or anyone else who touches the baby should do the same. Wash your hands thoroughly before preparing his food or feeding him.

As much of the time as possible when you are caring for the baby wear a dress that can be washed, and wash it often. At times when you do not wish to wear a washable dress wear a washable smock, apron, or other such garment that will cover your dress. This will prevent the baby from coming in contact with a dress that cannot be kept clean easily.

Three or four squares of cotton cloth will be useful for wiping the baby's mouth during and after feedings, for laying under his head so that the sheet will not be soiled each time he spits up, and for putting over the mother's shoulder when she holds him up to allow him to belch. They may also be used as washcloths. These squares may be from twelve to eighteen inches on each side and may be made of cheesecloth or any other soft, absorbent cotton material. If they are made of a thin material, several thicknesses should be used, bound or overcast at the edges. A diaper can be used for many of these purposes if it has been boiled. Unboiled diapers, however, should not be used near the baby's mouth.

DON'T'S FOR VISITORS

Friends and relatives nearly always want to play with a baby. It is good for you and good for the baby too to have some company. But in order to see that the baby is protected from possible harm that may be done by even the best-intentioned persons, take the following precautions.

Watch out for coughs and colds. Don't let anyone who has a cough or cold go near the baby.

Don't let anyone lean over a baby's crib. A person leaning over the crib many spray the baby with germs.

Don't let anyone play with the baby when you know he is tired and needs rest.

Don't let anyone—not even your own mother—pick up the baby without first washing her hands.

Have a clean cloth handy to throw over the shoulder of anyone who wants to hold the baby so that the baby's mouth will not touch the person's clothing.

Don't let anyone kiss the baby on the lips.

Don't let any visitor give the baby candy or anything else to eat.

A Word to Grandmothers

GRANDPARENTS are a blessing. The child who is privileged to grow up near enough the homes of his grandparents to enjoy close association with them is fortunate, indeed, for they contribute much to the richness and completeness of his world.

Sometimes grandmothers, especially, in their sincere eagerness to be helpful and to see that the baby gets the right care, unintentionally create doubt, confusion and resentment in the minds of new parents. They feel sure that their experience and their love and their close relationship give them the right to advise and criticize freely. Well, grandmothers have their rights and young mothers need their counsel and guidance provided it is based upon intelligent, unselfish interest in the baby's welfare rather than scorn of everything that is new and different from methods of a generation ago.

It is true that there seems to be evidence these days among leading authorities, of a rather definite change in opinion about some phases of child care. This does not mean that we are scrapping our scientifically sound knowledge of what constitutes healthful environment, good nutrition and methods of prevention and control of disease. It does mean that we are placing emphasis upon means of achieving desired results with less insistance upon rigid routines and we look with favor upon a more generous expression of good old-fashioned affection. In short the rocking chair and the lullaby are no longer severely frowned upon.

Grandmothers, we urge that you keep in mind the value of the positive approach. The young parents love their baby intensely and it is not in the least likely that they are following any but advice they believe to be the best they can obtain. You have a perfect right to offer a few helpful suggestions now and then and plenty of reassurance at all times. But don't allow yourself to feel hurt if you are not consulted on all minor matters. Avoid with utmost care the temptation to be critical or scornful of what seems new or unnecessary to you. If you'd like to be the kind of grandmother who is adored and respected in the years to come, make the right start now. It's up to you.

The Breast-Fed Baby

A HEALTHY mother's milk contains practically everything a young baby needs for nourishment. It is also more easily digested and less likely to disagree with the baby than cow's milk. Whenever large groups of babies are compared, it is found that on the whole the babies who have been breast-fed are healthier and have had fewer illnesses than those who have been fed cow's milk.

(But, if you cannot nurse your baby, do not fear that bottle feeding will harm him. It is a good, safe substitute.)

Nursing the baby is of some value to the mother in recovering from childbirth, for the baby's sucking at the mother's breast makes her uterus contract. This helps her body to return to its normal condition.

The Nursing Mother

Most mothers can nurse their babies.

The first and most important step toward successful breast feeding should be taken early in pregnancy. If she is convinced that nursing is best for both the baby and herself, she will plan to do whatever will make it possible for her to have an adequate supply of breast milk. Both before the baby is born and afterward, she will follow her doctor's recommendations as to what to eat and how to take care of her general health. After the baby is born the mother will make every effort to produce enough milk to feed the baby well.

The Sucking Baby

The sucking of a hungry baby—better than anything else—stimulates a mother's breasts to make milk.

For the first few days a thick, yellowish fluid called colostrum comes from the mother's breasts. During this time, if the baby is allowed to nurse at regular intervals, his sucking stimulates the mother's breasts, and gradually the true milk, which is thin and bluish, comes into the breasts.

By the third or fourth day there is usually enough milk for the baby, although sometimes it takes a week or two for the milk to become well established. Before the breast milk is well established it is important that the baby be put at the breast at every feeding time, whether or not there seems to be much milk in the breasts, so that his sucking will stimulate the breasts to produce milk. Failure to have enough breast milk is often due to the fact that the baby has not been allowed to suck regularly at his mother's breasts.

If, after the first few days of life, the baby is not getting enough milk to satisfy his needs, he may be given a cow's milk mixture after he has emptied the mother's breasts, but cow's milk should not be given in place of a breast feeding.

During the first three or four weeks it is desirable that the mother not omit *any* nursings. Once the milk supply is well established, however, she can miss an occasional nursing and have a short vacation from her baby without losing her milk. If it is frequently necessary for her to be away from the baby at feeding time, she should empty her breast at the time of the missed nursing, either by hand or with a breast pump. If she does this the breast will be stimulated almost as though nursed by the baby.

As the baby grows, the amount of milk in the mother's breast gradually increases. The quantity that the baby gets at a feeding depends largely on the energy, strength, and persistence with which he sucks. Emptying the breast completely helps more than anything else to produce milk.

If the supply of breast milk is plentiful only one breast need be given at a feeding, the other being given at the next feeding. If the milk supply is scanty both breasts may be given at each feeding; the breast given first at one nursing should be given second at the next nursing.

If the baby does not empty one breast at a nursing it should be emptied by hand or by a breast pump.

THE NURSING MOTHER'S DIET

The amount the breast-fed baby needs from his mother keeps on increasing until she begins to wean him.

Because of the baby's increasing need for food, the mother's appetite usually increases during the time she nurses her baby. A good appetite makes it easier for the mother to eat enough to supply both her own needs and the baby's. It is essential for the baby's health, and also for the mother's that she eat the right kind of food as well as enough food.

A good diet for a nursing mother includes the same foods that are in the diet of any other healthy adult. The amounts needed of some of them are greater than those needed by other people. In order to obtain the necessary amounts of these foods the nursing mother may need to have an additional small meal in the middle of the morning or in the afternoon or before bedtime.

MILK. At least one quart of whole milk a day is needed—fresh, evaporated, or dried. It is better if the mother can take a quart and a pint a day. The milk can be used in soups, desserts, and creamed dishes as well as for drinking.

Cheese may be substituted for part of the milk occasionally—two ounces of yellow cheese for a pint of milk. Cottage cheese may be used, but it does not supply as much bone- and tooth-building material as does yellow cheese.

Some skim milk may be used instead of whole milk, especially if the mother is overweight. If much skim milk is used it is more than ever necessary for the mother to take cod-liver oil or other fish-liver oil daily as a source of vitamin A.

FRUITS AND VEGETABLES. Five to seven servings a day of fruits or vegetables should be eaten. These can be divided as follows:

Cooked green leafy vegetable or cooked deep-yellow vegetable.
Raw vegetable or green salad.
Potatoes.
Any other vegetable.
Orange, grapefruit, tomatoes, or berries or melons.
Any other fruit.

Fruits and vegetables may be fresh, canned, dried or quick-frozen.

LEAN MEAT, POULTRY, FISH. Two servings a day of meat or fish are desirable. All meats are good foods, but it is the lean parts that supply the building materials for muscles and blood. Liver, kidney, and sweetbreads are especially good. Some of the less commonly used and inexpensive meats, such as tripe, brains, and heart, may be used also. All kinds of seafood may be used in place of meat.

EGGS. At least one egg daily is needed; two may be eaten if desired. Eggs may be used in cooked dishes, such as custard, as well as served plain.

CEREALS AND BREAD. Two or more servings a day of cereal or bread are needed. Flours and cereals made by grinding the whole grain, or all of it but the roughest outer parts, are more nutritious than those in which only a part of the grain is used. The germ and the outer parts of the grain, which are discarded in the preparation of white flour and refined cereals, contain minerals and vitamins that the body needs and that are particularly important in the nursing mother's diet. Some of the most important of this vitamin and mineral value that is lost in milling has been restored in the enriched white flour, bread, and the enriched and restored cereals now on the market.

Butter and Fortified Margarine. Butter may be used according to the mother's taste and pocketbook. Margarine that has been fortified by the addition of vitamin A has practically the same food value as butter, but other margarine does not.

A Source of Vitamin D. A fish-liver oil, such as cod-liver oil or other preparation with a great deal of vitamin D in it, is needed daily by the nursing mother. There are various preparations on the market that the doctor may recommend.

The amount of vitamin D needed by the nursing mother is considered to be 400 to 800 U. S. P. units daily. (For amounts of vitamin preparations that will supply 800 units, see page 205.)

It is wise to choose a source of vitamin D that also contains vitamin A. If the mother is taking skim milk instead of whole milk, or margarine without vitamin A instead of butter, she should make sure that she is getting enough vitamin A by taking cod-liver oil or other fish-liver oil daily.

Water and Other Fluids. Liberal use of fluid is desirable during the nursing period. It may be soup, fruit juice, or milk, as well as water. If the mother takes plenty of milk and fruit juice she may also drink tea and coffee.

A Food Containing Iodine. In most parts of the United States there is enough iodine in the water or the soil (and therefore in the vegetables grown in the soil) to supply all the iodine the nursing mother needs. In a few parts of the country, especially the Great Lakes region and parts of the Northwest, there is a deficiency of iodine in the water and the soil, so that it is necessary to use some special food containing iodine. Iodized salt is frequently used.

Cod-liver oil contains some iodine, as do all sea foods. Ask your doctor whether you need extra iodine.

In addition, a nursing mother may eat other foods to satisfy her appetite. These foods may include:

Bread and crackers made with unenriched flour.

Macaroni, white rice, and refined cereals that have not been restored or enriched.

Cake, pie and other desserts.

Sugar, sirup, jam, jelly, marmalade, candy.

Fats, such as the fat of meat, cooking fats, fat meats such as bacon and salt pork, and salad oil.

If a nursing mother gets enough milk, fruit, vegetables, lean meat, poultry, fish, eggs, and whole-grain or enriched breads and cereals, she as a rule may eat as much of these sweet, fat, and starchy foods as she wishes. If she is gaining weight too rapidly, however, these are the foods that should be decreased. No decrease should be made in milk, fruit, vegetables, eggs, or meat without instruction from the doctor.

If very highly seasoned foods or foods with a very strong flavor, such as raw onions, are eaten by a nursing mother the milk will have a strong taste, and her baby may refuse to take it.

THE MOTHER'S HEALTH

SLEEP AND REST. At least eight hours' sleep at night and one hour's rest during the day are desirable for every nursing mother, because if the mother is tired she may not produce enough milk for her baby. The 2:00 A. M. nursing can be stopped as soon as the baby will sleep through the night without it; this is usually before the end of the second month. There will then be only one nursing at night—at 10:00 P. M.—and the mother may have a long, unbroken sleep after this feeding.

FRESH AIR AND EXERCISE. Moderate exercise in the open air and sunshine, especially walking, is desirable for the sake of good health. If a mother has much work to do in the house she will not have strength for much walking or other exercise outdoors. She can try, however, to spend some time each day resting in the open air and sunshine.

Fresh air indoors is needed for health; and, besides, sleeping and living rooms are pleasanter if kept well-ventilated.

WORK. Overwork during the nursing period is undesirable for the mother. Often a mother who at first has plenty of milk for her baby finds when she goes back to her regular work that the amount is greatly reduced. Many mothers are not strong enough to under-take housework until at least six weeks after childbirth. By this time the milk flow has been well established.

A mother will have better general health if arrangements can be made that permit her to resume her duties gradually. If im-possible to provide or secure outside help, the father should do all he can to help the nursing mother get the rest she needs.

When the mother first begins to work again she can avoid fatigue by taking short rests between tasks. Lying down for five minutes several times a day may enable her to do more work than she would otherwise be able to do safely. To get more rest it is well for her to nurse her baby in a half-reclining or other comfortable position. This will give her fifteen or twenty minutes' relaxation every few hours.

CONTENTMENT. The mother who can lead an even, regular life without emotional upsets will nurse her baby the more successfully on that account.

Fright, grief, anger, worry, or any great excitement or lasting nervous strain can make a mother lose her milk entirely.

RECREATION. Some form of recreation is good for everyone. Recreation and outdoor life help to keep the mother happy and contented and help also to maintain the supply of breast milk.

REGULATION OF THE BOWELS. Constipation during the period soon after child-birth is very common because the mother's body does not return to normal strength for several weeks, and sometimes not for several months.

Every effort should be made to regulate the bowels by means of foods. Leafy vegetables are helpful, and also fruits, particularly apples, rhubarb, figs, and prunes. Eating whole-grain bread and cereals will frequently correct constipation. A glass of water taken regularly the first thing in the morning may help.

As the mother becomes strong, daily walks or other exercise may assist in making the action of the bowels regular.

It is well to make a habit of going to the toilet regularly once a day whether or not there is a desire to have a stool.

Laxative drugs should not be used except upon the advice of a doctor. Some of these drugs pass into the breast milk and affect the baby.

If the mother does become constipated an enema is a safe way of emptying the bowels.

BATHING. Many women perspire more freely during the nursing period than at other times. Sometimes this occurs only during the time the milk flow is becoming established, but sometimes it persists during the entire nursing period. The extra perspiration and the fact that a breast full of milk occasionally leaks milk made it necessary for the nursing mother to take extra pains with her toilet to prevent the odors of perspiration and stale milk.

ALCOHOL AND TOBACCO. The question is often asked, "Should a woman who has been used to smoking give it up during the months when she nurses her baby?" or, "Should a woman who has been used to taking an occasional alcoholic drink refrain from taking even that during the period she nurses her baby?" At present there is no evidence that if the mother smokes moderately or takes an occasional drink of an alcoholic beverage any harm will be done her baby; nor can it be said definitely that these things do not do harm.

CARE OF THE BREASTS

Often the success of breast feeding depends upon the care given the breasts. Before nursing the baby the mother should wash her hands with soap and water. She should then wash her nipple and breast with soap and water, using a clean cloth or a piece of absorbent cotton. The soap should be carefully rinsed off. After the nursing the nipple and breast should be washed again. Between nursings the breasts should be covered with a clean cloth held in place by the brassière. This cloth will soak up any milk that leaks from the breast, and it can be changed readily.

When the milk first comes in, the breasts may become painful. Usually this condition rights itself without difficulty as soon as the regular emptying of the breasts is established. Unnecessary handling of the breasts should be avoided. An uplift type of brassière that supports the breasts is needed. If the breasts become painful and tense (caked), an ice bag may make them more comfortable. A baby should never be weaned because of caked breasts, as it is only a temporary condition.

The baby's first efforts to nurse often make the nipples tender, but this should never discourage a mother from nursing her baby, as this condition lasts only a short time. The nipples usually become less sensitive in a few days or a week.

Great care must be taken to keep the nipples free from infection, for the tiny cracks of a sore nipple may develop into breast abscess.

A doctor should be consulted if the nipples are sore or cracked or the breasts are abscessed or if anything else interferes with satisfactory nursing.

Never allow the baby's mouth to come in direct contact with a cracked nipple. Let him draw the milk from the breast through a nipple shield. The nipple shield should be cleaned thoroughly after nursing and boiled before being used again. A lead nipple shield should not be used, as this is dangerous. If the baby cannot obtain the milk when a shield is used, the mother should express the milk from her breast by hand or with some type of breast pump and feed it to the baby from a nursing bottle.

During the first week or so the nursing of the baby makes the uterus contract so that frequently as the mother nurses her baby she feels pains in the lower abdomen. This is nothing to cause alarm; the pain disappears in a few weeks when the uterus has shrunk to normal size.

EMPTYING THE BREASTS

Before expressing the milk, whether by hand or by breast pump, scrub the hands and nails with soap and warm water for a full minute, using a brush. Wash the breast and nipple with a clean cloth and soap and water, being careful to rinse off all the soap. Dry the hands on a clean towel.

If the milk is to be given to the baby at once have ready a sterilized (boiled) glass to receive it (unless a breast pump that has a glass cup is used) ; also a sterilized nursing bottle and nipple. If your glass has no lip you should have ready a sterilized funnel also to use in pouring the milk into the bottle.

If the milk is to be given to the baby later, rather than imme-diately after it is expressed, it should be brought to a boil and then should be kept on ice in a sterilized bottle, covered with a sterilized bottle top.

EXPRESSING MILK BY HAND. The doctor or the nurse will show you how to empty the breasts by hand. One way to do it is as follows:

Place the balls of the thumb and forefinger on opposite sides of the breast, about one and a half inches from the nipple. This is usually at the edge of the darker-colored part. Press deeply and firmly into the breast until the resistance of the ribs is felt. Then bring the thumb and fingers tightly together well behind the base of the nipple. When the fingers and thumb are pressed deeply into the breast keep them there and repeat the "together" motion sixty to a hundred times per minute. Speed is important and is attained after some practice. The fingers should not slip forward on the breast or the skin may be irritated. It is not necessary to touch the nipple. Stripping the breasts in this way should cause no dis-comfort.

BREAST PUMP EXPRESSION. A breast pump is a convenience to a mother who must empty her breasts frequently. The simplest kind of pump consists of a glass cup and a rubber bulb. These pumps can be bought in most drug stores.

Before the breast pump is used, it should be washed with soap and water and sterilized by boiling five minutes. When washing the rubber bulb take care to clean all the grooves in the part that joins the glass.

USING OTHER MILK

OBTAINING BREAST MILK ELSEWHERE. Some newborn babies thrive so much better on breast milk than they do on cow's milk that it is worth trying to obtain breast milk for them if the mother is unable to produce it. In some large cities there are hospitals or breast-milk agencies that sell breast milk produced by healthy women and collected and handled properly. Breast milk that is bought should be boiled.

If it is necessary to obtain breast milk for a baby from some other source than the baby's own mother, your doctor should be consulted.

INSUFFICIENT BREAST MILK. If the mother's supply of breast milk is not enough for her baby's needs it will be necessary to give the baby a cow's milk mixture in addition to the breast milk. The doctor should be consulted as to whether additional feeding is necessary.

When a cow's-milk mixture must be given in addition to breast milk it is usually most satisfactory to give a small bottle feeding immediately after the breast feeding. This may be done at as many feedings a day as the doctor recommends.

The bottle should be given after the breast—never before—as the sucking of a hungry baby stimulates the production of breast milk.

When a bottle feeding is to follow a breast feeding, prepare the bottle of milk mixture and have it at hand, kept warm, ready to give the baby when he has emptied the breast. In this way the meal will be more satisfying to the baby than if he has to wait after nursing before he can have the bottle.

The milk mixture to be used depends upon the baby's age, weight, and special needs. Ask your doctor what mixture to use and the amount to be prepared. (See Bottle Feeding.)

PLENTY OF BREAST MILK. Even though the mother's supply of breast milk is abundant it is not wise to substitute more than one bottle feeding for a breast feeding in twenty-four hours until the time to begin weaning, because the amount of mother's milk is likely to decrease unless each breast is emptied completely at least twice every twenty-four hours.

An occasional bottle feeding accustoms a breast-fed baby to the bottle and thus makes weaning easier.

Weaning or Taking the Baby Off the Breast

What Weaning Means

WEANING means that the mother stops giving her baby her breast milk.

Partial weaning means that the baby gets part of his nourishment from his mother's milk, and part in the form of other foods, such as a cow's milk mixture, cereals, and vegetables.

Complete weaning means that the baby gets none of his mother's milk at all.

When and How to Start Weaning and When to Wean Completely

Usually, weaning is started when the baby is four months old. At this time, as a rule, a cereal feeding is given in addition to the 10 A.M. breast feeding.

The next step usually occurs when the baby is about five months old. At this age, a vegetable feeding is given at the 2 P.M. feeding time. The breast feeding at 2 P.M. is stopped. Instead, about five ounces of cow's milk mixture are offered after the vegetable feeding to get the baby used to taking cow's milk and to taking milk from a bottle. The mother need not worry that the baby will resist weaning. If he refuses to drink the milk mixture from a bottle, he may take it from a clean cup which has been boiled and cooled. This milk mixture is usually made by adding together three ounces of cow's milk, two ounces of boiled water, and one-half teaspoonful of cane sugar, or one teaspoonful of powdered maltose and dextrins. After about two weeks, he may be given four ounces of milk, two ounces of water, and one-half teaspoonful of cane sugar or one teaspoonful of powdered maltose and dextrins or corn sirup.

The usual time completely to wean the baby is when he is about nine or ten months old. The baby should not be weaned when he is sick, just getting over an illness, or when the weather is hot.

How to Wean Completely, Starting When Baby Is About Nine Months Old

When he is about nine months old, in addition to his other foods the breast-fed baby is usually being nursed at 6 A.M., 10 A.M., 6 P.M., and, in some cases, at 10 P.M. To take the baby off the breast completely at this time, the first step is usually to give a cow's milk mixture instead of the breast at 10 A.M., after the cereal. The milk mixture usually consists of four ounces of boiled cow's milk, two ounces of water, and one-half level teaspoonful of sugar; it is boiled for three minutes.

The second step, about a week later, is to stop the 6 P.M. breast feeding, and offer instead, the same kind and amount of milk mixture given after the 10 A.M. cereal feeding.

The third step, about a week later, is to replace the 6 A.M. breast feeding with a mixture containing six ounces of boiled cow's milk, two ounces of water, and one level teaspoonful of sugar. If the baby is still getting the 10 P.M. breast feeding at this time, it is stopped, and he is allowed to sleep through the night without being fed.

Then, in the fourth step (a few days later), the amount of milk in each bottle feeding is increased one ounce, the water decreased one ounce, and the sugar decreased one-half teaspoonful every two days, so that when the baby is about ten months old he gets whole boiled milk without any sugar or water added to it and is completely weaned.

If weaning becomes necessary during hot weather, it usually

may be done safely if the milk mixture is made and given in the right way and the cow's milk is boiled.

How to Wean the Baby Completely
Before He Is Nine Months Old

Complete weaning during the first few months may be a serious matter and should be done only when it cannot be avoided and when the doctor advises it.

GRADUAL WEANING. Whenever possible, the weaning should be done gradually. If the baby must be completely taken off the breast before he is nine months old, he usually is given, at first, a milk mixture made of equal parts of milk and water in place of the breast milk. Each ten ounces of milk mixture should contain two teaspoonfuls of cane sugar or corn sirup or three teaspoonfuls of powdered maltose and dextrins. The first day the weaning is begun, only enough of this milk mixture should be given from a bottle or cup to replace one of the breast feedings. The breast is given at the other feedings for that day. In a few days, a feeding of this milk mixture is given in place of another breast feeding, and so on until, in about ten days or two weeks, the baby is no longer getting any breast milk.

When possible, several days should be allowed to pass each time before giving the cow's milk mixture in place of another breast feeding.

After the baby is no longer getting any breast milk, the cow's milk mixture gradually should be strengthened, so that, in about three days after he has been taken off the breast, he is being given a mixture a baby of his age and weight usually gets.

If the baby is getting both breast milk and a cow's milk mixture, and for some reason must be taken off the breast, enough milk mixture must be added to take the place of the breast feeding. For each ounce of breast milk the baby was getting, one ounce of milk mixture is given. In this case, all the breast feedings the baby has been getting may usually be stopped in a few days.

SUDDEN WEANING. Sometimes, it may be necessary to wean the

baby suddenly for some good reason, such as when the mother has a severe illness, but this should not be done unless it is ordered by the doctor.

Trouble may arise in changing the baby from breast milk to cow's milk if the change is made too suddenly, and if the cow's milk mixture is too strong or is not properly made. Therefore, if the baby must be weaned in one day, the milk mixture may, at first, contain equal parts of water and milk with one teaspoonful of cane sugar or one and one-half teaspoonfuls of powdered maltose and dextrins or corn sirup for each six ounces of milk mixture in order to get the baby used to the new food. A feeding of such a milk mixture is given in place of every breast feeding the baby was getting. The feeding usually contains about two ounces more than the baby's age in months, but not more than a total of eight ounces. The amount of water in the mixture should then be lessened, and milk added, day by day. At about the end of five days, the baby is usually getting the amount of food that is suited to his age and weight.

If the mother's breasts become sore because of the sudden weaning, much can be done to relieve the pain. The mother should drink as little fluid as possible, and the breasts should be supported by a snug, but not too tight, brassière. An ice bag may be put on the breast for an hour or two several times a day. The breasts should not be emptied because, if they are, more milk will come into them.

HERMAN N. BUNDESEN, M.D.

Bottle Feeding

UNLESS there is very good reason, no baby should be taken off the breast during the first six months. Bottle feeding may begin at this time but it is best that a baby should be at least partly breast fed until he is seven or eight months old. On the other hand, if you cannot feed your baby at the breast, don't worry about it. Bottle feeding produces strong, healthy babies too.

Your doctor will help you decide whether fresh milk, evaporated milk or dried milk should be used for the baby's formula. There is nothing mysterious about this formula, because it consists of some form of cow's milk, sugar and water, and it will be prepared under your doctor's direction. This applies both to the young baby who cannot be breast fed and the baby who is old enough to be weaned.

FRESH MILK. This milk should be kept cool and clean. If you cannot get fresh milk from a dependable source or do not have a cool place in which to keep the milk, it is better not to use fresh milk for baby feeding. Fresh milk should be pasteurized before it is sold.

All fresh milk should be boiled before it is given to the baby.

EVAPORATED MILK. Evaporated milk is whole milk from which some of the water has been removed. As put into the can it has less than half the original bulk of the fresh milk from which it was made. It is sterilized in the can, and no sugar is added. All brands of evaporated milk now sold in the United States meet the government standards and are suitable for infant feeding.

Evaporated milk will keep without refrigeration until the can is opened. When the can has been opened the milk must be kept covered and in a cold place, just like fresh milk. It may be kept in the can.

When evaporated milk is diluted with an equal amount of boiled cooled water it has practically the same food value as fresh whole milk that has been boiled.

Evaporated milk is a safe and inexpensive milk for babies.

Evaporated milk must not be confused with condensed milk, which contains a large amount of sugar and therefore is not a suitable food for babies.

DRIED MILK. This comes in powdered form and is manufactured by removing practically all the water from fluid milk; no sugar is added. Dried milk may be made from whole milk, skimmed milk, or partly skimmed milk, and from sweet or sour milk. Be sure to read the label before buying dried milk so as to get the kind you want.

Canned dried milk will keep without refrigeration until the can is opened. After the can is opened and the powder has been exposed to the air the can must be kept tightly covered and cold. Damp or soiled utensils should never be used to dip out the powder, as this may contaminate what is left in the can.

Since a can of dried milk may not be used up for some time, dried milk should not be used unless the opened can of powder can be kept cold.

If dried whole sweet milk is mixed with water according to the directions on the can, it may be used in the same way as fresh whole milk and should be boiled.

Other types of dried milk may be used according to the doctor's directions.

Lactic-Acid Milk. Usually this is made for babies by adding lactic acid to boiled milk, although it may be made by adding a culture to the milk. The boiled milk must be cold before the lactic acid is added. Otherwise the milk is likely to form curds that will not pass through the holes in the nipple.

Vitamin-D Milk. This is milk—fresh, evaporated, or dried—that has had its vitamin-D value increased by some special process. The amount of vitamin D that these fortified milks contain varies but most of them have a vitamin-D value of 400 international units per quart of fresh milk or of evaporated or dried milk after sufficient water has been added to make a quart.

BOILING KILLS GERMS

It is of utmost importance to any baby who must be bottle-fed that the milk be boiled to make it safe. Boiling milk kills any disease germs that the milk may contain.

When milk has been boiled for five minutes it is also more digestible. The curds that are formed in a baby's stomach from boiled milk are small and soft and are more like the curds from breast milk.

Many of the digestive disturbances and other difficulties of bottle feeding do not appear when only boiled milk is given to the baby.

It is perhaps the one rule than can be laid down for all bottle-fed babies.

SUGAR

Your doctor will decide what kind of sugar is best for your baby's milk mixture. The kinds commonly used are: corn sirup, granulated sugar, a mixture of malt sugar and dextrin, milk sugar, and even honey. There are also proprietary or patent sugars for infant feeding.

Either granulated sugar or corn sirup is satisfactory for most babies. The dark kind of corn sirup is usually preferable to the light because it is likely to contain more minerals, especially iron. Sirup should be kept covered and cool.

Many infant foods on the market contain no milk but are intended to be added to the milk; they consist largely of sugars. This type of patent food should be added to milk in place of other sugar only as directed by the doctor.

THE FORMULA

The milk formula that is best for your baby should be planned by the doctor.

The amount and kind of milk and sugar and the amount of water that should be used vary according to the individual needs of the baby. Even though the doctor has planned a formula for the baby, it may be necessary for him to change it more than once, before a mixture suited to the baby's individual needs is found. After the right mixture has been found it will need to be changed from time to time.

Babies, even at the same age, vary a good deal in the amount of food they require. For example, very active babies need more food than babies that are less active. Let your doctor decide how much food a baby will need at different ages.

QUANTITY OF MILK. On his first day of life a baby is usually given no milk—only water, sweetened or unsweetened.

On the second day, if it is not possible to feed the baby at his mother's breast, cow's milk is begun, that is, one ounce of milk for each pound of the baby's weight. A seven-pound baby at this age usually needs seven ounces of milk in twenty-four hours.

From the fourth to the seventh day a baby needs as a rule one and a quarter to one and a half ounces of milk daily for each pound of his weight.

During the second, third, and fourth weeks the baby usually needs not less than one and one half ounces of milk daily for each pound of his weight, and he may need more.

From the beginning of the second month to the end of the ninth month most babies need one and one half to two ounces of milk daily for each pound of their weight.

When the baby is nine months old he will be taking a variety of other foods, so that it is seldom necessary to increase the amount of milk further.

After the baby is about nine months old, whether he has been breast fed or bottle fed, he may be given daily about thirty-two ounces (one quart) of cow's milk (boiled) unmixed with water or sugar. Some of this milk may be used in cooking the baby's cereal or may be poured over it.

AMOUNT OF SUGAR. During the first week of life a seven-pound baby, as a rule, will need one tablespoonful of corn sirup or granulated sugar added to the whole day's allowance of milk mixture. During the first month this may be gradually increased to two tablespoonfuls, during the second month to two and a half tablespoonfuls, and during the third or fourth month to three tablespoonfuls. Most babies will not require more than three tablespoonfuls a day of sirup or granulated sugar at any time.

At the beginning of the seventh month begin to decrease this amount of sugar gradually, until at the beginning of the ninth month no sugar is added to the milk.

One level tablespoonful of corn sirup or granulated sugar weighs the same as one and one-half tablespoonfuls of milk sugar or of a mixture of malt sugar and dextrin; therefore if either of these is used, one and one-half times as many tablespoonfuls will be needed as of corn sirup or granulated sugar.

AMOUNT OF WATER TO BE ADDED. As a rule during the first week of life a baby's milk is diluted about half and half with water; gradually less water is put into the milk mixture, more being given

MAKING THE EVAPORATED MILK FORMULA

EQUIPMENT NEEDED

- Pail or can with cover. Place wire mesh or cloth on bottom of pail.

- Six to eight nursing bottles and nipples.

- Clean quart jar.

- 6 or 8 squares of heavy paper, 4 inches square. String (1 for each bottle). Spoon, measuring cup, funnel, can opener, bottle brush.

- Evaporated milk. Sugar or corn syrup (white).

1. Wash your hands in hot, soapy water, and put on a clean apron before starting to make the formula.

2. Scrub all bottles, nipples and equipment to be used, in hot soapy water with a brush. Rinse in clear water.

3. Wash off top of the can in hot, soapy water and rinse in clear water. Then punch two holes in the top with the can opener.

4. Measure the amount of plain water needed into the quart jar.

5. Then add the number of spoons of sugar or syrup into the jar and stir to dissolve.

6. Measure the amount of milk called for in the formula and mix into the water and sugar in the jar.

6.

7. Measure into each bottle the amount of formula needed for the 24-hour feeding. Then place the nipples on the bottles and cover them with a paper square and tie with string around the neck of the bottle.

7.

8. Place the pail with the wire mesh on the stove with 3 inches of water in the bottom.

8.

9. Place the bottles of formula in the pail and, after the water has come to a boil, allow to boil with cover on for 20 minutes by the clock.

9.

10. At the end of the boiling, take the pail off the stove and keep covered in a cool place until time to take out a bottle for feeding.

10.

11. If you have a refrigerator, place the bottles in it until needed. Before feeding, warm the bottle in a pan of hot water until the milk feels warm when dropped on the inside of your arm.

11.

as drinking water. Some doctors prefer that the baby get all the water that he needs between feedings rather than in the milk mixture.

Throughout his first year a baby needs two to two and a half ounces of fluid daily for each pound of his body weight. If he does not obtain this much fluid in his milk mixture and fruit juices, the rest may be supplied as drinking water.

In hot weather a baby will need more fluid than in cold weather.

FEEDING SCHEDULE

Most babies do well if fed every four hours. The very young baby fed every four hours will have six feedings in twenty-four hours, usually, at 6:00 A.M., 10:00 A.M., 2:00 P.M., 6:00 P.M., 10:00 P.M., and 2:00 A.M.

As soon as the baby will sleep through the 2:00 A.M. feeding—usually by the second month—he will need only five feedings in twenty-four hours. Later, as a rule some time after he is four or five months old, he will also sleep through the 10:00 P.M. feeding. Four feedings in twenty-four hours will then suffice.

Some babies need to be fed at shorter intervals than every four hours. The baby fed every three hours will need eight feedings in twenty-four hours, or seven feedings if during the night the intervals can be longer than three hours.

The exact hours at which the feedings are to be given can be other than those suggested, so long as an appropriate interval is allowed between feedings.

Feedings should be given according to a regular schedule, arranged to meet the baby's needs and the parents' convenience.

The baby who is fed at four-hour intervals receives larger feedings than the one who is fed at shorter intervals. But even babies fed at the same intervals vary considerably with regard to the amount of milk that they will take at a feeding. For newborn babies it is well to offer a small amount at a feeding—say two to two and a half ounces—and to increase the amounts as the baby wants more.

FEEDING EQUIPMENT

If a baby is to be weaned before he is old enough to drink from a cup, or if he must be fed a milk mixture from birth, it is a great help if the mother is able to have a set of utensils especially for preparing the milk mixture and to keep these utensils together and not use them for anything else.

The utensils needed include (1) those needed for feeding, (2) those needed for preparation, and (3) those needed for keeping the equipment in good condition.

NURSING BOTTLES. Six to eight 8-ounce bottles, depending on number of feedings in twenty-four hours. Two 4-ounce bottles for water and orange juice.

Bottles made of heat-resistant glass cost more but will last longer. They should have no sharp corners, to permit cleaning thoroughly with a bottle brush.

BOTTLE CAPS. Cap covers that fit over the lip of the bottle and keep it tightly covered are more satisfactory than corks. If wax paper, held in place by elastic bands, is used, the bottle must be kept upright. Wax paper must never be used twice.

NIPPLES. Enough for a day's feedings and when giving water and orange juice. They should be easy to turn inside out for cleaning and they should be tested to see that holes are the right size. To do this put the nipple on a bottle of water, turn upside down and squeeze. Several fine streams should come from it. If the holes in the nipple are too small, the baby may get tired before he gets enough milk; if they are too large, he will get all his milk before he has sucked as long as he wants to. A baby sometimes starts thumb or finger sucking because he still wants to suck after he has had all his milk.

If the holes seem too small, heat an ordinary sewing needle to a red-hot heat, holding it by means of a cork, and enlarge the holes by poking the red-hot needle through them.

Several small holes in a nipple are better than one large one.

UTENSILS FOR PREPARING THE FORMULA

A saucepan in which to mix and boil the milk mixture is usually needed.

A funnel is usually needed in pouring the milk mixture from the saucepan into the nursing bottles. If the saucepan has a good lip a funnel may not be necessary.

A large measuring cup marked to measure ounces is convenient for measuring milk and water, but a nursing bottle marked in ounces is also satisfactory.

A tablespoon and a teaspoon are needed for measuring sugar. Measuring spoons, in sets of four fastened together on a ring, are inexpensive and are much more accurate than ordinary household spoons.

A knife should be kept for leveling spoonfuls of sugar or dried milk.

Strainer. A scum is likely to form on a fresh-milk mixture when it is boiled, and therefore a strainer is needed.

Egg beater. If dried milk is used an egg beater is needed.

Caring for the Equipment

A brush with a long handle and with long bristles, which will thoroughly clean the inside of the nursing bottles, is needed.

A kettle with a cover is needed for sterilizing the bottles, caps, nipples, and other utensils. Baby-bottle sterilizers, which consist of a kettle and a bottle rack, can be bought.

A wire rack for holding bottles when they are being boiled and filled is a convenience. This rack should fit inside the large kettle used for sterilizing as it does in commercial sterilizers.

A long-handled spoon is needed for removing utensils from the sterilizing kettle and for stirring the milk mixture.

Jars. Two small wide-mouthed covered jars, one for clean nipples, the other for used ones. The covers should be of glass or of a metal that does not rust. There should not be a paper top inside the cover.

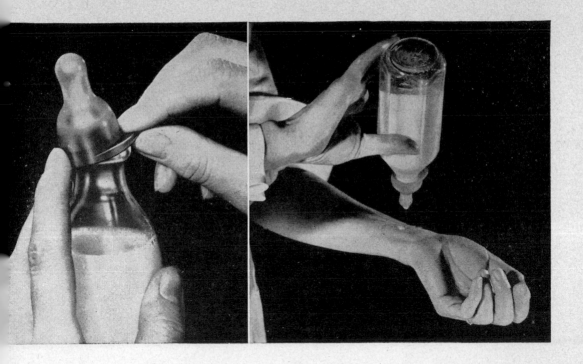

GIVING BABY HIS BOTTLE

(Upper left) It is easy to put on the nipple if bottle rests on a table. Nipple is held firmly with one hand, and stretched over the rim of bottle with the other. *(Upper right)* A drop on the wrist should feel warm, not hot. *(Lower left)* While feeding, keep bottle pointed straight toward his mouth and tipped so that nipple is always filled. *(Lower right)* If baby refuses last ounce or so, rest a moment, then try again. If he still refuses it, he has had enough. Bottle, nipple, and formula-making equipment must be completely sterile.

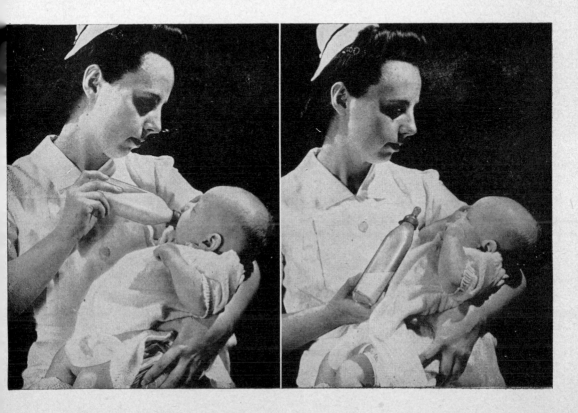

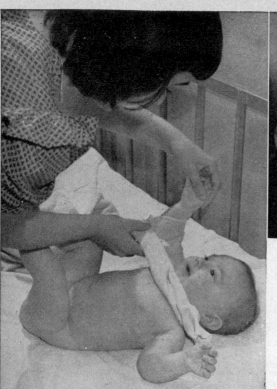

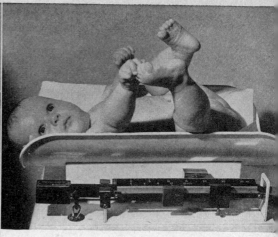

FOR BABY'S COMFORT AND HEALTH

(Left) Baby does not like to be turned over, o[r] to have his arms tugged at or his face covere[d] when you dress him. Shirts and sweaters wit[h] large head openings make the job of dressing g[o] more smoothly. (Above) Steady gain in weight i[s] far more important for baby than gaining a grea[t] deal within a short period. Your doctor will chec[k] baby's progress regularly. (Below) Concentrate[d] vitamin D is easily given by medicine dropper[.]

Left: U. S. Children's Bureau Photo by Philip Bonn[?]

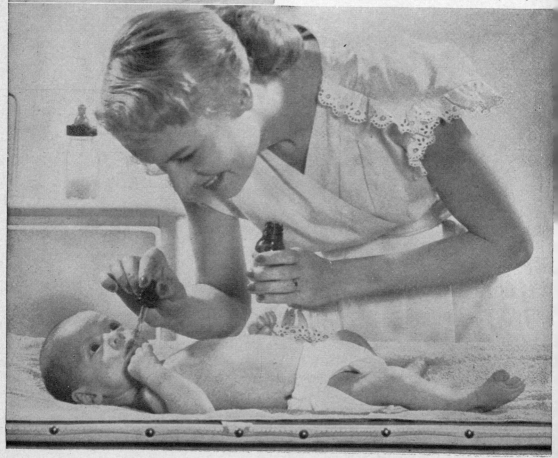

STERILIZING

All the utensils that come in contact with the milk mixture after it has been boiled must be sterilized—boiled or steamed for five minutes; those used before the mixture is boiled need only be washed thoroughly with hot water and soap.

After a feeding, rinse the nursing bottle and the nipple immediately with cold water. Leave the bottle standing full of water. Put the nipple into the jar for used nipples.

Before the mother starts to prepare the formula, she should wash and sterilize all the bottles and other necessary utensils in the following way:

Scrub the inside of each bottle with the bottle brush, using plenty of soap and hot water. Rinse each bottle carefully.

Place each bottle upside down in the wire bottle rack, which fits inside the large covered kettle. If a rack is not used, lay the bottles on their sides in the kettle.

Wash the bottle caps and the nipples with hot water and soap, turning each nipple inside out and seeing that all the soap is removed.

Then put the bottle caps and nipples into the large kettle along with the bottles and any other utensils that come into contact with the milk after it is boiled. Pour enough water into kettle to cover everything and put on the stove to boil.

When the water has boiled five minutes the utensils are ready for the next formula.

Let the kettle cool to avoid burning the fingers and take care in removing the articles from the kettle, so as not to let anything come into contact with anything that has not been sterilized.

Lift out the rack of bottles and let the bottles drain.

Lift out the jar for sterilized nipples. Using the long-handled spoon (touch only the handle), lift first the nipples and then the bottle caps from the kettle and put both into the jar.

The remaining utensils, such as the strainer and funnel, are less likely to get germs on them if they are left in the kettle until used.

If, after the nipples and bottle caps are taken out, the long-handled spoon is put back, with its handle propped against the side, the lower part of the spoon will still be sterile so that you can use the spoon in picking up the utensils.

PREPARING A DAY'S FORMULA

Always have a copy of the doctor's written order for the feeding fastened up in a convenient place so that you can refer to it every day.

Put a clock where you can see it while preparing the milk mixture.

Always wash your hands before beginning to prepare the milk mixture.

FRESH MILK FORMULA. Have ready the saucepan, measuring spoon, measuring cup, sugar or sirup, and knife (if sugar is used); and also the kettle containing the nursing bottles, bottle caps, funnel, strainer, and long-handled spoon, all of which have just been boiled.

Take the bottle of milk out of the refrigerator.

Unless the bottle has a cap *that protects the lip,* clean the top of the milk bottle by holding it under fast-running water and wiping it with a fresh paper towel.

Shake the bottle to mix the cream well with the rest of the milk.

Measure into the saucepan the required amount of milk and of water, using a measuring cup or a nursing bottle marked to measure ounces.

Measure into the saucepan the required amount of sirup or sugar, using the measuring spoon. If sugar is used, level each spoonful with a knife.

Stir the mixture to dissolve the sugar.

Place the saucepan on the stove and let the mixture boil (bubble) actively for five minutes by the clock, stirring it constantly.

Take the saucepan off the stove.

Put into each nursing bottle the milk mixture for one feeding, using the sterilized funnel and strainer.

If heat-resistant nursing bottles are used, strain the milk mixture immediately into the sterilized bottles.

If nursing bottles of ordinary glass are used, cool the mixture by placing the saucepan in a pan of cold water. Stir the mixture while it cools, using the long-handled spoon that was used for stirring it during the boiling. When the mixture is cool, strain it into the sterilized bottles, using the sterilized funnel and strainer.

Cover each bottle with a sterilized bottle cap.

Put the bottles into the refrigerator.

DRIED MILK FORMULA. Have ready the can of dried milk and the saucepan, long-handled spoon, measuring spoon, measuring cup, sugar or sirup, knife, and egg beater; and also the kettle containing the nursing bottles, bottle caps, funnel, and strainer, which have just been boiled.

Measure the required amount of cold water and pour it into the saucepan.

Measure the required amount of dried milk, using a *dry* measuring spoon and leveling each spoonful with a knife. Put the milk on top of the water.

Beat with the egg beater until the milk is well mixed with the water.

Measure into the saucepan the required amount of sirup or sugar, using the measuring spoon. If sugar is used, level each spoonful with the knife.

Stir the mixture with the long-handled spoon to dissolve the sugar.

Place the saucepan on the stove and let the mixture boil (bubble) actively for five minutes by the clock, stirring it constantly.

Take the saucepan off the stove.

Put into each nursing bottle the milk mixture for one feeding, using the sterilized funnel and strainer.

If heat-resistant nursing bottles are used, strain the hot milk mixture into them.

If nursing bottles of ordinary glass are used, cool the mixture by placing the saucepan in a pan of cold water. Stir the mixture while it cools, using the long-handled spoon that was used for stirring it during the boiling.

Cover each bottle with a sterilized bottle cap.

Put the bottles into the refrigerator.

USING EVAPORATED MILK. Have ready the can of evaporated milk and the saucepan, measuring cup, measuring spoon, sugar or sirup, and knife (if sugar is used); and also the kettle containing the

SAMPLE MILK MIXTURES FOR WELL BABIES OF DIFFERENT AGES

Age of baby	Weight of baby	Formula or milk mixture made with whole milk, granulated sugar¹, and water *For 24 hours*	Formula for milk mixture made with evaporated milk, granulated sugar¹, and water *For 24 hours*	*For single feeding*
3 days	7 pounds	Whole milk... 8 ounces. Water... 7 ounces. Granulated sugar¹... 1 tablespoonful. (6 feedings of 2½ ounces)	Evaporated milk... 4 ounces. Water... 11 ounces. Granulated sugar¹... 1 tablespoonful. (6 feedings of 2½ ounces)	¾ ounce. 1¾ ounces. ½ teaspoonful.
2 weeks	7¼ pounds	Whole milk... 12 ounces. Water... 6 ounces. Granulated sugar¹... 2 tablespoonfuls. (6 feedings of 3 ounces)	Evaporated milk... 6 ounces. Water... 12 ounces. Granulated sugar¹... 2 tablespoonfuls. (6 feedings of 3 ounces)	1 ounce. 2 ounces. 1 teaspoonful.
1 month	7¾ pounds	Whole milk... 14 ounces. Water... 6 ounces. Granulated sugar¹... 2½ tablespoonfuls. (5 feedings of 4 ounces)	Evaporated milk... 7 ounces. Water... 13 ounces. Granulated sugar¹... 2½ tablespoonfuls. (5 feedings of 4 ounces)	1½ ounces. 2½ ounces. 1½ teaspoonfuls.
3 months	11 pounds	Whole milk... 19 ounces. Water... 6 ounces. Granulated sugar¹... 3 tablespoonfuls. (5 feedings of 5 ounces)	Evaporated milk... 9½ ounces. Water... 15½ ounces. Granulated sugar¹... 3 tablespoonfuls. (5 feedings of 5 ounces)	2 ounces. 3 ounces. 1¾ teaspoonfuls.
5 months	14 pounds	Whole milk... 24 ounces. Water... 8½ ounces. Granulated sugar¹... 3 tablespoonfuls. (5 feedings of 6½ ounces)	Evaporated milk... 12 ounces. Water... 20½ ounces. Granulated sugar¹... 3 tablespoonfuls. (5 feedings of 6½ ounces)	2½ ounces. 4 ounces. 1¾ teaspoonfuls.
7 months	16½ pounds	Whole milk... 28 ounces. Water... 4 ounces. Granulated sugar¹... 1 tablespoonful. (4 feedings of 8 ounces)	Evaporated milk... 13 ounces. Water... 19 ounces. Granulated sugar¹... 1 tablespoonful. (4 feedings of 8 ounces)	3½ ounces. 4½ ounces. 1 teaspoonful.
9 months	18½ pounds	Whole milk... 28 to 32 ounces. (4 feedings of 7 or 8 ounces)	Evaporated milk... 13 to 16 ounces. Water... 15 to 16 ounces. (4 feedings of 7 or 8 ounces)	3½ to 4 ounces. 3½ to 4 ounces.

¹ An equal amount of corn sirup may be used instead of granulated sugar.

nursing bottles, bottle caps, funnel, strainer, can opener or ice pick, and long-handled spoon, all of which have just been boiled.

Although a can of evaporated milk does not need to be kept cold while it remains unopened, it needs to be kept cold from the time it is opened until it is used. The milk left in the can after a feeding has been prepared can be kept for the next feeding if it is kept in a cold place. The can should be covered so that no dirt can get into the milk. A small bowl or a glass turned over may be used to cover the can, or a piece of paper towel may be fastened over it with an elastic band.

WARMING THE BOTTLE. When a bottle of milk mixture is taken out of the refrigerator it is necessary to warm it for the baby.

Stand the bottle of milk mixture in a small, deep saucepan of warm water. Special bottle warmers may be bought, but they are no better than the ordinary saucepan. Heat the mixture rapidly. (While the milk is warming is a good time for the mother to wash her hands in preparation for feeding the baby.)

Usually the contents of the bottle become sufficiently warm (100° F.) in a few minutes. It is not necessary to wait until the water boils. Shake the bottle several times to make sure that the milk is warmed through.

Remove the bottle cap and put on a sterile (boiled) nipple taken from the covered sterile jar. Touch only the rim of the nipple.

The temperature of the milk may be tested by letting a few drops trickle from the nipple onto the inside surface of the mother's wrist, where it should feel pleasantly warm but not hot.

Never test the temperature of the baby's milk by taking a suck at the nipple.

The part of the nipple that goes into the baby's mouth should not be touched by anyone nor come in contact with anything until it reaches the baby's mouth.

BE SURE COW'S MILK IS SAFE AND FRESH

The problem of the milk supply varies greatly, depending on whether the family lives in a large city, in a small city or town, or in a village or rural district. In most cities milk is purchased from dealers who are required by law to meet certain standards. In smaller communities there is often less careful supervision of milk produc- tion, and so it is important to investigate the conditions under which milk is produced before selecting a milk supply. On the farm milk to be used on the premises or by the neighbors should be handled with the same care as is taken in the larger dairies.

In most large cities and in many small cities and towns, laws have been passed regulating the production and care of all milk sold and establishing standards for certain grades of milk. These standards take into account the composition of the milk (especially the per- centage of fat), the conditions under which it is produced, the number of bacteria in it at the time of delivery, and whether it is to be sold raw or pasteurized. Sometimes milk is sold just outside a city which cannot be sold in the city because it does not meet the city requirements. Such milk should be avoided.

Pasteurized milk should be bought in preference to raw milk whenever it can be obtained.

Several grades of milk are on the market in cities, but the stand- ards for a given grade are not uniform from city to city. Your health department can tell you what grades of milk sold in your community are suitable to give babies. In most cities grade A milk is milk from tuberculin-tested cows, which is produced under very good condi- tions and which has a low bacterial count.

Certified milk is milk produced under such good conditions that it meets certain special requirements of a medical milk commission. It is often sold raw. When certified milk is to be bought for a baby, buy certified milk that has been pasteurized rather than certified raw milk.

Certified milk is more expensive than other fresh milk, and it is not available in all communities.

Infant Feeding Problems

THE UNDERFED BABY

The baby who is losing weight or is showing no gain may not be getting enough to eat. Underfed babies are likely to be cross and fretful. They often wake up before feeding time and cry. They are more likely to suffer from colic than babies who are getting enough food, and many babies are thought to have colic when they are really hungry.

Occasionally an underfed baby will sleep more than a well-fed baby. The baby may eat for a short time and then stop and fall asleep, or he may cry after an exhausting attempt to obtain food.

The stools are scanty, often only brown stains.

The baby who has been underfed for some time seems weak, his body may feel flabby, and his skin may look pale.

THE BREAST-FED BABY. He may be underfed because his mother does not have enough milk, or because he is too weak to nurse properly or has a deformed mouth and cannot suck well.

The way to find out whether a breast-fed baby is getting enough milk is to weigh him before and after each feeding for a period of twenty-four hours, or better, forty-eight hours.

To do this, weigh the baby and whatever clothes and blankets are on him at the time that nursing started. At the end of the nursing weigh him again with exactly the same clothes and blankets. Do not change his diaper before this second weighing. The difference in the two weights represents the number of ounces of milk the baby has taken from his mother. The number of ounces the baby gets in twenty-four hours will show whether the mother is producing enough milk. A baby needs between two and three ounces of breast milk for each pound of body weight. The doctor will tell you whether the baby is getting enough milk.

If the supply of breast milk is not sufficient for the baby, steps can be taken to increase it. Until it is increased, he should get additional food.

To increase the mother's milk supply attention should be paid to her diet and hygiene. She should have plenty of rest and sleep and take the proper amounts of food and liquids. The breasts should be emptied completely at regular intervals. If the milk obtained from one breast is not enough, both breasts should be used at each feeding. Persistent efforts to increase the amount of milk will usually be successful.

If the baby is not able to suck properly, the mother's milk should be expressed from her breasts and fed to the baby with a medicine dropper, which has been sterilized by boiling. The baby's nose and throat should be examined by a doctor.

THE BOTTLE-FED BABY. He may be underfed either because he is not getting enough milk mixture or because his milk mixture is too weak. If the bottle-fed baby shows any of the signs of underfeeding described, consult the doctor.

THE OVERFED BABY

A baby's appetite usually regulates successfully the amount of food he takes, but occasionally a baby may take too much food. If he does his stomach will be overloaded, and he will be apt to spit up some of the food or he may even vomit the whole feeding. He may be fretful and cry; he may even have colic.

THE BREAST-FED BABY. When overfeeding occurs in a breast-fed baby it usually means that the nursing periods are too frequent or that the quantity of milk at one time is too large. To remedy this, the time at the breast should be decreased and the interval between feedings increased if less than four hours. Sometimes a little water before nursing will help. (Less frequent feedings will help regulate the oversupply of milk.)

THE BOTTLE-FED BABY. If overfeeding occurs in a bottle-fed baby it usually means that the milk mixture has been strengthened beyond the needs of the baby, or the feedings are too frequent, or the baby has been forced to take more than he wants. The doctor should be consulted.

SPITTING UP—HICCOUGHS

Spitting up or spilling over (not the same as vomiting) is usually due to air that the baby has swallowed. Spitting up is common in both breast-fed and bottle-fed babies. It can nearly always be prevented by "belching the baby." If, however, after every feeding the baby spits up even after he has belched it may be that he is either underfed or overfed.

Babies often have hiccoughs, and this should not cause anxiety. Give the baby a drink of warm water, or turn him over and pat him on the back, or pick him up. It may be necessary to lengthen the interval between feedings if it is less than four hours.

COLIC

A baby with colic cries vigorously, pulls his legs up, and gets red in the face. His feet may be cold. These symptoms may alarm the mother, but the condition is almost never serious.

Colic is caused most frequently by air in the stomach and can be relieved by getting rid of the air. Sometimes holding or rocking the baby will quiet his cries and make belching easier for him. A drink of warm milk or water (a trifle warmer than that usually given) will sometimes help him belch.

A breast-fed baby sometimes has colic when his mother is anxious or emotionally upset.

Colic may sometimes be caused by allowing the baby to become chilled soon after a feeding or by giving him his drinking water or his milk too cold.

If colic does not disappear when these suggestions are followed, or if it occurs frequently and is severe, and the doctor should be consulted.

"Colic medicine" should not be given except on the advice of a doctor.

Babies seldom have colic after the first three or four months of life.

STOOLS

The newborn baby's first stools are dark green, thick, and sticky, with little or no odor. They soon change in appearance as the baby begins to eat.

The stools of a healthy breast-fed baby are bright orange-yellow, though occasionally they may be tinged with green. When vegetables and other foods are added to the diet the stools change slightly. A breast-fed baby ordinarily has one to three stools a day; he may even have four.

The stools of a healthy bottle-fed baby are different from those of a breast-fed baby. They are much firmer and with slight odor. The color varies from lemon yellow, if white sugar is used, to dark or light brown if malt sugar is used. The stool is smooth and somewhat pasty in character. A bottle-fed baby ordinarily has fewer stools than a breast-fed baby.

Some well babies have infrequent stools; they may have one only every other day. Such a baby is not to be considered constipated, so long as his stools are soft and pasty. If they are hard and dry and the baby passes them with difficulty, he is constipated and the doctor should be told. Constipation is less common in the breast-fed baby than in the bottle-fed baby, but in neither baby is it to be looked upon as a serious condition. In the bottle-fed baby it can nearly always be dealt with by changing the formula, which your doctor will do if necessary. Never give castor oil or other cathartics except on the doctor's advice.

Loose, green, frequent stools are a sign that something is wrong, and a doctor should be consulted at once. Diarrhea is often a symptom of some serious disease, and it should not be neglected.

If any blood is seen in the baby's stool tell the doctor immediately.

Foods in Addition to Milk

EVEN mother's milk does not supply all of the baby's food needs. Therefore all babies can be kept in better health if they are given certain foods other than milk. The foods they will need in addition to milk during the first year are:

1. Orange juice or the source of vitamin C recommended by the doctor. This is introduced during the early weeks of life.
2. A dependable source of vitamin D—usually a fish liver oil concentrate.
3. Strained cereals.
4. Strained vegetables and fruit.
5. Egg yolk.
6. Strained meat—commercially prepared or fresh meat scraped and shredded before cooking.

These foods supply mineral salts, vitamins and other nutritional essentials that are lacking in adequate amounts even in whole milk. They are often unsuitable for the baby, however, in the form in which they are usually served to adults He needs the food but his digestive system is not sufficiently well developed to take care of lumps and coarse fiber. Improperly prepared food will upset him or at best do him very little good because he cannot assimilate it. Therefore, the doctor who has become familiar with your child's needs by frequent examinations must tell you when it is time to introduce new foods, what preparations to use and the amounts to give.

FIRST SOLID FOODS

When it is time to introduce new foods into the diet, school yourself not to display any concern over his immediate response. A mother often hastily concludes that the child does not like the new food because he rolls it around in his mouth and spits it out promptly instead of swallowing it. In reality he is only experimenting with something which is new in texture and taste. He needs a little time to get accustomed to these new sensations but nothing is gained by impatience or coaxing.

Toward the end of the first year, it is desirable to accustom him by easy degrees to foods which are a step nearer the consistency of those in adult diets. His chewing mechanism should be set in motion and stimulated even though he has not enough teeth to do a thorough job of chewing. Digestive upsets and stubborn aversions to foods may be avoided if coarser foods are introduced gradually.

Fruit juice is given to supply vitamin C. The juice of the citrus fruits such as orange, grapefruit, and lemon contains larger amounts of vitamin C than any of the other commonly used fruit juices.

Orange juice usually may be given without sugar, but grapefruit juice and lemon juice almost always have to be sweetened.

Tomato juice contains about half as much vitamin C as orange juice and therefore should be given in twice the quantity.

Citrus-fruit juice and tomato juice may be given either canned or fresh, as commercial canning does not destroy the vitamin C in these juices. Strained canned tomatoes may be used.

Occasionally, fruit juice may cause some digestive or skin disturbance. If it seems likely that the trouble is due to a particular fruit juice, another juice may be given. If the disturbance continues consult the doctor.

Fruit juice should be started when the baby is two weeks old. Start by giving one teaspoonful of strained orange juice daily. The amount can be gradually increased until by the time he is two months old the baby is getting three ounces a day.

Tomato juice and other fruit juices should be kept cold after the fruit is squeezed or the can is opened, so as to prevent much loss of vitamin C.

SOURCES OF VITAMIN D

Both breast-fed and bottle-fed babies need more vitamin D than they receive in their milk. Some food or other preparation to supply this vitamin should be given the baby by the end of the second week of life and continued throughout at least the first two years. It is usually better to give a preparation that supplies both vitamin A and vitamin D.

COD-LIVER OIL. Cod-liver oil and some other fish-liver oils are commonly given to babies because they are rich in vitamins A and D.

Ask your doctor which preparation is best for your baby and how much to give.

VIOSTEROL. Viosterol is vitamin D dissolved in a bland oil; it is not concentrated fish-liver oil. It does not contain any vitamin A, and therefore viosterol alone is not a substitute for cod-liver oil.

VITAMIN-D MILKS. There are several varieties of milk—both fresh and evaporated—on the market that have had the vitamin-D value increased by some special process. If such milk is used, enough additional vitamin D should always be given to insure that the baby gets not less than 800 units a day.

GIVING COD-LIVER OIL. When a baby is very young it is easy to feed him cod-liver oil with a medicine dropper. The oil should be gently dropped into the corner of the baby's mouth and then his lips closed until he swallows. Care must be taken not to squirt the oil far back into his mouth as this may make him choke. Some oils are put up in capsules made so that the tip can be nipped off and the oil dropped into the baby's mouth.

As the baby gets a little older it is easier to give him the oil from a spoon.

The baby should be held in a partly sitting position so that the oil will not go down the wrong way.

APPROXIMATE AMOUNTS OF COD-LIVER OIL AND OF OTHER PREPARATIONS NEEDED TO SUPPLY 800 U. S. P. UNITS OF VITAMIN D

If the cod-liver oil or other preparation contains in each gram the amount of vitamin D shown below—	The amount that should be given daily to supply about 800 units will be—
85 units	2½ teaspoonfuls.[1]
175 units	1¼ teaspoonfuls.
250 units	¾ teaspoonful.
400 units	½ teaspoonful.
1,000 units	40 small drops.[2]
5,000 units	8 small drops.[2]
10,000 units	4 small drops.[2]

[1] A household teaspoon holds four grams of cod-liver oil.

[2] This amount is approximate only. Usually a special dropper, which delivers small drops, is supplied with the preparation, and the label tells how many units of vitamin D are contained in one such drop.

A glass medicine dropper must be thoroughly washed with soap and hot water immediately after each using and the glass part boiled before it is used again. If the mother dislikes cod-liver oil herself, she must be careful not to let her expression or her actions show her dislike. If she does, the baby will learn to dislike it by watching his mother. Strange as it may seem to many mothers, almost all children like cod-liver oil.

Cod-liver oil and other oils containing vitamins spoil rather easily and therefore should be kept cold, covered and clean.

CEREALS

These cereals may be started when the baby is about four months old. Cereals made from whole grain, such as rolled oats and water-ground corn meal, are better for the baby than refined cereals, such as white farina and bolted corn meal.

Some cereals on the market have had vitamins and minerals added to them, and the doctor may recommend some of these.

Cereals need to be cooked thoroughly. Certain cereals, especially prepared for babies, have been thoroughly cooked at the factory and need merely to be mixed with warm milk or water.

The cereal that is cooked for the family may be used for the baby. For a young baby cereal with coarse fiber, such as cracked wheat, and any cereal that has lumps should be strained and it should be thin enough to run off the end of a spoon. If it is too thick it may be thinned by adding boiling water or part of the baby's milk mixture.

Begin with a teaspoonful of cooked cereal just before the 10:00 A. M. feeding and increase the amount gradually by a teaspoonful or two a day.

By the time the baby is about seven months old he may be taking from two or five tablespoonfuls of cereal twice a day. It may be made thicker so that he will learn to take some solid food.

EGGS

Egg yolk may be added to the baby's diet when he is about four months old. Some doctors add it in the third month or even earlier. The egg may be soft-cooked, or hard-cooked and mashed.

The first time egg yolk is given, give a very small amount (one-fourth teaspoonful or less) at the 2 P. M. feeding. Increase the amount gradually each day. When the baby is about nine months old he may be given a whole egg.

A very few babies are made sick by eggs. If your baby seems sick after he first gets egg yolk, do not give it again until you have told the doctor about it.

VEGETABLES

They should be started when the baby is about five months old and given once a day at the 2 P. M. feeding. Give a green leafy vegetable such as spinach, chard, beet greens, turnip greens—any green leafy vegetable that is in season—two or three times a week. On the other days, give carrots, green peas, green lima beans, asparagus, broccoli, or string beans, or any other vegetable that can be readily mashed through the strainer. Potatoes may be given occasionally in place of cereal at 10:00 A. M. or 6:00 P. M. but should not replace other vegetables. Begin by giving about a teaspoonful of mashed vegetables once a day and increase the amount fairly rapidly to two tablespoonfuls when the baby is six months old, three tablespoonfuls when he is seven months old, and four tablespoonfuls when he is eight months old. From this time on give four tablespoonfuls daily. Remember that these amounts are only average ones. Some babies will take more, some less. Do not try to increase the amount of vegetable faster than the baby is willing to take it.

Vegetables should be cooked until tender in a small amount of water, with a little salt, then mashed through a sieve or strainer. If any of the cooking water is left it should be added to the strained vegetable.

Use an uncovered pan for cooking vegetables with a strong flavor, such as cauliflower, but for all other vegetables use a covered pan, as this makes it possible to use very little water. Start the cooking with boiling water. Usually it is not necessary to add water to greens because enough water clings to the leaves after washing. Never add soda to vegetables; soda destroys some of the vitamins.

Canned vegetables may be used in place of fresh vegetables by mashing through a sieve or strainer. Some canned vegetables prepared especially for babies are on the market. Those prepared for young babies have been mashed through a strainer; those for older babies, cut fine. They need only be warmed. These canned vegetables are a real convenience, but they are more expensive. If only part of a can of vegetables is used at a time, the remainder may be kept in the can for the next day only if the can is covered and kept cold.

When home-canned foods are used, it is of the utmost importance to know whether nonacid vegetables (that is, all except tomatoes) have been canned in a pressure cooker with a gauge that has been tested recently and found to be reliable. If there is any doubt as to whether they have been canned by this method, nonacid vegetables should be boiled for fifteen minutes after they have been removed from the can even if they are to be served cold. Count the time after boiling has begun.

FRUITS

Apple sauce, apricot or prune pulp, and some other stewed fruits such as peaches, mashed through a sieve or strainer, may be given once a day, beginning when the baby is about seven months old. Bananas provide sugar in a form easily digested by a baby and are also a good source of several vitamins. Only thoroughly ripened bananas that have yellow skins with spots of brown should be given to babies. The ripe banana should be peeled, the stringy material scraped off, and the soft pulp mashed and fed to the baby with a spoon. Never give a baby any of a banana that has any green in the skin. The doctor will tell you at what age the baby may have banana and how much he may have.

MEAT

By the time the baby is seven months old he may have scraped liver or other lean meat with his 2:00 P. M. feeding. Scraped meat is prepared by scraping a piece of raw meat with a knife. The tough, fibrous part of the meat remains attached to the main piece, and the tender pulp is collected. The pulp should be cooked quickly in a hot pan with just enough fat to prevent sticking.

BREAD

After the baby's first teeth have come give him bread dried in the oven or zwieback after his meals. If commercial zwieback is used it is better to buy the unsweetened kind.

Bread made from whole grains, and enriched bread are better for the baby than bread made from unenriched flour. The whole grains contain minerals and vitamins that are lost in the process of refining the flour. These minerals and vitamins are valuable food substances for the baby. Whole-grain bread must not be confused with cracked-wheat bread or bran bread, which are made from refined flour with coarse particles of the wheat kernel added. Cracked-wheat bread and bran bread are not suitable for a baby.

Dried bread is much better for a baby than crackers because crackers soften in the mouth and give little exercise for the jaws and teeth. It is dangerous to give a baby dried bread while he is lying down, as it may choke him.

FOODS IN ADDITION TO MILK THAT ARE GIVEN TO BABIES AT DIFFERENT AGES[1]

2 weeks old	1 teaspoonful orange juice; 1 teaspoonful cod-liver oil.
1 month old	1 ounce orange juice; 2½ teaspoonfuls cod-liver oil.
2 months old	3 ounces orange juice; 2½ teaspoonfuls cod-liver oil.
3 months old	3 ounces orange juice; 2½ teaspoonfuls cod-liver oil.
4 months old	3 ounces orange juice; 2½ teaspoonfuls cod-liver oil; cereal; egg yolk.
5 to 6 months old	3 ounces orange juice; 2½ teaspoonfuls cod-liver oil; cereal, egg yolk; vegetables.
7 months old	3 ounces orange juice; 2½ teaspoonfuls cod-liver oil; cereal; egg yolk; vegetables; fruit; scraped meat.
8 to 12 months old	3 ounces orange juice; 2½ teaspoonfuls cod-liver oil; cereal; whole egg; vegetables; fruit; scraped meat; dry toast as soon as the baby has some teeth.

---

[1] Amounts of cod-liver oil are for standard cod-liver oil.

When Feeding Problems Become Behavior Problems

A COMMON TIME for the beginning of a feeding problem is when solid foods are first introduced. Most babies are at best doubtful about the first few mouthfuls. They wrinkle their brows, screw up their faces, and clack their tongues against the roofs of their mouths with at least a shade of disgust. The food is oozed out onto the chin. This bewilderment is understandable. The taste is strange, the consistency is strange, and the spoon is strange.

After two or three days the majority of babies seem to decide about cereal, which is the traditional first food. Within a week or two they are enthusiastic. But there are other babies who, on the second day, dislike the cereal more than on the first day, and on the third more than the second. If the mother persists in her efforts to force the substance in, the baby's obstinacy increases apace. When such a struggle has lasted for ten days the mother may call the physician with considerable alarm to say, "Doctor! Not only has the baby refused to take his cereal but this morning he refused his bottle too!" This example of how resistance once thoroughly aroused will spread to other areas, throws light not only on the development of feeding problems, but also on other behavior problems as well.

To prevent this battle over the first solid food the mother can be advised at the time the solid food is prescribed, "Take it easy. It will require several days, perhaps several weeks, for the baby to get familiar with and enthusiastic about this new food. There's no hurry. The only important thing is to ensure that he will eventually like it. A mere taste a day is plenty until he becomes eager."

Cereal so often causes rebellion that I have in recent years routinely suggested a fruit like applesauce or mashed banana as the first solid food. Fruit is nearly sure-fire. The baby may be puzzled for a day or two, but then almost invariably becomes enthusiastic. After a couple of weeks when he has become thoroughly prejudiced in favor of the idea of solid food, cereal can be added too. He is now in a mood to take cereal or anything else equally unpalatable. Whereas if he has started with cereal and has fought it for two weeks, he will in turn fight fruit or any other delicacy on principle.

The time when feeding problems most commonly begin is around the age of one year. The six- or nine-month-old baby is usually so hungry at mealtime that he opens his mouth and leans forward for whatever his mother puts on the spoon. Many twelve- or fifteen-month-old children lose this avidity, at least in spells. They have time to ask themselves, "What appeals to me today?" Another factor is the growing egotism and negativism which are normal and desirable developments at this age. The less ravenous appetite and the increasing arbitrariness in expressing choices bring to the surface normal and sometimes surprising variations in appetite.

The conscientious, well-instructed mother cannot "take it." She knows something about what a well-balanced meal consists of and she has been led to believe that it is her duty to get it ingested. She complains bitterly and incredulously to the doctor, "Last week he loved his spinach best of all, but today he wouldn't even touch it." The foods most commonly refused or taken in reduced quantities are vegetables, cereals and milk. These three have always seemed to the mother the very foundation of health and growth. She dare not let them be slighted. She urges or forces. The baby's obstinacy increases. It is already too late to ease the situation completely at the next routine medical visit. Mother and baby both have their backs up. Each has become disillusioned about the other. All this is hard to undo.

Don't be surprised if the baby's appetite falls off and he becomes more choosy. This is normal, otherwise he would become an obese monstrosity. He may turn against half his vegetables. Do not worry. Serve him the others. He may reject all his vegetables for days or even weeks. If this happens don't even serve them for two weeks. It will infuriate you to buy, prepare, and serve them only to have this whipper-snapper turn up his nose; and it will tempt you to try to force them. While he is off vegetables, serve him fruit twice a day. His fruit and his cod-liver oil will make up for the vegetables. He may temporarily cut down his milk intake to a pint a day or even less. A pint is enough anyway. If he goes below for any length of time you can serve it in milk puddings, milk-made cereal and cheese. His milk intake will probably go up again sooner or later if you don't turn it into an objectionable food by urging it. Instead of cooked cereal you can offer dry cereal, bread, potato, macaroni, tapioca, rice. Even if he wants none of these starches for considerable periods he will not suffer. If you will let your baby go on thinking of food as something always to be enjoyed, his nutrition will take care of itself, even though his appetite varies considerably in amount and in kind. But if during this period when he becomes more choosy you urge and force and make him feel that half the foods are his enemies, there's a good chance that you will make him thin and cantankerous.

Baby's Baths

AT LEAST twelve hours after the baby is born, and sometime before the end of the first day, most babies are given the first bath—an oil bath, which is to remove the white material left on the skin after birth. If the first oil bath does not remove all the white material, do not rub hard to get it off. If will come off at a later bath.

Some doctors, however, recommend that this material be left on until it disappears naturally. In this case it is usual to wipe the material from the baby's face and from the creases and folds of the skin with a little cotton dipped in oil, and not to give the complete bath until the baby is one or two weeks old.

After the first bath, the baby should have a daily bath of soap and water, or an oil bath if the doctor prefers this.

During the first few days of life, before the cord is off and the navel healed, the baby should not have a tub bath. After a dressing is no longer needed over the navel, a tub bath may be given. Some mothers, however, prefer to keep on giving sponge baths for some months.

Bathe the baby every day unless your doctor gives other directions.

Do it about the same time every day. It is best to do it before a feeding, and the 10:00 A. M. feeding is the one most mothers find convenient, although bathing may be done before any feeding. Do not bathe the baby within an hour after feeding him. In very hot weather it may make the baby more comfortable to bathe him twice during the day.

The room in which the baby is bathed should be comfortably warm—75° to 80° F.—and not drafty. If it is drafty a screen may be used to protect the baby. It is not wise to have the room so warm that the baby perspires.

When bathing a young baby, the mother should make sure that her hand supports both his neck and his back.

Getting Ready for the Bath

The mother should wash her hands with soap and water before picking up the baby to bathe him. She should have everything ready for the bath before taking the baby from his crib. The baby must not be left alone on the dressing table or in the tub while the mother goes off to get something that she has forgotten.

A place to put the toilet articles should be planned so that they can be reached easily. A shelf over the table may be convenient, or the top of the dresser, or a window ledge, or a separate table.

BATHING WITH SOAP AND WATER

The tub should be placed on or near the dressing table so that the baby can be moved from one to the other easily. If a tub is used, it may be placed inside or near the family bathtub; if this is done, it is usually easy to fill the baby's tub with a rubber hose attached to the bathtub faucet, and to empty the baby's tub into the family tub. Only a hose that is clean inside should be used.

The water for the baby's bath should be lukewarm (about 100° F.). Feel the water with your elbow to see how warm it is. If it feels neither hot nor cold, it will be right for the baby.

Any mild toilet soap may be used for a baby's bath. Soaps that float are likely to be convenient.

BATHING THE BABY

1. Wash your hands with soap and water, and put on a clean apron.

2. Put on table all equipment to be used.

3. Put warm water in the tub. The water should be comfortably warm when you put your elbow in it.

4. Place the baby on pad on the table covered with blanket and towel.

5. Clean baby's eyes, if needed, with cotton ball dipped in clean water, a separate cotton ball for each eye.

6. Clean baby's nose, if needed, with cotton ball dipped in water, a separate ball for each nostril.

7. Clean outside of baby's ears only.

8. Wash baby's face with water only.

9. Soap the baby's head with soap on the hand, using circular motion.

10. Hold baby's head over side of tub. Dip wash cloth in water and rinse head thoroughly. Then dry.

11. Undress baby and, until navel has healed, soap the body and wash the soap off with the wash cloth and water outside the tub. After the navel has healed, you can soap and wash the soap off with the baby in the tub. Then wrap in the towel and pat dry.

12. Care of cord: Dampen cotton with alcohol and pat cord, if still attached, or if navel has not healed.

13. Care of genitalia: Girl baby—moisten piece of cotton with oil, using downward stroke to cleanse parts. Boy baby—follow doctor's order if newly circumcised. Otherwise, gently pull back foreskin and cleanse with oil on piece of cotton.

14. Dress baby.

When everything is ready for the bath, undress the baby, leaving on the diaper, and wrap him in his blanket.

Wash the baby's face with clear water, using a soft washcloth. Lather his scalp thoroughly with your hand; then, holding him up with his head over the side of the basin or tub, dip the washcloth into the water and rinse his scalp quickly. In this way you can wash his head easily without getting soap into his eyes. Dry the face and head gently with a soft towel. Do not be afraid to wash the top of the baby's head thoroughly. By daily care "milk crust" or "cradle cap" may be prevented. (If it forms, rub in petroleum jelly or oil each night and wash the head thoroughly in the morning.)

Next unwrap the bath blanket and remove the diaper; if the buttocks are soiled, clean them with cotton dipped in oil.

SPONGE BATH. If a sponge bath is being given, soap the baby on the table. Go over his entire body gently with your soapy hand or a soapy washcloth. Be sure to wash the creases in his neck and arms, between his fingers, between his toes, and in each groin.

Rinse all the soap off the baby by wiping him with a washcloth dipped in clear water. If any soap is left on his skin, especially in the creases and folds, it may cause irritation.

When the bath is finished, dry the baby thoroughly, pat on a little oil, and dress him.

TUB BATH. If a tub bath is being given, the baby may be put into the tub and soaped in the water, or he may be soaped on the table, as with the sponge bath, and then put into the tub for rinsing.

When you are ready to put the baby into the tub put your left arm and hand under his head and shoulders, grasping his left arm at the shoulder so as to hold him securely. With your right hand holding his feet and legs very firmly, lower him gently into the tub.

After he is in the tub keep on holding him with your left hand, resting your arm against the edge of the tub. Your right hand will then be free for washing and rinsing the baby. (If you are left-handed, of course, the hands are reversed.)

If the mother prefers to soap the baby first and then rinse him in the tub, she should remember that unless a baby that has been soaped is held securely he may slip out of her hands.

As the baby gets older he usually likes to play in his bath. If a tub with a firm bottom is used, some of the water may be let out of the tub when the bath is finished and the baby allowed to lie flat on his back in the tub and kick and play for a time. Care must be taken to see that he does not splash water in his face nor turn his head into the water.

When the bath is finished, take the baby out of the tub, dry him thoroughly, pat on a little oil, and dress him.

Cleaning Special Parts

Eyes. A baby's eyes may be washed with a soft cloth when his face is being washed. They do not need any other cleaning.

Ears. A baby's ears can be washed also when his face is washed. Do not try to poke into them with anything other than a soft washcloth.

Nose. Usually the baby's nose needs no cleaning other than that which is given with the washcloth when his face is washed. Sometimes, however, a little mucus stays in the nose, and it needs to be removed. This is best done by twisting a small piece of cotton, moistening it with water or mineral oil, and inserting it in the baby's nostrils with a twisting motion of the fingers. Keep hold of one end of the cotton so that it does not get out of reach. Never use cotton twisted onto a stick or other sharp instrument.

Mouth. A baby's mouth does not need to be cleaned. The saliva keeps it clean. If you try to clean it you will probably put more dirt into it than you take out.

Genitals. The baby's genitals need to be cleaned gently with the washcloth and soap and water during the bath.

In a girl the lips of the vulva should be separated and the parts washed.

In a boy the foreskin should be pushed up so that the tip of the penis can be cleaned. This can be done by putting two fingers on the penis and pushing the skin away from the tip, much as you would work your finger into the finger of a snug glove. Clean the part of the penis under the foreskin with cotton dipped in clear water or in oil. Then gently pull the foreskin back into place. The foreskin should never be left pushed up after cleaning.

Sometimes, if a mother has trouble in learning to clean the baby's penis, her husband or a public-health nurse can show her how to do it. If the foreskin cannot be pushed up easily, the doctor should be told. He may be able to loosen it so that it can be pushed up easily. If not, the baby may need to be circumcised.

NAVEL. Wash the navel gently but firmly with a soft washcloth and soap and water.

GIVING AN OIL BATH

Plain mineral oil may be used for an oil bath. Mineral oil does not get rancid, even without special care. Vegetable oils, such as olive oil and cottonseed oil, become rancid easily, especially when the bottle of oil is warmed again and again, as it is for a baby's bath; and rancid oil is irritating to a baby's skin. Commercial baby oils are usually mixtures of mineral oil and a vegetable oil such as cottonseed oil. They are usually perfumed, and some contain a chemical that prevents rancidity but may irritate a baby's skin. They are more expensive than plain oils.

For an oil bath warm the bottle of oil by letting it stand in a basin of warm water. Pour about half an ounce of the warmed oil into a clean shallow dish into which your fingers or pieces of cotton can be dipped easily.

Get everything ready, and then put the baby on the table, wrapped in a cotton blanket. Uncover part of his body and gently wipe it with your fingers or with absorbent cotton moistened with oil. Clean the rest of his body in the same way, never leaving him entirely uncovered. Care should be taken to wipe under the arms, between the fingers and toes, and in all creases of the body.

Wipe off any oil remaining on the baby's skin and dress him. If any oil is left over throw it away.

AFTER-BATH CARE

If the baby tends to chafe or have diaper rash, oil is usually better than powder to put on him after his bath, as oil protects his skin from urine and stool. If oil is used, put a few drops in your hand or on a piece of cotton and pat it into the creases and folds of the baby's skin. Wipe off any excess oil with a little cotton. In hot weather it is better not to use oil.

If you use powder on the baby do not use much, as it may cake and irritate his skin. Wipe off excess powder, especially in the folds of the skin. Take care that the baby does not breathe in any powder. Always put your hand between the baby's face and the powder can when powdering his neck and chest.

Talcum powder is suitable for a baby, but do not use a powder containing stearate of zinc.

MAKE BATHING A PLEASURE

Usually babies enjoy the bath, but sometimes a baby dislikes it. Especially is this so if he has been frightened at some time while being bathed. Water splashed onto him, soap in his eyes, water that is too cold or too hot, and the feeling of not being firmly supported are the things most likely to frighten a baby.

Try to avoid these things, but if you find that your baby does dislike the tub bath, give him a sponge bath for a few days, each day bringing him closer to the tub and using more water over his body. Usually in a short time he will go into the tub willingly. Never force a child into a tub.

BATHING DO'S AND DON'TS

Place the dressing table against the wall.

Make sure that the tub is on a solid support and that there is no danger of its falling.

Never put the baby into the bath while the tub is standing on a stove or heater.

Make sure that the bath water is not hot, as hot water will burn a baby's delicate skin. Test the temperature of the bath water by putting your elbow into it. If the water feels neither hot nor cold it is safe for the baby.

Never bathe a baby close to a stove.

Never use stearate of zinc, nor powder containing stearate of zinc.

Protect the baby from breathing in powder of any kind. Do not let the baby play with the powder can, even when you think it is empty.

Never use a toothpick or other sharp instrument to clean a baby's nose or ears, no matter how well covered with cotton it may be.

Never leave a young baby while he is in the tub. Never leave a baby alone for a moment with the water running.

When you take a safety pin out of the baby's diaper, stick it into something at arm's length above you, such as a pincushion, where the baby cannot reach it. When safety pins are not in use keep them in a closed container where the baby cannot reach them.

Always support the neck and back of a young baby when he is not lying flat.

Remember that a baby who is covered with soapsuds is slippery and needs to be held firmly so that he will not wriggle out of your hands.

Habits Begin at Birth

WE now know that a happy and healthy child, and one who is most likely to become a well-adjusted adult, is to no small degree the product of the habits formed in infancy and early childhood.

With the young baby this centers around the forming of good eating and sleeping habits—to be followed later by toilet training.

GOOD EATING HABITS

Almost all babies enjoy eating. They learn very early in life that eating gives them pleasure. This feeling of pleasure is due not only to the relief of hunger but also to the things that go along with eating—the warmth of the mother's breast, the holding, the rocking, the human contact of being handled and cared for.

As the baby grows up the extra things he wants along with his food change. The older baby wants to hold his bottle, and the still older baby wants to help feed himself with a spoon.

Good food and pleasant surroundings are necessary for the greatest pleasure in eating, but it must not be forgotten that even more important is the need of being hungry at mealtime. If we offer a baby food at regular times we usually find that he is ready for it at these times. Before we know it, he has developed good habits of eating; this in a baby merely means that he enjoys eating at regular times.

The First Nursing

The baby's first nursing at his mother's breast is his first step in the development of his habits of eating.

To make the first nursing successful both mother and baby should be ready for it by having had a good rest after delivery (about twelve hours).

The baby will probably be hungry, and he will probably be crying. If he is brought to the mother and laid down beside her and allowed a little time he will probably nuzzle around a little before he discovers the nipple. Do not hurry him. When he is ready he will grasp the nipple with his lips and after a few experimental movements with his lips he will probably settle down to suck. The baby will not get much food at this nursing and will probably stop sucking in a short time. It is not wise to try to make him suck longer than he wants by putting the nipple in his mouth again and again or by any other means.

When he has stopped sucking offer him a drink of boiled, cooled water from a nursing bottle.

If he does not suck, it may be that he is not hungry and needs to wait a little longer before nursing.

Later Nursings

As soon as the milk comes into the breast the baby will want to nurse longer. He should always be allowed to nurse until he is satisfied or until he has emptied the breast. Sometimes a very young baby will not suck long enough to get sufficient milk. Gently rousing him will usually be sufficient to make him continue nursing. It may be necessary for the mother to try to keep him awake long enough to get enough milk.

After the mother is out of bed her position for nursing should be as comfortable as possible, so that she may relax during the nursing period. Some mothers prefer to lie down to nurse the baby; others find sitting in a chair more comfortable, especially a rocking chair.

"Burping" the Baby

After the baby has finished eating, the mother should hold him up over her shoulder and pat him gently on the back, to help him get rid of the air he swallowed as he nursed. It is sometimes three to five minutes before this air is raised. There can be no doubt when it occurs, because the baby makes a loud belching noise. If the air comes up when the baby is lying down, a mouthful of milk is likely to come up with it. This spitting up of a mouthful of milk is not the same as vomiting. Spitting up can usually be prevented by "belching the baby" after feeding.

If the baby is not nursing well, it may be because he has swallowed an unusually large amount of air and needs to get rid of it. If this seems to be happening, stop the nursing and hold the baby over your shoulder for a few minutes.

Bottle Feedings

For the baby who cannot be breast fed the first feeding from a bottle should be given in much the same way as a first feeding from the breast. The baby should be held in the nurse's arms; he should be allowed to nuzzle around, feel the rubber nipple with his lips, let go of it if he likes, and take his time in settling down to suck. He should be allowed to take as much as he wants of the milk. Later, when the mother is giving the baby his feedings she should hold him in her arms in much the same way as though she were feeding him from her breast.

Do not give a young baby his bottle while he lies in his crib, and never prop his bottle up for him and leave him alone to eat. When holding a bottle for a baby always tip it so that the nipple is kept full of milk. If the nipple is not full of milk the baby sucks in air, which sometimes makes it hard to take the milk or causes coliclike pain.

The baby who is fed from a bottle should be "belched" just as is the breast-fed baby.

Quiet, Unhurried Feedings

Whether the mother feeds her baby at the breast or from a bottle she should not be disturbed while feeding him. She should be comfortable, quiet, and unhurried. She should try to arrange her other activities so that, during the feeding time, she will not be interrupted nor called upon to attend to other matters.

The baby, to enjoy his meal, needs to be dry and comfortable, and during his early months he needs the holding and cuddling that accompany feeding.

An older baby often likes to play during the feeding period. The mother should see that the baby does not become so interested in the play that he forgets to eat. She can do this by not showing interest in the play until he has finished eating.

Feeding Intervals

Because babies are all different, each baby should be allowed to select his own times for being fed. Instead of scheduled hours, the "clock" of the baby's hunger should be the mother's guide. Babies do not get hungry at the same intervals.

At first a baby may eat very irregularly, but within a month or two most babies settle down to a fairly regular schedule, with perhaps three or four hours between feedings. The mother who breast feeds her baby can nurse him any time he seems hungry. With a bottle-fed baby feeding is not so simple. It is out of the question for most mothers to prepare as many bottles of his formula as a baby might demand, and it would be dangerous to feed him out of a bottle that had sat around half-empty for a while.

As young babies sleep much of the time, the problem of arriving at feeding times that suit both mother and baby need not be a troublesome one. If the baby sleeps for longer periods during the day than at night, his mother may find it helpful to waken him for regular feedings during the day. Coaxing him into staying awake more during the day may help his mother to get more sleep at night. If the baby wakens before the family needs to get up in the morning he may be held off for a few minutes. Bit by bit he will gradually learn to adapt to his family's needs. Babies can learn to adapt, as well as parents.

Parents must expect some irregularity at first and not be disturbed by it. When a mother feels uncertain she should not be afraid of letting her own good sense be her guide.

Not all of a baby's crying is due to hunger. Sometimes when a baby cries a short time after being fed all he needs is to be picked up, patted to relieve him of any air bubbles, and have his diaper changed. At other times a baby may go back to sleep after being turned over, talked to, or held for a few minutes.

After three or four weeks many babies begin to skip a middle-of-the-night feeding, and by the time a baby is four or five months old he may begin to sleep through the night without a late-evening feeding. Often by the end of his first year a baby is ready to change to a three-meal-a-day schedule.

Baby's Appetite

A baby will eat until his hunger is satisfied. A baby does not always want the same amount of food at each meal any more than a grown-up always wants the same amount. If the baby has been exercising vigorously he may want more than the usual amount. On the other hand, for some reason he may not want as much as usual. Trying to force him to take more milk than he wants may make eating so unpleasant that he will not be eager to eat the next time. Sometimes lasting dislikes start in just this way—forcing a baby to eat. This is more apt to happen to a bottle-fed baby than to a breast-fed one. The mother of a breast-fed baby cannot see how much milk her baby has taken, and so she is not likely to urge him to take more than he wants, but the mother of a bottle-fed baby knows how much he has eaten and may be worried if he does not finish his bottle. The baby's appetite is the best guide to the amount of food he needs.

Length of Feeding Time

The usual length of time for feeding either at the breast or from a bottle, is between ten and twenty minutes. Occasionally a vigorous baby may take enough milk in five minutes, and a feeble baby may nurse so slowly that it will take him the full twenty minutes to obtain a meal. It is usually not wise to allow a baby to nurse at a breast after it is empty. If the baby empties the breast in five minutes and still appears to be hungry he may be given the other breast. If the baby is unable to get as much milk as he wants from both breasts, he may need to be given extra milk from a bottle.

For the bottle-fed baby the holes in the nipple should be adjusted so that he will take his feeding in ten to twenty minutes. If the holes in the nipple are too small the baby will have to work so hard to get his milk that he will be tired out before he has had enough. If the holes are too large the milk will come so fast that the baby will want to suck some more after he has had all his milk. This may lead him to start sucking his fingers. Try to keep the baby awake until he has had enough milk, but do not try to force him to finish a bottle.

Starting Solid Foods

When the baby gets his first taste of cereal, he is starting a new experience. We should like him to enjoy it and to want to repeat it. Just as the first nursing is important in the development of the baby's habits of eating, so too is his first approach to another kind of food and another way of eating.

Up to the time when cereal is first given to the average baby he has never taken any food except liquids and knows but one way of satisfying his appetite—namely, sucking, from which he gets great satisfaction. When a small amount of cereal is put into his mouth he does not know what to do with it. When the spoon touches his lips it at once stimulates sucking movements, but sucking movements do not necessarily result in his swallowing the cereal. They are more likely to result in his spitting it out, because he does not yet know how to swallow it.

If the cereal stays in his mouth, you can see him feeling it with his tongue, turning it over, finding out for himself what it is. His

THE FIRST SOLID FOODS

When Baby tries new foods, do not be concerned if at first he spits them out. He needs to become accustomed to new tastes and textures — to learn how to swallow solids.

U. S. Children's Bureau Photo by Philip Bonn

SELF-SERVICE

Include foods the baby can pick up in his fingers while he is learning to master a spoon, and don't be too quick to help. Before long, the child will be managing well enough to join in a really pleasant, sociable luncheon.

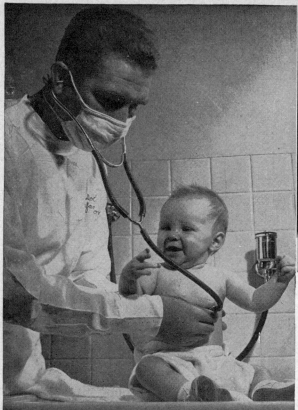

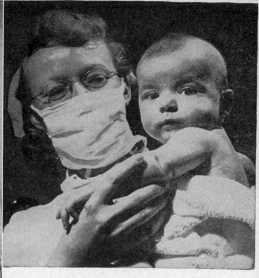

GUARDING BABY'S HEALTH

(Above) Baby's first check-up should be a complete physical examination from head to toe. Periodic examinations that follow will include checking his heart and lungs (left), examining his eyes and ears (below), and other body openings.

Three Lions

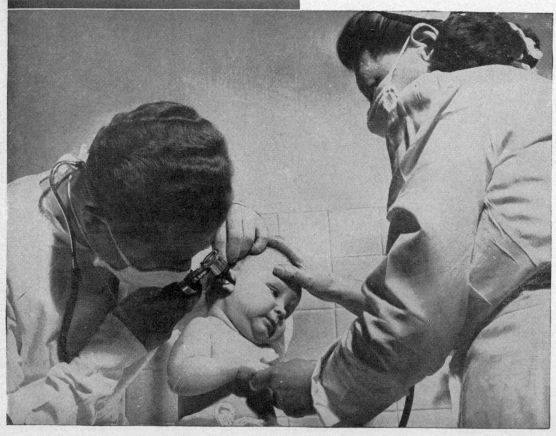

face often shows surprise or curiosity. If now you will encourage him by looking pleased and speaking of the "nice cereal" and by telling him to swallow the cereal, you will let him see that you are pleased with his attempt. If he pushes it out of his mouth with his tongue, give him another small portion to try again. Do not laugh at his funny faces. Treat the situation as a serious but pleasant lesson in eating. Praise him for trying; do not scold him for not doing it right the first time. He will thus learn to associate eating with pleasant words and looks.

By allowing the baby during his first year to get used to eating some foods that are not in liquid or semiliquid form, as an introduction to solid foods, the mother can avoid later difficulties in feeding.

When giving a new food, give only a small amount—two or three tastes the first day and four or five tastes the second day. Gradually the baby will get used to the new food and learn to swallow it. If he continues to make faces and push it out, it is because it is still new to him, not because he does not like it. He has to learn how to eat it. Whether he learns to like it or not depends upon whether he learns to associate pleasure and satisfaction with eating it. This association depends largely upon your attitude and behavior. Take for granted that he will like every new food. Offer it to him in small amounts every day until he eats it well. Never ask him whether he likes it. Do not let the expression of your face show that you think he does not like it. Do not suggest to him in any way that he may not like it. A little baby is not too young to understand your attitude, even though he may not understand your words.

Many babies learn quickly and well to eat new foods, but some babies learn slowly. Offer new foods to the baby when he is well. If a new food is offered when he is coming down with a cold and his appetite is not good, he may take a dislike to the food that will last after he is well again.

Do not be anxious nor worried if your baby is slow in learning or if he refuses to eat. If you are, the baby will know it, and he will soon learn to get extra attention from you by continuing to refuse. All babies want attention; give your baby plenty of attention when he eats well, and do not give him extra attention when he will not eat. Be patient and persistent. Do not coax. If the baby refuses to eat a food, take the food away without showing any excitement, offer it again a week or so later, and the baby will very likely have forgotten his objection to it. Always give the new food before the nursing or the bottle feeding, when the baby is hungry. Never give more than one new food at a meal. Praise him when he does well with a new food.

A baby learns to like a large variety of foods if they are given to him in such a way that he gets satisfaction out of eating them. He will not cry for foods that he has never tasted; do not let him taste foods you know are not good for him.

Time to Give Up the Breast

The change from breast to bottle feeding is a big step for the baby in growing up. Later steps will be easier if the baby finds this one pleasant.

If the change from breast to bottle feeding is made gradually so that the baby gets accustomed little by little to the new method of feeding he will take the step forward gladly. If the change is made suddenly he may resist it.

If when the time for weaning comes the baby is familiar with the bottle he is likely to be willing to take a whole bottle feeding instead of a breast feeding, once a day. He will take the bottle more readily if he is held in his mother's arms for the bottle feeding as he is for breast feeding. Otherwise he has to get used to a new position as well as to a new method of taking food.

In an emergency there may be no time for gradual weaning, and a baby may have to be taken off the breast suddenly. If this happens every effort should be made to make the sudden change as easy as possible for the baby. It will help to make the weaning easy for him if the nurse, or whoever gives him the bottle, holds him in her arms while feeding him.

Holding the Bottle

Many babies like to hold the bottle when they are seven or eight months old. When this happens it means the baby is growing up and is beginning to want to take a more active part in his world. At first the baby puts his hand out and touches the bottle in his mother's hand; later he grasps it, and finally he holds it some of the time—though he is apt to tire before the feeding is finished. Still later the baby may wish to hold the bottle entirely by himself. When this stage is reached the baby may be given the bottle in his crib. The bottle should be taken away from him as soon as he has emptied it.

Some babies never want to hold the bottle. If your baby does not want to hold it, do not try to make him do so.

Learning to Use Cup and Spoon

When a baby sees his mother using a spoon to feed him he usually wishes to use one also. Let him have a spoon—even if he is messy. The joy that a baby gets from directing a bit of cereal into his mouth is taking the place of the joy he got when he was younger at being held in his mother's arms at feeding time.

While the baby is struggling to get a few bits of cereal into his own mouth, the mother may sit near by and use another spoon to get the rest of it in. Sometimes a baby wants to put his food into his mouth with his hands. Let him do it occasionally. It adds to his joy in eating.

A baby likes to hold his cup, as he likes to hold his spoon. Steady it for him but let him do as much as he can.

When a baby seven or eight months old is being weaned his milk may be given him in either a bottle or a cup. Many babies at eight or nine months learn at once to drink from a cup, and thus will not need to learn to give up the bottle a few months later.

Sometimes giving up the bottle for the cup is a big problem for the baby. Let him take his time about it. Offer him a cup and let him play with it. Let him have a few sips from the cup just to become familiar with it. Soon he will want to take more and more milk that way. It makes little difference at exactly what age bottle feeding is given up for good. It makes a great deal of difference to the baby's future mental and emotional health that he does not feel cheated out of something important to him, but that he does feel that he is giving up a baby way for a grown-up way.

GOOD SLEEP HABITS

Habits of sleep develop in much the same way as habits of eating. A tired baby learns that sleeping is pleasant. If we make him comfortable—by feeding him, by making him dry, and by adjusting his covers to the temperature—and if he is tired he will go to sleep, and we shall soon find that he has developed the habit of sleeping at regular times.

Sleep habits, like eating habits, so easily established in early infancy, will be maintained only if the baby continues to get satisfaction out of them.

If a mother disturbs her baby's sleep by waking him up to show him off to friends or to go out with her she soon finds he does not want to go back to sleep.

He first learns to associate going to sleep with the pleasant feeling of food and warmth and sleepiness he had after his meal. He does not associate going to sleep with the uncomfortable feeling he has after being waked up and disturbed. If this happens often he may not wish to sleep immediately after his feeding. And his mother will complain, "The baby just won't go to bed at six," or "The baby won't go to bed until I do."

How Much Sleep Does a Baby Need?   Just as some babies need more food than others of the same age, some need more sleep. This is to be expected, for every baby is a little different from every other. It is not possible to make exact rules as to how much sleep babies need.

As a rule a very young baby sleeps from twenty to twenty-two hours of the twenty-four; a baby one or two months old, about eighteen to twenty hours. When the baby is about six months old, he is likely to sleep fifteen to seventeen hours—twelve hours at night with only one interruption for feeding, two or three hours in the morning, and one or two hours in the afternoon. Some babies need less than these amounts of sleep; some need more.

During most of the first year the baby usually requires one long nap and one short one during the day. Soon after the first birthday, or even before then, most babies give up the short nap and have one long nap a day in addition to the night's sleep.

When a baby gives up the short nap it is usually time to put him on a three-meal-a-day schedule. The long nap may then be taken before or after lunch.

Some Sleeping Don'ts

Don't give the baby any sort of medicine to make him sleep, except under the doctor's orders. All soothing sirups and other similar preparations contain drugs that are bad for a baby, and many of them are exceedingly dangerous.

Don't take the baby up after he has gone to bed to show him off to visitors.

Don't take the baby out in the evening to movies, nor for an automobile drive. Good habits of sleeping cannot be maintained unless the baby is put to bed every night at the same time. A baby who is taken out in the evening not only loses some part of his long, unbroken sleep, but he may be over-stimulated by lights and noise and may be exposed to persons with colds or other communicable diseases.

Don't leave the baby alone in the house during the daytime or at night, not even if he is sound asleep.

Don't let the baby get into the habit of going to sleep with a bottle.

TEACHING BOWEL AND BLADDER CONTROL

Sometimes a mother's eagerness to have her baby learn to keep clean and dry leads her to begin such training before he is ready for it. She may often succeed in having him move his bowels into a vessel, and she may cut down the number of diapers she has to wash by holding him over a pot to urinate after he has slept or eaten, but she must not get the impression that he is being trained. For until a baby is ten or twelve months old, his nervous system is not enough developed to enable him to form any association between the act of voiding and his feeling of need. Until he has reached an age when he makes this connection, any real training is impossible.

When a baby can sit alone easily and has bowel movements at a fairly regular time, which will probably not be much before nine months, bowel training may be begun. If, however, the baby's regular time of evacuating is disturbed by attempts to get him to use the toilet, so that he begins soiling himself at odd hours, training should be discontinued for a month or so and started again when a regular time is again established. A mother's overemphasis on cleanliness or the frequent use of suppositories sometimes results in a child's acquiring the habit of constipation.

When a baby begins to show that he understands when you praise him for moving his bowels or urinating while on his toilet seat, it is time to begin real training. This means putting him on the toilet at certain regular times—when he wakes in the morning, just after each meal, before and after naps, and at intervals in between. Keeping a record for a few days of the hours at which he is wet or has had a bowel movement will help in planning a schedule so as to anticipate his needs.

When the baby begins to walk, diapers should be discarded for pants. Many children seem to grasp more easily the idea of going to the toilet for emptying the bladder when they wear pants instead of diapers.

Children usually learn night control of the bladder between the second and third birthdays, after control during the day is well established. The mother must remember that as she is trying to establish the "dry" habit it will not help to leave the wet clothing on. If the child wets himself by accident the pants or diaper should be changed at once. He should be praised when he keeps dry. He should not be scolded when he has an accident. (See page 232, Avoiding Behavior Problems.)

INFANT THUMB SUCKING

Thumb sucking or finger sucking develops in a great many babies during the first year, most frequently between the fourth and tenth months of life. A baby explores everything within his reach. He looks at a new object, feels it, squeezes it, and almost always puts it into his mouth. He knows how to suck because he has learned to get his food in that way, and naturally he sucks on whatever he puts in his mouth.

Frequently the baby discovers he can suck his fingers, and so the habit of thumb or finger sucking develops. Usually the child will outgrow the habit unless too much fuss is made over it.

If a baby sucks his fingers it is sometimes helpful in the very beginning to see that he is allowed to suck longer during his meals than he has been doing. The breast-fed baby may be allowed to stay at the breast an extra few minutes; the bottle-fed baby may be fed by means of a nipple with somewhat smaller holes, so that it takes a little longer to get the milk.

Keeping the hands occupied with some toy is an excellent way of diverting his attention from sucking. Punishment or restraint is never helpful.

HANDLING GENITALS

Babies want to handle and investigate everything that they can see and reach. When a baby discovers his genital organs he will play with them, and he learns that pleasant sensations can be had by handling his genitals. A wise mother will not be concerned about this, and will not punish the baby.

The baby will not spend much time handling his genitals if he has many other interesting things to do. As with thumb sucking, sometimes an older baby persists in handling his genitals because he gets comfort and pleasure from doing it. Giving him comfort in other ways will help.

PLAYING WITH STOOL

Almost all babies will play with their stool if they have the opportunity. This is natural during babyhood and it will be outgrown. Don't scold a baby for doing it; just clean him up as soon as he has a bowel movement.

Avoiding Behavior Problems

A STORY of a stormy battle over weaning will often be found in the past of children with behavior disturbances—suggesting that the kind of resentment created by this particular struggle may be unusually long-lasting and bitter. Certainly the pediatrician is familiar with the common complaint that a feeding problem centering around milk started abruptly at the time of an attempted weaning to the cup.

WEANING CONFLICTS AND THUMB-SUCKING

How should weaning be managed and at what age? Experience suggests that there is no simple or single answer. Babies are born with a strong instinct to suck quite apart from the instinct of hunger. In some babies this desire to suck appears to weaken and disappear in the last half of the first year. Others seem unwilling to begin to give up sucking until the first half of the second year. The baby will show in various ways how ready he is for weaning from breast or bottle, and it seems fair that his readiness should be the main guide of parent and physician. If one questions mothers of eight- or nine-month-old infants about their attitudes toward the bottle, toward the cup, and toward thumb-sucking, the answers fall between two extremes. Of one baby the mother will say, "He seems to be bored with the bottle. Half the time he only chews on it or plays with the nipple. When I offer him milk from a cup he takes it enthusiastically. He isn't doing any thumb-sucking." At the other extreme is the baby whose mother says, "Oh, Doctor! How he loves his bottle. All the time he is eating his food, he is watching the bottle out of the corner of his eye and when it's time for the bottle, he's all eagerness. He clutches and fondles it while he's drinking and always finishes it to the last drop. He's very suspicious of milk in the cup and will take only a sip at most. It's not that he doesn't know how, because he takes his orange juice well from the cup. He is doing a lot of thumb-sucking." Many babies of course fall between these two extremes, and the thumb-sucking is not necessarily so highly correlated with the other signs of sucking need.

For the sake of the discussion let us consider the two clear-cut types. The baby who at eight or nine months is getting bored with breast or bottle and is taking milk eagerly from the cup seems ready for weaning and it would seem entirely proper to tell his mother, "Gradually over a period of weeks, put more and more of his milk in the cup at each meal until the bottle is done with." Another gradual method is to substitute the cup for the bottle first at breakfast, then at lunch, then at supper, allowing a couple of weeks between each change. If during the process the baby shows reluctance to go further, the mother should follow his cue. There is often a temporary increase in the desire to suckle during illness, during the miserable stage of teething, or during any episode which upsets his spirits.

If the baby at nine months still loves his bottle dearly and is suspicious of milk from the cup, present-day teaching emphatically advises against attempting to force the issue. Experience with forced weaning shows that many babies will react violently with an absolute and often long-lasting refusal to tolerate the cup. An occasional baby will go on a complete hunger strike for several days and another may become generally resentful and hostile. It is true that many babies who have been deprived of a bottle against their wishes, will, after holding out for two or three days, apparently decide to let bygones be bygones. But one cannot tell ahead of time which will give in and which will remain adamant. From the sharp distinction that many a baby makes between orange juice and milk from the cup, it is clear that he is not primarily suspicious of the cup itself. He apparently feels deeply that milk from bottle or breast has been and still is his chief emotional gratification and perceives that milk-in-cup is a threat to its continuance.

It will help to prepare the infant for eventual weaning to offer him a sip of milk a day from the cup beginning at five months. At that age he will try almost anything. At ten months he has become wise enough and opinionated enough so that he is apt to object to anything newfangled on principle. Unfortunately, however, the babies who seem destined to be long suckers may take the sip a day for several months and then turn sharply and indignantly against the cup at about the age of ten months.

If a baby falls into the group of those who are still devoted to the bottle and suspicious of the cup at nine or ten months, the chances are good that he will stay of the same opinion until he is at least fourteen or fifteen months. Then he will relent gradually. But even when initial progress is good he is apt to want the supper bottle for several months more. It is important that during this age of suspicion of the cup, between, say ten and fifteen months, the mother refrain from urging the cup or withholding the bottle, since this seems to increase his dependence on the bottle and postpone his readiness for weaning.

Thumb-sucking is obviously related to the sucking instinct and the problem of weaning. Until recent years it was universally considered just a bad habit which ought to be broken quickly before it became ingrained. We now know that the baby sucks his thumb because he has not had full satisfaction from the breast or bottle; that babies whose bottles take a long time to empty are less apt to thumb-suck than those who drink their milk quickly through large nipple holes, and babies who have few nursings in the twenty-four hours are more apt to thumb-suck than those who have frequent nursings. I have repeatedly seen thumb-sucking begin at the period when an infant was able to reduce his bottle time from twenty to ten minutes because of his growing strength and the aging of the nipple, or when he was suddenly weaned to the cup at an early age. I have the impression that there are two other etiological factors. First, there seem to be wide constitutional differences in the amount of sucking craving in different babies. Second, the important time to insure complete sucking satisfaction is in the first three or four months of life. Many babies are unable to get their thumbs into their mouths except by accident before the age of three months and therefore can give their mothers only vague signs of their unsatisfied craving at the period when correction is most vital. Incidentally thumb-sucking that occurs only just before feeding seems to be merely an expression of hunger.

If thumb-sucking in early infancy is primarily the result of a deficit in sucking satisfaction at breast or bottle, the prophylaxis and treatment should consist in providing longer and more frequent opportunities to nurse. For the breast-fed baby this means allowing him to nurse as long as he feels the urge rather than stopping at any arbitrary number of minutes. Sometimes a baby taking both breasts at each feeding and being removed after ten minutes on the first, stops spontaneously after five minutes on the second because he is too full (with the initial copious flow), even though he has not had his quota of sucking. In a few cases this can be solved by prolonged nursing at only one breast. But if the milk is insufficient at least the baby can be allowed to nurse much longer on the first breast before being shifted to the second.

Just as soon as the bottle-fed baby begins to suck his thumb, or, more important, shows signs of *trying* to, one should inquire whether he has recently been able to drain the bottle in a shorter time and suggest a new set of nipples with smaller openings.

Occasionally one can suggest more frequent feedings in the young infant if he is willing to take them and his mother to give them. Few mothers, however, take kindly to the idea of reverting to a three-hour schedule unless they are excessively alarmed by thumb-sucking. It is sensible though, when the baby is beginning to thumb-suck, to advise against omitting the 10:00 P.M. and the 6:00 A.M. feedings for a while longer, even though the baby seems ready for the change in other respects.

If the feedings are lengthened or made more frequent and the thumb-sucking still persists, the hypothesis that the baby is trying to make up insufficient nursing time will dictate emphatically that no effort should be made to interfere with the thumb-sucking. The aim, of course, should be to give the baby every opportunity to suck by any means that he can use.

By the time a baby is a year old thumb-sucking appears to be no longer primarily a need to satisfy the sucking instinct but has become a comforter. He no longer sucks it a certain number of minutes every day but only on special occasions: when he is going to sleep, when he is fatigued, when he is frustrated, when he is bored. There is no longer any point in trying to increase his nursing time. The constructive thing with the one-, two-, or three-year-old child is to survey his daily life to see whether he has enough playthings, play space, and playmates to make life absorbing. Is he being treated at home in such a way that he feels secure and happy? Whether or not constructive changes can be made in his daily routine and handling, it seems wise to advise the parents to make no direct efforts to stop the thumb-sucking. The normal tendency is for the child to give up the habit gradually as he acquires inner security and interest and absorption in the world around him. Efforts to stop the habit from the outside, whether they consist of physical restraints, punishment. nagging, or teasing, seem only to increase the child's need of his thumb. Sometimes a child who has practically given up thumb-sucking does it only when a certain relative is near by who has always made most fuss about it. We all know dozens of cases where every form of physical restraint and moral intimidation were used without beneficial effect. If the parent objects to this *laissez-faire* attitude toward thumb-sucking on the basis that the teeth are being made crooked, the answer again is that letting the child alone is often the quickest way to stop the thumb-sucking and the threat to the teeth.

A physician might summarize his discussion with a mother about weaning and thumb-sucking as follows: "Every baby is born with a strong instinct to suck. The intensity and duration of this instinct seem to vary in different individuals. We should consult the baby about the time for weaning from the breast or bottle. One infant at nine months is bored with the bottle, enthusiastic about milk from the cup. He seems ready for gradual weaning. Another at the same age rejects the cup and shows a deep devotion to the bottle. He may not be ready until fifteen months or later. Do not force for fear of making him balky or resentful. Urging may prolong his dependence on the bottle. Thumb-sucking in the early months suggests that the infant is not getting sufficient suckling satisfaction at breast or bottle. At the first sign try to prolong the nursing time and to retain frequent feedings. By the age of one year thumb-sucking appears to have become a comforter when the baby is tired, bored, or frustrated. Constructive treatment consists in insuring that his life is as happy as possible, counting on him gradually to give up the habit as fast as he is able. In a persistent case efforts to interfere directly seldom succeed and may prolong the habit."

BOWEL TRAINING

There is a widespread but unfounded belief that good health is acquired through meticulous regularity of bowel movement. In order to get the baby started early on this mythical road to health, and also for the sake of general elegance, it has become the style in our twentieth-century American civilization to put a lot of effort into and to take great satisfaction from early and rigorous toilet training. Often to the parents' despair training has broken down at a later stage of the child's development and the child has resisted retraining until an abnormally late age. The psychoanalysts have felt that in certain individuals these over-vigorous training efforts created permanent distortions of the personality.

In the early months of infancy the movement of the bowels is a fairly simple reflex. It is true that when the reflex evacuation occurs at a predictable time of day the assiduous mother can catch the movement in an appropriate vessel. But it is more the mother who is trained than the baby. As the infant gets into the second half of the first year and acquires voluntary control of the lower half of his body, he acquires more voluntary control of the bowel movement too. For instance if the mother rushes him to the potty too abruptly he may become startled and cease pushing. As he gets into the second year he acquires not only further control, but also a genuine interest in the movement as well. He turns around to see what he has done, babbles about it, even plays in it if he has not been inhibited. He gradually takes a possessive proprietary attitude toward it, brings his mother in to admire what he has done.

Each of us has been told by at least one happy-go-lucky mother that her baby trained himself to the toilet in the second half of the second year without her making any effort. The child, naturally, in the course of his social development reaches a stage where he wants to deposit his movement in the same place that the rest of the family use, just the way he wants to use his mother's toothbrush or mop.

Observation of children trained for the bowel movement at different age periods suggests that the age at which the baby is first set on the toilet is not of primary importance. There are babies trained early who stay trained without gross evidence of personality distortion. There are babies trained early who rebel during the second year and suffer tragic changes in character during the prolonged conflict with a severe parent. And among the babies whose training has been postponed until after the age of twelve months some get into trouble and others do not. It seems to me that the most important factors are *how the mother goes about it and how the baby feels about it during the second year.*

If during the second year when the baby is becoming more possessive of his movement a stern and exacting mother is going at his toileting hammer and tongs, it is clear why a conflict will occur. It is as if the grim mother were saying by her behavior, "It isn't your movement, it is mine. You must produce it for me, when I say, where I say." This seems to offend his sense of proprietorship and arouses the negativism which is his handiest weapon at this period. It doesn't take an outrageously demanding mother to start a conflict during the second year. Many babies at this age get so sensitive about their rights and interests that they rebel against minor degrees of maternal insistence.

There are other factors in toilet rebellion besides the mother's demanding attitude. Of vital importance is the comfortableness of the bowel movement. The baby who has had painfully hard movements on frequent occasions will naturally dread the toilet seat as soon as he learns what is expected of him there. The request, "Now do your duty," when translated by his experience means, "Now hurt yourself." It is no wonder that he resists sitting down, or if sitting, that he procrastinates. I believe that a large proportion of the babies who resist training come from the group who have had painful movements. This puts on the physician the responsibility of carefully preventing or curing all painful constipation throughout the first two years of life.

Another factor of great importance is whether or not the infant is naturally regular. The baby who always moves his bowels within ten minutes after the first meal of the day is practically never a training problem. He moves so quickly and thoughtlessly that there is no reason for his mother to become insistent. It is when the movement occurs without any regular rhythms that the mother is tempted

to become overstrenuous and demanding in her efforts to put him
on the toilet often and to keep him there for long periods, to use
strong disapproval when he fails, and to act as if he had redeemed
himself when he succeeds.

There are three common forms that the resistance against training
takes. The first is reluctance to sit on the toilet or even to go into
the bathroom. The reluctance may be mild and transitory or it
may develop into violent rage and terror. Another baby is more
subtle and polite. He may sit down willingly but nothing happens
so long as he is on the toilet, whether he is kept there five minutes
or fifty. The movement occurs promptly after he has gotten up.
Mothers complain, "He seems to have forgotten what he's put there
for." But a baby who has been performing well for several months
does not forget that easily. There is more indication that he has
moved on to a new phase of awareness and resolved to get matters
back under his own control. The third form that resistance commonly takes is for the infant to retain his movement not only while
he is on the toilet but afterwards, too. He acquires a constipation of
purely psychological origin. The retained movement, however, becomes hard and painful to pass. He now has two reasons for withholding.

At this stage the determined mother is apt to use suppositories or
enemas. Almost invariably this intensifies his resistance and alarm.
A suppository used for two or three days in the first stages of toilet
training may not be harmful though some would prefer not to use
them even then. But suppositories or enemas after the child has
begun to resist training are dangerous in the extreme and should
never be recommended.

What does happen to a small child's personality in the course
of a long struggle against training? He is first of all made unduly
obstinate and hostile. This in itself is an unfortunate influence at
such an impressionable age. But worse than the hostility is the insecurity which usually keeps pace with it. The small child cannot
consistently defy his mother without becoming uneasy and guilty
and this throws his whole personality out of balance. Such is the
case when a boy of four has developed a compulsion to touch constantly the seat of his pants and then sniff his fingers. He is obsessed

with the fear that he has soiled his pants even though he has not actually done so for a couple of years. In less dramatic form it shows up in the little girl who runs crying to her mother every time she gets a speck of earth on her hand. The fear that was impressed on her in the earlier training period has spread to include dirtiness in any form.

One might summarize a sensible discussion with the parent about bowel training as follows: "It is normal for many individuals to move the bowels irregularly. Do not try to change this as long as the movements are comfortably soft. Every child gradually acquires control of his bowel function and becomes willing to dispose of his movement in a way that is locally conventional. You do not need to become concerned about this process. It seems unnatural to do anything before the baby can sit up. It is important to keep his bowel movements soft so that he will not dread defecation. When you begin to put him on the chair or toilet do it casually and briefly. This means putting him on it at just the right moment, an easy job with the regular baby, but one calling for ingenuity or postponement of the whole program when the movement comes at any time of the day. Do not make it a moral issue. Between one and two years it is normal for the baby to acquire a proprietary interest and pride in his movement. During this period he may show resistance to your efforts to capture his movement. He may object to going to the bathroom or wait until he gets up to move his bowels, or become constipated. Relax your efforts gracefully until he feels more cooperative. Your persistence, especially if you resort to suppositories or enemas, will only increase his rebellion and distort his personality."

BLADDER TRAINING

Control of the urinary bladder, like control of the bowels, is something which the child gradually acquires by himself through physiologic development. The most that the parent can accomplish is to persuade the child to void in the conventional receptacle a little earlier than the child would have gotten that idea by himself. During most of the first year the bladder retains little urine and voids frequently though there is considerable variation in different individuals. A great majority of babies do not retain their urine for as long as two hours until they are approximately fifteen months old. By this age they have usually acquired enough conscious awareness of urination to comprehend the purpose of toileting if the mother has gone at it in a sensible way. At this period, however, the mother has to take all the responsibility. The child becomes aware of what is about to happen only a few seconds ahead of time and participates voluntarily only to the extent of standing still. During the second half of the second year he shows increasing voluntary control. If his mother has been teaching him that she expects the urine to go into the toilet, he now retains the urine for a few seconds beyond the stage of comfort and may signal his mother with some sound that signifies urgency. He may on the other hand forget to warn her until it is too late. Most children still need to be watched and reminded into at least the first part of the third year.

Night control is not usually acquired until after the child has taken over the responsibility of keeping himself dry during the daytime. But as should be pointed out to parents, retention of urine at night is a normal development in the inherent maturing of bladder function and has little to do with whether the child is picked up during the evening. It is true that a dry bed is secured a little earlier if the long night interval is broken. But the child would not be caught dry, either at 10:00 P.M. or 7:00 A.M., unless the bladder were already tending to longer and longer retention. That it is not the parents' training efforts that make the child dry at night is shown in another way by the rare child, usually a girl, who jumps the gun and becomes dry at night before the age of a year and before her parents have made any move at even daytime training.

What are the causes of delayed control both day and night? First of all there is the apparently wide variation between individuals in the maturing of bladder function as is shown not just by individual cases but by the observation that on the average boys are slower than girls.

Training itself, if it is done in the wrong spirit, sometimes works to postpone voluntary control. The child between one and one and a half who is rigorously set down once an hour and kept there for long periods sometimes rebels against this unnatural imprisonment and becomes firmly determined never to void in the proper place. This resistance shows up more often in prolonged night wetting. A two-year-old son of ambitious parents is at first caught dry about half the time at 10:00 P.M. and 7:00 A.M. The eager parents redouble their efforts and pick him up at 9:00 P.M., midnight, and 6:00 A.M. At first their zeal is rewarded but after a few weeks of this night work, coupled with exhortations and admonitions during the day-time, he gets wetter and wetter. Instead of being warned by these negative results the parents resolve to torture themselves and the poor child even further and take turns getting him up every two hours right through the night. Again there is partial success at first. But after a while the boy's resistance becomes so ingenious, even in his sleep, that he wets before two hours are up.

At least in some individuals tension and uneasiness of many kinds seem to be readily communicated to the bladder, rendering it less capable of relaxing and of retaining urine. It is common for the two- or three-year-old who has been dry at night for six months to begin wetting again temporarily when he moves to a new house, or when his mother leaves him to go to the hospital, or when the new baby sister comes home, or when he is frightened by a dog, or after he has gone to the circus. If almost any kind of emotional disturb-ance, small as well as great, can cause a child to relapse temporarily into enuresis, it is easy to see why a child who lives in a constant state of tension during his early years never has sufficient equanimity or inner relaxation to become dry in the first place.

When the physician is consulted because a young child is still wetting his bed, the first question should be whether there are ten-sions operating to postpone the child's normal inherent progress to dryness. In one case the child needs only a little more time to feel at home in a new situation. In another the friction between himself and his parents centers around a feeding problem. More commonly it is apparent that the mother's handling all day long is characterized by pushing, nagging, and unnecessary interference. Occasionally the only problem is that the parents are expecting perfect control at an age when a good proportion of children are still wetting regularly or intermittently. Certainly if the parents are going at the enuresis by intensive methods that are bringing diminishing returns they should be called off. This is done not with the promise that this new technique will bring immediate success, but that in the long run it will work in the right direction. In the meantime less harm will be done to the child's personality.

The physician is often troubled with the question of whether he should recommend a complete urological examination. There are cases, of course, where the symptomatology or the results of urinalysis demand further investigation. But in a great majority of cases of slow bladder control there is no reason to suspect an organic cause. The point is that hospitalization, anesthesia and instrumentation, with or without pain, are all alarming to small children. This danger should be given serious consideration in deciding whether or not to investigate further.

One might summarize a discussion of urine training with the mother as follows: "Urine training is largely accomplished by the child himself. The child's bladder, through a normal process of maturing, comes to retain urine for longer periods. Simultaneously the child acquires a conscious control of voiding. Your baby, if he is average in this respect, will, in the neighborhood of a year and a quarter, begin to retain his urine for about two hours at a time. He will also be wise enough at this stage to see what you are after when you put him on the toilet. If you put him on only when he is dry after two hours, you will insure three things: (1) His bladder function is ready for cooperation. (2) His bladder at that moment will be full. He will urinate soon. Therefore you will not have to antagonize him by keeping him on for a long time. (3) Your training efforts will be gradual since you will only find him dry occasionally at first. After some months he will begin to take the responsibility of telling you when he needs to urinate. In time also his bladder will learn to retain urine throughout the night. Inner security and emotional relaxation are necessary for this progress of bladder function."

BENJAMIN SPOCK, M.D.

The Baby Grows and Develops

I T IS almost impossible to realize the changes that will take place in a helpless, newborn baby in a few months. During his first year he will grow faster than at any other time in his life. He will develop so rapidly that before you know it he will be pulling himself up, exploring everything he can reach, showing his likes and dislikes, and become an active member of the family. All babies follow the same general path of development, although they may differ considerably in the age at which they reach certain places in the path. As a baby's body grows in size he learns not only how to do certain things but also to understand what goes on around him.

The baby has great curiosity and he tries to satisfy it by looking, listening, smelling, tasting, handling.

As the baby develops he moves different parts of his body and gains more and more control of it. At an early age he finds he can raise his head. He also finds out how to use his hands. At first he moves his whole arm; later he learns to take hold of objects with his hands.

He also finds he can make sounds. At first he makes them by accident, but slowly he gains control over his voice and makes sounds at will. Much later he combines the knowledge he has gained by listening to the people and things about him with his own power to use his voice, and he begins to imitate what he hears. That is how he learns to talk.

Some force within the baby makes him develop in these ways. But his full development depends not only upon this inner drive to learn and to act, but upon influences outside himself. No person can act entirely according to his own needs or desires. Behavior is influenced by circumstances and by the actions of other persons.

244

This is true even in earlier babyhood; the baby soon learns to adapt his behavior to the conditions and people in his home.

WEIGHT

The baby changes in weight rapidly during his first year—more rapidly than at any later time in his life.

In the first few days after birth all babies lose some weight. It takes a few days for the baby to become accustomed to life outside his mother's body; during these days he does not take much food, and consequently he loses some weight.

After the first loss in weight the normal baby begins to gain and gains rapidly throughout infancy.

Babies vary a great deal in the number of ounces they gain from month to month and also in the amount they weigh at any given age.

How much any baby should weigh at a given age depends upon such things as—

THE SIZE OF HIS PARENTS. If both parents are large, it is to be expected that their baby, too, will be large and will therefore weigh more at each age than will the baby whose parents are small.

THE TYPE OF BODY OF THE CHILD. The long, slender baby will not weigh so much in proportion to his length as the short, chubby one, even if both are healthy.

THE SEX OF THE CHILD. Boys are a little heavier than girls.

It must not be thought that because a baby does not weigh as much as some other baby of the same age he is sick or undernourished. He may be light because he is naturally a small person.

If a baby does not gain weight, or loses, or suddenly begins to gain very rapidly, the doctor's attention should be called to it. Keep a record of your baby's weight; it is only by comparing his present weight with his previous weight that the doctor can tell whether or not he is gaining as he should, considering his age and sex, his body type, and his race and family.

It is a great mistake to compare your baby's weight with the weight of a friend's baby. Your baby and her baby are different. You can expect at least as much difference between the babies as exists between you and her, or between your husband and hers.

TEETHING

The teeth begin to develop about six months before birth and keep on developing during the entire period of childhood. Nearly all the teeth of the first set—the deciduous or milk teeth—are already partly or wholly hardened at birth. As the baby grows the teeth grow also; and if he is healthy, some teeth begin to cut through the gums at about the sixth to the eighth month of life. From then on new teeth appear at intervals, until the baby is about two and a half years old when, as a rule, all the twenty teeth of the first set have come through.

By the end of the first year many babies have six front teeth although some healthy babies have only two. If a year-old baby has no teeth at all the doctor should be consulted. The diet may be at fault, or some disease may be slowing the baby's growth; racial and family traits may account for delayed teething.

There is a good deal of difference in the age at which the various teeth come through the gums, but the order in which they come is the same for almost all babies. First the two lower front teeth appear; then after a time the four upper front teeth. After this, it is usually some months before more teeth come through. Then two more lower teeth appear in the front of the mouth. In a few months two teeth appear in the lower jaw—one on each side—near the back; then two in the upper jaw, opposite these. Later four eyeteeth come through—two upper and two lower. After a while the four back teeth come through, and then the temporary set of teeth is complete.

While a tooth is coming through the gum the baby may be irritable or fretful and may not eat well, but teething alone rarely accounts for illness. The illness should not be attributed to teething until all other possible causes, such as a cold, an abscess in the ear, and other diseases, have been ruled out by the doctor.

The permanent teeth develop during the last months before birth and during the first year of life, though they do not come through the gums until the sixth to the tenth year. Whether they will be strong and firm depends largely upon the food the baby gets while they are forming. If the child is to have good permanent teeth—straight, strong, and regular, with upper and lower sets meeting to form a good chewing machine—his baby teeth must be kept in good condition. He needs his baby teeth to chew his food and hold the jaws in shape so that the permanent teeth will have plenty of room. Exercise in biting and chewing helps to develop strong, healthy teeth and jaws. When the baby is about eight months old begin giving him some dry, hard bread or toast at the end of a feeding but watch him carefully until he learns how to eat hard food.

The child's gums should be smooth, firm, and a light pink color.

HIS SENSES DEVELOP

A baby learns by seeing, hearing, tasting, smelling, feeling. Some of these things he can do well at birth, others not until later. As these powers develop they give the baby increasing ability to learn about his world.

SEEING. Babies do not see very much soon after birth. Some of the special kind of cells that are used for seeing are not fully developed in the baby's eyes at birth. Gradually, during the early weeks of life, these special cells develop; and by the time the baby is three or four months of age his eyes are more or less complete, and he is able to see shapes and colors fairly well.

Even before complete vision has developed the baby shows that his ability to see is increasing. He fixes his eyes on his mother's face and follows a moving light with his eyes by the first or second month. Soon after this he shows that he recognizes familiar objects—he opens his mouth when a feeding is offered, and he stops crying when his mother leans over him, before she picks him up.

HEARING. Unlike seeing, hearing is well developed at birth. A very young baby is easily startled by noise and will show fright at a loud sound. Babies learn to distinguish between sounds at an early age, and they respond to sounds long before they are able to understand speech. A baby learns that the soft voice of his mother is associated with being made comfortable. Often when a baby hears his mother's voice he will stop crying in anticipation of the comfort to come. Most babies enjoy being sung to, and they seem to respond to singing when only a few weeks old.

TASTING AND SMELLING. It is probable that babies are able to taste their food. Most babies seem to prefer sweet-tasting substances, but sometimes a baby is found who seems to prefer sour milk.

Smelling probably is well developed at birth. Young babies seem to notice the odor of milk and will root about with their mouths to find where it comes from.

FEELING. Babies feel pressure and pain, they feel heat and cold, they are uncomfortable when their stomachs are empty. Even a very young baby is aware of various sensations and will cry if he has disagreeable ones, but it is not until he grows older and his brain and nervous system develop that he is able to tell, for example, the difference between discomfort due to hunger and discomfort due to a pain in his ear.

LEARNING TO DO

As the baby is becoming aware of his world he is also learning to do things. He develops the ability to move his arms and legs at will, to change his posture, to stand, and finally to walk. He develops also the ability to make sounds and later to control these sounds so as to make words. These things and many others are not taught to the baby; he develops to the point where he can do them.

A new ability appears as soon as the nerves and muscles concerned are developed enough to permit them to work together. Just as before birth, in the mother's uterus, the baby begins to kick as soon as he has developed sufficiently, so with advancing development after birth he begins to creep, stand, and toddle.

The ability of babies to learn to do things depends partly upon their ability to take in what goes on around them. The baby who is born deaf and never hears anything does not develop the power of making sounds that mean anything.

The normal baby, however, develops more and more skill as his growing body responds to the drive from within and the stimulation from without.

The way a baby holds his body depends first upon the strength of his muscles and secondly upon the development of his nervous system.

The first muscles to come under the baby's control are those of the head and neck; next come the muscles of the arms and chest.

The muscles of the feet and legs are the last to be brought under control.

HOLDING THE HEAD UP. When a newborn baby is lying on his abdomen he can usually raise his head from the bed, but he cannot keep it up; his head bobs up and down and finally rests again on the bed. When lying on his back a newborn baby is not able to raise his head at all because the muscles in the front of the neck are not so strong as those in the back.

At about one month of age the baby, when lying on his abdomen, can, as a rule, hold up his chin, and a little later he can lift his head by raising his chest. Soon after this he can lift his head and chest from the bed by putting his weight on his hands. During the third or fourth month most babies learn to lift the head when they are lying on their backs. At this age a baby is usually able to hold his head up without support for four or five minutes if he is in a sitting position with support at his back, but he soon gets tired.

SITTING UP. By the time a baby is four or five months old he usually begins to show some interest in sitting up, although at this age the large muscles of his back are not strong enough to support his weight and he is apt to slump over to one side when he is in a sitting position. If given proper support so that his back is erect, a baby of this age can sit up for fifteen or twenty minutes. Many babies enjoy this change in position. Considerable care must be taken, however, to see that the baby does not become tired and that he does not slump over. When sitting up he needs not only support at his back but also a firm surface under him—a firm mattress, the floor, or the floor of a play pen—not a soft cushion.

At about seven or eight months a baby can usually sit alone without support for a short time. At this age he is beginning to be able to pull himself back into a sitting position whenever he topples over.

CREEPING. At about five months of age most babies learn to turn over, first from the stomach to the back and later from the back to the stomach. Some babies roll over and over and manage to move a considerable distance in this way.

When the baby is placed on his stomach he kicks and squirms and sometimes discovers that he can push his body forward by movements of his arms and legs. Sometimes the movements of the arms may actually move him backward with a sort of swimming movement. He does not move rapidly in either direction by this method. Gradually, as the baby gets older and his muscles become stronger he learns to move about by raising himself from the floor—first on his hands, later on his hands and knees, and still later on his hands and feet. Movement about then becomes much easier as he learns to use his hands and feet alternately. This going on all fours is similar to the walking of animals.

Some babies never creep but move themselves about by other methods before they learn to walk.

LEARNING TO STAND. As the baby gets a little older he will try to put all his weight on his feet and to stand up.

Children vary a good deal in the age at which they begin to stand. Some will try to stand as early as seven months. Some may not attempt it until as late as ten or eleven months. Never urge a baby to stand; he will do it himself as soon as his muscles are strong enough to support his weight.

When the baby first begins to stand alone he will keep his feet far apart to give himself balance, he will try to dig his feet into the floor, and he will hold his arms out to balance himself. At first he will fall many times because he is top-heavy and has not learned to balance his body.

Soon after a baby has learned to stand he will try to walk. At first he will hold to some firm support with both hands. Later he will need support with but one hand. It is often a long time after a baby is able to walk well when holding on to something before he will finally give up the support and walk alone.

GRASPING. A newborn baby will grasp a finger or a rod if it is placed across his palm and will hang on to it with enough strength to support his weight. This act in the newborn is automatic, and the ability to perform it is lost after about two months. Toward the end of the first year he will again be able to grasp objects with similar strength, and then the act is under control of his will.

TALKING. By about the sixth week of life or a little later the vocal cords come sufficiently under control of the brain to enable the baby to make cooing sounds. At first the baby makes these sounds at random, but soon he is able to make them at will. When babies discover that they can do this they usually spend much time practicing their newly acquired skill, and they then find that a variety of sounds is possible. These cooing and "ah-ing" sounds are like the movements of the arms and legs in that the baby discovers by himself that he is able to make them. He is not taught to do it; he develops to the point where he can do it.

BECOMING A MEMBER OF THE FAMILY

In the first few weeks after birth what the baby does depends almost entirely upon his physical needs, but before long he begins to notice and respond to his environment, which includes the people around him. He learns to adapt his behavior to that of the family. It is with respect to this type of development that parents have their greatest role in helping their children.

From the time of the baby's birth some of his desires are met with resistance; for example, his desire to satisfy his hunger. When he becomes hungry and begins to root around for something to suck, and then begins to cry, his mother cannot always be prepared to feed him immediately. The baby must get used to waiting for his food. He will suck his fingers, he will cry, but he will wait. Each conflict between his desire and his environment means that some adaptation must take place.

If the baby does not have to wait too long for his feedings when he is hungry, or for a change of his diaper when he is wet and uncomfortable, he will probably adapt himself easily to the idea that there cannot be someone dancing attendance upon him at every moment. But if, time after time, he has to endure discomfort a long while without relief, though he may finally become accustomed to this state of affairs, the adaptation may be slow and difficult.

Easy adaptation helps the baby to grow into a happy, likable member of his family; difficult adaptation is apt to result in habits of resistance toward everything and everyone around him. Parents can help the baby to develop a happy, pleasant personality by fitting his daily schedule and other things about him as nearly as possible to his needs, so that he will not be called upon to make adaptations that are too difficult for him.

A newborn baby has emotional needs; and if these needs are met his adaptation to the world is easier than if they are not. He needs, for example, to be made to feel safe and secure. If a baby does not feel safe and secure he is apt to develop ways of behaving which are really an effort to get the sense of security he needs. A child who is spoiled, who is constantly demanding attention, may be the child who is afraid because he does not feel safe and secure.

A baby needs to be loved; he needs to be picked up and cuddled occasionally; he needs to snuggle down in the warmth and comfort of his mother's arms. At feeding time, especially during the early months of her baby's life, the mother has a good opportunity to hold and fondle him, and it is at these times that the baby feels the love and comfort he needs.

SOCIAL DEVELOPMENT

Usually the smile begins to appear about the end of the first month of life, and in the course of a few days after the first few mouthings it becomes the full-fledged toothless grin of babyhood. Through his smile, especially when it is combined with the gurgling and cooing noises of developing speech, the baby makes friendly human contact with the people about him. The baby learns that he is able to please his mother with his smile and his gurgles, and he soon learns that this kind of behavior brings him pleasure, too. This is the beginning of the baby's adaptation to people.

Later the baby learns that other behavior of his produces the same kind of pleasant response not only in his mother, but in others too, and so he repeats that behavior consciously in order to get the response he likes. He learns to imitate people, and he finds that it pleases them if he tries to play pat-a-cake or peek-a-boo in imitation of their motions. As the baby learns new accomplishments, he will persist with those that give him most satisfaction, and his satisfaction comes partly from the accomplishment itself and partly from the interest and approval of those about him.

MANAGING THE ANGRY BABY

The times when your baby will be most likely to show anger during his first year will come when you have to restrict his activity while you dress him or wash his face, when he has to wait for his food, or when he wants something he can't have. A problem he can't manage, like getting his foot caught under him in his high chair, is another cause of anger.

All these are times when he feels thwarted. All through life the natural thing is to feel anger when we are thwarted, or when our freedom is interfered with. So it's an important responsibility for parents to help babies learn to manage their anger.

When a baby doesn't know what else to do, he flies into a rage. He can't help it: his body must get rid of the extra energy that anger has stirred up in it. At first he has no other way than the natural one of wild screaming or hitting out.

We can help in two ways. We can keep down the number of occasions when he's severely thwarted, and, when he must be, help him to learn better ways of managing his anger than by kicking and screaming. This can only come gradually, as he grows. Offering just a little help when he gets in a pinch—like turning the milk bottle upside down so the toy he's dropped in will come out again—will give him a hint about how to go to work on a problem, instead of getting angry.

If we keep a baby's days simple, we cut down the number of times he's likely to get angry. Some of the ways of preventing anger are: dressing him quickly; not keeping him waiting long to be fed or changed; and giving him only those toys he's not likely to have trouble with. We'll do ourselves and him a service if there aren't a lot of forbidden things around for him to get into. Keeping him out of trouble is much easier than smoothing things over afterward.

When we first see temper in a baby, we don't always stop to think he's going to need this force in his life. He'd be easier to handle if he always gave in to us, never showed spunk or a will of his own. But the energy anger arouses will help him many times to do away with obstacles—if he learns to use it right.

Anger can be fruitless and exhausting. The baby who gets so

angry he bangs his head on the floor or holds his breath is not learning a good way out of trouble. But he may be learning to get what he wants, because he frightens his mother.

Showing Anger by Breath-Holding

Breath-holding itself is nothing to be concerned about. When an angry baby holds his breath until he is blue in the face, no wonder his mother is alarmed. It looks as though he would injure himself. But he won't.

When a baby's lungs need more air, he *has* to take a breath. His body's reaction is automatic, beyond his control. So don't worry if he holds his breath. What you do need to be concerned about is not letting him have his own way when he shouldn't. For if this happens a few times, the baby finds he has discovered a way of lording it over you. For a little creature who is ordinarily helpless among big powerful adults, this is quite a find. No wonder he uses it!

Perhaps breath-holding would never happen a second time if a baby's mother simply turned her back and walked away when her baby began to hold his breath over something she couldn't safely let him have or do. Quickly turning his attention to something interesting is another way to handle breath-holding.

A baby who bangs his head on the floor in his angry moments won't injure himself. Like the baby who holds his breath, he will stop sooner if he has no audience.

Frequent show of temper in a baby should serve as a warning signal to his parents. They might ask, "Is he being told 'No! No!' too often? Being opposed too much? Are we giving enough of *ourselves* to the baby? Do we put more effort into taking things away from him than into finding things he might learn about through touching, tasting, and handling? How about the routine things we have to do for and to him every day, like washing his face, and putting him to bed? Are they being done in a way that he finds easy and pleasant to submit to?" Another thing you may want to consider is whether someone is hurrying to pacify him at every least display of temper. It won't hurt a baby to get rid of his unreasonable temper by crying a little, but punishment for anger only makes him crosser.

Even in his first year a baby is beginning to form patterns of behavior. The way his natural explosions of anger are handled can incline him to feel and act rebellious, or good-humored.

DEVELOPMENT IN FIRST TWO YEARS

THREE MONTHS:
Holds up head if supported, discovers hands, recognizes parents.

SIX MONTHS:
Sits up with support, turns over and begins to crawl, reaches for objects with both hands, laughs.

NINE MONTHS:
Sits erect alone, pulls self up on play pen, reaches with one hand, recognizes voices, has two teeth.

ONE YEAR:
Stands with support (walks twelve to seventeen months), plays with blocks and ball, holds cup and spoon, understands when spoken to, has six teeth.

TWO YEARS:
Runs, is steady on feet, helps dress and undress, feeds himself, hears music, tries kiddie car, has twelve to sixteen teeth.

Taking the Baby Outdoors

A BABY should get as much fresh air and sunshine as possible but that does not mean he should be taken outdoors in all kinds of weather. He will be better off in a well-ventilated room than outdoors when the weather is either extremely cold or hot.

IN COOL WEATHER. After two months it is all right to take the baby outside if the sun is out and there is no wind blowing. Wind does more harm than is usually thought. It stirs up the dust which is laden with all sorts of bacteria. Remember that the baby's resistance in the early months has not been built up.

IN COLD WEATHER. Under two months of age, it is better not to take the baby out of doors. After two months, always use the middle of the day to take the baby out. If it is very cold, then do not keep the baby out for more than fifteen minutes at a time. In bad weather you can give the baby plenty of fresh air by opening the window in his room and either using the ventilator or putting a screen in front of the open window.

SUNSHINE: Sunshine contains the valuable vitamin D. Also, it contains the ultraviolet rays, which are so helpful in changing some of the mineral elements of the body into bone formation, which is vital to the child's welfare. To get the maximum benefit of these rays, the sun must shine directly upon the skin. Window glass and clothes filter out most of the ultraviolet rays.

In most parts of the United States babies cannot get enough sunlight throughout the year to provide them with all the vitamin D they need.

Even in summer, in most places it is difficult to give a baby enough sunlight, for some days are cloudy and some are so hot that the baby should not be exposed to the sun very long. Some localities are so smoky that the babies get little benefit from the sun at any time of the year. It is best, therefore, for babies to get vitamin D not only from sunshine but also from some other source.

Vitamin D can be given to babies by using a special kind of lamp that produces ultraviolet rays or it can be given them by mouth in foods or special preparations.

A sun lamp should not be used without the advice and supervision of a doctor. Sun lamps are relatively expensive and for most babies it is just as satisfactory to give vitamin D in food or special preparations. For many years cod-liver oil has been the principal food for supplying vitamin D.

SUN BATHS

SEASON OF THE YEAR. Naturally only in warm weather can the

TAKING BABY OUTDOORS

When a baby is properly clothed, cold weather need not keep him indoors. The best time to take him out is the middle of the day. However, if it is very cold, the baby should not stay out longer than fifteen minutes.

SUNSHINE AND VITAMIN D

baby should get as much sunshine and fresh air as sible. A play pen that provides plenty to do and see l keep the older baby occupied for an hour or so. by should always be protected from the wind. oid direct, hot summer sun in middle of day.

Right: U. S. Children's Bureau Photo by Philip Bonn

THE NEW BABY AND THE OLDER CHILD

It is natural for an older child to be jealous of a new baby. Besides preparing him for the baby's coming, parents must make him feel that his place is *not* being usurped by another. Letting him help with the baby's care will show him that the baby is also his, and helps to relieve his fears.

baby be exposed unclothed out of doors. This also depends upon your geographical location. Always protect him from the wind. In hot weather, great caution must be used not to burn the baby. His delicate skin cannot take too much sunshine at one time. In the hot summer months do not go out in the extreme heat of the day; do not expose the baby longer than five minutes on each side of the body. In the shade there is no reason to limit the time that much. It is the direct rays of the sun that are the active ones.

If your baby is fair, with thin, white skin, be especially careful. Slight reddening and tanning of the baby's skin will show that he is benefiting from the sunshine, but not all babies tan, even in the sun. Gradually both the time the baby remains in the sun and the amount of his body exposed can be increased. But it should be remembered that too much sunlight may be harmful to the skin.

The baby's eyes will not be injured by sunlight unless the rays enter his eyes directly. If the baby lies with his feet away from the sun and his head slightly raised, his eyes will be protected by his forehead and eyelids. A baby old enough to sit up will protect his own eyes by turning and bending his head. As the baby gets older, much of his playtime can be spent in the sunshine, with few or no clothes in summer and with suitable warm clothes in winter.

BABY'S TOYS

A baby wants to suck and bite everything, and therefore all his toys should be of the kind that can safely be put into his mouth. They should be washable and should have no sharp points or corners. They should be so large that they cannot be swallowed, and they should not have bells or whistles that can come out and be swallowed. Rubber or bone toys are excellent.

When a baby's rattle is old it may come apart, and the little stones in it come out. Be sure to discard a rattle before this happens, as the baby might choke on one of the stones if he got it into his mouth.

Some painted toys are unsafe because if the baby sucks them the paint will make him sick. Before buying painted toys inquire whether the paint used is harmless to babies.

If floating celluloid toys for the bath are bought, it should be remembered that the very light ones break easily. When celluloid toys are broken, throw them away at once; the sharp edges of such a broken toy are dangerous to a baby.

Be careful that the string you tie toys to the crib with isn't long enough to get looped around the baby's arms or head.

Don't worry for fear your baby will pick up germs from his toys. Most of the germs on the toys will be his own, and won't hurt him. If other children use his toys, wash them often. Plastic-covered toys are easier to keep clean than cloth-covered ones.

Have a place to keep his toys so that they will seem freshly interesting when you get them out. Give him only a few things at a time to play with, as he will explore their possibilities better that way.

Some of the things you can make are:

Stuffed animals (when stuffed with discarded nylon stockings they can be easily washed and dried).

Large wooden beads or spools, strung on a stout shoe lace and tied securely.

Blocks cut from odds and ends of wood, and sandpapered to remove roughness and sharp edges.

Older babies like things they can "put into and take out of." Many such playthings cost nothing, like a milk carton to put clothespins in and dump out again, or different sized cans vegetables came in (the tops removed with a can opener that leaves the edges smooth). A baby needs very few bought toys. He enjoys the pans, big spoons, lids and pails he pulls out of the kitchen cupboard as much as anything you could find in a store.

A Word About "Sitters"

EVERYONE agrees that parents need an occasional evening out if they are to be cheerful, well adjusted people. Arranging for a responsible person to stay with the baby is sometimes a problem. The practice of "baby-sitting" is quite well established in most communities but the supply of competent sitters is seldom equal to the demand. In cities where bureaus have been organized to furnish trained and dependable persons at specified rates per hour this service may be used with confidence. Elsewhere the parents must make all necessary arrangements for themselves.

A FEW GOOD SUGGESTIONS

1. If the sitter is someone you don't know personally, make sure she (or he) —whether adult or teen-ager—has references from someone you do know, or from an employment agency that you can trust. (Because a person or an organization advertises in a newspaper does not mean that the person or organization is necessarily trustworthy.)

2. Always ask the sitter to come, the first time, long enough ahead of the time you expect to leave so that you can get acquainted. A reliable sitter will want to have time for careful instructions about what she is expected to do and what not to do. She should be given the following information, some of which you should write down:

Telephone number where you (or some responsible person) may be reached

Telephone number of your doctor

What time you will return

What to feed, at what time, where, and how

The routine you follow in changing the baby

What to do if he cries

Where extra clothing is kept

How to regulate the heat in the house

3. Except in the case of a very young baby, under four months, give the baby a chance to see and get used to the sitter beforehand. This is especially necessary if he is going to be asleep when you leave. The terror a baby may feel when he is old enough to tell people apart and wakes to find himself with a stranger is something no child should be exposed to. Babies of from four to six months are beginning to be quite conscious of strangers, and some of them are very timid about being held by them, or even approached.

The sitter should know something about how you handle the

baby, the order in which you do things, for example, and under what conditions you pick him up and rock him if he cries. This will make taking care of the baby easier.

4. Be as considerate of the sitter as you want her to be of you. This means paying her at a fair rate, being careful to get back when you say you will, and seeing that she gets home safely if it is late.

In return, you can require certain things of her, such as that she shall let you know in advance if she can't come; that she shall not come if she has a cold; that she shall not entertain friends during your absence without having first asked your permission.

It is good for a baby to have his mother leave him sometimes. We usually say it the other way around—that it's good for the mother. But it is also good for your baby to learn that he can be independent of you, and still be happy.

THE WORKING MOTHER

A mother who must leave her baby in someone else's care during the whole day, or some part of it, feels happier about it if the baby is handled in much the same way that she would handle him.

It can be taken for granted that the fewer differences there are in a baby's care, the more comfortable he feels. For example, if a person puts the baby's shirt on over his head, when he's used to having his mother put it on over his feet, it may bother him. Or, suppose the person caring for the baby during the week holds him and rocks him to get him to go to sleep. In such a case, he will probably cry if he's not rocked when his mother takes over during the weekend.

The baby will be easier to take care of if he is not confused by changes. Of course no two people will do things in exactly the same way. They can agree, though, on some of the main features of the baby's care. No one sets out to make it hard for the baby's mother. If each watches how the other does certain things, like bathing and feeding, it will make it easier. Written instructions about some details of the baby's care will be helpful. Let the baby get used to the caretaker before you leave him. If he shifts gradually from you to the new person he won't feel anxious when you go.

Your main concern is that the person who cares for the baby shall be warm and motherly and really enjoy babies. A mother should try not to be jealous of the affection her baby gets to feel for his part-time "mother." Instead, it is important for her to be glad the relationship is so good he can feel this way. There may be times when the baby acts as if he liked his caretaker better than his own mother. This is upsetting. But try to remember, if you find this happening, that it is necessary for a young baby to trust those who take care of him.

It is hard on a baby to have frequent changes in the person who cares for him. It is worth a good deal of effort to find someone who you are pretty confident can stay for a fairly long period if you have to have a caretaker.

If you should have to board your baby away from home, be sure the home you pick out meets the standards set by your state health and welfare departments.

Child Care and the Doctor

CHILD care is perhaps the most important task any parent ever undertakes. The parents have a responsibility not only to their child but also to the community to see that the child grows into an adult who can use fully all the talents and capabilities that he had within him when he was born. The father shares the responsibility with the mother. From the baby's birth they work together to see that this most important job is well done.

A young mother and father need the doctor's help in planning for the health of their baby.

It is desirable that the doctor, who will be the mother's main guide in caring for her baby, be one who is trained in the care of children. In some communities there are no doctors that specialize in the care of children, and in such places the family doctor will advise the mother.

The way a mother will go about selecting the doctor will depend on whether she intends to have a private doctor—whether a specialist or a general practitioner—or to go to a clinic or child-health center.

If a mother intends to have a private doctor supervise the care of her baby, she must find the right doctor.

After the mother has picked out a doctor—and it is a good plan to do it before the baby is born—she should have a talk with him about (1) when he wants to see the baby, (2) under what circumstances he wishes her to get in touch with him by telephone, and (3) what to do in case of emergency. She should talk over with the doctor what will be cost of his services. It is best to have a definite understanding with him on this subject.

If a mother intends to go to a clinic or child-health center and if she lives in a place that has a local department of health, the simplest thing to do is to telephone to this department and ask where the nearest child-health center is and when it is open.

In small communities a county or a district health department can generally be reached, either by telephone or by mail; or, if there is a public-health nurse in the community, the mother can ask her for the information.

Baby's Examinations

Throughout the baby's first year he should be seen regularly by a doctor, preferably a pediatrician—a doctor trained in the care of children.

During the first half of the baby's first year visits to the doctor should be made at least once a month; during the second half, at least every two months.

At these visits the mother will have an opportunity to talk over the baby's diet with the doctor and also any problems that have arisen since the last visit.

Even if there are no special problems, the doctor will want to know at each visit what has happened to the baby since the last visit. It will be helpful to him if the mother is prepared to answer such questions as the following:

Has the baby been well? Has he had any diseases? Any accidents?

Has he been active and playful? Or listless and cross?

Has he been eating well?

Have his feedings been given regularly?

What has he been fed? Is he getting cod-liver oil or some other good source of vitamin D? Is he getting orange juice or some other source of vitamin C?

Does he vomit or spit up his food?

Do his bowels move regularly? How often? What do his stools look like?

Does he sleep well? How many hours? Is he restless during his sleep?

Have any other members of the household been sick?

It will help the mother as well as the doctor if she has written down whatever she thinks she should tell him and any questions she wishes to ask him, so that she will not forget about them.

The doctor will make a thorough examination and from his findings and what the mother tells him, can judge whether or not the baby is growing and developing as a healthy baby should.

Sometimes the doctor may want to examine the baby's urine. If he does he will tell the mother how to collect it.

Sometimes he may want to make special tests to find out things about the baby he cannot tell in any other way.

At some time during the baby's first year he will recommend that the baby be given protection against various diseases.

The doctor will keep a record of his findings each time he examines the baby, so that at later examinations he can compare them with the previous ones. This helps him to judge how the baby is growing and progressing and to keep in mind any unusual conditions that he wants to watch.

After the examination the doctor will talk to the mother about the condition of her baby and will make suggestions about his care. If the mother needs further instruction to help her carry out the doctor's suggestions, she can, in many communities, get such help from a public-health nurse.

Avoiding Disease During Infancy

Doctors list four ways of protecting a baby from most diseases: (1) Making sure he is fed enough clean, nutritious, digestible food. (2) Keeping him away from sick people. (3) Inoculating him against disease. (4) Keeping the mother in good health before he is born and while he is nursing.

EATING THE PROPER FOOD

CLEAN FOOD. Food may look quite clean, may even taste all right, but still it may have so many germs in it that a few mouthfuls will make a baby seriously ill. Germs may get into a baby's food in many ways.

The germs that cause the most trouble in a baby's food come from human beings, although germs from animals may also make the baby sick.

Disease germs from the nose or throat of someone handling the baby's food may be carried into his food by a fine spray, which is constantly being thrown into the air from people's noses and throats, especially when they cough or sneeze. If these germs get into the baby's milk they will grow. If the milk is warm they will grow very rapidly.

Disease germs from human beings get into a baby's food in two ways: (1) They are carried on the skin of people who do not wash their hands after going to the toilet; (2) they are carried on the feet of flies, which feed on human filth and then walk over food, leaving footprints of contaminated material.

Disease germs may come from any animal; those from cows cause the most trouble in babies' food. Milk for babies should come only from tuberculin-tested cows, and no raw milk should be given to a baby. To safeguard the baby against these infections only pasteurized milk should be bought.

When the weather is hot, special care is necessary to keep milk free from germs. Most of the danger for which hot weather is blamed, especially during weaning, can be avoided if the baby's milk is free from germs.

Not only milk but everything else that the baby eats must be clean; that is, free from harmful germs. All the food must be protected against flies, rats, and mice. Food, especially cooked food, should never be left where any kind of animal can touch it.

Anything that is not clean contains germs. For this reason everything that comes into contact with a baby's food should be clean. Every cup, spoon, or other utensil that touches a baby's food should be boiled before it is used.

The mother should wash her hands thoroughly before preparing the baby's food and before feeding him.

Nutritious Food. The baby's food must be adequate in quantity and contain all the substances necessary to make healthy tissues.

If a baby's food is inadequate in total amount, or if several of the substances necessary for health either are absent or are inadequately supplied, general malnutrition develops. General malnutrition can be prevented by making sure that the baby receives all the necessary food substances in sufficient quantity.

If a baby's food does not supply enough of any one of the necessary substances a deficiency disease, such as rickets and scurvy, may develop. These diseases can be prevented by making sure that the baby receives enough of the right foods.

Easily Digested Food. Not only must a baby's food be clean and be adequate to nourish him, but it must be such that he can digest it. Babies are not able to digest all the foods that grown-ups can digest.

KEEP HIM AWAY FROM SICK PEOPLE

Babies are very susceptible to diseases that they can get directly from sick people. A baby should never be taken to visit a sick friend, especially if the friend has a cough. No one who is ill should be allowed to go near a baby. No one, not even the mother, should ever kiss the baby on the lips or breathe into his face.

Guarding Against Colds. A mother should take every precaution to protect her baby from colds. It sometimes takes tact and firmness for a mother to prevent well-meaning friends from playing with the baby. Whether a person has a cold or not, he should not lean over a baby nor breathe into his face.

When the mother has a cold, it is sometimes very difficult to protect the baby adequately. If it can possibly be arranged, someone else should take care of the baby for a few days until the mother has recovered. If this cannot be arranged, the mother must take as much care as possible not to allow her breath to come near the baby. She should use a gauze mask or tie a handkerchief over her nose and mouth when she handles the baby and, of course, she should wash her hands carefully before touching the baby or his food.

When a baby has a cold the mother should see that he has the proper treatment and that he does not spread the cold to others. She should keep other children away from him and should not allow him to cough in her face.

Family epidemics of colds are difficult to prevent; the only way to prevent them is to keep the sick members of the family away from the well ones.

PREVENTING TUBERCULOSIS.   Tuberculosis of the lungs is a serious and often fatal disease in infancy. Babies get tuberculosis of the lungs by being near a person who has tuberculosis. To prevent this type of tuberculosis in a baby, keep him away from anyone who has the disease, even if it is his mother or father or some other relative, and from anyone that has a cough.

If any member of the household has the disease, either that person or the baby should be removed from the home. If the mother has active tuberculosis when the baby is born, he should be taken away at once. She should neither nurse him nor take care of him. Babies should be kept away from any person with a chronic cough, since frequently such a cough is due to tuberculosis, whether recognized or not. Many mothers, not knowing that old persons have tuberculosis, fail to keep the baby away from an old person with a cough.

PREVENTING GONORRHEA.   Diseases transmitted through the nose and throat are not the only ones that babies can get directly from other people. The delicate mucous membranes in the eyes of babies

and in the vagina of baby girls are places where the germs of gonorrhea grow rapidly. The germs may get on the fingers of an adult
who has the disease in an active form, and the germs may be transmitted to the baby if such an adult takes care of the baby. This
disease is serious. If it is in the baby's eyes and is not promptly and
adequately treated, it may cause permanent blindness; if in the
vagina, it may cause considerable trouble for the baby and danger
to others. Mothers should see that no one in the household, including
employees, has active gonorrhea. If the mother is aware that anyone
in the house has a discharge from the genital region, she should see
that that person is examined by a doctor.

If the baby's eyes are inflamed, the doctor should be told.

Employing Help. If the mother plans to have someone help
her in the care of her baby, she should hire only a person who will
not infect the baby. Before a helper is engaged, it is a good plan for
the mother to have her examined by a doctor. The important things
to guard against are diseases of the lungs, especially tuberculosis, and
active gonorrhea or syphilis.

INOCULATION

Every baby should be inoculated against diphtheria and smallpox.
Under certain circumstances a baby should be inoculated against
typhoid fever. If the doctor recommends it a baby should be inoculated against whooping cough and tetanus (lockjaw).

Suggested Plan for Immunization

1. Have the baby vaccinated against smallpox at three months of
age.

2. Have him vaccinated against whooping cough at seven months
(three injections).

3. Have him immunized against diphtheria at nine months (three
injections). Tetanus immunization may be given at the same time.
Have a Schick test made six months to a year after the diphtheria
immunization is given.

Caring for the Sick Baby

IT usually rests with the mother to decide whether her baby is sick and there is need to call the doctor.

If the baby is being seen regularly by a doctor he should notice any slowly developing signs of disease before the baby becomes seriously ill. It is the mother, however, who will be most likely to notice any sudden change that indicates the need for medical care. She knows her baby better than anyone else and will be the first to recognize any change in his usual behavior or appearance. For example, she can tell whether he is more restless in his sleep, more irritable, or eating less than usual. She knows when he has a running nose or coughs, and should recognize a skin rash, diarrhea or vomiting as warning signs. At any of these signs she should take his temperature and if it is above 101° she should put him to bed and notify the doctor.

If he is hoarse, has convulsions, or there is blood in his stool she should telephone the doctor immediately.

WHAT TO DO BEFORE THE DOCTOR COMES

1. Put the baby in a bed in a quiet, cool place where he can easily fall asleep.

2. Keep other children away from him.

3. If the baby is vomiting or having diarrhea, stop all food but offer him small amounts of boiled water frequently. If he continues to vomit stop giving even water for a while. At the end of two hours if the vomiting has stopped, try giving him some boiled water, and continue giving it to him frequently so long as he does not vomit it.

4. If the baby is neither vomiting nor having diarrhea give him as much or as little as he wishes of his regular feeding of milk. Never try to make a sick baby eat.

5. Save the baby's stools for the doctor to see.

6. Take his temperature every four hours.

7. Keep a record on paper of—

    a. The baby's temperature each time it is taken.

    b. The times he passes stool.

    c. The times he urinates.

    d. The times he vomits and the amount vomited.

    e. Anything else you think important.

8. Do not give medicine.

How to Take a Baby's Temperature.　Every mother should learn how to take a baby's temperature. It is a good idea to buy a thermometer and learn how to use it when the baby is well. Then if he should get sick the mother will be able to take his temperature with the least possible disturbance to him.

Buy a rectal thermometer (one with a thick bulb). Ask the doctor, the druggist, or public-health nurse to show you how to read it and how to shake down the mercury.

Before taking the baby's temperature, read the thermometer and be sure the mercury is well below the normal mark. Smear the bulb of the thermometer with petroleum jelly or cold cream. Place the baby downward on your lap, separate the buttocks with one hand and with the other put the bulb end of the thermometer about an inch into the rectum (the place where the stool comes from) and leave it there for three minutes by the clock. Keep the baby quiet and hold the legs firmly so that the thermometer will not break. Do not leave the baby nor let go of the thermometer while it is in the rectum. At the end of three minutes take the thermometer out and put the baby back in his crib. Read the thermometer and write down the baby's temperature and the time of day it was taken.

Wipe off the thermometer, wash it thoroughly with *cold* soapy water (hot water will break it), and finally rinse it and put it away.

The Meaning of Temperature.　A baby's temperature normally ranges from 98.6° to 99.6° F. If it is 101° F. or higher, the doctor should be notified. A baby is more likely than an adult to have fever when he is ill, and when he has fever it is likely to be higher than that of an adult. A rise in temperature frequently accompanies even a slight upset. A daily rise in temperature, even if slight, that lasts a long time is often just as important a symptom as a higher temperature that lasts a short time. It may be even more important. A baby who is sick may have fever at any time of the day or night, but it is likely to be higher in the evening than in the morning.

After a baby has been sick for some time his temperature in the morning may be subnormal; that is, below 98.6° F. When this occurs the baby needs special care to keep him from being overtired.

GIVING AN ENEMA. For an enema, use a bulb syringe with a soft-rubber tip holding two to three ounces of water. Put one-half teaspoonful of salt into a glassful of warm water. To fill the syringe, put the tip of it into the glass of slightly salty water, squeeze the bulb while holding the tip under water; then release it and it will fill by suction. Let the baby lie on his back across your lap or on a table with the buttocks somewhat raised by a folded towel under his hips. (This position will cause the water to run up into the bowel more readily, and the towel will catch any drip.) Grease the tip of the syringe with petroleum jelly. Lift the baby's legs with the left hand and with the right put the tip into the rectum for about an inch and slowly squeeze two or three ounces of the water from the bulb. If gently and slowly done, this causes the baby little or no discomfort, though if he is badly constipated the starting of the bowel movement may be somewhat painful.

When the water has been put in, take out the syringe and hold the buttocks together for a few minutes to keep the water in before placing the baby on the chamber. The water sometimes comes out as the syringe is taken out and therefore the mother's clothing should be well protected. If the first enema does not bring a bowel movement, give another one.

Occasionally the water does not come out. If this happens do not worry. The water will do no harm.

A soap stick or other suppository may be used instead of an enema. Neither enemas nor suppositories should be used over long periods, as they may irritate the rectum.

CHILDHOOD ILLNESSES. The causes, symptoms, and treatment of the common ailments of childhood are discussed at length later in this volume. Consult the Index, under the name of the specific illness.

For Baby's Protection

Do not ever leave a baby alone in the house, whether he is awake or asleep. It is equally dangerous to leave him in the care of small children or to let a child take him out in a baby carriage. Never leave a baby alone while he is in a bathtub.

If parents wish to go out in the evening, they should have a responsible person—not a child—stay with the baby to meet emergencies. Parents may be able to arrange to take turns with other parents in staying with the children.

If the baby is to be kept safe everyone in the family should see that nothing is brought near him that might injure him. The other children should be trained to keep scissors and knives out of his reach, and the younger ones should be trained to let matches alone, for their own safety and the baby's.

A play pen will keep the baby away from many dangers.

Never use a baby powder containing stearate of zinc, because if stearate of zinc is inhaled, a serious and often fatal form of pneumonia develops. Never give a baby a can of baby powder as a plaything, even one that seems to be empty. If he puts the top in his mouth, he may inhale the powder.

The mother should keep her fingernails and the baby's short and smooth so that the baby will not be scratched, and she should have no unprotected pins or needles in her clothing or anywhere near the baby.

The mother should not put pins in her mouth, for if an older baby sees her do this he may do it too.

SMOTHERING. Special precautions should be taken to prevent smothering. Babies have been smothered when in bed with an older person who, while sleeping, rolled onto the baby or pulled the covers over him. A baby should sleep alone. Sometimes a baby is smothered when his head becomes buried in a feather pillow or a feather bed; neither of these should be used for a baby.

CHOKING. Straps for keeping the baby in bed and drawstrings at the neck of sleeping bags and outdoor garments have caused chok-

271

ing as a result of their getting twisted and tight around the baby's neck.

The baby may choke on any small object. For this reason small toys and toys with small parts that might come off, such as whistles, should not be given to him; small objects such as beads, coins, and pins should be kept away from him; and he should not have small hard things to eat, such as peanuts.

BURNS. To prevent burns, which are far too common among babies, keep the baby away from such dangerous things as heaters, hot liquids, and flames of all kinds. Older babies frequently are burned as a result of pulling at tablecloths and upsetting hot coffee or soup. A fire screen is necessary if an open fire is used.

Make it a habit to turn saucepan handles toward the back of the stove.

Part Three

ONE TO SIX YEARS OLD

What Makes a Good Home

WHAT children need more than anything else is a home where parents like children and enjoy them. This means far more that just liking to play with them. It means taking time to study a child's interests. It means helping him develop step by step, whether in skills with hands and body, making friends with others his own age, or delving into the world of books and ideas. It means listening to a child and trying to understand his language. It means giving close attention to changes, knowing how and when the child's growth is best served by helping him, and when he's better off if left alone.

Parenthood at its best is not a set of rules but an art calling for a sensitive awareness of a child's world. Parents who can take this view are likely to find the whole process of growing up an exciting challenge, and can weather the storms of childhood too. For children aren't always amiable and amusing; often they're stubborn, unpredictable and—when you come right down to it—even hostile and hateful to those they love. This is part of growing up; to steer them through it takes understanding and wise management. Enjoyment, then, means having patience and continued interest during even the least agreeable moments with children.

A good home depends primarily on parents who have formed a going partnership. This doesn't mean that they never disagree, or even that they never quarrel. But it does mean that the parents have some sort of united front and have come to an understanding on the major principles of child rearing. If they have done this, their children will know it and will take the minor disagreements in their stride. They will sense the difference between quarrels that are deep and bitter and those that don't really matter. They will know when their parents are loving and loyal to one another just as they are to them. Of course when quarrels between parents grow out of deep-lying anger and bitterness, the difficulties with children will be greater.

Fundamentally constructive relationships among the members of a family create what we call a good home. For a child's sense of security is based on the *feelings* of people around him far more than on his parents' financial condition or the material things they give him.

Parents are human, of course. They have their own ups and downs and worries. When the circumstances of their lives get too hard they're bound to become depressed or irritable—and this makes children anxious. Sometimes parents feel so insecure that they stop noticing what their children are thinking and feeling. When children sense the parents' insecurity, they feel insecure too. But parents don't have to be perfect. Nobody should expect them always to be controlled and calm; parents need to blow off steam occasionally. If it doesn't happen too often it may clear the atmosphere all round. If they hold to a fairly consistent course, their children will weather the minor upsets.

CHILDREN NEED TWO PARENTS

To children, Father and Mother represent everything that is manly and womanly. They tend to model themselves after their parents; when they're young their dearest wish is that some day they may be like them. If one or the other parent is missing from the home, this vision becomes blurred, and the child's conception of what a man or woman should be like tends to be confused.

When a child loses one or the other parent, therefore, there is special need for careful thought and planning. If there's no step-mother or father to fill the empty place, then a child will be fortunate if a relative or family friend who is interested in him plays an important part in his life and serves as a kind of parent-image on which to build his own vision of himself as a grownup.

A serious breach between parents, with or without separation, is always a threat to a child. He is tempted to use one against the other for his own interests, or is torn with doubt as to whose side he should be on. If he sees his parents permanently angry and hateful toward each other, it's harder for him to master his own anger and his own aggressive impulses. The rock on which his house is built is no longer a rock, but something unsure and shaky.

When there has been a divorce, the situation, in many respects, may be calmer. But even in this apparent calm there's always the danger that the child, especially the very young child, may silently feel that he has been deserted, or abandoned by the absent parent. No matter how much he is reassured, he can't help suspecting that this is because somehow or other he's been "bad." If it's at all possible, it's best to let the child keep friendly relations with the absent parent. But this will be possible only when each parent makes a sincere effort to refrain from bitter criticism of the other. If the child grows to feel that his father or mother is not a "good" person, he will feel in turn that he, too, is not "good." If he grows up really knowing both parents, the strengths and weaknesses of each will gradually become apparent; he will form his own judgments.

Divorce is a wounding process for everyone concerned. But the parent who really has at heart his children's best development will try, in every way possible, to spare them its damaging effects. If bitterness and rancor can be avoided, even a home broken by divorce can have a wholesome quality.

Sometimes, in spite of everything, divorced parents can't achieve this goal. Perhaps the absent parent fails to stay sensitive to what's going on inside the child; he forms other ties, loses interest, neglects birthdays and other special days, fails to send letters. If he disappoints the child on cherished plans and in general deeply disturbs his faith, then the relationship may better be broken. But this isn't a solution to be adopted lightly. Everything should be done first to try to work out a really loyal and satisfying relationship between a child and his absent parent. If the loyalty is there, faults, even serious ones, aren't apt to be damaging. What may be damaging is the *unknown* absent parent on whom a child may build every kind of fantasy of the "perfect" parent, the "rescuer," the person-who-sets-everything-right. Such an image discourages a child from facing his real problems. Far better a flesh-and-blood parent from whom a child learns to take the bad with the good.

PLAY

All children need things to play with and a place to play. But it isn't necessary to provide expensive toys to keep a child constructively happy. Anything he can hold and handle freely will fascinate a young child. Common household objects, like pots, pans, spoons, clothespins, cartons, the garden hose, a tub of water and dozens of others, may be excellent toys for small children.

If a child has no room of his own, his mother should arrange for him to have a corner, a shelf or a drawer all to himself where he may keep his own treasures and possessions safe from marauding brothers and sisters.

If he cannot have many toys of his own, he should be given a chance to explore the house, to climb stairs, to handle objects. In most cases he can be taught to adventure without hurting himself or breaking anything, but if there are accidents he should not be scolded too severely. Keep valuable or easily broken things out of the way. Simple furnishings are best while children are young.

A child should be welcome in every room in the house as long as he behaves with reasonable consideration for others. This applies to the kitchen too, where even little children may sometimes "help" with a meal.

Wise parents always try to find ways for their child to do the things he enjoys doing, instead of trying to stop him from being active. They try to find out how to make the things he wants to do safe for himself and for others. Then they let him go ahead to his heart's content.

A SENSE OF HUMOR

When household chores pile up for Mother, when Father comes home tired from a long day in shop or office, and Johnny is especially trying—when you feel you can't take another thing— then is the time of times for a sense of proportion and, if you have one, a sense of humor! There's nothing more relaxing for both parents and child than a good laugh together. When you are tense and tight, your child gets worried. When you are relaxed, he relaxes too. A good corny joke that child and grownup enjoy together helps keep the atmosphere in the home easy and good-natured.

But laughing *with* a child is a very different matter from laughing *at* him. Teasing by adults is a form of laughing at a child which should be avoided at all costs. It can be terribly painful. The child doesn't understand what it's all about and feels bewildered, humiliated and finally angry. Remember always that even the youngest child has his dignity to uphold. When he is teased or laughed at he feels very small and helpless, as well as insecure. Making a child feel small shows fundamental disrespect for him, and a lack of sensitivity to his vulnerable spots.

WORKING MOTHERS

It is possible to have a good home even if a mother goes out to work. But it takes extra planning and extra consideration on the part of each member of the family. Working mothers should try to arrange their hours so that they can be with their children for at least a part of each day. In a child's mind, nothing can take the place of a mother who gives him his supper, puts him to bed, tells a story or sings a song. Because the time that working mothers have with their children is bound to be short, it's especially precious. It's important that constant distractions shouldn't come between mother and child during the time they have together. This doesn't mean that the father shouldn't be there too whenever possible; and other members of the household may be in and out. The important thing, however, is that the time set aside for a child should be given to him whole-heartedly.

Lots of mothers have no choice—they have to take jobs and do the best they can. But a mother who can choose might well ask herself in advance if she really has what it takes. She may find she is tired after a day's work, and there will be household chores to do when she gets home. Her husband will be entitled to attention too; older children will be in and out with their demands. Everything will seem to fall on Mother's shoulders and she may resent it. If she is of a stable nature and organizes her life well and easily, she may be able to play this dual role. She will realize that family life in her case has to be concentrated into a few hours instead of spread over the day. How well she handles those few hours will make all the difference in the happiness of her family. Will she be able to give herself whole-heartedly to each member while she is with him, for however short a time? Everything depends on the answer to this question.

UNDERSTANDING CHILDREN

In a good home, parents know that children will be children, and are patient with them. If parents don't know much about children, they try to find out. They read articles in newspapers and magazines or books. They listen to experts on radio and television. They talk to older friends who seem sensible and have done a pretty good job of raising their own children. They go for help to trustworthy and experienced people—a doctor or a public health nurse or a social worker.

Parents learn what to expect of children at various ages and don't demand that a two-year-old should act like a six-year-old, or a six-year-old like a twelve-year-old. They must know, too, when to stop babying their child, when to let him have more freedom, and how to encourage increasing independence. They learn that no two children are alike; they study each child and treat each one differently from the others.

After they have listened and absorbed all they can, parents stop trying to remember or to follow rules or practice "techniques." They "act natural" with their children, having confidence in their own intuitive wisdom and good sense. If all these fail, then parents may consult a child guidance expert or trained family counselor.

In a good home, each individual—whether child or grownup—is respected and loved for what he *is*, not for what someone wishes him to be. He is encouraged to be himself, to grow at his own speed, to have his own unique character and temperament. He is never made to feel either inferior or superior to other members of the family.

Although it is impossible for parents to love each child in just the same way, it is possible to treat each child fairly, and to avoid favoritism. A child who thinks he is being treated unfairly by his parents, whom he loves and respects above all other people, is an unhappy and resentful member of the family, spoiling the harmony of the whole.

Successful parents are those who can remember what it was like to be a child. They put themselves in their child's place and feel as he is feeling. If this kind of sympathy is kept alive between parents and children nothing very seriously wrong can happen in their relationship. You may live with relatives who don't share your ideas and who make life hard. You may have a struggle with money problems or with illness. There may be divorce or death. Yet you may still have a good home, for at bottom it depends not on outer circumstances but on the understanding, sympathy, and love that exist between parent and child.

WAR—COLD OR HOT

What makes a good home in peacetime and boom years isn't really different from what makes a good home in time of national calamity. Steadfast loyalty, understanding, affection and all the small things of daily life that spell love and home—these are what count at any time.

But when parents are anxious, harassed and sad, they will surely find it harder to give their children the attention and thought that they need. Some will turn to their children as a solace for loneliness and fear; others will feel depleted and emptied of what they know they should give. Yet both kinds of parents love their children.

It's hard, too, to teach children the great lessons of kindness and brotherly love in a world where fathers and brothers may be called to go out and kill. Parents will need to come to grips with this problem, so that they can explain to their children why violence, though a great evil, may sometimes be necessary. A child's life—especially an older child's—is enriched when parents think deeply about troublesome problems and share their thinking with sons and daughters.

When fathers leave home for a military life in camp, there is great gain for all in joining him whenever possible, no matter what the adjustments or how frequent the moves. A united family is always the child's greatest source of strength.

But when it is no longer possible, and a father must really be absent, then he should be kept as real and present to his children as all the small reminders of his personality can possibly make him. Even separation doesn't have to mean real loss. The absent father whom a child loves and reveres, and who can somehow be made a part of the child's daily life, is still a father who counts. He is still an indispensable part of the family—a vital part of the child's fundamental equipment for living. Even in wartime, a feeling of solidarity can be kept alive.

Whatever holds parents steady will be of the most help to their children. Keeping busy about the home has helped many people in time of stress. Some find great solace in religion. Working shoulder to shoulder with others of like mind and conviction on the great issues of the day is another way of finding a kind of equilibrium. All of us need to hold before our children mankind's hope for a peaceful world. We need to tell them of the efforts men are making to achieve this end. But this hope will have more meaning and reality both for us and our children if we actually ally ourselves with others who are working for these ends—and if we give ourselves wholeheartedly to that work.

Anna W. M. Wolf

Building Family Ties and Respect for Parents

At an early age the child begins to have special feelings about his family. Although he cannot put into words the ways in which his family is unlike other families in the neighborhood, he is conscious of the differences and is being affected by them.

His family is the "best," of course, in his estimation. Every child needs to feel this reliance on his father's and mother's ways as being the "right" ways. Fortunate are those parents who set up ways of managing their family life that will stand up under the child's examination later on when he begins to compare his home life with that of his friends. If parents are honest with each other and try wholeheartedly to see each other's point of view, if each reminds himself that he must give up something of what he wants in deference to the other's desires, the spirit of real cooperation that results will keep their child feeling that his family life is a good life. If his home satisfies him, he can more readily understand the individual differences in feelings and behavior that make other children think of *their* family ways as being right, too.

There will come many a time later when the child will want to do what *other* children are allowed to do—stay up later, go to more movies, have more money to spend. But if the foundation of reasonableness and friendliness has been laid in the early years, he is not going to be too rebellious when his parents sometimes have to say "no." He will have had plenty of proof that they really love him, really want him to be able to have good times and do the things that seem so desirable to him; in other words, he will be ready to admit that there must be some good *reasons* back of their refusal.

What are some of the things in family life that build up a child's respect for his parents?

1. Enjoyment by parents of each other's company.
2. Respect for each other's opinions.
3. A truly self-reliant outlook on life.
4. Treatment of the child with respect as an individual, a person worth consulting.
5. Enjoyment in doing things together as a family.
6. Sensible use of family income and joint decisions about its use.
7. Skills or traits in each family member that the others are proud of.
8. Recognition of lasting values rather than desire for excitement and amusement.
9. Acceptance of community responsibility.

STRENGTHENING VALUES IN FAMILY LIFE

1. Enjoying each other's companionship is possible only if parents have interests in common.

Many young parents do not realize until it is too late that they must build up enjoyment in each other's concerns if they are to live on a firm basis of understanding. Too often each goes his own way, with tolerance of the interests of the other but no real effort to get together. A man's wife may not find it possible to become tremendously enthusiastic about his hobby of stamp collecting, but if she enjoys reading, a book that throws light on an event commemorated by a certain stamp will give them something to talk over. Her reading indicates to her husband that she doesn't think his hobby childish. A man whose wife likes to do fancywork as they sit together of an evening may find that by reading aloud he can make interesting to her the sort of thing in which he takes keen delight but which she would never read by herself.

An interest in music, photography, gardening, carpentry, or almost anything else can serve to make family life richer if each partner enters into the other's absorbing interest.

2. Respect for each other's opinions is possible only if each considers the other as important as himself. Because the home background and training of the two partners are not at all alike, it is easy to see why very different attitudes grow up. A man may have had a father whose unflattering opinion of women made his son unwilling to let his wife have a share in family planning. A woman may tend to show little respect for her husband's opinions because she, as an adored only child, was allowed to rule her mother and father. It will take effort for these two types, or others somewhat like them, to develop habits of respect for their partner's ideas.

3. A truly mature, self-reliant outlook on life is reached only through practice in responsibility. A girl who has been pampered or one who has developed a self-pitying point of view because of early hardship, a man whose father has tried to keep him bowing to his will or one who has been less outstanding in school or in sports than his brother, may find that the final growing up has to come

after marriage. Recognition of one's need for a more realistic outlook is the first step in changing one's habits.

4. Treating one's children with respect is not likely to come about unless one tries to learn what children are like and what to expect of them as they develop. Sometimes it is necessary for a father to interpret the children to the mother, though more often it is the other way round. But the more anyone knows about children, the more he realizes how worthy they are of consideration.

5. Enjoyment of family companionship comes from having had fun together many times. To one family walking may be fun; to another, playing games; to a third, gardening; to still another, entertaining guests. The main thing is to try out many things than can be done as a group. Some of them will bring pleasure that will build up warm feelings of oneness.

6. Sensible use of the family income depends to a great extent upon training in using money but also upon the amount of respect parents feel for each other. If either the husband or the wife feels that the other is extravagant or stingy or not always sensible, there is bound to be some arguing and disputing. Because it is more often the man who provides the income and because men have so long held the purse strings, many men unthinkingly expect to make decisions as to how money shall be spent. They have not stopped to remember that in our present way of living it is the wife and mother who must know about how to buy, about comparative costs of food and clothes and rent, and that the family will be better served if decisions are made jointly.

If husband and wife talk over the advantages of buying a new rug now or putting it off, of renting a house in one neighborhood for the sake of the school or in another for the sake of the fine yard, the children are learning while they listen. They are learning (1) that talking things over is a good way of bringing out all sorts of ideas and feeling, and (2) that it is a democratic way of living in which no one person dictates what the others shall do. As they grow older, they will get in on the discussions, too; Molly will have a chance to tell the family why she thinks dancing lessons should be included in the budget, and Mark will ask, if Molly is going to have that money spent on her, won't it be fair for him to have a like amount to buy a camera?

7. If each member of the family has some trait or skill that the rest can be proud of, family unity will tend to be stronger. Even while children are very little they begin to show personality differences. Molly's family is pleased because already, as a 4-year-old, she is so friendly that everyone likes her. Two-year-old Mark may have a very different temperament, but he may show a quickness of observation that is very well worth encouraging. If Father is proud of Mother's skill in cake making or house decorating, and if Mother is sure no gardener has a "greener thumb" than Father, the children just naturally expect that things they do well will be pointed out, too. It is wholesome for everyone in a family to be proud of everyone else (but totally unnecessary for outsiders to have to hear about it). And there is usually something for which each one can be praised if we stop and hunt for it.

8. Parents who have asked themselves what they mean by "good family life" are trying to find the values in their way of living. Of course, people seldom live up to the ideals they have, but they certainly won't live up to ones they haven't even thought out.

The valuable parts of family life are the byproducts of all the work that goes into making a home. It isn't how varied or well-cooked the food on the table is (though that helps) so much as it is the atmosphere at the family table; it is not the cost of the curtains at the window so much as it is the eagerness with which the children look out of the window to see their father coming home. It isn't what kind of car the family has, but what kind of planning they have shared in saving for that car (agreeing on beans instead of steak for dinner, for instance) and how they enjoy themselves when they go out in it.

The family's attitude toward life is what makes the difference. If the parents have lived lives in which excitement to fill in the vacant spots was all they hunted for, the values of their family life for their children will be very different from those of parents who never have time enough to do all the creative, interesting things they have piled up ahead of them.

Feeding children's stomachs with suitable things takes a great deal of parents' energies and thought, but just as vital to a child's growth are the thought and effort put into building up the resources of his mind and personality.

9. Acceptance of their responsibility in the community in which they live is one way parents can round out family life. Children are very proud of parents who enter into the life about them, who are taking part in and contributing to the community and not just receiving from it.

When a family chooses a home because it is "in a good neighborhood," they immediately have to shoulder part of the responsibility for keeping the neighborhood "good." If they are *really* community-minded, they will already have been interested in the school and active in community school projects, not just selfishly for their own children but for the good of all children.

Having children is what often starts people toward becoming community-minded,

A New Role For Fathers

THE traditional role of Father was that of provider and disciplinarian while the training of the child was regarded as "woman's work." Only when the child was so troublesome that his mother could not handle him was he turned over to Father for a good, sound spanking. Is it any wonder, then, that the child learned to fear or even hate his father?

If a father is to be loved and respected by his children, his role must be broadened to include more pleasurable contacts with his children. He must be a part of their lives, not an outsider whose feelings are hurt because he is excluded from the inner circle of family life.

Here are some of the roles the father of today must play if he is to contribute what he can and should in the lives of his children:

A Lover

It has been said, and rightly so, that the father's greatest contribution to his children is to make their mother happy. Studies of problem children have shown, in a large proportion of the cases, that they come from homes marked by parental discord.

So long as a man maintains the role of lover, showing his wife the little attentions which made her fall in love with him during the days of their courtship, she will be happy. And, because she is happy, she will create a happy, wholesome home environment for her children.

Admirer and Rooter for Mother

Even when a husband questions his wife's judgment in handling a problem at home, he should back her up in front of the children and discuss the matter later when the children are not present. Furthermore, he should take advantage of every possible opportunity to point out how much Mother does for the family, and how much she contributes to the family's happiness.

Standing together goes a long way toward building family solidarity, love and respect. Nothing could be worse for children than discord between the parents, nor the example set by one parent who belittles or even ridicules the other in front of the children.

An Important Arbiter

Family life never does, nor could it be expected to, run a completely smooth course. There are bound to be some clashes, some hurt feelings, and some bitter words. Because the mother is with the children almost constantly, she is likely to get a somewhat prejudiced point of view. Here is where Father can step in and act as arbiter. As a newcomer to the scene of trouble, his viewpoint is likely to be unimpaired by bias or prejudice.

A Playmate

A strained relationship cannot last for long between pals. The father who wants to be a real friend to his children must share their play. Even when the child is a baby and can play only the simple games of "Peek-a-boo" and "Little pigs went to market," he finds it fun to play with Father. Later there are the running games, ball games, card games and athletic contests for Father to join in.

If Father is to be a satisfactory playmate to his children, there are three cautions that he should keep in mind. He must not dictate what the play will be. Let the children decide that. He must not be so expert that he will always win. It's not much fun to play when you haven't a chance of winning. Finally, Father must forget about dignity and come down to the child's level. Sitting on the floor instead of a chair will go a long way toward reducing Father to the child's status.

A Funmaker

Every home needs a funmaker who always has a joke ready when things get tense and who will plan surprise entertainments for the family. A busy mother frequently becomes too weighted down with the day in, day out care of the home and children to retain her sense of humor or to be able to think beyond the immediate needs of the family. Here is where Father can take over. Letting him suggest a movie, a picnic, or a ride in the car will help to compensate in the children's eyes for all Mother does for them and will put the two parents on an equal footing.

A Teacher

While schools and Sunday schools assume the responsibility for part of the child's education, there is plenty left for the parents to do. Teaching the child the meaning of right and wrong, good sportsmanship, wholesome attitudes toward sex and how to get along with people are just a few of the lessons that must be learned at home. Mother and Father together can do this job better than either parent alone.

An Ideal

Every child follows the pattern set by his parents. Because the father is not at home as much as the mother, more attention is focused on him when he is there than on the ever-present mother. Getting to meals on time, being polite and courteous, keeping his possessions in order, sharing home responsibilities, being cheerful and a good sport, are just a few patterns of behavior Father can set for his children. A father who is a real hero in his children's eyes has achieved the pinnacle of success of fatherhood.

What We Do and Don't Know About Children

So we moderns understand our children? Only in a measure. There are many things about them which we know full well. But a core of almost instinctive knowledge is offset by many misconceptions which cause us to act on false premises and unwarranted impulses. A map of our present knowledge of the child's mind would be comparable, both in truth and error, to a fifteenth-century map of the world. Vast areas remain to be explored.

The developing child is the most complicated of all bundles of atoms. It takes him a long time to grow up, and he must do his own growing. We may provide him with favorable opportunities for growth, as a baby, as a school child, as an adolescent, but we cannot impart the essence nor the mechanisms of development. Emily Dickinson must have had something like this in mind, when she teasingly asked, "Can you teach me how to grow, or is it unconveyed, like melody or witchcraft?"

The sequences and gradations of growth are most transparently revealed in the development of motor abilities. In attaining the upright posture and the ability to walk, the infant traverses over twenty progressive stages. At one stage, he merely erects his head as he lies prone; at another stage he crawls "on his stomach"; later he get onto hands and knees, creeps backward, then forward; still later he rises to his feet and walks. Each stage is a developmental link in a lawfully ordered chain of events.

"Learning" to walk causes no disciplinary problems. We freely recognize the limiting mechanisms of growth. We guide and protect the child; but we respect the growth factors, and place a great deal of confidence in them.

Similar growth gradations determine the patterning of the fine motor skills of the infant's eyes, hands and fingers. At sixteen weeks he can pick up a tiny pellet with his eyes, but not with his hands; at twenty-eight weeks he crudely rakes at it, in a pawlike manner; at forty weeks he plucks the pellet with precise pincer prehension.

Such gradations govern the patterning of behavior at all ages. Banging comes before poking; vertical crayon strokes before circular and oblique; towers before bridges in block building; jargon before articulate words; nouns before prepositions; solitary before social play; perceptions before abstractions.

Teachers and parents are usually ready to recognize these natural progressions in the training of practical skills. But as soon as the scene shifts to the less neutral fields of manners, morals, and competitive school work, the child runs into danger of being misunderstood. The issues become heated with emotion.

Often he is soundly scolded and even punished for shortcomings which are mainly due to his immaturity. He is arbitrarily held to standards of conduct and of success, which take scant account of his readiness in terms of growth. This is the most fundamental and far-reaching mistake which our culture makes in the management, the care and education of children. We can correct the mistake only through a more rational appreciation of the laws of child development. These laws apply to morals as well as to the motor skills of posture, of locomotion and manipulation.

Our culture is surcharged with moral directives and ethical norms which must be preserved if civilization is to survive. But time-tested wisdom is still intricately mixed with persisting error. We cling to oversimplified absolutes. It is almost impossible to set aside adult preconceptions of what a child ought to do, and so we fail to understand what the child does, and what he actually is.

All this leads to arbitrariness; that is, to lack of understanding. Obedience is exacted for its own sake, although our demands should be tempered to a child's capacity to obey. Apology is exacted, when a little face-saving banter, supported by a sense of humor, would be the better part of wisdom. Parents (and grandparents) frequently become emotionally 'burned up" by a child's poor table manners—an exaggerated emphasis, which may result in very injudicious discipline. Manners, like morals, do not yield to arbitrary authority. They depend chiefly upon the long-prevailing atmosphere of the home, and the current maturity of the child.

Needless to say, we are not placing a premium on "badness" and license. Mere indulgence does not accomplish constructive prevention. But an insight into the developmental logic of misbehavior will enable parents and teachers to use enlightened methods of management. In all disciplinary situations the adult can keep an eye on himself as well as on the child. He should feel certain that he is not demanding too much in terms of the gradations of growth. He must be sure of steps 1, 2 and 3, before he exacts steps 4, 5 and 6. First the blade, then the ear, then the full corn of the ear.

The basic development of the ethical sense takes place in the first ten years of life. This sense is not a special faculty: it is a complex product of growth. The child is born with dispositions and potentialities which undergo progressive organization from the moment of birth. His moral capacities at the age of three are significantly more mature than they were a few months earlier.

Look, for example, at the patterns of social behavior typical of the 2½-year-old level of maturity. The parents of our nursery-school children tell us repeatedly that of all ages this is the most perplexing, yes, the most "exasperating." The 2½-year-old is reported to be contrary and unreasonable. "He doesn't know what he wants." "He can't make up his mind."

When he acts, he seems to oscillate between two opposites. Unable to make a single, decisive choice, he makes two—two contradictory choices. His timing is poor. Sometimes he obeys; and then again, "without reason," he refuses. Every avenue of culture is a two-way street to him. So he goes both ways, making confused distinctions between Yes and No, Come and Go, Run and Stop, Give and Take, Push and Pull, Grasp and Release.

This paradoxical behavior, however, might well remind us of an earlier stage when he was learning to creep; he had just mastered the creeping stance, but he could go neither forward nor backward, so he remained on the spot and rocked back and forth. In his personal social behavior, he is now in an equivalent transitional stage. He is learning to shift gears, and soon he will forge ahead. Soon he will be an amenable three-year-old, capable of making a voluntary choice between two alternatives.

Three is a delightful age. For one so young, the child has himself well in hand. What is more, he likes to please and to conform. "Do it dis day?" is a characteristic question, which shows he is sensitive to the demands of culture. Indeed he foreshadows the man of good-will on whom the fate of nations should rest.

But his moral nature is still in the making. He will not always remain in his present state of relative equilibrium. At the age of four he feels the push of growth in many new directions. He is sensitive to praise and blame, and he needs new kinds of motivations when questions of obedience arise. He tends to go out of bounds. He tells tall tales; he cannot stick to the truth, because he barely discriminates between fact and fiction; he has been known to "cheat" and to take objects that are not his own.

Wisely managed, the expansive four-year-old becomes conforming again at the age of five. He invites and accepts supervision. His ready obedience has an attractive quality. He is reputed to be very good. Developmentally speaking, five is indeed another period of relative equilibrium, reminiscent of three.

The tides of development, however, soon take the child into more troubled waters and into new transitions. By the age of six he may lose some of his angelic five-year-oldness. At times his behavior becomes brash and combative, as though he were at war with himself and with the world. At times he becomes hesitant, indecisive, over-demanding and explosive, with strangely contradictory spurts of affection and antagonism. At other times he is engaging and companionable.

We need to know more about this complex, transitional psychology, because the child is now, officially, a school beginner. And our schools, both public and private, are committing grave errors of mental hygiene for lack of understanding of this critical period. Even the roots of juvenile delinquency may reach back to mismanagement and neglect of the six-year-old.

Normally, there is a growth trend toward recurrent equilibrium. The seven-year-old has himself better in hand. He is less impulsive, more pensive. He has established firmer relations with his companions and his teacher. He is in an absorptive, assimilative phase. Day by day he grows in mental stature.

Near the age of eight, he enters a more expansive phase (reminiscent of age four). He shows more initiative and spontaneity in going out to meet his environment. He fraternizes with his schoolmates.

The ten-year-old is in still better touch and tune with his environment. He can be relaxed and casual as well as alert. He takes things in stride; he works with speed and likes the challenge of school tasks. He is peculiarly receptive to social information, and susceptible to prejudices, good and bad. He can participate in elementary discussions of social problems—racial minorities, crime, labor and management, black market. It is a golden period for planting liberalizing and stabilizing ideas, prior to the teens which impend.

And so the cycle of mental growth continues on a fluctuating, and more or less spiral course. At ascending levels of maturity the ethical sense becomes organized as part of the total action system of the child. The foundation and much of the framework of human personality are laid down in the first ten years of life.

Herein lies the cultural significance of all the life sciences which contribute to a better understanding of our children. Given a sound inheritance (and this is a most important "given"), the welfare of these children will depend upon favorable political and economic conditions. But these conditions cannot be made favorable without the aid of scientific knowledge. The humanities alone, without the directive light of science, are unequal to the problems of social control.

It is said that man needs new moral techniques, and greater self-knowledge to manage a technological civilization. How can we possibly arrive either at the techniques or the self-knowledge, without a deepened understanding of the laws and the very mechanisms of child development?

The most constructive cultural force that can be released in the years which lie ahead is an intensified conservation of the development of infants and young children. This must be a socialized conservation, felt and effected by the people, as well as by political leaders. This would entail vast extensions of pre-parental and adult education, and a more nearly universal form of developmental supervision under medical and public health auspices. The life sciences, therefore, will have a basic cultural function in a yet more technological era.

ARNOLD GESELL, M. D.

WORD GROWTH

One gauge of a child's development is the growth of his vocabulary during pre-school years. Studies of vocabulary increases by M. E. Smith list the average vocabularies of children as follows:

Age	No. of Words
8 months	0
10 "	1
1 year	3
15 months	19
1½ years	22
21 months	118
2 years	272
3 "	896
4 "	1,540
5 "	2,072
6 "	2,562

Outgrowing Babyhood

THE average child from one to six grows and develops very much like all other children of his age. Among many other things, children learn during this period to use their hands skillfully, to walk steadily, to run and to skip, to talk easily, and to play happily with other children.

But there are normally great differences in the rate at which children grow and develop and in the age at which they are able to do certain things. Some walk at thirteen months, others not until eighteen months. Parents must not be impatient for their child to do the same things that another child of his age can do. It is a mistaken idea that a child who is slow to walk or talk is necessarily backward. Children who are mentally dull are slow in learning to do these things, but a great many very bright people too have been slow in learning to walk and talk.

Parents can expect that their children will do things in the same order: that is, a baby will always be able to sit before he can stand, to use his hands well before he can use his legs and feet, and to creep before he walks. This is because growth proceeds from the head downward. The arms and hands are skillful before the body is, and the legs and feet are the last to develop.

Parents can do nothing to hurry this development; it comes as the child's body matures. But they can try to see that nothing interferes with the unfolding of their child's powers. They can help him learn to use his hands by letting him hold his spoon and cup as soon as he wants to try. And they can talk to him, walk around the room with him, let him see and handle many kinds of objects.

Most children at one year weigh about three times what they weighed at birth and have grown from eight to ten inches in height. After growing very rapidly during this first year, a child slows down during the next few years, so that he puts on only four to five pounds a year. This slowing down in the child's development is perfectly natural; there will be times of rapid growth alternating with times of slower growth.

As the child develops out of babyhood, he gradually loses the chubbiness that is characteristic of most babies and lengthens out into slimmer proportions. As he begins to be very active, his weight will be made up more of muscle than of fat. Often he does not seem to be eating so much for his size as he did when he was a baby, but if he is gaining regularly this need not disturb his mother.

One very noticeable change is that the child's head, which made up one-fourth of his body length at first, does not grow nearly so rapidly as other parts of his body. It was so large at birth that even with this slow rate of growth a child's head at the age of five is almost as large as it will ever be. Its circumference grows less than an inch after this time. The brain is half as large at birth as it will be in adulthood; and when a child is six his brain has about completed its growth in size. Changes in the brain cells and nerve connections that make it more and more mature will be going on for many years, however.

At birth the upper part of the child's face was far larger than the lower part. This changes as the teeth come in and the jaws develop. The child's neck, short and inconspicuous when he was a baby, lengthens.

The infant's arms, short in proportion to his trunk at birth, begin to grow in length. So do his legs, though at a slower rate. The legs of a two-year-old are much shorter in proportion than the legs of a four-year-old, and much less strong, so that the younger child depends much more on his arms than on his legs in climbing.

Because of different family and racial backgrounds, children vary so much in physical growth that two children of the same age are seldom alike in height or weight. The average height of a three-year-old is about thirty-eight inches, but some will be only thirty-three inches tall, while others will be forty-three inches. In general, children follow the body build of their parents, but they may not follow it to extremes. If a father is extremely tall, for example, his son may not be so tall, as there is a tendency away from extremes and toward an average. Moreover, children are affected, just as their parents were, by such things as food patterns, climate, and other influences of environment.

The child who is large as a baby will be likely to grow faster than a small baby; one who is large at two will usually be taller and heavier than the average at four, and at later ages, too. Probably because of better diet and for other reasons, recent generations of children have tended to be taller than their parents or grandparents.

Many children grow about three inches a year during this period. They usually add about five pounds a year in weight between the ages of one and two, and after that gain about four pounds yearly until they are six or seven. Growth tables that were formerly so much referred to tended to give parents concern if their child did not measure up to the "average" for a given age; they are no longer considered useful. Each child's physical state is now judged by his own individual growth rather than by comparison with an average of the weights and heights of a great many children.

Growth differs at different times of year. Children in the United States grow more in height in the spring and early summer and put on weight more rapidly in the fall.

Changes keep going on in the makeup of the child's skeleton, too. The bones of the baby are relatively soft and flexible and contain less bony tissue and more marrow than they will later. As the child grows older, the bones thicken and become stronger; they gradually have more mineral content and less soft tissue. When a child's bones are less hard than is normal in early childhood, as they are if he has rickets, pressure on them may easily cause deformities. The bowlegs of a child who has rickets result from the position in which he sits or lies or from attempts to stand when the legs are not strong enough to carry the child's weight. Fortunately, such children are not seen so frequently nowadays as in the past because most parents know the advantages of exposing babies to sunlight and giving them fish-liver oil in the first months of life.

Boys and girls differ in this matter of growth. Although girls are usually a little shorter and lighter in weight than boys at birth, their bony structure is further developed. From being about a month ahead of a boy at birth, the girl forges ahead more rapidly and at the age of six years her bony structure is about a year advanced over that of a boy of the same age. Because their skeletons and nervous systems are more developed, girls learn more easily than boys of the same age to dress themselves, to write, and to do other things that depend on skill in using the bones and muscles of the wrist.

HE LEARNS TO WALK AND TALK

With each passing day after the baby begins to walk and talk he is leaving babyhood farther behind him. He is no longer entirely dependent on someone else to satisfy his every want and is learning to do more and more for himself.

A few babies walk as early as eight or nine months; others do not manage it until they are sixteen to eighteen months old. A large, heavy child is not likely to walk so early as a small-boned, less fat baby. On the average we may expect a baby to walk at thirteen to fifteen months of age.

Perhaps mothers would not be in such a hurry for their babies to walk if they realized that for a while it means more rather than less work for them. Although a baby gets his clothes very dirty while he is creeping, the chances are he will get into things so much after he walks that this will be more bother.

Since the baby who is beginning to walk cannot yet talk, he must find out as much as he can of what he wants to know by touching, tasting, handling, and throwing. He explores by climbing, and so has to be watched for possible tumbles; he runs and sometimes can get away from his mother amazingly fast. He will no longer be content to stay in his play pen long at a time, for he can see far more interesting things to do outside it.

When the time of walking comes, a baby needs the muscle-strengthening exercise he gets by climbing steps and lifting boxes. He should have a chance to run freely so that his unsteady legs, planted far apart in his first walking days, to help him balance his body, may gain strength and sureness. By the age of two he will be fairly sure on his feet and will be using his body easily and skillfully.

TALKING. Sometime between the eighth and seventeenth months a child usually learns to associate certain sounds with an object or person.

Many babies have two or three words that they can use correctly by the time they are a year old. For the next six months or so additional words come slowly, with one word serving the purpose of a whole sentence.

Nouns, or the names of things, are what he is interested in first, but it will not be long before verbs begin to be added in great numbers. It is when the child is able to move about freely that verbs of action—"run," "go," "fix," "come"—become very important.

By the time he is three, a child is using a great many verbs and also pronouns, though he still gets them mixed up. From the third year through the sixth, children add between five hundred and six hundred words to their vocabularies each year. This tremendous increase is not strange, considering that a child in this period is usually not quiet for more than four minutes at a time and asks more than three hundred questions in a day!

Girls tend to talk a little earlier than boys and to be slightly superior in language ability throughout the early years. By the age of five most children have learned to speak clearly, with few of the letter confusions ("dat" for "that," "aw" for "all," "wain" for "rain") that occurred earlier. Twins, being so closely associated with each other that they do not have good speech to copy, are likely to be somewhat slow in language development and cling to their poor pronunciation longer than other children. They catch up in the early school years, however. Parents can help very much by speaking clearly and carefully so that their children have good speech models to copy.

Many bright children not only begin to use language earlier, but their pronunciation is better and they speak with greater ease throughout the main period of development.

Boys tend to have a larger vocabulary than girls, for they are likely to gather general information on a greater number of subjects.

YOUR CHILD'S GROWTH AND DEVELOPMENT

At One Year

The year-old child is a creeper and a climber. He can pull himself up to a sitting position and while sitting he can turn himself around in various directions. Although he can stand if supported by his hands, he usually prefers to be on his hands and knees. Such "walking" as he does is often done on all fours. Some children can stand alone at one year, and some even walk forward, but this is the exception rather than the rule.

Toward the end of the first year, the child can hold a cup and may use a spoon clumsily. Generally, however, he prefers to pick up bits of food with his fingers. By this time he will probably have been weaned from the bottle. At bedtime he likes to help pull off his socks, although he may spend considerable time trying to put them back on again. This is the period when the baby is becoming a child and his parents can best help him to develop by encouraging him to do things for himself.

The young child likes to play with many little things at a time and takes delight in picking them up and dropping them. This repeated picking up and dropping represents a process of learning. The baby, having learned how to hold an object in his hand, must now learn how to unclench his fist to drop it. And he learns by doing a thing over and over again.

Around one year the baby will often say "da-da" and wave "bye-bye." He enjoys playing "peek-a-boo" and throwing things down from his high chair or out of his play pen. He loves an audience and is often a great mimic.

Most children at one year have six teeth.

At Two Years

The two-year-old is a "run-about." Although not yet very sure-footed, he has passed through the wobbly months when bumps and tumbles were very frequent. By holding on to a hand or a rail he can go upstairs, one step at a time. He can throw a ball and ride a little three-wheeled car.

He builds blocks into small towers, pulls open drawers, and delights in taking things out and putting them back. He likes to fill and empty things over and over again. Washing is wonderful fun and he goes in for this with much dabbling and splashing. If he has been allowed to feed himself, he can generally eat rather neatly by the end of the second year. He likes to help undress himself.

At two years he may speak in short sentences as well as single words. "Dis is mine," "Daddy aw' gone," "Wanta wide car," "Gonna pway blocks," are good examples. Nursery rhymes are beginning to interest him. Some two-year-olds will occasionally surprise their parents by reciting short jingles that have been read to them.

Parents should not be too disturbed if a child around this age begins to say "no" to almost everything. This "no" or negativistic stage is not an unusual phase in a child's development.

It used to be thought that a baby should be taught bowel and bladder control before he was a year old. We now know from scientific studies that such attempts at early toilet training are useless because the nerves and muscles necessary for such control are not fully developed until sometime in the second year of life. In a few infants regularity in bowel movements seems to be established in the early months of life, but this is the exception rather than the rule.

Generally, however, bowel control can be accomplished by fifteen or eighteen months. As for bladder control, many children at two years have learned to keep dry, except perhaps at night.

Most children at two years have sixteen teeth.

At Three Years

Of all the preschool years, the third year is one of the most fascinating in the growth of the child. The three-year-old can *do* things. He can run and jump and climb; he can ride a tricycle. He bustles back and forth, up and down stairs, and can even turn corners and stop abruptly.

He can *do* things with his arms and hands and with his legs and feet. He delights in playing with modeling clay and in his sand box. He can make a train or a tower out of blocks or cubes. He can fold a piece of paper crosswise or lengthwise and can draw crosses on paper with crayons. He can put away his toys when playtime is over.

The three-year-old will help with dressing as well as with undressing himself. Sometime between three and four he usually learns to unbutton buttons—much to his delight. If he has hooks within his reach he can hang up his own coat and hat after being outdoors. Since little girls develop more rapidly than little boys, some three-year-old girls are able to dress themselves with very little help.

With supervision the three-year-old can wash his hands and put his towel back on his own rack or hook. He can eat without much spilling and can drink from a cup with enthusiasm, particularly at fruit-juice time.

At three the child speaks in short sentences and usually with animation. He pays great attention to adults, listens to their words, and watches their faces for clues as to their approval or disapproval. He is willing to accept suggestions from grown-ups, such as "Shall we put the blocks away now?" or "Let's put on our hats and coats now," and acts on them with vigor. He likes to listen to simple stories and nursery rhymes and he loves being a bear or a doggie or a horse. He is very curious about people and things around him and asks many simple questions.

Most three-year-olds sleep through the night without wetting the bed and if given a hand with buttons, when necessary, can go to the toilet themselves during the day.

Most children have all twenty of their "first teeth" at thirty months.

At Four Years

If three can be called the age of "doing," four is the age of "finding out." "Why" and "how" are two of the words most frequently used by the four-year-old.

Not that the four-year-old is not a "doer" also, because he is, of course, very active. He can run, jump, and climb with much more ease, grace, and sureness than the three-year-old. He can pitch a ball and build a house with blocks. He likes to play with other children.

In addition to asking many questions, the four-year-old can carry on a running conversation with another child or an adult. He likes to listen to stories and nursery rhymes. Stories that he particularly loves he wants to hear over and over again with not the slightest change in detail. *Peter Rabbit* and *The Three Bears* are often great favorites at this age.

At four the child can dress and undress himself if his clothes are simple and buttons within reach. He can go to the toilet without any help at all.

From Five to Six Years

The five-year-old usually can hop—even on one foot—skip, and turn somersaults. He can handle his sled or wagon with ease.

He likes to cut and paste and draw pictures. He likes clothes and loves to dress up. He prefers playing with other children, especially in group projects such as building houses, garages, switch yards. In the home he likes to help his mother with the washing and the sweeping and his father with the hammering and the painting. He can be very skillful in handling tools and utensils if they are suited to his size.

The five-year-old is more reliable than the four-year-old. He likes to feel independent. He loves to hear and to tell stories, but he is more serious than the four-year-old. When he asks, "What is this for?" or "How does this work?" he wants, and should have, a thoughtful answer. Not in language or detail which he would not understand, but nevertheless an honest answer.

To sum up—the five- to six-year-old is sure of himself and generally dependable; he has learned to do what is expected of him in the household. He washes and dresses himself, goes to the toilet alone, and has an interest in helping with home chores. He plays well with other children but when alone can amuse himself in all sorts of ways from skipping about to drawing pictures.

Building Healthy Bodies

THE good health habits that are formed in the first six years of a child's life lay the foundation for future health. The child who leads a well-ordered life, with wholesome, well-planned meals, plenty of sleep, and adequate play in the sunshine is most likely to grow into a healthy adult.

Parents are learning more and more that it is wise to go to a doctor to keep their children well rather than to go to him only to cure illnesses that might have been prevented. Besides giving the child regular health examinations, the doctor will give him protection against certain diseases and will tell the parents what they can do to guard against other diseases. He will advise the parents as to the child's health habits.

The healthy child is active, alert, and interested in everything. His color is good and his eyes are bright. His skin is smooth, his muscles firm, and his body straight and strong. He is gaining in size and weight. His mother may find him a strenuous companion, with his never-ending desire for activity. He is probably noisy, getting pleasure out of banging and shouting and singing. But when it is bedtime he sleeps soundly. He is hungry at mealtimes and needs no coaxing to persuade him to eat. His bowels move regularly. His teeth are clean and in good condition. He does not have pains or aches.

The child who is "not really sick" is usually the same child as the one who is "not really well."

Too many people are satisfied with a child that is "not sick." Ill health is often excused or explained on some ground or other and considered unavoidable.

Nothing short of really healthy children should satisfy parents, for every child is entitled to the best health possible.

REGULAR MEDICAL EXAMINATIONS

Every child should be examined by a doctor at least every four to six months. At these regular examinations, if it is possible, the same doctor should see the child. In this way the child will get to know the doctor well and the doctor will be able to follow the child's progress much better. Then, too, the doctor will understand the child's condition better than if he has never seen him before.

He may be a pediatrician—a doctor who is a specialist in the care of children—or the family doctor. Or it may be that the mother has been taking her infant to a well-baby clinic (or child-health center) and plans to continue doing so until the child is ready for school.

The visit to the doctor's office should be a pleasant experience. A child should be taught that the doctor is his friend. A mother who threatens to "call the doctor if you aren't good" makes a great mistake. It is next to impossible for a doctor to examine a screaming, struggling child properly. On the other hand, if a child has been told in advance that he is being taken to the doctor and what the doctor will do, he will usually learn to look forward to his visit with the doctor with pleasure rather than dread.

It will help the mother as well as the doctor if she has written down whatever she thinks she should tell him and any questions she wishes to ask, so that she will not forget them.

At the examination the child should be completely undressed. After being weighed and measured by the nurse or the doctor, the child will be examined by the doctor.

After the examination the doctor will talk to the mother about her child's health and will make suggestions about his care. He will recommend that the child be immunized against diphtheria and smallpox, if this has not already been done, and will advise her about immunizing and guarding against other diesases.

A mother should be sure, before she leaves the doctor's office, that she understands just what he wants her to do. Since he is an expert in health, she will find it well worth her while to carry out his orders to the best of her ability.

REGULAR VISITS TO THE DENTIST

From the time a child is two years old he should be taken to the dentist every six months so that his teeth can be examined and cleaned and any small cavities filled or defects repaired.

A child who goes to the dentist from the age of two is not likely to develop fear of the dentist or of having his teeth fixed. Many dentists nowadays make a specialty of caring for children's teeth. The "baby teeth" need home care and the dentists's care just as much as the permanent teeth do.

If the first few visits are only for inspection or cleaning, as is likely to be the case, the child will often actually enjoy going to the dentist.

If cavities or defective fissures appear in the child's teeth, they should be filled promptly.

The child with a sore tooth tries not to bite on it and may avoid coarse foods that need to be chewed or may chew on only one side of his mouth. If the cavity becomes very large, the root of the tooth is likely to become infected and the tooth may have to be pulled out. The shape of the jaw may suffer, from either lack of exercise or loss of teeth, and the permanent teeth that are being built may not have room enough to come in straight. If a child has a tooth in which decay has destroyed or exposed the nerve, he should be taken to the dentist often so that the dentist can give the necessary treatment that may save the tooth.

Perhaps the most important teeth in childhood—and the most neglected—are the six-year molars. These four permanent teeth, which come in sometime between the fifth and seventh birthdays, do not take the place of any baby teeth but come in directly behind them. For this reason they are often wrongly thought to be baby teeth. The six-year molar is the sixth tooth from the front on each side; there are two in the upper jaw and two in the lower.

The six-year molars are the first permanent teeth to come through. If they are lost, the other teeth are likely to come in crooked and the dental arch may be poorly formed. As soon as the chewing surface of each of these teeth has appeared, it should be examined by a dentist to see whether there are defective fissures. Great care should be taken of the six-year molars.

TEACHING GOOD HEALTH HABITS

Teaching a child to do habitually and without conscious effort the things that make for good health is one of the first duties of parents. The health habits have to do with the daily activities of the child— eating, sleeping, playing, eliminating, and keeping the body clean and suitably clothed. Most of these habits should be learned in the first three or four years of life. Once learned, they may last a lifetime.

To help a child form good habits, we must see that he gets satisfaction from the things we want him to do. We must also see that he does *not* get satisfaction from doing the things we do *not* want him to do.

In planning a routine for the young child the life of all the members of the family should be considered. It is not desirable to have the plans of the family revolve completely around the children. Certain things, however, are of absolute importance, such as the daytime-nap period, outdoor play, regular mealtimes, early bed hour, and regular visits to the toilet. A regular schedule will benefit the whole family in the end.

A definite daily plan or schedule, made to meet individual needs and followed conscientiously, will prove a great saver of the mother's time. Children who live by such a plan are usually ready for bath, meals, and bed when the time comes.

PLANNING A DAILY SCHEDULE

The child's day should be planned so that both his needs and those of his mother and other members of the family are well met. In fact, his needs cannot be satisfactorily met unless his mother's are, too. If she does not plan so that she will not be overburdened, she will be in no condition to be sunny and pleasant. Fitting her day around the child's routines in such a way that she does not become completely exhausted by night will help her to be a good companion to her husband, too. A child might about as well go dirty and hungry as have parents who are not getting along with each other. It is the duty of both parents to cooperate for the child's sake.

A plan for a child's day, then, should be built around his four needs—for food, for rest, for activity, and for a mother who can stress the important things and not let unessential details use up her time and strength.

After the first year most children are ready for a schedule built around three meals a day. There are several good ways in which a daily schedule can be planned. It is up to the mother to work out one that will be best suited to her child, herself, and the rest of the family. If, for example, it is more convenient for a mother to have bath time come just before lunchtime in the late morning, there is no reason why the bath should not be given or taken at this time instead of before supper.

Once a routine has been established, it is a good idea for a mother to stick to it as it usually gives her more free time for other duties and much-needed leisure besides. The child, too, will benefit from a regular routine and so will the family.

The following schedules for the one- to three-year-old and the three- to six-year-old are given merely as examples of the way in which schedules can be planned. They are meant only as suggestions, for the mother will wish, of course, to establish her own routines for her own children.

Suggested Schedule for the Child From One to Three

Around 6 to 7 a. m. (depending upon when the child awakens):
Citrus-fruit juice (now or later with breakfast).
Sleep or play alone in crib.
Wash and dress child before breakfast or right afterward.

Around 7:30 a. m.:
Breakfast.
Fish-liver oil (may be given with citrus-fruit juice, if preferred).
Play, out of doors when the weather is suitable.
Sunbath, if weather permits.
(Offer some water during this time.)

Around 11:30 *a. m.:*
  Noon meal.
  Nap (undress child for nap). Cup of milk after nap.
  Play.
  (Offer more water during this time.)

Around 5 *p.m.:*
  Bath.

Around 5:30 *p.m.:*
  Evening meal.

Around 6 to 6:30 *p. m.* (an hour or 2 later in very hot weather):
  Bed (lights out).

If the child takes a long nap in the morning instead of in the afternoon, he should be undressed for his nap at a regular time—usually about 10:30 or 11 a. m.—and then have his dinner at 1 or 1:30.

Most children want to go to the toilet when they first wake up, after their nap, and before they go to bed at night, in addition to having to urinate at other times during the day. Whatever time of day the child's bowels move regularly should be an established time for him to go to the toilet.

For the Child from Three to Six

Morning:
  Wash and dress child.
  Breakfast.
  Play out of doors when weather is suitable.
  Sunbath, depending on weather.

Mid-morning:
  Fruit juice.

Noon:
  Lunch or dinner.
  Nap (if preferred, nap can be taken right before lunch). Cup of milk.
  Outdoor play.

Evening:

Dinner or supper.

Bath.

Bed.

Water should be offered freely between meals.

From the time a child is three he can usually go to the toilet by himself at regular times. But he may still need help with buttons for a little while.

PLANNING MOTHER'S TIME

All through the preschool years naps lasting too far into the afternoon should be avoided, so that children will be sleepy enough to go to bed very early in the evening. The child needs a long, uninterrupted period of night sleep, and his parents need a time to relax and to be free from having to take care of an active youngster.

The mother who is on the alert to use her time wisely will plan to get a rest during part of the time her children are napping. But instead of getting some rest, many women tend to use every minute of the time a child is asleep to get housework and laundry out of the way. Ten minutes with a book, or fifteen minutes flat on her bed, will probably mean the mother can get much more work done later than she would have without this little relaxation. Doing some darning out in the sun while the baby is in his sand box will sometimes be much more sensible than washing the dishes then just because it is the time of the morning when breakfast dishes are "supposed" to be done. Trying out several schemes to find out when the washing of diapers fits in best or when the trip to the store should be made, will probably pay for the time it takes. Carefully planned use of one's time, following an orderly schedule but allowing for occasional breaks in routine, will result in much greater happiness for both mother and child.

A mother who says she is "too busy" to get to the grocery until late afternoon may be deceiving herself, for she wastes time in going when the store is crowded with women who have no other time to do their buying. A half-hour trip to the store with his mother in the middle of the morning, on the other hand, would in many cases make a nice break for a child, who may be too tired to eat if he plays continuously right up to lunchtime. Getting out of doors may also make his mother more interested in eating a good lunch, which many young women neglect to do. But if the other mothers in the block do their shopping at another time, the pleasure of visiting with them may make it seem desirable to fit her routine into theirs. The main thing is to try several ways until you have a schedule that works satisfactorily both for the baby and for any other children in the family.

If there are two or more children under school age, the mother will find it necessary to plan very carefully in budgeting her time and in working out a schedule to met all needs. She may be tempted to push the younger one ahead too fast, or to keep the older one back at the baby's pace. Of course, it simplifies her day if the two children can do some things on the same schedule. There are some activities that can be arranged this way—meals, for example or time of starting the nap—but in other activities the children need to be independent of each other. The four-year-old girl may be quite capable of playing outside with the neighborhood children, though little brother of eighteen months is not ready for group play without an adult around. It is not fair to sister to keep her inside until mother has time to take both children out, nor is it good for little brother to push him out with the older children until he is able to fend for himself. Adjustments in routine should be made in a family to take into account different levels of development, even of children close together in years.

How the Small Child Learns

THE speed with which a small child learns can tax a parent's ability to keep pace with him. In this eager quest for knowledge the parent must be ever alert to the need for providing the opportunities for learning useful things rather than acquiring habits that will have to be unlearned later on.

Everything the child sees or hears is contributing to his learning. He learns by imitating others as well as by suggestions we are not conscious of giving him; by trying over and over again to lace his shoes or something else he wants to do.

Between the time children learn to walk and the time they go to school, they cram in more learning than they possibly can in that amount of time later, for they are learning with every bit of their bodies. Their mouths, their ears, their noses, their eyes, their feet, and their hands are all channels for the knowledge that pours into their minds. They learn what different sounds mean, how to get feet into shoes and buttons into buttonholes; they learn to use speech, so that they can tell others about their wants and interests.

Parents can find a great deal of enjoyment in setting the stage so that their children make the most of these tremendously important years if they will keep in mind some of the rules upon which learning is based.

Learning is dependent upon the development of all parts, structures, and organs of the body until they reach maturity; it takes place by degrees.

How a child learns will depend upon the readiness of his body, especially of his brain and nervous system, for whatever it is we want him to do.

We are sure to fail if we try to teach a child something before he has developed enough to undertake it. Sometimes people try to bring about the dry habit in a baby whose nervous system has not matured enough to make control of the bladder possible. To sit quietly in church or to remain quiet at the table while grown-ups

313

enjoy a long-drawn-out meal is very difficult for 2- and 3-year-olds because they have not developed to the point where they can bear to be inactive for so long.

If attempts are made to force a child to learn things he is not ready for, his lack of success is all too likely to make him unwilling to try to learn other new things.

Waiting until the proper stage of development has been reached is important, but just as important to a child's habit training is an opportunity to do things when he *is* ready. If he is not allowed to experiment and practice when he has an urge to do so, he may lose the desire to learn. This is sometimes true, for example, of a child whose mother does not take advantage of his interest in feeding himself when it appears. By continuing to feed him she gradually builds up in him a feeling of pleasure at getting this attention that is greater than the pleasure he would have in doing something for himself. This loss of desire to learn can happen in connection with playing with other children, dressing himself, or any other part of his learning experience.

LEARNING BY ENJOYMENT

A child, like everyone else, has to do a thing over and over again to learn to do it well. When he takes his first steps, a baby's movements are clumsy and unorganized. Only after many attempts and many months does he succeed in emerging from the staggering, wavering stage of walking to the sure, confident gait of the three-year-old.

It is the same with everything he learns; holding a spoon, building with blocks, steering his wagon—all have to be practiced over and over.

But why do some things take so much more repetition than others? Why does a baby learn the thumb-sucking habit after only a few tries and yet take so long to learn to keep dry? This brings up another very important part of learning; that pleasure-giving acts become habits much more quickly than things that give no special satisfaction. Thumb sucking gives a child pleasure, but it is no fun for him to keep having his clothes taken off and to have to sit still on the toilet.

Because he tends to repeat what he enjoys, it is worth while for us to try to make enjoyable those things we want a child to learn. Going to bed, washing, eating desirable foods are some of the things we want the child to make habitual, so we must make them simple and pleasant. A story at bedtime helps to make going to bed enjoyable. Having the things a child needs for washing handy for him and letting him do as much as possible himself about getting clean, encourages the enjoyment of cleanliness. A small-sized fork, foods that are attractive to look at as well as to taste, a cup or glass that can be handled easily, help a child to learn good eating habits. In the earlier stages, letting a baby have a spoon and try to help feed himself when the food is easily managed (like mashed potatoes) is a good plan, for he finds it pleasant to be active in satisfying his own desires. A happy atmosphere at mealtime too will encourage him to form good eating habits.

Of course, we must be equally careful to see that a child has no chance to attach unpleasant feelings to the things we want him to learn. Thus, we must see to it that he is not uncomfortable on the toilet seat when we are training him for toilet habits. We must be sure not to nag and scold him when he is learning to feed himself. We must make sure that he has interesting things to do when we are teaching him to play alone. When he is learning to play with other children, we must try to arrange it so that his first experiences are happy.

Handicaps to Learning

1. If we insist too much or too frequently that a child do a certain thing over and over, we shall dull his interest and may even lead him to develop a resistant attitude. If, for example, we insist on a child's feeding himself for a whole meal while he is still very far from expert at it, we are hindering the building up of good eating habits. If we interrupt his play too frequently to put him on the toilet, we risk having him hate the whole business.

2. If a mother is too concerned about her child, she may actually

slow up or interfere with his learning. Too great anxiety over whether a child eats enough, sleeps enough, learns to keep dry early enough, often has the effect of making him resist learning. If she talks too much about his eating, sleeping, toilet, or other habits, she causes feelings of unpleasantness, and this is just the opposite of what she is trying to achieve.

3. If the parents are impatient at their children's slowness and fumbling in learning to do things that seem simple and easy to grown-ups, they may hinder good habit formation by making a child stubbornly refuse to try, or fearful of trying, new things. If we tried to look at things through children's eyes, and to feel things through their skin and muscles, we would be slower to criticize and correct when they make mistakes or seem clumsy.

Such things as getting a button into a buttonhole, getting peas up off a plate, and closing a door gently all involve delicate, fine muscle movements that require many trials, with many errors, before they are fully mastered. We should praise the child's successes and not show irritation over his failures.

Making Learning Easy

Children will learn desirable habits more cheerfully and quickly if parents remember to arrange things so that learning is made easy and simple. Clothes, for example, should be made in such a way that the child can get into them easily and can fasten them himself. Table arrangements should take into consideration the difficulty a child has in handling dishes and silver. When he is eating at the family table, his chair seat should be high enough so that his arms can move freely above the level of the table; his feet should rest firmly on a stool or box provided for that purpose.

LEARNING TO DO THINGS FOR HIMSELF

Because small children enjoy playing in water, the first steps in teaching them to keep clean are often easy. As with feeding or dressing themselves, they find satisfaction in personal accomplishment. At the same time, they are gaining confidence in their ability to do things for themselves and becoming more self-reliant.

Before he is two, a child can wash his own hands if the basin is placed on a low bench or if a box or step is provided by means of which he may reach the washbowl comfortably.

While a child is learning to wash, he should be allowed time enough so that he won't have to be hustled on to the next thing—a meal or bed or dressing; and if we want to keep his attitude toward getting clean pleasant, we won't talk about what a poor job he has done.

Many three- and four-year-olds love to try to comb their own hair, brush their teeth, and wash their own faces. If a low-hung mirror is provided, they can see how successful their efforts are.

By the time a child is four or five, he can often bathe himself fairly well, with a little help about back, neck, and ears.

At these ages children enjoy cleaning up the bowl and tub, and so may be taught to leave them clean, although, of course, they won't do a perfect job. The idea back of such training is, of course, that what is done with pleasure will more readily become a habit, and that a routine of toilet behavior will become almost second nature by everyday repetition.

If a child is trained to have bowel movements at certain times of day, to bathe and to brush his teeth regularly, we may expect him to have such habits pretty well established by the time he goes to school. Everything that he learns to do for himself will add to his belief in his own ability and will increase his self-reliance when he later comes to do such things as going on the streetcar alone or making purchases at a store.

Learning to Dress Himself

A baby of a year can take part in dressing only to the extent of holding out his arm or leg when his mother is putting a garment on him. At fifteen months he may pull off his shoes and by eighteen months is often taking off his socks or slipping out of his overalls.

By the time a child is two he is usually interested in helping to put on clothes as well as to take them off. He doesn't do it very well, but his interest suggests the importance of having his clothing very simple, so that his efforts will be successful. If the trousers of his suit are laid out in front of him, and if they are clearly marked in some way so that he can tell back from front, there is some chance he will get them on right-side-to.

For the next months it will be very worth while to make it easy for the child to help himself. While the child is learning to dress himself, lay out the clothes in a certain order and help by saying, "Shirt first, now the socks," so that the child will begin to learn the right order. Brief, clear suggestions, quietly given, using the same simple words every day will bring better results than hurried or difficult directions; every time a child successfully accomplishes a thing, the habit you are trying to help him learn will be strengthened.

Little girls are often somewhat more interested in and quicker at learning to dress than boys; this may be due to their slightly more advanced development. A girl twin will often be amusing in her eagerness to help her brother, for example.

A three-year-old can usually do a good part of his dressing, although he still sometimes gets pants or sweater on hind-side-to and makes a hit-or-miss job of lacing his shoes. He will probably be doing so well about dressing when he is 4 that he needs help only with buttons that are in the back and with his shoelaces. Ordinarily, he will be unable to tie the laces in a bow until he is five or six.

As the child develops control of his muscles, it is important, then, to provide clothes that promote self-help. A little girl can get into a dress with loose raglan sleeves easily, but she finds one with fitted armholes more difficult. If a little boy's suits are of the knitted type, with an elastic waist band in the pants and a jumper top on which a pocket shows which is the front, he can deal with dressing with much less irritation than if he has a suit with pants that button onto the blouse all the way around.

Buttons should be large enough to be handled easily by fingers not yet able to manage tiny buttons and holes. Zippers are well liked, provided they are put in so that they don't catch the edges of material. Snap fasteners are hard for young children to deal with; so are hooks and eyes and crocheted buttons with loops.

The more things that fasten in front the better; little girls' dresses can just as well be made with an opening down the front—something to watch for when buying dresses.

It is easier for a little boy to go to the toilet alone if he has pants that can be slipped down or that are wide enough in the legs so that he can push the pants leg aside when he urinates. Underwear for little girls should have broad elastic in the sides of the waist band. Narrow elastic constricts the child's abdomen if the band is tight enough to stay up.

Outdoor garments are harder for a child to manage than his indoor clothing, as they are bulkier and heavier. A one-piece garment has fewer places for wind or snow to enter, but a child can use the toilet more easily when wearing a two-piece garment.

Galoshes and rubbers should be bought large enough so that they slip on easily, but even so, some help with them may be needed even by the four- or five-year-old.

Though the four-year-old can manage his dressing pretty well, it still helps to have his clothes laid out in an orderly way. He will almost certainly do better in a room by himself than with another child to distract him and talk to him. If he dresses in the same room with his father or mother, he may sometimes enjoy "racing" to see who can finish first.

Once the child has learned how to dress himself, you might think it would not be necessary to urge him to. But to the four-, five-, and six-year-old, dressing is no longer an exciting novelty that he is proud to be able to do; it is "old stuff." At six especially, children often are somewhat bored with getting their clothes on, and they often tend to dawdle. They have not yet come to accept the dressing business as a necessary evil, the sooner out of the way the better.

When a child is old enough to go to school, his eagerness to get there may mean that he speeds up his dressing. But this may not last long. A certain amount of pokiness must be expected as a child becomes more interested in a great many other things than he is in putting on his clothes by himself. Nagging and hurrying him will make things worse rather than better. Although it is a great temptation to talk to a child in an effort to hurry him up, he soon becomes deaf to his mother's urging. Removing all possible distractions, pointing out to him on a clock in his room just how far the minute-hand has to go before it will be time for him to be dressed, thinking up new little incentives that will make him feel important ("It will be your turn to pour the orange juice this morning"; "If you are quick you'll have time to shovel a path to the garbage can for me"; "Will you bring in the newspaper for father as soon as you are dressed?") are some of the things it will pay to keep in mind.

Perhaps it seems unnecessary to lay so much stress on encouraging a child to dress himself without help. But when we see children of nine or ten, or even older, who are still dependent on their mothers to help them with their dressing, find their mittens, and turn their coat sleeves right side out when they are wildly trying to get ready for school, we feel pretty strongly that much more careful planning could go into the business of training children to be self-reliant.

The following suggestions should be helpful in this respect:

1. Make use of the baby's and young child's first interest in putting on his own clothes.

2. Praise the child's accomplishments when they show effort on his part, even if what he does seems very trivial from a grown-up's point of view.

3. Allow plenty of time for a child to get into his clothes when he is at the stage of wanting to do it "all by 'self." If he tires toward the end of a job, make your help as unobtrusive as possible ("Now when mother fastens your coat, you'll be all ready to go out," or "I'll put on one shoe, you put on one shoe"). If the parent doesn't suddenly or impatiently take over the job, the child is likely to look upon her help as cooperation rather than interference.

4. Arrange clothing so that the child will get a feeling of order: "First your sweater; now your leggings; next is your cap; now, the mittens."

5. Let the routine be the same every day, so that the child will

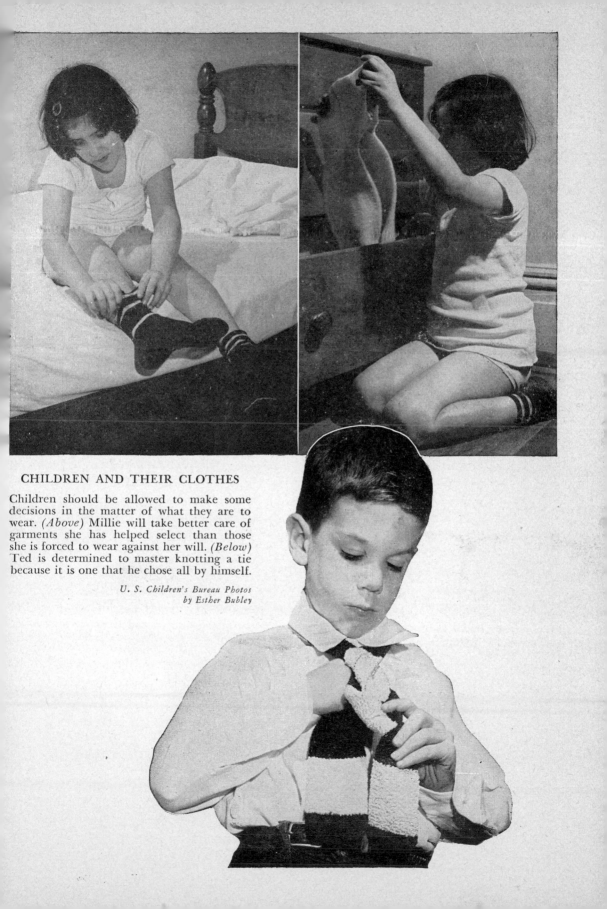

CHILDREN AND THEIR CLOTHES

Children should be allowed to make some decisions in the matter of what they are to wear. *(Above)* Millie will take better care of garments she has helped select than those she is forced to wear against her will. *(Below)* Ted is determined to master knotting a tie because it is one that he chose all by himself.

U. S. Children's Bureau Photos
by Esther Bubley

LESSONS IN SELF-RELIANCE

At an early age most children try imitating their elders. Moreover, it is always fun for them to play with water, whether in cleaning the teeth, bathing or helping with the dishes. Encourage these attempts at self-help for they build confidence, dexterity, and the habit of cleanliness.

see the reason for dressing; that is, don't allow dressing *after* break-fast one morning and insist that the child be dressed *before* eating the next. Children accept things that fall into a routine and are confused by irregularity.

6. As soon as a child is old enough, let him get out and put away his own clothing. This means having drawers and hooks low enough for him to reach, a place for him to put soiled clothing, and a chair or rack upon which he may hang his clothes at night.

7. When a child starts going to school, teach him to get ready at night the things he will need in the morning. If such things as cap and mittens, a clean shirt or dress, and so on, are laid out at bedtime, there will be far less confusion in the busy morning hours.

8. If a child must be ready for breakfast at a certain hour, call him early enough so that he has plenty of time to dress. Remember that each step takes longer for him than it would for you. Also, keep in mind that each child differs in his rate of speed.

LEARNING THROUGH ASKING

Having learned to talk, the small child is no longer limited to what he can see, hear, taste, smell, and feel. Now he can ask about them too. In the number and variety of questions he can ask is tangible evidence of his mental growth.

Throughout the day his active mind is seeking the answers that will give him a sense of security and of being a part of his parents' world. There is no limit to his curiosity or to the kinds of questions he may ask, and a parent is often hard-pressed to provide a satis-factory answer.

Whether a child's questions are amusing or disconcerting, they do suggest the opportunity his lively interest affords us to add to his information and enrich his mind. There is a remarkable differ-ence at six years of age between those children who have had much conversation and many good picture books and magazines to look at and those children whose background has not provided these advantages.

Sometimes grown-ups are at a loss to know how to answer

children's questions or don't want to take the time to. The temptation is great to say, "Oh, you're not old enough to understand," and let it go at that. If a child meets this response over and over, he may become discouraged and lose faith in the very persons who should be stimulating him to learn.

Unfortunately, putting a child off is most likely to occur when he asks important questions about where he came from and what it means to be born and to die. The kinds of answers children get to the hardest questions of all will affect them more than we realize. An adult who acts embarrassed and hesitant tells a child something by his manner. He tells him that these are "forbidden" topics, about which people feel very strongly.

Unless a mother prepares herself to be frank and truthful when her child bursts out with an unexpected tough question, there is danger of damage to the relationship between her and the child. If she takes pains to equip herself so that she can talk naturally when he asks questions about his body, her frankness will encourage him to come to her again when he is puzzled. If she is the one who tells him things, she can be sure of giving him information that is true, but if he has to rely on what he can pick up from the discussions of other children, he will almost certainly be misinformed.

Questions About Death

One of the half-truths that should be avoided is telling a child that dying is "just like going to sleep." Many a child has been terror-stricken at the idea of waking up in a box deep in the ground and not being able to get out. To tell a child that he will go "up into Heaven" when he dies is not much more comforting, for to a very young child the idea of going to a far-away place and being separated from his parents is almost unbearable. It is more sensible to point out to him that he is not at all likely to die, that nowadays children are given such good care that they do not need to worry about dying. If his attention has been called to death because of the loss of some older person in the family, he may be told that they were content to leave. If death comes to one of his playmates, some parents may like to express their belief that such a child is with grandmother (or some loved person who has passed on), so that the child's imagination will not dwell on how he would feel at being removed from his parents. The idea of being with God is a very vague one to his mind, which deals only with things he can see or touch.

It is not so much what is told a child as how it is done. A little child has such faith in his parents that he is ready to accept with comfort what he feels they believe. The forms of their belief, of course, will depend on the religion of the family.

Because little children may suffer feelings of great insecurity from seeing grief in adults whom they think of as strong and able to deal with anything, it is just as well for them not to attend funerals until they are old enough not to be frightened by the sorrow of adults.

Although it is very hard for a child to have a pet die, this sort of experience may really be of value to him, for he comes to understand that death is inevitable through a milder sorrow than he would feel at the death of a loved person. By degrees he is able to accept the idea that everything and everyone must die; but, seeing also the rebirth that takes place each spring, he can be given some idea of how life goes on even though some plants die.

A little child's curiosity is usually very easily satisfied. All that is necessary is to answer his question of the moment, without trying to go into long explanations that are beyond his understanding. A mother who complains that her child is not content with brief, specific answers but demands more than she believes he is ready for, has probably made her remarks emotional instead of answering as casually as she would if he had asked about the dust motes in a ray of sunlight.

What children really want is to feel that their parents can be relied on. If the father and mother never let them down by silencing them or telling them they are too young to know or making them ashamed of having asked, they will continue to think of their parents as the natural source of information. They may, and very often do, forget the explanation that is given and ask the very same thing over again later on. When this happens, parents can feel pretty sure their manner has been so normal and natural that the child is building up no inhibitions.

Food for the Preschool Child

FROM the first year on, and particularly during the preschool years, the child is forming food habits that may stay with him for years to come. Although not growing as fast as when he was a baby, he is using up more energy, so his food must provide fuel for the body, as well as the materials for building bigger muscles and bones and new teeth. Whether he refuses or accepts the variety of new foods that continue to be offered him, will decide the difference between the good and bad food habits he acquires during these most important years.

A child who has been given enough of the right kinds of food as a baby will not have to make any sudden changes in his diet when he reaches his first birthday. On the contrary, the changes in the kinds and amounts of food he is given and in the way they are served should be made so gradually that he does not notice them.

The following table shows the main groups of foods that are given to children of preschool age and the quantities that healthy children of average size and appetite may be expected to eat.

Most foods are equally suitable for grown-ups and for children of various ages. Of course, the youngest members at the family table will eat smaller quantities of most foods and they will need to have meat, vegetables, and fruit prepared for easy handling and for chewing with less than a full set of teeth. A few foods that the rest of the family eats should not be offered to the children from one to six, but they will not expect to have them unless some grown-up puts the idea into their heads.

The same meals, with slight variations, will take care of a two-year-old and a five-year-old as well as their parents and older brothers and sisters. Unless the family eats its evening meal early, the children of preschool age will probably have their supper by themselves.

Eating a meal is not easy for a young child. Parents should see that the food is prepared and served so that it appeals to the child. It should also be fixed so that he can eat it with a minimum of help from older members of the family and without getting tired out in doing so. This does not mean preparing meals just for the preschool child. It does mean giving some thought to combinations of foods on the child's plate and to the appearance, form, flavor, and temperature of the food. Attention to a few details makes all the difference in the world in the way children respond to their food. Here are some suggestions for making meals appealing and easy to eat:

Teaching Him to Eat New Foods

Children like best the foods that they know best. Plan to use not more than one new food at any meal. Give only a small portion of the unfamiliar food the first time. Introduce it in the same meal with some food the child likes especially. If the child accepts the little that is offered, serve that same food again within a few days and increase the size of the portion slightly. Keep on in this way until the child accepts this food as an old friend; after that, it can be served as often as it appears on the family table.

Children like very simple foods; they usually like foods served separately rather than combined with others so that it is hard to tell the different foods apart. For example, they tend at first to like meat and potato by themselves better than as hash.

FOOD SHOULD BE APPETIZING AND APPEALING

Color makes foods appealing to children. They also like food cooked in individual dishes, such as a cup custard, and they are pleased with an occasional surprise, like a few pieces of fruit at the bottom of the cup.

FOODS INCLUDED IN A GOOD DAILY DIET FOR CHILDREN FROM 1 TO 6[1]

FOOD	AMOUNT NEEDED BY EACH CHILD DAILY	AVERAGE SIZE OF SERVING FOR EACH AGE		
		1 YEAR OLD	2 AND 3 YEARS OLD	4 AND 5 YEARS OLD
Milk	3 to 4 measuring cups	1 cup as a drink at each meal		
Eggs	1 egg	1 whole egg		
Meat, poultry, or fish	1 to 2 oz. (2 to 4 table-spoonfuls)	1 oz. (2 table-spoonfuls)	1½ oz. (3 table-spoonfuls)	2 oz. (4 table-spoonfuls)
Dried beans, peas, lentils	1 serving 2 or 3 times a week when meats and eggs are hard to get	Strained in soup	3 table-spoonfuls	4 table-spoonfuls
Potatoes	1 serving	2 table-spoonfuls	3 table-spoonfuls	4 table-spoonfuls
Other cooked vege-tables (a green leafy or deep-yel-low vegetable of-ten)	1 to 2 servings	2 table-spoonfuls	3 table-spoonfuls	4 table-spoonfuls
Raw vegetables (let-tuce, carrots, cel-ery, tomatoes, etc.)	Small amount	....	A small piece, or two	
Fruit for vitamin C	1 medium-sized orange or ½ to ¾ cup tomato juice	Whole day's amount in one serving		
Other fruit (apple, banana, peaches, prunes)	1 to 2 servings	¼ cup	⅓ cup	½ cup
Cereal, whole-grain, restored, or en-riched	1 serving	¼ cup	⅓ cup	½ cup
Bread, whole-grain or enriched	1½ to 5 slices	½ to 1 slice	1 to 1½ slices	1½ to 2 slices
Butter or fortified margarine	1 to 2 tablespoon-fuls	1 teaspoon-ful	1 to 3 tea-spoonfuls	1 to 3 tea-spoonfuls
Sweets	A simple dessert at 1 or 2 meals	¼ cup	⅓ cup	½ cup
Fish-liver oil	Enough to pro-vide 400 to 800 U. S. P.[2] units of vitamin D			

[1] All measurements in this chart are level, measuring cups and measuring spoons be-ing used.
[2] United States Pharmacopoeia.

Children learn to like some foods that have a strong flavor—onions, for example—but they usually prefer to eat only one strong-flavored food at a meal. So turnips and peas are better dinner partners than turnips and cabbage. Most children like foods that are not highly seasoned or spiced or very sour.

One crisp food in a meal appeals to the child and teaches him to chew as well. Foods that are gummy, sticky, or stringy are almost always unpopular. It often helps to stir a little more milk than the rest of the family likes into the portion of mashed potatoes or a cornstarch pudding that is to be given to a young child. Gelatin desserts should be quivery rather than stiff.

Many young children like most of their foods lukewarm. This is another reason why soft foods like cream soups and sauces should be thinned a little for children; otherwise they may be too thick by the time they have cooled to the temperature that the child prefers.

MAKING EATING EASY

Until children have acquired skill in handling table silver, it will be helpful to serve many foods, such as toast and pieces of raw vegetable, in strips that can be picked up in the fingers. Meat should be cut into small pieces unless it has been ground or minced before cooking. One mashed vegetable on a plate keeps slippery foods like lima beans and cubes of meat from being pushed off the plane onto the tray or table. Some cooked vegetables and fruits should be cut into bite-size pieces so that they will be easier to handle.

A child who is learning to feed himself needs some help from the tools that he is given. Plates, bowls, cups, and glasses should not be easy to tip over or otherwise spill from. Spoons, and later, forks, and knives, when the child begins to use them, should fit small hands.

The usual "baby spoon" with a curved handle is a poor implement, but one with a short straight handle is more easily managed. The bowl of the spoon should be round and shallow. The fork also should have a short straight handle and wide blunt tines. An adult's salad fork, if blunt, makes a good fork for a child. A child seldom uses a knife at this age.

EATING BETWEEN MEALS

Some preschool children, especially the younger ones, will need something to eat oftener than three times a day. They will probably be hungry at about the same time each day, and a regular plan can be made for a light lunch that will satisfy hunger without taking away the appetite for the more hearty meal that is to follow. The food offered at this lunch should be a regular part of the child's diet; it should be something that supplies minerals and vitamins as well as energy. Many children will welcome tomato juice or fruit juice with a plain cooky or two, or a slice of bread and butter. The child who has a between-meal appetite only for candy or ice cream is probably not genuinely hungry.

FOODS AND FOOD VALUES FOR THE PRESCHOOL CHILD

Milk

As the child grows older, milk still contributes more than any other single food although it is relatively less important than it was during the first year of life. Milk is outstanding as a source of the mineral calcium and the vitamin riboflavin and is also a good source of the best quality of protein, of vitamin A, and of thiamin (vitamin B_1). The preschool child is somewhat less dependent on milk for these essential nutrients than when he was a baby because he is eating a wider variety of foods. If a preschool child takes three cups of milk readily and has a good appetite for the other important foods in his diet, he is probably getting enough milk. A few children will not take more than one pint voluntarily and if they are persuaded to drink more will not eat enough other foods. Under these circumstances the doctor should be consulted to see whether the child is getting all the nourishment he needs from the combination of milk and other foods. Many children will not eat enough other food if they drink all their milk at the beginning of a meal. In such cases it is wise to give most of the milk at the end of the meal.

Any form of safe milk (whole fluid, unsweetened evaporated, or dried) is suitable for children of preschool age.

Cheese

Mild American cheese, cottage cheese, and cream cheese combined with other foods are suitable for young children but need not have a very large place in the diet of children who will take enough milk as milk. Cream cheese has a high proportion of fat and less protein than other cheese. Other forms of cheese are good sources of protein. Those made from whole milk are rich in vitamin A. American cheese is high in calcium.

When cheese is used in cooked foods for young children, it should be grated or cut fine and cooked at a low temperature. For example, in making macaroni and cheese it is better to add the cheese to the white sauce than to arrange it on top of the food in the baking dish and melt it in a hot oven.

Eggs

Eggs are important for proteins, iron, vitamin A, and riboflavin. The yolk has more all-round food value than the white.

Eggs fed to children should be cooked at a low temperature so that they will cook evenly throughout. They may be soft-cooked, hard-cooked in water that only simmers and does not boil, coddled, poached, or used in custards and other puddings. When eggs are cooked in fat, as in scrambling, frying, or making omelets, only enough fat should be used to keep the egg from sticking to the pan.

A few children are sensitive to egg in any form, in which case the doctor should be consulted.

Meat, Poultry and Fish

FOOD VALUE. These foods contribute chiefly protein, iron, thiamin, riboflavin, and niacin. Liver is especially rich in these minerals and vitamins and also supplies vitamin A. Salt-water fish and shell-fish are rich in iodine.

Any form of poultry or lean meat, including the lean portions of pork and ham, and organs such as brains, liver, sweetbreads, and kidneys, may be given to young children. Pork should always be thoroughly cooked. Highly seasoned meats, such as many kinds of sausage, very salty meats, and meats containing large quantities of fat are not suitable foods for children of this age. Liver may well be given to children at least once a week. Beef, lamb, pork, and chicken livers are as high in nutritive value as the more expensive calves' liver. Children usually like all these kinds of liver.

Fish and shellfish may take the place of meat frequently in the diet of the young child. Oysters resemble liver in food value; only cooked oysters should be given to children.

Bacon should not be considered a substitute for lean meat; when it is cooked until it is crisp and the fat drained off, it supplies principally flavor to the child's other food.

How to Prepare. For the most part, meat, poultry, or fish for young children should be broiled, stewed, roasted, or baked. It should not be highly seasoned nor served with gravy containing enough fat to float on the surface. If fried, it should be cooked with great care so that it does not absorb a large amount of fat. The fat should be hot enough to cook the food quickly but not hot enough to burn. The food should be coated with flour or crumbs that will form a protective coating and keep much fat from soaking into the food. The cooked food should be drained on absorbent paper before serving so that any excess fat will be left on the paper.

To serve, the meat or fish should be cut into pieces small enough for the child to eat easily. This may mean chopping or grinding for the youngest preschool child and cutting in pieces for the older ones. Fish should have all the bones removed.

Fruits

Food Value. All fruits help to meet the child's need for iron, thiamin, and riboflavin. Citrus fruits (oranges, grapefruit, tangerines, and lemons) are the child's most important sources of vitamin C, which is also found in large quantities in strawberries, cantaloupes, and the guavas and mangoes of the semitropical regions of the country. All raw fruits supply some vitamin C. The dried fruits are better than average sources of iron. Yellow-fleshed fruits, such as yellow peaches and apricots, and prunes contain also considerable quantities of vitamin A.

The citrus fruits are the most important fruits in the young child's diet because he eats so few other foods that contain large quantities of vitamin C. Early in the preschool period, the child will take his orange or grapefruit as juice, fresh or canned, but by the time he has enough teeth to chew well, he can be given sections of fruit to eat. The whole sections contain more vitamin C than the juice. The child over two may be given ripe strawberries as well as small pieces of ripe but sound melon. For the greater part of the year, however, oranges or grapefruit will be the main source of vitamin C among the fruits, and tomatoes or tomato juice among the vegetables.

PREPARING FRUIT. Cooked fruits, including canned fruits and cooked dried fruits, can be given to children; a large amount of sugar should not be used, only enough to make them taste good. The sweeter dried fruits, prunes, for example, may be sweet enough without added sugar. Only mild, ripe fruits which can be peeled, such as apples, apricots, bananas, and peaches, should be given raw to children under two years of age. The fruit should be thoroughly washed before peeling, and any overripe parts thrown way. In introducing any raw fruits it is best to start with a small quantity and make sure that it does not have too much of a laxative effect before giving more generous servings. Fruits for very young children should be scraped or mashed, and berries that have large seeds should be cooked and strained.

After the age of two, children can have all kinds of ripe fruits, raw or cooked. Tough, stringy, and overripe portions should be removed, as should the pits of such fruits as apricots and prunes.

Vegetables

FOOD VALUE. Vegetables in general are important chiefly for minerals and vitamins, some vegetables more than others. Most vegetables contain some fiber and so help to promote regular bowel movements.

Thin, dark-green leaves, eaten raw or properly cooked, are valuable for iron, vitamin A, thiamin, and riboflavin. Greens, such as turnip tops and kale, are even richer in some of these nutrients than spinach.

The deep-yellow vegetables, such as carrots and sweet potatoes, are valuable chiefly for vitamin A.

Tomatoes, raw, cooked, or canned, and tomato juice are very rich in vitamin C and a good source of vitamin A. Tomato juice contains about half as much vitamin C as orange juice, and, therefore, should be given in twice the quantity.

White, or Irish, potatoes, cooked in their skins, are a good source of vitamin C, especially when new, and also contribute iron. Both white potatoes and sweet potatoes are energy foods.

Dried beans and peas and soybeans are good sources of protein, iron, thiamin, and riboflavin.

PREPARING VEGETABLES. Tender, raw vegetables may be served to young children over two to give them practice in chewing as well as to furnish food value. These include strips of young carrots or young turnips, celery hearts, leaves of lettuce or cabbage, and tomatoes. It is important that any raw vegetables given to children be safe for them to eat. Care should be taken to make the home vegetable garden safe. If there is any reason to suspect that vegetables may have come from polluted soil, they should not be served raw. Vegetables that are to be eaten raw should be washed only in water that is known to be safe for drinking.

Among the cooked vegetables the green and deep-yellow ones should be served most. Those that have a mild flavor will probably be accepted most readily. They should be cooked in a small quantity of water in a covered container and only until tender. In introducing the stronger-flavored vegetable, such as turnips and onions, it is more important to cook them so that they will appeal to the children than to save every last bit of vitamins and minerals. This may mean cooking in a fairly large quantity of water and draining off the water.

Vegetables should be lightly salted and served with a little butter, fortified margarine, cream, milk, gravy, or white sauce. No other seasoning is needed or desirable. The vegetables should be in pieces small enough for the child to eat easily; for very young children some vegetables may well be mashed.

Corn and those kinds of dried beans and peas that have tough skins should be rubbed through a sieve before they are served to the youngest children in this age group.

CANNED VEGETABLES. Vegetables canned according to safe methods are as good for children as those cooked at the time of serving. When home-canned foods are used, it is much safer to boil them for 15 minutes even if they are to be served cold. Stir the contents of the saucepan so that all parts are equally hot; watch the time after boiling has begun.

These precautions are advisable because vegetables may have been contaminated with certain bacteria that grow in some soils and cause a dangerous type of food poisoning, botulism.

The chopped vegetables packed in small cans for the younger preschool children are useful principally when the child is traveling and the mother may have difficulty in getting properly prepared vegetables. Both home-canned and commercially canned vegetables should be tasted to see that they are well seasoned before they are served. Day in and day out young children and their parents will all be better off if enough vegetables are prepared for everybody. The servings for very young children should be separated before seasoning is added for the family, then mashed or cut up according to the child's stage of tooth development.

Quick-frozen vegetables cooked only until tender are perfectly suitable foods for children.

Cereals and Bread

All forms of cereal and bread furnish energy and protein. Cereals, flour, and bread that are made from the whole grain or those that have been enriched or restored by the addition of minerals and vitamins after milling, are also important sources of iron, thiamin, riboflavin, and niacin. The label will indicate when bread, flour, or cereal is made from the whole grain or has been enriched or restored. These are the grain products that should be emphasized in children's meals. Young children like whole-grain breads and cereals, and if these are served regularly, children will grow up liking them.

The special, highly fortified baby cereals that some doctors recommend for babies can be replaced in the preschool period by the same cereals that the family eats. In general, the cereals that require cooking in the home are more economical and may well be served most often. However, those ready-to-eat cereals that have been made from the whole grain or have been restored, are nutritious foods and usually well liked by children, especially in hot weather. They usually absorb considerable milk, an advantage for children who find it difficult to take enough milk as a drink. The least desirable forms of breakfast cereal for young children are: (1) Those that contain large quantities of coarse bran, and (2) those that are so fluffy that a whole bowlful weighs very little and does not meet the child's need for energy.

Hot rolls, biscuit, corn bread, and other hot breads that have a crisp but tender crust may be given occasionally to children in the last half of the preschool period. These children may have a small serving of waffles, thin, tender pancakes, or French toast when other members of the family are having them.

Bread should be spread lightly with butter or fortified margarine. The addition of syrup or jam converts bread and crackers into a dessert and, like other desserts, this combination should follow and not replace the main part of the meal.

Crackers should be given to young children only occasionally; those that are neither very sweet nor heavily salted are to be preferred. Melba toast, made from bread dried in the oven, is a satisfactory and inexpensive substitute for crackers.

Butter or Fortified Margarine

Butter and fortified margarine supply energy and vitamin A. Children of preschool age need only enough butter or fortified margarine to spread thinly on bread and to season vegetables, or in milk sauce or soup. Foods that have been made with considerable fat, such as pastry, poorly fried potatoes or doughnuts, may prove difficult for the young child to digest and may take away his appetite for the simple foods that should be the mainstay of his diet.

Sweets

The amount of sugar that is used in sweetening fruits or simple desserts is all that the young child needs. Children usually like cereal without added sugar if they have never been given any other kind. A few raisins or chopped dates may be added to cooked cereal for children over two. Children are perfectly happy also with crisp molasses cookies; plain, unfrosted cake; buttered bread spread with molasses (a rich source of iron); a gelatin dessert that is mostly fruit; or a milk pudding. Among the frozen desserts, milk sherbets or ice cream made with a custard base are better than ice cream that is richer in fat. Concentrated sweets, like frosted cake, ice cream with a rich sauce, or candy, are almost sure to crowd out more important foods from the child's diet. If candy and other sweets are given to children, it should be only at the close of a meal and in small amounts.

Fruit Juices and Other Beverages

Fruit juices are important foods for young children. Most children like them and will take them plain. The special milk drinks, many of them flavored with chocolate, are sometimes resorted to when children seem to dislike ordinary whole milk. Many parents have found, however, that children tire quickly of these drinks. It is best to save them for special occasions.

In serving fruit beverages to children, it is important to know whether they really contain fruit juice. Some of the commercial fruit beverages contain little or no fruit juice; they are a poor investment at any price.

No beverages that contain a stimulant are suitable for children of this age; these include not only coffee, tea, and strong cocoa but also many of the carbonated bottled beverages of the cola type.

Vitamin D

Sunshine helps the child grow normally. It gives his body the power to use food so as to help build straight bones and sound teeth. Sunshine is considered "direct" when the rays fall on the skin without having to pass through clothing or window glass, both of which greatly reduce the beneficial effect. When sunshine reaches the skin directly, vitamin D is formed in the body.

But the child does not usually get enough vitamin D through

	FAMILY MEAL	TWO-YEAR-OLD CHILD	FIVE-YEAR-OLD CHILD
Morning	Orange (1) Oatmeal (½ cup) with cream Whole-wheat toast (2 slices) Butter Milk or coffee (1 cup)	Orange juice (4-6 table-spoonfuls) Oatmeal (3-4 table-spoonfuls) with milk Whole-wheat toast (½ slice) Butter Milk (1 cup)	Orange (1) Oatmeal (½ cup) with milk Whole-wheat toast (1 slice) Butter Milk (1 cup)
Noontime	Egg salad Potato (cooked in jacket) Peas, fresh (½ cup) Whole-wheat bread (2 slices) Butter Fruit cup (⅔ cup) Milk (1 cup)	Hard-cooked egg or beef ball Potato (cooked in jacket) Sieved peas (½ cup) Whole-wheat bread, stale or toasted (½ slice) Butter Pear, cooked and mashed (4 tablespoonfuls) Milk (1 cup)	Hard-cooked egg (1) Peas, fresh (½ cup) Potato (cooked in jacket) Whole-wheat bread (1 slice) Butter Fruit cup (⅔ cup) Milk (1 cup)
Evening	Beef balls with spaghetti String beans (½ cup) Carrot and cabbage salad Whole-wheat bread (1-2 slices) Butter Apple Betty Milk or coffee	Well-cooked whole-grain cereal (4 tablespoon-fuls) with milk (2-4 tablespoonfuls) Stale bread (1 slice) Butter Apple sauce (¼ cup) Milk (1 cup)	Beef balls (1) String beans (½ cup) Carrot strips (3 pieces) Whole-wheat bread (1 slice) Butter Apple Betty (½ cup) Milk (1 cup)

Note.—Fortified margarine may be used in place of butter.

sunshine. Nor can he get enough from the common foods; few of the foods have it and these only in very small amounts. Therefore, it is necessary to give special foods or other preparations, such as fish-liver oil, that supply vitamin D. Your doctor can best advise you which of the many preparations of this vitamin to give your child and how much to give. Some additional form of vitamin D is needed by young children all through the preschool years.

LEARNING GOOD EATING HABITS

By the time they are a year old, most babies have learned to eat many foods. About this time they begin to want to help feed themselves. Because it is fun to be active in satisfying one's desires, the child grabs the spoon and sticks it into the food himself. If he succeeds in making a bit of food cling to the spoon long enough to get it to his mouth, he will be likely to try again.

As we have said, learning anything means repetition. Because a child is more likely to repeat something that is pleasurable, the pleasanter we can make it for him to feed himself, the better. If, for example, his mother tries to help too much, the child's efforts may slow down because it is no fun to be interfered with. If she gives him foods that are hard to manage (cereal that is too liquid, a piece of bread that crumbles), the pleasure in trying to feed himself is lost. While a child is learning to feed himself, it is especially important to serve food that he likes well enough to make the effort. He should be allowed to use his fingers, too, as this way of getting food to his mouth comes naturally to him.

With each passing week, the child's nervous system is maturing, so that he becomes better able to twist his wrist and get the spoon up to his mouth right side up. That he is unable to do this before reaching a certain stage of development reminds us again how useless it is to begin training for any skill until a child has matured enough to be ready for it.

At the outset a child's mother should let him feed himself during the early part of his meal, when he is hungriest, and then quietly feed him the rest of the meal herself. To choose times when he is not tired and sleepy is important.

The main things to keep in mind are:

1. When a baby shows a strong desire to feed himself, it is time to let him try.

2. Much practice is necessary to perfect any skill, so you must expect the baby to be messy about feeding himself for a good while. What little he wastes will not be so costly as the resistance you may set up by constantly correcting him.

3. The repetitions must be pleasant if the learning is to proceed well, so scolding or hurrying is taboo. A plate with raised sides; a low cup with a handle, rather than a glass; a spoon and fork with short, straight handles—all will help.

It is necessary to give a great deal of help while a child is learning to eat by himself, but it will usually be better if a mother does not give the child all her attention. His high chair, or small table and chair, may be placed in the kitchen, where she can be working but can still keep an eye on him to see when he needs help. If his mother sits down with him, she is likely to become irritated by his slowness and to keep fidgeting at him to hurry. A child's unavoidable spilling and general awkwardness will not be the occasion for so much comment if he eats alone or with another child.

Should a Small Child Eat with the Family?

In some homes it will be more convenient if the child eats at the family table fairly soon. In others everyone will be happier, if he is fed separately. Each family will have to decide for itself which works out better; but it is safe to say that the youngest is better off eating alone if adults or older children are constantly correcting him for the way he holds his spoon, or reminding him, while he is still very inexpert, not to spill his soup. A young child will not want to sit at the table throughout a meal of several courses, and it is unfair to expect it of him. Another reason why it may be better not to include a young child at the family table is that his mother will have more freedom to enjoy her own meal if he eats beforehand.

If a child does eat with the family, everyone must be careful not to make unfavorable comments about the food. Children love to copy someone they admire, so if Father turns up his nose at a certain dish, they are likely to follow. If a member of the family is on a diet or cannot eat some things, care should be taken not to make these peculiarities a topic of conversation. Many families, by talking too much about food, concentrate children's attention on it rather than on enjoyment of companionship.

A child who eats with the grown-ups should not be given tastes of unsuitable foods. If this practice is not started, a child will take for granted having different food from that of adults.

If, for any reason, the meals for adults cannot be served at regular hours (if, for instance, the father is a physician or is working at something that often keeps him overtime), it will only stir up trouble to have the children eat with the grown-ups. Little children need to have their meals served with great regularity, as is shown by the greater frequency of cross behavior in children whose mothers are careless about this.

Small or Large Appetites

Children differ greatly in their food needs. A child who has a very small appetite may be just as healthy and grow just as well as one who eats a great deal more. Some children burn up their food very fast; others, less strenuous and excitable, need less food to supply their energy.

Even children with good appetites often lose interest when they face a plate piled with food. Small servings don't so overwhelm a child, and second helpings can be served if he shows an interest in eating more. New foods especially should be introduced in very small amounts; a child will eat a teaspoonful of squash or onions when he might make a scene over having a tablespoonful.

If a child is happy and lively, is growing and gaining weight as he should, and is eating a sufficiently varied diet, it may be assumed that he is probably eating enough for his needs.

Loss of Appetite

There will be times when a child does not eat so well as at others. If a mother learns to recognize some of the reasons for lack of interest in eating, she will be able to handle such times better.

When a child is coming down with a cold or any form of illness, he usually cares little about food. In fact, lack of appetite in a child who usually eats well is one of the first signs of illness.

If refusal of food occurs without any obvious reason, it is a good idea to watch the child carefully for a few hours in order to note whether there are any other signs that he feels out of sorts. If he is listless or whiny, is easily irritated by little things, or acts different in other ways from his usual self, it may be well to take his temperature. Because a runny nose is one of the first noticeable symptoms of some early childhood diseases, the mother should watch for it especially.

If the child is not ill, he will probably be ready to eat by the next meal. If he does turn out to be ill, it will be better for him to have eaten lightly.

A child whose appetite has not returned after an illness must be re-educated by slow degrees. It may have been necessary while he was sick to encourage him to eat and to provide special foods in order to tempt him. Once he is well again, this sort of thing should be tapered off and his regular diet substituted. If no comments are made about the child's eating, if he is encouraged to be out of doors as much as possible, and if he gets plenty of sleep and rest, his food habits should fairly soon be back to normal.

Sometimes refusal of food is due to a child's not being active enough to make him hungry.

Appetite is best kept lively by a well-balanced program of play—indoors and out—rest, and sleep. A child who is used to vigorous outdoor play may be much less hungry if there is a change in his routine that prevents his working off energy out of doors. In winter, if the weather is very bad, the windows of his room may be opened, and he may be dressed in out-of-door garments to play in the open air although he is inside.

Still another reason for a child's having little or no appetite is an emotional upset. If a child has been frightened or alarmed, or if he has been through an exhausting scene in which his will was pitted against that of an adult, he will be in no condition to eat. If he has just come home from some exciting event, like the circus or a movie, the chances are his body is reacting wisely in telling him to avoid eating.

It is not good sense to urge food upon a child who has been under any emotional strain. The amount of food excited young children leave untouched at a birthday party or when they have the new experience of eating at a restaurant, shows how nature postpones hunger till the body is ready to take care of food.

Refusing to Eat

Any discussion of eating habits that omitted refusal of food as a way of getting attention would be leaving out one of the problems mothers meet most frequently.

Partly, no doubt, because of the present-day interest in nutrition, partly because, not having big families on their hands, many mothers now have more time to worry about their child's eating, a distorted situation has grown up in many American homes. The parents in these homes may become so concerned over their children's nourishment that the children discover they have at their disposal a very effective way of getting attention and sometimes, of getting their own way.

Once the mother recognizes that this stalling about eating is a device her child is cleverly using to get notice, it would seem a simple thing to stop giving it. That this is not so is shown by the number of parents who beg for help in handling their children's failure to eat.

They are told, "When the child gets hungry he will eat. Let him alone. Don't let him see that you are concerned. Better still, don't *be* concerned."

Many parents whose child's unwillingness to eat has become a real "problem" will try the plan of quietly removing the child's food if he has not eaten in a reasonable length of time. But then, if the child's long-standing practice doesn't stop at once, they become worried and begin coaxing again. Children don't starve because they go without a meal or two or even three. If a child is in good physical condition and your physician suggests it, it is safe to follow for as long as a week or two the plan of offering food and taking it away with no comments if it goes uneaten.

But the very mother who has got deepest into this kind of trouble is the overanxious, overcareful one who finds it hardest to pull out. The one who has merely blundered into the habit of talking too much about her child's eating habits, or whose child's lack of appetite is due to some temporary thing, finds it pretty simple to right-about-face. But the mother who allows a child to rule her finds it hard to put on an unworried smile. It takes courage for such a person to seem to neglect her child's health by being unconcerned when he does not eat. It is hard to break a habit in which a woman has so much personal interest as in her feelings about her children.

The parent who tends to be too emotionally tied up with her child will not succeed in doing a good job until she learns to stand off and look at her behavior as she would at someone else's. In order to *act* casual and unconcerned she has to *feel* casual and unconcerned. This does not come about without practice and very real effort.

Malnutrition

Malnutrition may be the result of poor eating habits, although it may also be caused by other things. Some children, for example, may have a good diet but their bodies may not make use of all the nutrients they need to be well nourished. Many children, however, are malnourished because they have not learned to eat the right kinds of food in sufficient quantities. Correcting these poor food habits often leads in time to restoring the children to a satisfactory state of nutrition.

After the mother has provided a large enough variety of foods, she has to see that the child eats all of them and not only those that he likes best or is most familiar with. A child who is allowed to drink as much milk as he likes may not be hungry enough to eat vegetables and meat. Another child may be filling up almost exclusively on bread and butter—good foods, of course, but not containing all the elements needed in his diet. A little cleverness on the part of parents may prevent or correct these poor eating habits. If

the child tends to drink his milk first, it can be withheld until vegetables and meat or egg have been eaten. The foods about which the
child is least enthusiastic can be offered to him at the beginning of
the meal when his appetite is the keenest, and he can be made to
understand that he is expected to eat these foods before he gets
others. Because sweet foods are usually well liked, a finicky child's
dessert should not be put on the table until he has finished the main
part of his meal.

Lack of appetite due to chronic infection, decayed teeth, or
other physical conditions, cannot be expected to clear up until the
underlying causes have been taken care of. The importance of frequent physical check-ups to prevent such things, or to catch them
before they become serious, is evident.

Dawdling at Meals

Sometimes young children cause a great deal of annoyance by
dawdling at meals. These are likely to be children who eat less
heartily than children who set to and finish promptly. Urging and
talking about their slowness may only result in their eating less.

Such children are often better off eating alone, as there are
fewer distractions to slow them up. If the mother of a slow-eating
child is herself inclined to do things rapidly, she will have to be
extra careful not to keep jogging and nagging at him. Many a child
has become a real "problem" because he enjoyed the fuss that was
made over his slowness.

Forming Good Sleeping Habits

SMALL children require an abundance of sleep and rest, since the
faster a child is growing, the greater his sleeping needs. By establishing regular hours for his rest and sleep you are greatly contributing
to your child's well-being.

Besides getting from eleven to thirteen hours sleep every night a child should take a nap or rest in bed for at least an hour or so in the middle of the day. Even after he no longer naps in the afternoon, he needs some time for quiet relaxation in order to avoid being overstimulated. The great majority of children continue to nap at least occasionally until they are between four and five.

Many schools now arrange for periods of rest on mats or cots, and children well beyond kindergarten age often fall asleep when given a chance to do so. This suggests that mothers might profitably include a rest period for children who have reached the age of five or six and are in school part or all of the day. A child who is new to the large group he mingles with in the schoolroom is likely to be so keyed up by his school experience that he has very great need of planned rest at home.

REST PERIODS AND NAPS

Young children usually eat their noon meal better if they have been allowed a few minutes to calm down from play. Perhaps coming in and washing up, taking off outer garments and shoes, and putting on a dressing gown will afford enough quieting down, but in some cases actually lying down for five or ten minutes will be better. This is the practice carried out at nursery school, after long experience.

If a child's nap immediately and invariably follows his noon meal, he will go to bed more willingly than if he is sometimes allowed to play around for half an hour or so afterward. One of the reasons for getting a child undressed for his nap before his dinner is that he will then be less tempted to run out of doors after he has eaten. Since cutting down the things that stimulate a child has much to do with his being in the mood for sleep, the relaxation that follows eating will help in getting him to sleep.

If from babyhood a child has slept while the household noises were going on, he should not be bothered by ordinary sounds; his closed door should be enough protection. Although light in itself should not bother him, it is one of a number of things that may make it less easy for him to go to sleep; consequently to pull the shades down at naptime and to turn out the light at night will be useful. Once babyhood is past, a child has eyes and ears for so many things that it is just as well to plan the setting for sleep with this in mind.

By the time a baby is a year old he has probably changed from two naps a day to one. This nap should come (whether he is one year old or four) early enough in the day so that he can have some time out of doors while there is still sunlight. The length of the nap will be shortened greatly between the ages of one and five but the length of night-time sleep will hardly be changed at all; children usually sleep eleven to twelve hours at night throughout this period.

The one- and two-year-olds will probably take a nap of about two hours; three- and four-year-olds gradually reduce their sleep to about an hour. If the nap is postponed too long, a child may be so tired that he sleeps too late, loses out on the time when he should be out of doors, and may not be ready to go to bed at a suitable hour.

Although it is not recommended that children be wakened from a nap, it is sometimes necessary. If a child has acquired the habit of taking a nap lasting too late in the afternoon, it is well to rouse him gently and unobtrusively. Opening his door or closing his window will probably suffice. To rouse him suddenly is not good, as it may make him irritable.

A child who is outgrowing his nap may be told that he need not go to sleep but may rest. Such a child sometimes falls asleep, once he is relieved of the necessity of proving that he does not want to. If, after three-quarters of an hour or an hour of quiet (with a book or a toy for quiet play) he has not fallen asleep, he should be allowed to get up. Being alone will have rested him a good deal.

Some children fight sleep for fear of missing late-afternoon fun. A promise to wake them at a certain hour should dispose of this fear. Anyhow, it is better for the child to lose an occasional nap than to have battles and tense situations over sleep.

It does no good to expect children to go to sleep "as soon as their heads touch the pillow," for very few do. Some children take fifteen minutes, some half an hour, before they drop off.

BEDTIME

One of the good arguments in favor of getting children to bed early is the need of a time of relaxation for the mother. But if she wants her children to go to bed willingly, she must be very careful not to let them think that she wants to get rid of them. A child who feels that his parents are in a hurry to get him out of the way will try to stay up as long as he can. If, on the other hand, regular hours have always been held to, and going to bed has always been made a pleasant routine by being associated with conversation, stories, or music, it will be accepted as a matter of course.

Giving a child a few moments' notice before bedtime so that he can wind up what he is doing is a great help. He will more readily accept leaving his play if there is a definite hour for going to bed; and having the burden put on the clock keeps a child from feeling that personal pressure is being put on him by his mother or father.

In many families young children are fed and put to bed before their parents eat. This is an especially good thing to do if the family dinner hour must be as late as 6:30 or 7, but there should be some time when children can be with their father. Having them eat their supper as early as 5:30 or 6, then get ready for bed and have a period of quiet play while the mother is getting dinner for the rest of the family works out well in many cases. If the family eats at 5:30 or 6, it may be simpler to have the children eat with the grown-ups. As they will not want to linger over their meal, they may be allowed to leave the table and busy themselves until their mother or father is ready to get them into bed.

The hour for going to bed will depend on the family routine. Although children differ in their sleep needs, the average child will sleep about eleven hours at night. Thus, if his parents are very early risers, they will want him to get to bed by 6 or so. If they do not have to get up until 7 and do not want him to waken them when he has had his sleep out, they may prefer letting him stay up until 7 in the evening.

One of the good reasons for a regular bedtime is that when children go to bed later than usual, they generally do not make up their lost sleep by sleeping later in the morning.

A good rule is to arrange things so that a child has plenty of chance to sleep eleven or twelve hours without being disturbed by the bustle that is sure to occur when others get up. Each year a child may be allowed to stay up a little later than the year before. If this is made a rule, the younger child will not tease to stay up until an older child goes to bed, as so often happens when no plan is in force. Even a very little child can see the sense of having privileges added as he grows.

SLEEPING PROBLEMS

When children fail to go to sleep fairly promptly at night, it is usually due to one of these causes:

EXCITING PLAY NEAR BEDTIME. This is often the only time a father has to see his children, and he may play with them then in an overstimulating way. Romping is thoroughly enjoyable to young children, but it may leave them keyed up and in no condition to go to sleep. A story hour or singing time with their father gives them and him just as much pleasure, without poor results. Stories read or told at this hour should be carefully chosen, as preschool children are very imaginative and tend to be more disturbed than adults realize by the adventures told in stories.

If the child is worn out because of too strenuous play with other children late in the day, his hour for coming in may need to be set ahead, or he may have to be limited to play with one other child late in the day.

THE LATE NAP. When a child is not sleepy after being in bed a considerable time, it may be that his nap is coming too late in the day. His whole schedule may need changing. Perhaps he is a child who needs less sleep than the average, or he may be getting too little physical exercise.

EXCUSES FOR DEMANDING ATTENTION. If a child makes a nuisance of himself by insisting on a drink of water, a handkerchief, or a trip to the toilet, wants to have his bedclothes straightened out or a noise explained, we may be fairly sure he is making these demands for attention because he has found they work. All children like to feel they are important, and if a child discovers that he can make his parents step lively to satisfy every whim, he can think up a whim a minute—it is such fun to be the center of things.

The cure for such behavior is to be sure that he has enough of your love and attention at all times and then be firm. Listen to him and talk to him at suitable times and refuse to be bullied at others. Be sure that all his needs are cared for before he goes to bed; tell him that when you say good night and close the door, it is final. If you say it firmly and convincingly, he will believe you.

PHYSICAL DISCOMFORT. If no other cause for restlessness and failure to sleep can be found, the physical conditions under which a child sleeps should be checked.

Children are more often too hot than too cold, as many mothers tend to cover them too warmly. A child heats up and also cools off more quickly than an adult. His bed covers should never be heavy. If his room is very cold, it is better to put on an extra night garment, such as a sweater or shirt, than to load him down with covers.

In very warm weather it is often desirable to let a child stay up until the temperature in his sleeping room makes going to bed bearable. An electric fan, placed so that it does not blow on the child, is sometimes helpful, as its hum tends to encourage sleep.

BAD DREAMS. In the case of a child whose sleep is often disturbed, who cries out or talks in his sleep and has night terrors and bad dreams, several things must be considered. It may be that he gets too excited and overstimulated in play during the day, and that he is overtired, but more frequently the cause for such behavior will be found in feelings of insecurity and fear that his parents have not recognized. Worries unexpressed in words or actions during the day come out while he is asleep. If an explanation for such disturbances cannot be found by the child's parents, help should be sought from the family physician or a guidance clinic, if one is available.

WHEN ILLNESS UPSETS ROUTINES. Illness is very likely to disturb a child's sleep schedule as, being in bed all the time, he sleeps at irregular hours. Also the idea of bed becomes unpleasant to him because he has been uncomfortable or in pain there.

If he fails to slip back into his old sleep habits after he is well, it may be a good idea to make some change in the physical set-up so that he will not be reminded of the unpleasant time in bed. Perhaps his bed can be moved to a different corner or he can have some new pajamas or a new doll to take to bed with him. Any little change that will tend to connect feelings of pleasure with nap or bedtime may help. It is especially necessary to see that he gets outdoors as much as possible, for exercising in the fresh air will make him ready for sleep. If, while he is convalescing, he cannot play vigorously, he can be out on a porch or go for walks.

It is particularly inadvisable to show concern over the disturbed sleep habits, as such anxiety will only establish the poor habit more firmly.

TRAVELING AND OTHER CAUSES. Traveling or moving often results in days or even weeks when getting a child to sleep is difficult. Making sure something is present from the old familiar surroundings is a great help. If a child cannot have his own bed, a familiar blanket or other bed covering will be soothing. Being wrapped in his mother's well-known dressing gown may remind him of home enough to put him at ease on the train. Anything that takes away the forlorn newness may be useful.

It is wise to make the child's new daily routine conform as closely as possible to his former one. Thus, if a period of outdoor play has been part of his regular morning at home, it will pay to continue the same plan in the new place, even if it means leaving the settling you are eager to do and taking him outside yourself.

A visit is harder to manage than moving, as it is necessary to conform to the conditions under which another family lives. Many mothers of young children do not realize how thoroughly upsetting to a child's regime it is to have to adapt to a new place, new faces, new ways of doing things. Even with the greatest good will on the part of the hostess, the child's mother is likely to find well-established habits being broken up. Visiting and travel are especially hard on sleep habits, and this fact should be thoughtfully weighed when a trip or a visit is being considered.

Even though the mother has good control over the situation as far as convenience of arrangements, hours, and so on are concerned, young children are likely to be so overstimulated and excited by changed conditions and new people that they will not sleep as usual even though they have a chance. Young children need a stable, calm environment, and trips and visits which seriously upset important habits should be as infrequent as possible.

A routine too strictly followed can cause trouble by making a child completely dependent on a certain set of conditions. For this reason it is not a good idea always to put a child to sleep in the same bed, to have him take the same toy to bed with him right along, or to let him become attached to one blanket. Although overdependent behavior is more likely to appear in children in whose lives there are lacks or insecurities, other children, too, from force of long-continued habit, may find it hard to adjust when conditions make changes necessary.

Guiding Your Child Toward Emotional Balance and Control

EVERY child lives in two worlds. One is the world around him. With his parents' help, the child soon manages to see the sense of it and accept it. Not so the other world. For this is a world within himself, a world of sudden, unpredictable emotions that often leave him confused and unsure of himself. He can, in time, learn to make himself at home in it, but the affectionate guidance of his parents will lighten his task considerably.

Children are not born with specific fears and loves and hates. As they grow, however, they do have unpleasant experiences that cause fear, and they do begin to have such pleasant experiences with people that feelings of love develop.

If a baby slips in his bath and swallows water, he may be afraid for a long time of being put into the tub. If a child gets his own way by an emotional scene, he may resort to this behavior over and over again.

We cannot separate what we want to teach a child from his *feelings* about what we want him to learn. Whether it is eating or dressing or sleeping or playing, we have to remember that it is not *our* interest in the habit that is going to be effective, but the *child's* reaction. The way we go about training will be all-important.

Emotion is useful, for it is associated with changes in the body that give us the additional energy needed to meet difficulties. Because we feel emotion when we are stirred by facing a problem, we find in ourselves the extra power we must have to cope with it. A child can run faster, for example, if he is afraid, can hit harder if he is angry.

But when emotion becomes so strong as to prevent action—when the child is "paralyzed" by fright, or so angry he "can't see straight"— it is an enemy. If a child is so upset by seeing a car come straight at him that he cannot think what to do, he is in great danger. Because of their lack of experience in handling upsetting situations, we must protect children as much as we can from coming up against things that floor them. If their problems are not too big to solve successfully a good part of the time, they stand a better chance of learning to handle them well and thus of gaining confidence in their ability to meet tougher problems. If we did not, for example, protect little children from many things that might frighten them, they might suffer from many unnecessary and damaging fears.

OVERCOMING FEAR

What are the kinds of fear situations that little children most often encounter and that, improperly handled, may lead to habitual help-lessness in the face of danger?

Any startling sudden occurrence—a loud noise, a fall, an unex-pected movement—is likely to produce the body reaction that we term fear. A siren, clanging fire bells, the whir of a vacuum cleaner are all startling things to a child ignorant of what they mean.

Fear of dogs, common in young children, results from a dog's loud barking and sudden jumps and bounds; it is not caused by any inborn fear of dogs. Watching someone feed a dog, saving bones for it, listening to amusing stories about dogs are some of the possible ways of breaking down the fear, once it has come about. Bringing into the family a young puppy that the child can play with and see is harmless is often successful in getting rid of his fear.

That children's fear of dogs dies out pretty much after they have been in school a year or so shows the effect group pressure has. Seeing that other children feel friendly to dogs gradually helps the fearful child to overcome his own fear.

Fear of thunderstorms is another example of a reaction produced by sudden noise, but it may be taken, as well, for an instance of—

Fears We Communicate to Children

If a child's mother is afraid of storms, the child will almost always be afraid, too. Though he doesn't reason it out, his unconscious attitude is, "If this great big person on whom I depend for safety is afraid, there must surely be something to fear."

Most parents would do a great deal to keep their children from acquiring unserviceable fears. But these same parents are sometimes unwilling to make the effort required to give up their own pet fears. However, as more and more mothers become aware that they are responsible for the absorption of fear by their children, they will undoubtedly take steps to rid themselves of these burdens before they burden the children too. Fear of deep water, of going places alone, of meeting new people; fear of pain, or darkness, even of such minor things as insects, are some of the kinds of fears mothers should cure in themselves. They can be overcome, and saving children from them makes the effort worth while.

First of all, a mother should look her own fear in the face. She will often find that it is absurd and useless, often a hang-over from an unhappy childhood experience. Even if she cannot recall its origin, the chances are that thinking about it will show up the fear as nonsense that had better be gotten rid of. A fear of snakes is very common but usually unjustified, especially among people living in parts of the country where there are no poisonous snakes. A fear of lightning, understandable enough in a child, seems rather foolish when one stops to think how few houses or people are ever struck by it. Fear of deep water can be done away with by having some strong, trusted person teach one to swim.

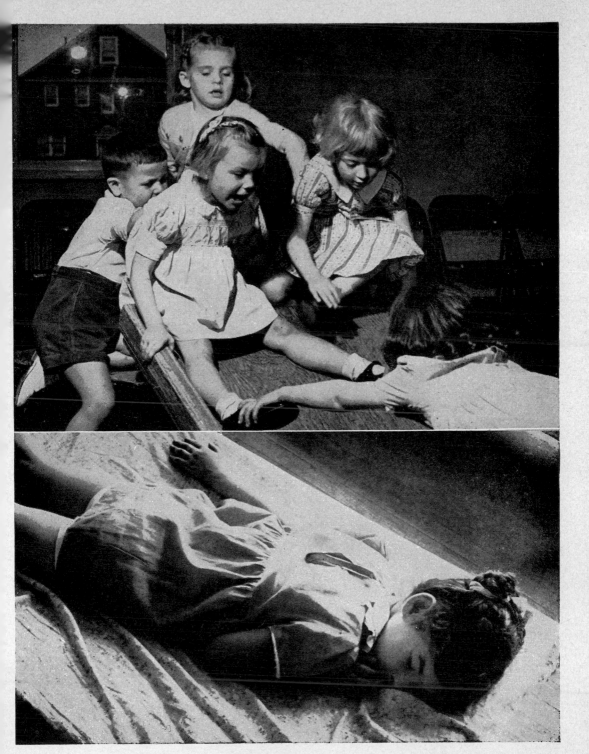

Play Schools Assn.

THE NURSERY SCHOOL

With trained supervision, ample room, and play equipment, the nursery school offers advantages that of necessity are lacking in many homes. *(Above)* Here small children learn the give-and-take of group play, and *(below)* also obtain the necessary rest and nourishing food that are part of a good nursery school's health program.

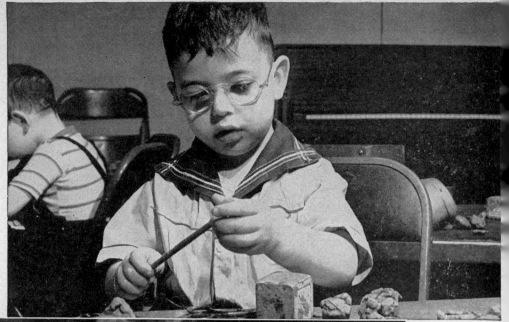

MEN AT WORK

Young nursery schoolers find full scope for creative play in an atmosphere keyed to their gradually developing skills and abilities. They work with clay, accomplish engineering feats with blocks, and engage in a wide variety of other absorbing activities.

Children are often frightened by what they hear adults talk about. Discussion of dentists and doctors as persons to be avoided, war talk that is gloomy, talk about family troubles, are some of the things that may be disturbing to a child.

Hardest of all to do away with and most damaging to a child's personality is that uneasy fear which comes from vaguely sensing a situation that he does not understand, such as tension or bickering between the two persons who mean most to him. If the adults in a child's life are deeply disturbed, it is almost inevitable that the child will suffer. For the adults to try to hide their insecurity will not be enough. If the adult is continuously disturbed and unhappy, he may expect his child to feel the tension and to react in some way—by fear of being left alone, perhaps, by night terrors, by bed wetting, by thumb sucking, by cruelty to pets, or by bad relations with playmates —any way in which the tension may be released.

Parents are sometimes the cause of a kind of fear that they would be the last to bring about if they were conscious of what they were doing. This is a fear caused by their ambition for their child to shine. It is very hard on a child to be expected to be the "best." This attitude in parents usually does not reach its height until the child is in school, when they sometimes do a great deal of pushing to make him excel in marks and in athletics and other contests. But even earlier some mothers aspire to have their children the best-dressed or the most healthy or the best-mannered. The three-year-old in nursery school who, when she was setting the table in the doll-play corner, put a block at each place, which she called "good table manners," was subtly telling tales on her mother's preoccupation with her behavior at table.

Children who feel the pressure of living up to impossibly high standards of cleanliness, of speech, or of other matters that betray their parents' desire to "show off" their youngsters show fear, often not in the obvious ways but by their nervous habits.

Closely allied to this is the dangerous practice of talking about "what people will think." Many people have suffered hampering fears all their lives because of early repressions by parents who themselves were overcautious and fearful lest their actions be criticized. Independence of thought should be one of the child's rights, as little interfered with as possible. Confidence in one's own good judgment can grow only in an atmosphere free from overmuch concern about criticism.

Another type of fear caused by parental behavior is fear of punishment. A child who cringes before his parents as a result of harsh or frequent punishment is anything but emotionally healthy. Deception and lying often start as protective measures against pain or humiliation.

Any situation in which a child feels inadequate is likely to produce fear. Being subjected to the overfriendly advances of a stranger, suddenly coming upon older children in masks on Hallowe'en, being separated from his mother in a crowded store, are the kinds of incidents that cannot be guarded against completely, but these things will have relatively little effect on the child who feels basically secure.

Guarding Against Fears

Much can be done to keep children from acquiring fears. Explanations that add to a child's knowledge are helpful, for ignorance is at the back of much fear in children, just as it is in grown-ups. Parents who take pains to tell their child that policemen are friendly and useful are preparing him against the tales he may hear from other children about policemen as threatening and bad. Explaining to children how harmless thunder is, demonstrating perhaps by letting him see what a loud explosion even one paper bag blown full of air makes when it bursts, may interest him enough to make him listen to the thunderclaps with amusement.

Fear of doctors and nurses, or even of people who remind a child of them because of some similarity in dress or appearance, may be guarded against, even though it is not always possible to have a child's earliest remembered associations with a doctor or nurse pleasant. Taking the edge off a child's uneasiness by letting him help the doctor "work" something—the always fascinating stethoscope, perhaps —or asking the child to do something (like ringing a little bell) as soon as the doctor pricks him, may serve as a helpful distraction.

Many parents nowadays take their child to a dentist as soon as he has all his first teeth or earlier still if the teeth show stains that can easily be removed. This early visit is for the purpose of building up a friendly acquaintance before any work is needed. The first visit can be purely social, or the child might go with his mother when she is having her teeth cleaned. The child whose first visit is made under these conditions, who then has his own teeth cleaned by the funny little brush that his friend, the dentist, perhaps lets him start whirring, is going to feel secure enough so that later, when a cavity may have to be filled, he will be less apprehensive and readier to accept a little discomfort.

Of course, the mother and the dentist, in this case, must not say, "This isn't going to hurt." Few things are more upsetting to a child than to have adults, whom he should be able to trust, deceive him. Fears multiply when a child doesn't know when to believe a person and when not to.

Some Suggestions for Dealing with Fears

Careful experiments have shown that some treatment does, and some does not, do away with fears. A time-honored but useless method is ignoring a child's fear in the hope that he will outgrow it. Ridiculing fear in a child has just as bad, or even worse, results, for it often drives the fear underground.

Among methods that are good, building up a child's self-confidence holds first place when the fear is one that can be overcome by teaching some habit that actively combats it. Thus, a child who is afraid of physical hard knocks can build up belief in his ability to hold his own by boxing with his father.

If the methods used aim at making what was a feared situation a pleasant one, the results are pretty sure to be good. Thus, getting acquainted with a jolly policeman may be all that is needed to remove fear of policemen; concentrating on some very pleasant feature of a trip downtown, like buying a new picture book or hair ribbon, may drive away fear of the dentist or doctor to be visited; spending a few happy days in a home where there is a friendly, gentle dog may do more toward helping a child like dogs than hours spent in telling him "the dog won't hurt you."

Of course, everything possible should be done to learn *why* and *how* a fear has come about, because if this is cleared up, sometimes half the battle is over. It does no good to ask a child why he is afraid, for he usually does not know. In many cases it will not be possible to find the cause of the child's attitude, but patient, quiet observation and real thought may reveal it. Sometimes the best a parent can do is to give unobtrusive support and comfort.

When the cause of the fear cannot be discovered, long and painstaking effort may be necessary before the child is free from it.

THE ANGRY CHILD

By the time they are a year old, most babies have shown a good deal of spunk, of which their parents have good reason to be proud. They enjoy this evidence that their child is a real personality. One baby will refuse certain foods over and over, no matter how cleverly his mother tries to introduce them into his diet. Another will show remarkable tenacity in his efforts to reach something outside his play pen and will struggle mightily to get it.

We would have cause for alarm if babies were always docile and yielding. (Man would not have got very far by such behavior.) We want them to be bold and demanding enough to stand up for their rights.

In discouraging children from being too demanding we have to be careful not to squelch their determination, their desire for independence. What we should like to see them achieve would be a nice balance between an aggressive and a submissive attitude. They are most likely to attain this goal of knowing when to push ahead firmly and when to give in if they have great personal security.

A young child tries to get his own way because to him it is the *only* way. We try to help him grow out of this self-centeredness by encouraging him to make strong efforts when what he wants is desirable, and by avoiding as often as we can situations in which we have to say "no."

Anger and resistance are the natural responses to being blocked. Children show this by having temper tantrums when they have to be interrupted to be washed, dressed, or taken to the toilet. They burst out if they are interfered with at play. Hunger and fatigue are other kinds of thwarting situations that produce anger.

At about the age of two, children show anger more often than they are likely to when they are older. Because a child cannot yet put into words how he feels about something he is expected to do, he may burst into tears or stoutly say "no." If he could express himself, he might say, "But I don't need to go to the toilet yet. I want to finish building my house." His helplessness should make us thoughtful enough to give him a little warning when we must interfere with what he is doing. If we can somehow interest him in the new thing we want him to do, we may avoid a scene. "Is your teddy bear getting sleepy? Let's take him upstairs with us," or "We have a new cake of soap to wash with tonight. Oh, but it smells good," are examples. A negative reaction to commands at this age is so common that the foresighted mother tries to avoid conflict by giving as few orders as possible and making requests instead.

Since hunger and fatigue are among the commonest causes of anger, we should see to it that the youngster does not have to wait too long for his dinner or his nap. Children whose meals are served regularly and who have plenty of sleep actually have far fewer tantrums than those whose mothers do not follow schedules so carefully.

If there are adults in the family, the mother should try to have each of them use the same methods with the child. It is confusing to a child, for example, to have grandma say he may play with her workbasket, only to have Aunt Bet take it away from him.

Handling the Angry Child

But supposing he *does* get angry? What shall we do?

If he is angry because he is sleepy or hungry, we have to try as matter-of-factly as we can to get him fed and into bed. If we can be calm ourselves it will help. What use is there in being disturbed and annoyed when that will only add to our child's anger and our own trouble?

If he is angry because a toy thwarts him—a wheel won't go over a board, a paper tears when he tries to fold it—we can give a little help and try to plan so that he won't have difficulty like that often. If we choose play materials wisely, according to his ability, there should not be too many times when he comes up against something too tough for him.

If anger is frequent in connection with daily routines, a good scrutiny of the schedule is in order. It may be possible to let the child make more decisions, especially as he becomes able to talk freely. To be asked, "Shall I give you your bath now or just before you have supper?" gives a child a sense of power. It sets him up to have some "say" in his own affairs, and there are certainly times when giving a choice is just as convenient for the mother.

Suppose the anger comes about, as it often does, because a child has found he can get attention in that way. Better to call down wrath upon your head than not be noticed at all, the child seems to argue, though, of course, he does not consciously reason it out. Ignoring such tantrums and giving more attention of a desirable sort—reading to him, talking with him, spending more thought on constructive things for him to do—is the answer in probably nine cases out of ten.

The mother who says she cannot ignore a screaming, kicking youngster usually means she has not found out how to use ignoring as a constructive method. Leaving him and going about her business may work better than she thinks it will. The minute he hasn't an audience his pleasure in the performance begins to die down. Naturally, if she herself is so angered by his temper that her attitude in ignoring him is hateful, ignoring will only cause him to feel more hostile. But if she can treat his anger as not too serious a matter, if she is prepared for it just as she is prepared for other primitive ways of acting in early childhood, like eating with fingers, it will be more likely to subside.

Of course, if a mother begins by ignoring an attention-getting piece of play-acting, if she then becomes irritated and switches to pleading, to scolding, and finally to spanking, she is defeated by her own jumble of techniques. The child in such an instance senses his mother's feeling of helplessness. As *he* is the one who is usually helpless and in her power, he now feels he has won out.

Keeping a child by himself is sometimes useful when he is angry and wants to see if he can make an adult give in. Told he can play by himself until he is ready to be more agreeable to the wishes of others, children or adults, he often comes to his senses very quickly. A child should not be kept apart long, however, and should never be confined in a way that will make him fearful, as in a closet.

Many a mother, trying to explain something to an angry child, has discovered that he might as well be deaf for all the good her talking does. It is a very good idea to try to explain things to children, but it is useless to try to reason with an angry child. The fewer words the better, until he has cooled down.

It has already been pointed out that a child between the ages of eighteen months and three years tends to say "no" to every suggestion. If he is not constantly being given directions and commands, he has less chance to build up this habit of balkiness.

If parents could only train themselves not to be shocked when their young children express their anger by saying "I hate you!" or by calling them names, they would improve their relations with their children. The average father and mother have forgotten the feelings of resentment they had in early life toward their own parents who, in the process of trying to help them become acceptable members of the family and of society, placed many curbs upon them and inevitably aroused antagonism. A child drains off his resentment if he is allowed to express it. He has no hesitancy in coming right out with his feelings among playmates, but he is not supposed to injure the dignity of his parents by expressing his feelings toward them when he is thwarted. If he is made to feel guilty over these natural reactions, if he has to suppress them or be punished, his feelings may be in a turmoil. But if his parents can say to his expressions of hate, "Of course you feel that way. I used to, too, when someone made me do something," he doesn't store up guilt over his conflicting feelings about his mother and father. We might as well admit that it is perfectly possible to feel hate and love at the same time.

Parents are sometimes afraid a young child who is allowed to talk back when he is angry will form the habit of doing this. Actually, being allowed while very young to let off steam this way, without reproach, may prevent the forming of worse habits of sulkiness and obstinacy. A child very soon learns (if his parents set an example of courteous behavior) that people do not continue to act in this childish way. He is usually eager for his companions to like him, and they exert a great influence upon his learning to control his outbursts of anger and to limit them to appropriate occasions. Furthermore, parents who try to react tolerantly to such natural expressions of a child's feelings will find themselves bringing about fewer situations in which such feelings are aroused.

Let Your Child Have His Say

HAVE you ever stopped to consider whether your child can literally call his soul his own, or whether his life is so guided by your wishes and decisions that he has little or no say about what he would like to do or think or say or have?

There is no question that it is easier for parents to plan the details of a child's life than it is to leave many of the decisions up to the child himself. Furthermore, there are fewer chances for errors in judgment which the child will later regret if decisions are made for him.

But the child does not see it that way.

The child whose life is completely planned for him feels abused. He believes that no one is interested enough in him to be willing to ask his opinion or to try to find out what his wishes are.

Even though the adult decision may be exactly what the child himself would decide, the fact that he has had no say in its making is enough to cause him to rebel against it. It is a form of self-assertiveness which any child with spunk is bound to display.

Every child needs practice in making decisions. It is essential if he is to learn to make wise ones. A child who rarely has opportunity to make his own decisions feels at a loss when he is forced into a situation where he must decide things for himself, free from adult aid.

To make a child feel that he is recognized as a person, with rights and privileges of his own comparable to those of other members of his family, here are certain areas in a child's life in which he should have a voice in making decisions about matters which are of direct concern to him.

WHAT HE EATS. Of two or more equally nourishing foods, there is no reason for a child not to express his preference for one rather than for the other. In planning the day's menus, let your child have a chance to suggest one or two food items that he would like to have. Then, if it is not practical to have them, this can be explained to the child and he can have an opportunity to make other suggestions.

WHAT HE WEARS. In the selection of his clothes, even a three-year-old is old enough to express an opinion. Every child likes his clothes better when he has some say about them and he takes better care of them than he does of garments that he is forced to wear against his will.

WHAT HE PLAYS WITH. If play is to be fun for a child, he must be allowed to select the toys he enjoys most and to play with them in a way that will give him maximum enjoyment. So long as his play is not injurious to himself, to others, or to the household equipment, the child should be free to make his own choice about what he wants to do in his playtime and how he wants to do it.

WHOM HE PLAYS WITH. Friendships cannot be controlled by arbitrary standards set by parents. A child must be free to select friends to his liking and to associate with them without constant interference and criticism on the part of his parents. Unless a child has given undeniable evidence of exercising a bad influence on other children, there is no reason why other children should not be permitted to play with him if they enjoy his companionship.

WHAT HE THINKS. This is likewise a child's privilege and, as such, should be respected. Even a tiny tot can and should have his likes and dislikes, his interests and his opinions. Instead of trying to mold a child's thinking into a pattern, wise parents will encourage their children to think for themselves.

And, finally, *what he says* should be respected. A child should be encouraged to express his opinions frankly at home. Otherwise, how can parents know whether their children's thinking is straight and logical or distorted and biased?

Of course the child's thoughts will be childish and will be expressed in an immature manner. Nevertheless, he should be encouraged to express his thoughts in his own way. Furthermore, he should never be made to feel that his thoughts are too trivial to count. How can a child be trained to play any other role than that of a meek follower throughout life if he is treated as such in childhood?

ELIZABETH B. HURLOCK, PH.D.

Discipline Through Affection

"How can I get my child to do what I say?" Parents have asked this question times without number, and probably will continue to do so throughout many generations to come.

Implicit in the question is the fundamental problem of all education: How can people in general and children in particular learn what they are supposed to learn?

Parents seldom think of it in this way, however. To some, the question means: "How can I discipline (or punish) Jimmie if he doesn't do *what* I think he should, *when* I think he should?" Such parents are so concerned with finding a device or trick to bring about the response they want that they lose sight of the end they are really trying to attain. Discipline, for them, becomes largely a matter of punishment, rather than an essential step in the slow building-up of a child's learning of what is "right" or "wrong," acceptable or not. These parents, and some teachers also, unfortunately, believe that children learn nothing unless they are punished, and unless the whole procedure is unpleasant.

We know that this is not so. Children learn the best and most important things, without being taught, from those who love and care for them. The infant, lying in his crib or on his mother's lap, knows instinctively when she is pleased with him, and when she is not. If she smiles and holds him securely, with gentle affection, he feels comfortable and content. If her face is cross, her body tense, and she dresses or feeds him impatiently or with angry jerks, he senses that something is wrong. Then he is not at ease.

Children of all ages, big and little, learn to give up many of the things they want to do or have in order to keep the atmosphere around them peaceful and pleasant. And they do so without knowing it themselves. Parents seldom recognize how much self-disciplining occurs every day in childhood.

THE BEST BASIS FOR GOOD DISCIPLINE

In the long run, discipline is effective, not when it is dependent on punishment but when it is based on love and affection. When children feel loved and accepted, they learn not only what *not to* do, what displeases parents; they also follow positive suggestions more easily, with less resistance. When, for example, the time comes for a child to give up drinking milk out of a bottle, it is easier for him to take it from a cup if his mother is sympathetic and understands how hard it is for him to make the change.

In the same way, Johnny, aged twelve, will be readier to accept his father's advice to keep away from the movies on Sunday, so that he may finish his homework, if he has the feeling that his father stands by him in most situations.

This kind of relationship between parents and children is the best basis for good discipline. It is found where parents from the beginning accept their children naturally, showing them the love and devotion that they feel. Of course, there is great variation in the amount of affection parents have for their children, and in the ways they show it. This does not mean that children have to be swamped by demonstrations of affection. In fact, they will sometimes let you know, even when they are little, that you are getting in their way. But a pat on the shoulder, a kind word and encouraging comment at any age are reassuring evidence of the close tie that binds parents and children together.

The mother who is able to give her child these evidences of affection shows it also in other ways. She accepts him for what he is. Any disappointment that George is not the little he-man, or Mary, the blonde, blue-eyed angel she had hoped for is soon forgotten. She knows that she will find other traits about which to be pleased and proud. She understands that children don't become perfect all at once: that there is a certain amount of trial and error about the business of growing up that all children must go through. She is not put out when Mary, now nearly three, finds her new blocks more interesting than going to bed; and when Jimmy, aged seven, can't be bothered to hang up his coat when he is dashing in to listen to his radio program. In other words, such a mother understands, on the whole, something of the way in which children develop, what she can expect at various ages and stages, and how one child's response may differ from another's in a similar situation, according to his individual temperament.

THERE IS NO MAGIC

Knowing all this, she is more apt to set standards for her children that are in keeping with what they actually can live up to. But even in the best of families—where relationships are warm and strong, and where children have been given the opportunity to be as independent as their years and abilities will allow—here, too, will come times and occasions when the children need to be controlled and corrected. Their judgment is not always as good as they think it to be; some situations may be dangerous in ways they cannot understand. Then the question is: What does one do about it?

There is no rule-of-thumb answer. We found that out long ago, although many parents are still looking for magic formulas. When children must be controlled, it is important that parents act, and do so with sureness and despatch. What they do, actually, is not as important as the way they do it. If Johnny is about to climb on a window sill from which he may fall three stories to the street, you waste no time. You remove him from his perch, planning to have window guards put up to safeguard the next adventure. If you can act in a firm yet kindly fashion, so much the better. Children will accept quiet firmness much more readily than if you scream at them in order to make your point. At the same time, you can direct a child to other things he *can* do.

Such situations are easily seen and rather easily dealt with. It is the subtler problems that are more confusing. Persuading children to accept family routines raises issues that are less clear-cut. How much leeway, for example, can one give at bedtime? How much responsibility should children take in caring for their own things and in helping around the house? How about fighting between sisters and brothers? Should they be allowed to fight it out, or should a parent interfere? These are some of the questions parents are trying to answer with fairness both to their children and themselves. In each case they have to decide between the things on which to take action, and those which the children can be allowed to work out for themselves.

CORPORAL PUNISHMENT ISN'T THE ANSWER

In practice, parents often tend to act in one of two extreme ways. They either punish too much, and too often, or they do nothing, letting the children go their own way. It is startling to find, for example, that many parents still have no better way of influencing their children than by hitting them. A twelve-year-old girl says her father hits her when she doesn't put her light out on time at night. A mother spanks her six-year-old son because his teacher writes each day that he doesn't pay attention at school. For many months a baby, now two years old, has been rocking back-and-forth on his knees before going to sleep. The doctor has advised hitting the child every time he starts doing this, and mother and child sometimes battle it out for hours. These are true experiences reported by parents themselves. Sometimes one sees a letter in a magazine or newspaper in which an individual or a group of parents recommends the indiscriminate use of corporal punishment with a cruelty and sadistic satisfaction that is frightening.

Most parents, however, turn to this extreme as a last resort, and because they think that nothing else will work. It usually is the end step in a long course of happenings that has carried both parents and children away from positive feelings of love and understanding. Outside influences are often instrumental in bringing about this change. Sometimes it is a relative or an "in-law," who criticizes the children, comparing them unfavorably with other members of the family. Sometimes it is the other mothers on the block who, unable to understand or accept the normal aggressiveness of an active small child, suggest in no uncertain terms that he is badly brought up and a menace to the neighborhood. Frequently the school finds that a child is not doing well and passes the responsibility back to the parents, who have no other way of handling the problem than through "discipline."

The child's failure to live up to what is expected of him, either by the school, the family, or his parents, is a painful and bitter experience for a mother or father. They feel a deep sense of their own failure in their most important job. Angry and upset at themselves, as well as at their children, they strike out in the only way they know.

And yet the intelligent parent cannot help seeing that this kind of treatment actually does no good. In spite of punishments, the little boy still has to rock himself to sleep; the six-year-old is still incapable of better work at school; the twelve-year-old girl is not helped to handle the matter of bedtime herself. In all these situations, the children become confused and resentful, while the cause for their so-called "bad" behavior is, if anything, intensified. Constant nagging, criticizing or complaining will bring about equally unfortunate results.

Again and again we have to remind ourselves that children's behavior is not random and haphazard, as it appears on the surface. It is really purposeful: children act in accordance with their deep inner drives and feelings. A child sucks his thumb because doing so gives him comfort and satisfaction. Punishing him will only increase his need for this kind of solace. More affection and understanding are the best cure for thumb-sucking. This is not "spoiling" him; it is contributing toward his sound development.

TO SPANK OR NOT TO SPANK?

Some mothers are always nagging and scolding their children, yank them when they cross the street or get into busses, and slap them whenever they do something Mother doesn't like. These mothers may be tired and cross, but they do not understand that they make their children cross and irritable, too, and make things harder for themselves.

If you let yourself go occasionally, and slap or spank when you are excited or upset, it probably isn't too serious, provided your child is left with the feeling that he has been punished only for something he has *done,* and that you love him anyway.

But if you find that you are punishing and slapping repeatedly, you may be sure you are on the wrong track.

Spanking may stop your child for the moment, but you don't know what else it may do.

It may make him angry and resentful, or humiliated and ashamed. Or he may become hardened and pay no attention to it; or just so afraid that he can't trust himself to do anything.

None of these feelings helps him to learn what it was that he did wrong or why, or how to act the next time.

The best that can be said for spanking is that it sometimes clears the air. But it isn't worth the price, and it usually doesn't work.

THE GOAL: FIRMNESS WITH KINDNESS

How about the parents who do little or nothing to control their children? Some of them have been confused by recent psychological discussions which stress the need for more freedom and self-determination in childhood. Others use these ideas to rationalize the fact that they are afraid of their children (though they themselves may not recognize the fact). Some are just unwilling, or unable to assume the responsibility of taking a definite stand on anything. So the children rule the home, getting what they want, browbeating or wheedling their way through life. There are many families in which this kind of situation exists, and neither the parents nor the children are happy in it.

Children never feel comfortable if they know that they are "getting away with something." Whether they are five or fifteen, they need to know how far they can go; and they feel better when parents set up definite standards which they can use. Bill, at fourteen, may grumble when the family puts a limit on the number of week-day nights he can stay out with his gang. But he is probably relieved when he does not have to make the decision about the time when homework must be done.

If Jane, who is four, feels like pushing the baby around when he gets in her way, she may be glad to accept the rule that big girls don't push; especially if her mother lets her see that she understands why Jane would like to do so, and how she feels inside. If Jane were allowed to hurt the baby, she herself would be quite disturbed about it.

In other words, adults need to safeguard children from doing things that may bring consequences with which they cannot cope. In situations of physical danger and health, in social situations which they cannot yet judge for themselves, and in those which arouse childish aggressive feelings, they need to know that their parents understand and can control their behavior.

This is perhaps the most subtle and most challenging part of a parent's job. It takes art as well as skill to set up flexible, yet effective standards and controls for children as they develop, and to do it in a way that is acceptable to them, gaining their cooperation rather than their resentment. Here again, the answer lies not so much in the specific details of what one does as in the feeling tone behind it. Firmness and kindness together create one kind of atmosphere. The firmness that becomes hard and sharp, through anger and vindictiveness, creates an entirely different atmosphere with different results.

No mother or father will be able always to respond to children in an ideal way; nor should they hold up that kind of expectation for themselves. Occasional bursts of irritability are only human, after all. And children will accept them as such if they know that they can count on their parents' basic love and understanding.

The child who feels alone, struggling against criticism and hostile feelings, has little chance. The child who knows that there are adults who will help and guide him when he needs it, and who will, at the same time, allow him to go ahead because they have confidence in him—for this child the doors of life are open wide.

Aline B. Auerbach

Naughtiness Is Preventable

WE ARE all familiar with children who, "when they are good, they are very, very good but when they are bad, they are horrid." In fact, far too many children are naughty far too much of the time. The mother is completely exhausted at the end of the day and the father returns from his work to a scene of bedlam. While childish naughtiness, whether it be wilful disobedience, fighting, wrangling, sneakiness or any one of a dozen other varieties, makes life a nightmare for the parents, it is equally bad for the children.

Naughty children are tense, nervous, high-strung creatures. They cannot relax at bedtime, with the result that they get too little rest. Their emotional tensions interfere with proper digestion. Stomach upsets and other digestive disturbances are the aftermath.

Of equal seriousness are the psychologic effects. The developing personality of a naughty child takes on a form which may readily persist throughout life. The man who, for example, bullies his business subordinates, is behaving as he did in childhood when he bullied and teased his smaller playmates.

Perhaps the most serious consequence of naughtiness is the fact that a naughty child is an unhappy child. The more he gets into trouble, the more often he is punished. The more aware he is then of the fact that he is losing the respect and approval he craves from others. This makes him unhappy. In revenge, he tries to get even by being naughtier than ever. The result is a vicious circle.

Naughtiness should be controlled and it can be, if handled properly. Children are not good by luck nor will strict discipline and harsh punishments "drive out the devil from within them." Control of naughty behavior will come only when the causes that predispose the child to misbehave are corrected.

Scientific research has shed light on the causes of naughtiness. This information, if used in handling children in home and school, will go a long way toward eliminating the disciplinary problems that have made child-rearing a difficult and nerve-racking job.

The most common causes which pave the way for childish misbehavior are as follows:

1. FATIGUE. The times of the day when children are most troublesome coincide with the periods when physical fatigue reaches its peak. These occur in the late morning and late afternoon, shortly before the scheduled meal times, and just before bedtime. The remedy for naughtiness caused by fatigue is quiet and rest.

A good policy is to keep individual records of each child's "naughty periods." This should be done consistently for at least a week to discover just when troublesome behavior is likely to start. Then rest periods can be planned to begin at least one-half hour before trouble usually starts.

As a further aid in warding off naughtiness, a "snack" of some easily digested food such as fruit juice, milk, fruit or crackers might be given. Hunger frequently accompanies fatigue and together they lead to trouble.

2. TOO LITTLE SPACE. Children, like plants, need space in which to grow. When cooped up in cramped quarters, they get into one another's way, and trouble is inevitable. Ideally, children should have plenty of space indoors and out in which to romp and play freely. The closer one can approximate this ideal, the less troublesome children will be.

3. IDLENESS. In mistaken kindness, far too few adults give children duties and responsibilities which they are capable of assuming. Children must have some outlet for their energy. Unless directed, it is just as likely to be expended in mischief as in good deeds. Idle hands, as everyone knows, are apt to get into trouble.

In every household, there are a hundred and one duties which a child can not only perform but enjoy. They make him feel important and use up some of the energy which might otherwise go into trouble-making. When carried out under direction, they will cut down much of the work usually performed by a too busy mother.

4. TROUBLEMAKERS. It is unusual in a group of several children if one is not a troublemaker. The troublemaker gets keen enjoyment from putting other children up to mischief and even keener enjoyment from seeing them take the consequences when they are caught.

Since children are highly suggestible and easily persuaded to do mischievous things, much of their naughtiness can be controlled by spotting the troublemaker and putting an end to his mischief. Any adult who is with children for a short time can readily pick out the one who stirs up trouble.

Once the troublemaker is spotted and has had to take the entire blame for the misdeeds of others, he will find that causing trouble is not as much fun as he formerly believed. A few experiences of this sort are usually enough to cure him.

ELIZABETH B. HURLOCK, PH.D.

Make-Believe and Truthfulness

IN HUMAN life, the ability to imagine is an invaluable asset. Without it we would not have progressed beyond the level of animals. The wonderful accomplishments of science would not be possible without it. Yet imagination must be guided and controlled if it is to be a useful part of a child's equipment.

For example, a child can be so much alone that he comes to depend too much upon the pleasure he gets from imaginary companions and is unable to adjust very well to real ones, who don't always do his bidding like the ones created by his fancy. A child whose imagination is allowed to run away with him is not very well prepared to meet a world of facts; thus, a boy who boasts that *he* could make a better model plane than one another child is flying should have a chance to see how hard it is to fit together fragile bits of wood and paper.

The distorted imagination, however, usually seen in older children, is not to be confused with the airy imaginings of little children, who are only gradually becoming aware of the difference between reality and invention. Because it is hard for parents to enter into the world of a little child, they sometimes deal unwisely with the fancies of children, even calling them "lies" when there has been no attempt to deceive in the adult sense of that word.

Thus, a three- or four-year-old may be heard telling a friend that he has "hunderds and hunderds" of dollars in his bank. An adult who finds fault with him over this exaggeration is ignoring the fact that to the youngster one coin is as good as another. He is only aiming to give an account of all the birthday money that came his way.

The mother who finds it hard to enjoy her child's imaginative play is denied a great experience, one that is worth a great deal of effort to have. If she learns how to enter into imaginative play with her child, she will find that their companionship benefits, that the child appreciates her living through these experiences with him. It helps her, too, to avoid the "bossiness" that is such an enemy of good discipline. A child who feels the "oneness" created by his mother's sympathy is less likely to be resistant.

Take, for example, the matter of getting a child to go willingly to bed. The mother who is abrupt and matter-of-fact, who simply says, "Time to get ready for bed now," is far less likely to gain the cooperation of her child than she who observes what he is doing and remarks, "Shouldn't the truck go back to the garage pretty soon? Drivers must have a rest after they've driven a lot of hours, so they won't have an accident." Or the wise mother may weave what the child is doing (perhaps playing with a doll) in with a bedtime routine: "While you're undressing, I'll read you the story about the doll that had to sleep in the snow when she was lost, and how she finally found a home."

Many mistakes in handling a young child's imagination come from parents' fear of their child's developing a habit of untruthfulness. There is nothing to be concerned about on this score if pains are taken to see that the child knows when he is making things up. "That was a fine make-believe story; now tell me a *true story*" is one way that has been successfully used to help a child check up on himself and distinguish between invention and real life. Carefully pointing out to a child, as one reads to him, which are true stories based on fact and which are purely imaginary is another way of helping him to understand the difference between the real and dream worlds. He enjoys equally hearing that "Jack Frost has got in, you see, and left your window silver white" and the explanation in a simple science book of the way frost crystals form on a windowpane. He likes to hear about old Dobbin, who pulls the milk wagon and knows without being told just which houses to stop at, but he also wants to hear about Pegasus, the winged horse of the old Greek myths.

One of the reasons parents must be careful in the handling of their children's imaginative chatter is that a child can easily use this as a means of getting attention. If there is a great to-do over his tales of having seen lions or tigers or his exaggerated account of something that happened at school, he may be encouraged to make up more stories. It is fun to be able to cause a stir among the grown-ups.

If this way of getting attention is being used increasingly, parents might well ask themselves what purpose it is serving for the child. It sometimes shows that a child is not allowed to feel important and so uses any means he happens on to make himself somebody who is listened to. Children who are denied satisfaction of some of their natural desires make up for it by fantastic stories which they *wish* were true.

Such puzzling behavior as when a child brags at kindergarten about how many toys he has at home or "talks big" about how he has traveled or what important things his father does, is often a clue to insecurity and lack of self-confidence. Such a child may be one who longs for the toys he is denied but sees other children having as a matter of course; or perhaps he is a fatherless child who is envious of children with fathers.

Punishment for such tall tales is, of course, foolish. Instead, it is necessary somehow to build up the child's feeling of adequacy.

Another thing that puzzles parents is to know what to do when they are not sure whether or not a child is telling an untruth. Surely it is better to slip up occasionally than to make relations with a child tense or unfriendly by acting suspicious of him. A father and mother who trust a child have an enormous advantage in getting him to behave well over parents who show they don't know when to believe him and when not to. Nothing more thoroughly shatters a child's morale than to have his parents' belief in him break down.

STANDARDS OF HONESTY

It has been shown by painstaking study that the upright behavior of his parents is a powerful influence on a child's character. Scrupulous honesty and straightforwardness on the part of his family are as catching as measles. If sincerity and integrity are invariable rules in the home, there is little danger a child will not reflect them in his actions.

This must not be taken as suggesting that rigidity and severity, seeing everything in blacks and whites, is a favorable setting for the desirable development of character. Methods of training that frighten a child into being "good," that lay down such strict rules that a child's natural impulse is to try to evade them, are as poor as laxity and indifference.

"But how does lying come about?" asks the perplexed parent, who knows that children seem to lie as the sparks fly upward. "Are they natural-born liars?"

They certainly are not natural-born truthtellers! They are only little human creatures who have, necessarily, a great impulse to protect themselves from harm. If we accept from the outset that young children's untruths usually have this self-defending motive, we may deal differently with them.

Many of us practically force our children into telling untruths because we are so eager for them to be upright and honest. If our efforts are directed toward giving them reason for feeling secure and self-confident, we shall come out better. They won't *have* to lie.

A child's first deliberate untruth is often caused by his fear of punishment. Asking a child, "Who did this?" or "Did you do this?" when he knows from the tone of your voice that you are upset (over the scribble on the wall, the broken dish, or the picked-at-frosting) makes him deny having done it even if he has.

Parents should try to avoid such impulsive questions. Punishment for such offenses is worse than useless if it leads to a child's trying to hide his guilt another time. Very often a child's *feeling* that he has done wrong is punishment enough in itself.

Then, too, questioning a child may lead to his stubborn, continued denial of something he would not hesitate to admit if the matter were approached more tactfully. For example, asking which of two children marked on the wallpaper may leave you completely thwarted, or it may result in one child's gleefully tattling. Simply commenting on how ugly the wall looks and saying that crayons will have to be put away unless they can be used properly will certainly bring no bad results, and it may be all that is necessary.

With regard to breaking things, it is important to remember that children are very seldom *deliberately* careless. Adults would not enjoy being taken to task for such mishaps; how can a child be blamed for trying to avoid having reproach heaped on him?

When a child takes cake or candy or money or anything that has been forbidden, we might well ask ourselves if we have not brought about the trouble by putting temptation in his way. It will be helpful if we remember that young children have not yet built up habits of resistance. They are very easily tempted, and they may not be able to resist taking money or anything that they like very much when it is there right at hand. Only by slow degrees will they be able to be strong. It is not a good idea to leave money around where it is easily found. If children see us going casually to a purse or drawer to take out money for something we need, they may do the same thing when they want candy. One of the best arguments for even very young children's having a tiny allowance of their own is that they begin in this way to get an idea of "mine" and "thine."

One of the best ways of encouraging a child's understanding of property rights, of what is his and what is not his to handle or use, is for us to make sure that he has belongings of his own. Only through the feelings of satisfaction he has in *his* toys or *his* books or *his* pennies will he be able to grasp the fact that other people feel the same way about their possessions.

This business of having one's *own* things is the first step in the journey toward generosity and sharing. A child of three who has a wagon is better able to understand how another child feels about sharing his tricycle than one who has no such toy. With a little help he is able gradually to learn to share and to take turns.

When a Child Still Sucks
His Thumb

A CERTAIN little three-year-old sucks his thumb a hundred times a day. His mother, as she herself would tell you, has done everything she can think of to stop him. If you were to watch her a few hours, you would realize how troubled she is. She alternately reasons with the little boy, scolds him, threatens him. You hear her say, "You make me ashamed of you," or "I don't want a little *baby* around me," or "What will your Daddy think?" Sometimes she merely reminds him, or takes his thumb away from his mouth without saying anything. Other times she grabs him impatiently and gives the offending hand a resounding smack. At night she carefully ties both thumbs in a bulky woolen mitt.

Now this is a *good* mother, conscientious and well meaning. She dotes on her little boy. Indeed, if she cared less about him, she would not be so concerned over the thumbsucking. Without being quite aware of it, she regards her child's thumbsucking as a sign of failure on her part. She could also give you many reasons why she thinks that, for his sake, it is imperative to break the habit at once. What she has not yet learned is this important truth—that the chief danger of thumbsucking lies not in the habit itself but rather in the way parents and teachers handle it.

THUMBSUCKING IS GENERALLY HARMLESS

Many mothers fear that thumb- or finger-sucking may be harmful. They feel duty-bound to stop a child from sucking his thumb or fingers because they believe it is babyish or improper and that unless halted, it may go on forever. They fear that it will injure the thumb, that it will carry germs to the mouth, that it will make a child introverted, that it will spoil the shape of the teeth and jaw.

There are no facts to justify these fears. Not only is concern needless, it is also unfortunate when it is translated into direct or immediate action in order to stop the thumbsucking. In such instances, the mother may unwittingly make the habit into a more serious problem.

Thumbsucking *can* affect the shape of the teeth and jaw but the effect is usually not permanent. It depends partly upon the way the sucking is done. If the child presses his thumb *hard* against the roof of the mouth or teeth, there is a possibility that the shape of the mouth will be altered, at least temporarily. However, since in most cases the jaws come back to normal position when the thumb-sucking ceases, parents' concern is usually unnecessary.

Thumbsucking Satisfies Other Needs for the Older Child

For the older baby and the young child, thumbsucking seems to have a rather different meaning. It is no longer just a sign of insufficient sucking, but has become a sort of *comforter*. It is now more of a habit, in the old-fashioned sense, to which the child turns when he wants a little comforting. When he feels that he is not loved enough, not safe enough, not good enough, he resorts to his earlier satisfaction. The act of sucking his thumb comforts and assures him. It is a natural impulse which he does without reasoning.

Children practically always give up thumbsucking by the time they are five or six years old, whether it has been a constant target for correction, or whether there has been *no* effort on the part of the parents. For one thing their contact with children of the same age or older makes them want to give it up as a matter of pride. By school age it is clearly not a social asset among their playmates. Also, as they grow up and become more outgoing they have less need to cling to babyish comforts.

Thumbsucking Conveys a Message

The child who constantly sucks his thumb is (without realizing it, of course) telling the world that he's not quite satisfied with certain things about life. There's a little something missing which he needs. He's telling this to his mother just as the infant, by his cry, is telling her that he is hungry or cold. To ask, to plead, to force the child to give up thumbsucking does not get to the bottom of the problem.

It's like asking a child to stop crying when he is cold instead of giving him a blanket.

Furthermore, to put pressure on the child to forsake his thumb-sucking only serves to add new tension to his already distressed frame of mind, and may even increase the amount of thumbsucking. He may feel that here is just one more satisfaction taken away. Other signs of tension such as sucking his tongue may crop up, as a result.

In many cases, it seems that the parents' constant efforts to correct it only prolong the habit. And some authorities think that the reverse is also true—that is—if a child is allowed to suck his thumb all he wishes, he will give up thumbsucking sooner than if urged to stop it.

There are, of course, many different degrees of thumbsucking. There is the youngster who sucks his thumb or fingers for a few minutes at night before he goes to sleep, or whenever he is sleepy in the daytime, or when he is tired or hungry or feeling frustrated. This is so natural and so commonplace and so completely lacking in significance that you need not give it a second thought.

But occasionally one sees a child who sucks almost constantly, who would rather suck than eat, and who indeed may sit through an entire meal absorbed in his sucking and not eating. This youngster is certainly saying that things are not right with his world and that he needs help in finding more constructive satisfactions.

Then there is also the little one who has given up thumbsucking but suddenly starts it up again. Observation will almost always show that something has happened to upset his equilibrium. What he needs is not a direct attack on his thumbsucking but some ironing out of whatever difficulties are causing him to resort to the comfort of his thumb again.

WAYS OF HANDLING THUMBSUCKING— A POINT OF VIEW

Parents whose children suck their thumbs will need to be prepared for the criticism of other parents, or perhaps relatives. This is embarrassing, and sometimes irritating. But one needs to develop a point of view. True, any of us would *prefer* that our child not be a thumbsucker. But try to keep in mind that it is not really very important, that he *will* grow out of it, that he is not doing it just out of wilfulness but out of a need. Try not to let yourself be drawn into nagging or punishing or any other unwise direct attack on the problems just because someone else thinks you should make the child stop.

The Do Not's

Do not use force to restrain the child in any way. Even in the earliest months do not tie or bind his hands so he cannot reach his mouth. Do not use mits or thumb-guards of any kind, nor elbow splints nor anything to keep his arm from bending. Avoid the kind of sleeping garment that holds his arms down. Do not put bitter or disagreeable substances on his fingers, or commercial preparations which are supposed to stop thumbsucking.

Do not punish. Do not scold, wheedle, coax, "remind" constantly, nor threaten that he will injure his fingers or make his teeth crooked. Avoid bribes or rewards or the "gold star" technique. Do not say "If you love me you'll stop," "You're a big boy now." "Aren't you ashamed to be such a baby," or use any similar incentives or threats.

The Do's

The "Do Not's" are nice and specific. The "Do's" are much more general. They require looking at the child's life as a whole and trying to provide all the essentials of a happy childhood.

With the young baby—provide longer and more frequent sucking periods. Make the hole in the nipple smaller, or, if breast fed, let him nurse as long as he wishes. Postpone weaning. Try using a pacifier or a rubber nipple stuffed with cotton.

With the older baby—make sure he is not sucking his thumb just because he is bored. Is he kept in a play pen too long? Does he have enough toys, enough stimulation?

With the child of two, three or four—notice when he sucks. If it is only occasionally, forget about it. If it is when he is lonely, frightened, feels deserted, try to provide more satisfactions and greater security.

With the child of five or six—if he seems to be trying to overcome the habit himself, discuss it with him. Encourage him. Assure him that he will get over it.

With any child any age—look at his life as a whole. See if you can't find the root of the problem. Does he have too much of some things, too little of others? Too much excitement, too little? Too many companions, too few? Too much mothering, too little? Always try to notice the kinds of situations which seem to bring on thumbsucking. Is it when he feels left out of things? When he can't keep up with older children? When his little sister gets more than her share of attention? These may tell you what is really troubling him and what lies at the bottom of his thumbsucking.

NINA RIDENOUR, PH.D.

When a Child Still Wets

Y ou can scarcely blame a mother for being upset if her child is still wetting himself long months after she thinks he should be dry. For one thing there is the nuisance of extra laundry. Also she hesitates to let him go places, such as visiting, or to nursery school, until he is dry. But even more important than these appears to be her *embarrassment* because her child is showing up at a disadvantage.

It is part of our cultural pattern to feel proud when a child does things early for his age. The child who learns to use the toilet at an early age is thought of as a "good" child and reflects credit on both himself and his parents. "I shouldn't boast," a mother will say, unable to keep the pride out of her voice, "but Mary Lou has been dry since before she was fifteen months old." By the same token, parents are worried or ashamed when their children are slow in learning toilet control or if, having once learned, they suddenly return to wetting again.

In the last decade or two, many of us have been placing too much emphasis on early toilet training. Perhaps that is part of the speed-up in tempo of living which we are seeing everywhere. Actually many children in this country would be better off if adults were less concerned about their toilet training. Indeed our very word "training" is unfortunate because it indicates that "training" is something which parents do *to* a child. In reality, achieving control of his elimination should be something which a child is permitted to *learn for himself* with some helpful direction from the parents, but without any coercion.

However, since "training" is the accepted word and there is no other well-understood term to express what happens, we shall use it here—keeping in mind the warning that "training" can be a dangerous idea if it is permitted to mean "to impose a set of rules." Here we want it to mean "to help to develop."

The very young child who is placed on the toilet too often does not achieve the voluntary control which he appears to achieve. As is frequently said, "It is the mother who is trained, not the child." What appears to be control is only mechanical action. Because the child has no real understanding, he is easily thrown off his training later. Also, the insistence on training gets him to feeling balky and makes him want to go against his parents' wishes instead of wanting to do what they want him to do. This makes for bad relations between the parents and the child, and will show up in other clashes of will.

EARLY TRAINING MAY BE THE CAUSE OF WETTING PROBLEMS LATER ON

It is now well understood that too early training, too much training, or too strict and severe training may be one of the major causes of wetting that persists or that begins again after the training period has ended. To shame, punish, threaten, bribe or reward a child for behavior on the toilet is to exert high pressure methods which may cause wetting at a future date, especially if other things are troubling him at that time. It is much better to take things easy. Don't rush. A few extra weeks of diaper washing when the child is one and two may save months of panty and sheet washing when he is three, four and five.

It is important to keep in mind what toilet training is like from the young child's angle. To him urine and faeces are not yet objects of disgust and to withhold them for a particular time or place is not natural. However, since it is requested, he tries to please. But in order to carry out this difficult new idea, he must first set in motion a complicated machinery which involves both his mind and his muscles. To demand too much of him when he has neither skill nor understanding will undermine the first beginnings of his newly developing self-confidence.

Some of the mistakes to be avoided in toilet training are:

starting too early

taking the child to the toilet too often, or keeping him sitting there too long

trying to establish a rigid toilet schedule

making the whole thing seem too important

If your child is now three or four or five, many of these mistakes are already a part of the past as far as you are concerned. However, an understanding of these points may give you some of the explanations for your present problems. Don't worry about past mistakes. They've been made by countless other mothers, often on good "authority." There is still a lot you can do to help your child with his problem.

SOME CHILDREN ARE DRY LATER THAN OTHERS

If one says that a child "still" wets, what is meant by "still"? That is, how old should a child be before he is considered "too old" to wet? In this area, mistakes are likely to be made in the direction of expecting too much of the child. It is practically impossible to say when any one child "should" be dry—and perhaps it is just as well not to try.

Children differ in this as they do in every other characteristic. Some achieve it without effort many months before others. Some children are dry in the daytime by their second birthday but this is exceptional. If it happens, well and good; but it is by no means a goal to be aimed at. Some children are dry both night and day by their third birthday though occasional night wetting usually lasts until three and a half. After three, and even four years, though, there are bound to be accidents—times when there are temporary breakdowns of control.

Persistent wetting beyond the age when most children have learned control is called enuresis. It can refer either to wetting which has never ceased, or to wetting that occurs after the child has achieved control. Although the deep, psychological reasons for these two kinds of reaction may differ, in general the over-all handling which parents need to understand is more or less the same for both.

Though enuresis is rarely due to physical reasons, a check-up by the doctor is often advisable. There should always be an examination of the urine if enuresis persists.

WHAT TO DO WHEN WETTING IS A PROBLEM

These are the points to be kept in mind in the handling of the three-, four- and five-year-old child:

Don't make an issue of toilet control. It is only one of the many things children must learn.

Don't use threats, shaming, rewards, punishment as a means of training.

Don't bribe the child with candy or a special treat for good behavior.

Don't demand that he tell you in words that he wants to go to the toilet.

Don't give him the idea you'll love him more when he stops wetting. Never say, "If you loved me, you would" or the opposite, "Aren't you ashamed to be such a baby?"

Try giving him a little extra to drink in the mornings and early afternoons so that his body will contain extra fluid and he will not be thirsty. Then give him a little less to drink in the late afternoon and early evening. But do not carry this to extreme nor expect it to be a cure-all. It may help a little with some children.

Don't show your annoyance if you can help it. Better still, try not to feel annoyance. Even with the four- and five-year-old, regard wetting as a not unusual reaction to something that has gone wrong in the child's life. It is a sign that the child needs your help.

Try to be casual. Give him more assurance. Show him that you know he will do better some day. (*He will!*) Give him more affection and praise. Help him to develop his skills, to grow in independence and self-confidence.

Following these suggestions may not make your child dry right away, but it should help him to be happier, more relaxed and out-going. And the happy, relaxed child is likely to achieve dryness a good deal earlier than the tense, high-strung child.

ACCIDENTS ARE TO BE EXPECTED

When a child who is dry most of the time wets himself, it is often referred to as an "accident." Actually "incident" may be a better word, because an "accident" usually refers to something which is un-expected and unfortunate. An occasional wetting in the three- and four-year-old is entirely normal and is therefore to be expected. The only thing unexpected about it is the exact moment at which it occurs.

Treat these slip-ups casually; never scold. It may help you if you recognize that these things happen most often when the child is excited or upset, or when he has played too long, or is in strange surroundings. If the child is inclined to worry about his "incidents," it may be necessary to assure him that he has done nothing to be ashamed of, and that all little boys and girls have that happen once in a while.

THE CHILD'S UNEASINESS MAY BE THE
CAUSE OF WETTING

A small child has so much to learn, so many things to attempt! When too much is expected from him by adults, his troubles start piling up. He becomes worried and upset. He feels unable to juggle all the things expected of him so he drops one; that one is often urinary control.

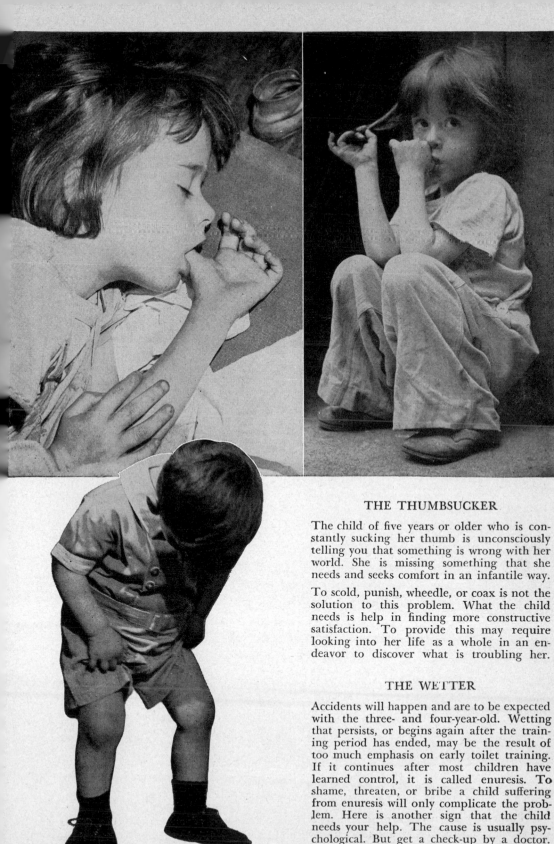

THE THUMBSUCKER

The child of five years or older who is constantly sucking her thumb is unconsciously telling you that something is wrong with her world. She is missing something that she needs and seeks comfort in an infantile way.

To scold, punish, wheedle, or coax is not the solution to this problem. What the child needs is help in finding more constructive satisfaction. To provide this may require looking into her life as a whole in an endeavor to discover what is troubling her.

THE WETTER

Accidents will happen and are to be expected with the three- and four-year-old. Wetting that persists, or begins again after the training period has ended, may be the result of too much emphasis on early toilet training. If it continues after most children have learned control, it is called enuresis. To shame, threaten, or bribe a child suffering from enuresis will only complicate the problem. Here is another sign that the child needs your help. The cause is usually psychological. But get a check-up by a doctor.

U. S. Children's Bureau Photos by Esther Bubley

Three Lions

DOUBLE TROUBLE?

Twins may mean extra expense and care but there are advantages in that they are company for each other, and toilet training and learning self-help present fewer problems.

Parents know and recognize that certain things—such as excitement—will bring on wetting. There are a number of other causes, though, that are not ordinarily associated with the problem. These are such things as being expected to achieve too much in good behavior, manners and the like; finding things in his home at sixes and sevens; having too many people asking him to do this, do that; being with relatives who don't understand children; a new baby sister or brother whose presence makes him jealous; sickness which keeps him in bed or indoors for a length of time; moving to or visiting another house; going to a new school—any change in the normal routine of things.

HELP HIM TO WANT CONTROL

There may be other deeper reasons for his trouble. For instance, sometimes when relations between a child and his parents have got off to a bad start, the child seems to use the enuresis as a "weapon" against the parents, "to get even" with them for some of the bad feelings he has inside. Or the enuresis may seem to be part of a pattern of stubbornness.

If the parents sense this attitude, the important thing to understand is that they must not in turn try "to get even" with the child. Tit-for-tat behavior never solved anything. They may think he could control himself if he wanted to—and in a sense that may be true. But then the thing is not to *make* him control, but to *help him want to control*. Remember that a child would rather have his parents' approval than their disapproval even though occasionally the opposite may seem true for a short time.

If a child has been dry for a while and then starts to wet again, do not pay too much attention to the wetting itself. Try instead to analyze the child's total life situation and improve things for him as much as possible.

HIS IDEAS ABOUT URINATION MAY BE CONFUSED

Children are often mixed-up as to the difference in the functions of the sex and eliminative organs since they are near each other. If a child has feelings of shame or secretiveness concerning sexual matters, he is likely, due to his confusion, to transfer some of these feelings to the eliminative functions.

A casual, matter-of-fact attitude is the best way to help clear up this confusion. When a little girl, for instance, stands in front of the toilet and tries to urinate "like Daddy" or her brother, don't be shocked. Most little girls try this at some time. Don't scold her for wetting the floor. Instead use this as the logical time to give her one of her first lessons in sex education. Explain to her that boys and men have a penis, so they stand up; all girls and women have a vagina so they sit down.

Some little children have fears connected with going to the toilet. For instance, a child may be afraid of being flushed down the toilet. (He should be given a potty or a child's seat over a pot.) Such fears cannot simply be laughed off since they are very real to the child. They call for soothing and reassurance.

Children like to make jokes and play games that deal with the toilet. This is a harmless and natural interest which they should be allowed to express. In fact, when a child seems unduly concerned with the function of elimination, encouraging such play can give him a needed outlet. For instance, give him a toy potty or join in when he plays doctor or nurse. Of course, it is wise to explain to him which of these games or jokes may be frowned upon by the conventions of the outside world.

FURTHER SUGGESTIONS

When a child insists upon performing toilet in public or watching others at the toilet, treat the matter calmly with some remark such as, "It is not clean to urinate in the yard" or "People like to be alone."

Of the many words taught children to express urine and urinate, bowel movement and defecate, the best ones are probably those especially coined for the purpose (such as "wee-wee," or "B.M.") Words that have another meaning in ordinary conversation (such as "duty," "business," "try," "go," "number two") are better dropped. The child may retain their toilet meaning when he is grown up and avoid their use in conversation because of an embarrassing association.

Most nursery schools handle the wetting problem well. They take wetting incidents in their stride and make nothing of them. But if you find that your child's school makes an issue of the matter in training your child, it may be well to consider removing him from the school until a time when wetting is no longer a problem.

NINA RIDENOUR, PH.D.

When a Child Masturbates

THE very word "masturbation" makes some people feel like blushing. To many of us it brings to mind furtiveness, shame, distaste or danger. For hundreds of years masturbation has been pictured as a shocking, harmful habit leading to disastrous consequences. As a result many parents are quite naturally disturbed when they find that *their* child masturbates.

Surrounding this whole subject there exist some dangerous untruths which, believed by thousands of people, have caused vast harm to children and unhappiness to their parents. To give little boys and girls the best kind of childhood, parents must know the truth about masturbation. They must have the *facts*.

To approach the subject soundly one must first throw out many of the ideas that have accumulated through the ages, ideas which even some books on medicine and child care have helped to spread.

THESE ARE THE FACTS

Let's get rid of the untruths first . . .

Masturbation will not injure people's bodies or make them unable to marry.

It will not cause them to "go crazy."

It is not something perverted or to be looked upon with shock or horror.

And now here are the important truths . . .

All little children do a certain amount of masturbation. In its milder forms, masturbation is not serious and is to be expected.

Brief or occasional masturbation should cause no concern whatsoever. When it is indulged in excessively, it indicates that the child is tense or worried about something and it therefore becomes necessary to find the cause of his tension.

It is not the *habit* which is serious or harmful but the *worry and anxiety* it causes to both parents and children.

Masturbation is not a *cause* of other problems but it can be a *symptom* that other things are wrong in the child's life. When it is excessive it is a signal of emotional distress.

IT IS NATURAL FOR YOUNG CHILDREN TO HANDLE THEIR GENITALS

A child may, with no intent to stimulate the genitals (sex organs), pluck at his clothing if it is too tight, or touch the genitals when he wants to go to the toilet but this is not considered masturbation. Masturbation is the touching or handling of the genitals purposely for the sensation it creates.

Little children are natural explorers. They learn about a new world by feeling and touching new things. Sex is no exception. A child has a healthy curiosity and is interested in exploring all parts of his body (and other peoples' too). He sticks his finger into his navel and his nose and his mouth, and experiments with his toes and fingers. When by chance he touches his genitals and finds that this produces a sensation he is likely to repeat it. To him this is in a class with other sensations derived from the sense of touch—sucking his thumb, twisting a lock of hair, caressing a soft piece of silk or a woolly toy animal.

WHEN PARENTS ARE UPSET AND ANXIOUS

To adults it is sometimes a shock to realize that a little child does have sexual feelings and that by touching himself he derives a mild form of sexual pleasure. Parents fear that a child who shows sexual feelings early in life may grow up to be too strongly sexed or in some way abnormal. Actually a moderate amount of handling the sex organs is normal and will be found in all children. The feeling in the genitals is one of the many kinds of sensations which the body gives, a sensation which the child naturally wishes to explore and to enjoy occasionally. Small amounts of masturbation, therefore, can and should be ignored; it is only frequent or excessive masturbation which requires special attention for the sake of the child's well-being.

Perhaps you are one of the many adults who have believed, all your life—ever since *you* were a child—that masturbation is unhealthy, shameful, bad, etc. If so, you are bound to feel troubled when you discover that your child masturbates. Your natural reaction is to try to put a stop to it immediately by the most direct means. But immediate, direct action may have the very opposite result from that which you hope to achieve. You may find that the masturbation has increased or that other seemingly unrelated problems have sprung up.

So, in order to help your child, the very first thing to do is to stop worrying about masturbation. Keep in mind this well established fact: some handling of the sex organs is completely normal and to be expected. *All children do it.*

THE CHILD'S PROBLEMS INCREASE

When you have overcome your own disturbance concerning this part of children's behavior, you will be better able to avoid the mistake so often made by adults. That mistake is to let the child know you think he is doing something bad.

To the small child, *to do something bad* is the same as if *he himself* were bad. When he feels he is a bad person he feels guilty. This, in turn, makes him begin to fear that his parents do not love him because of his "badness." Then he starts worrying because to him the love of his parents is the most important, the most necessary thing in his whole world. He could not exist without it. His happiness and his very life depend on their taking care of him—and they will take care of him only if they love him. To lose their love would be the worst thing that could happen to him. The fear of losing love is the root of anxiety.

These emotions—guilt, fear and anxiety—spell trouble. They are the basis for the child's worries. They are the underlying cause of many behavior problems of childhood and may lead to unwholesome, unhappy attitudes in adult life. They may be the causes, too, of other problems such as nightmares, temper tantrums, aggressive behavior and habits such as bedwetting and thumbsucking at a later age. They are also at least partly responsible for the ingoing, introverted personality for which masturbation is sometimes mistakenly blamed.

Therefore, if a child's parents show directly or indirectly that they think masturbation is bad, they only increase the child's problems. Disapproval, scolding or punishment intensifies the child's guilty and fearful feelings. It may happen that the more he is forced to think about masturbation, the harder it is for him to refrain. A vicious circle is set up. The more he masturbates the more he worries; and then the worry causes still more masturbation. Threats may possibly make him stop (they probably won't) but even if they *appear* to be "successful," they are likely to stir up other anxieties.

THESE ARE GOOD WAYS TO APPROACH THE PROBLEM

Give the child every assurance that he is both safe from harm and a good child.

Avoid words, attitudes or actions that might make the child afraid or ashamed.

Give praise and affection at special times, such as when he is going to bed, or has been disappointed or has had trouble with other children.

See that he gets plenty of opportunity for happy relations with his playmates as well as activities which capture his wholehearted interest. If he shows any strong interests let him pursue them.

Answer his questions, both the ones he asks and those which are obviously troubling him but which he cannot express.

Let children of the opposite sex see each other when undressed. However young a child may be—two or three or four—he should be given an explanation when he shows interest or puzzlement over the sex differences. Tell him in a casual, matter-of-fact tone: boys and men have a penis, girls and women have a vagina.

Answer his questions about babies in a way he can understand. If his natural curiosity is satisfied at each stage of his development, he will be more likely to have a normal, healthy attitude towards sex and avoid some of the pitfalls of anxiety and fear and confusion so often associated with the subject.

PUNISHMENT IS UNWISE

Any kind of punishment either by means of words or force, or even mild reprimands on the subject, is extremely unwise. The chief danger of punishment is that it makes the child feel guilty—that he is bad, naughty. The child is likely to have a stronger feeling of guilt about his activity than about the other things he does. His ideas are vague and confused and his imagination vivid. He may build up pictures of the terrible things that will happen to him because of his naughtiness, thus sowing the seeds of more fears and more anxiety, and increasing his emotional difficulties.

Another reason for avoiding punishment is that it may play upon and confirm the fear which he may already have to some degree, that is, fear of injury to his genitals. Many children do worry for fear their genitals are impaired in some way or that something is lacking. When children first become aware of the differences in the sexes, they are likely to experience some anxious moments.

A little girl, for instance, frequently asks why she doesn't have a penis like her little brother and in playing games may show her wish to have one. Girls often assume they have been injured or that there is something wrong, missing or unfinished about themselves. Boys often have similar thoughts when they see little girls and consequently may fear that the same thing will happen to them.

Punishment for masturbation, therefore, only increases their fears. What they need is the exact opposite: reassurance. Masturbation is less likely to cause anxiety if children get the right kind of reassurance than if they are punished.

THREATS ARE PUNISHMENT TOO

People often think that "to punish" a child means to do something to him physically and that merely "threatening" him with punishment is not punishment itself. Actually it is more accurate to regard as punishment anything which frightens the child or makes things unpleasant for him.

The use of threats by parents to make children stop masturbation is far more prevalent than one would ordinarily think. Studies have shown that both the threats and the measures used are frequently shockingly severe. Over and over again parents admitted—often with pride—that they had warned a child that his genitals would be injured, that he would not be able to urinate, that he would get a hernia, or that he would be a cripple or "not grow strong." Some parents resorted to more drastic measures such as putting red pepper on the child's fingers or tying the legs to a high chair. Slapping the hands was one of the most frequent of the mild punishments.

These parents cared about their children and thought they were doing the right thing. Such lack of knowledge can nevertheless have tragic results, no matter how well-meaning the parents may be.

SOME SUGGESTIONS FOR PARENTS

Do not use any harsh or severe methods to break masturbation such as threats, punishment, scolding, humiliation or mechanical restraint. It is better not even to use mild reprimands such as "It isn't nice;" "people won't like you." Never tell the child that he will injure himself, get sick, become infected or not grow. And never slap his hands or use any other kind of punishment or restraint. Do not offer rewards in order to make him give it up.

Ordinarily it is better not to call the child's attention to his masturbation or discuss it, especially if he is very young (only three or four). However, he is pretty likely to hear about it from other adults sooner or later, and possibly in such a way as to upset him. Therefore, if he is old enough, say five or so, it may be advisable to say "Some people think that does not look well. It is better not to do it when you are around others." If he has been scolded elsewhere, or if he seems to be trying to get over the habit, discuss it with him, reassure him, tell him that it is not important but that some people object.

WHAT TO DO—TO HELP YOURSELF

Remember that a certain amount of masturbation is only a part of normal growing up.

If you are worried, try not to show your concern. This will not be easy if you yourself were taught that masturbation would cause all sorts of dreadful things. But it becomes easier as you gradually grasp the fact that you do not *need* to worry.

Try to understand that some masturbation is to be expected in all young children and indeed in older children too. There is little reason for distress.

WHAT TO DO—TO HELP THE CHILD

Look at the child's daily life as one complete picture. Analyze its parts and see if they add up to one happy whole.

Here are the questions to ask yourself:

Does he have plenty of physical activity—space to run and climb, a chance for outdoor play?

Does he have companions of his own age? Is he included in the group when he plays with other children? Is he liked by other children?

Does he have appropriate things to play with? Not expensive toys —but things to push and pull and tug, things to put in and take out and drag around, paints, clays, crayons—things which he can handle in his own way? Is he allowed to take a few favorite toys to bed with him so that before he goes to sleep and after he wakes up, he has things to keep him happy and busy?

Does he have reason to feel loved and accepted in his own home—with not too much expected of him, not constantly scolded or punished? Does he have assurance that he is growing in ability and independence?

When the answer to most of these questions can be "yes," masturbation is not likely to be a problem.

NINA RIDENOUR, PH.D.

The Fingernail Biter

O F all the typical nervous habits of childhood, such as picking the nose, blinking the eyes and making grimaces, nail biting is the most common. The reason for nail biting is typical of all such evidence of nervousness.

Healthy young children are very active and only gradually develop to the point where they can sit still or keep quiet long at a time. Freedom of movement is necessary to their growth. If it is interfered with to any great extent, we may expect an outburst of some kind by means of which they "let off steam." To tell a child to "sit still" is about as useless as telling a lively young colt to stop prancing. If he is forced to be inactive for a long period, to keep from talking, or to live up to standards of behavior that are beyond his powers, we must expect some reaction.

In some children the result may be irritable behavior; others become very resistant to control; still others will respond to the pressure by developing some bodily habit, like nail biting, that shows up the inner restlessness.

A parent who takes note of the times when a child bites his nails most will probably find that it takes place under conditions of excitement, overstimulation, or unhappiness. (Once it has become a habit of course, the nail biting may appear at any time, especially when the child is bored or tired or suffering from excitement and tension.) This suggests the importance of keeping the child from being subjected to too great excitement. Young children should not be taken often to the movies, to the circus, to fairs, or to other places where there are crowds and where many things are happening. Sitting still in a movie and having his emotions stirred by exciting or distressing scenes that he does not understand is the very kind of strain which a child ought not to have to bear.

Anything that causes the child inner tension, such as fear or worry of any sort, makes conditions just right for the growth of the habit. If his mother is anxious, if there is quarreling that upsets him, if too much is expected of him, he may unconsciously try to ease his feelings in this or a similar way.

Parents should try to remove the cause of the strain and substitute a more desirable activity—something to do with the hands, some occupation that will keep the child actively busy. Scolding, threats, constant mention of the habit, only make it worse. Care should be taken to keep the child's nails in good condition; if they are short and smooth, with no hangnails, the temptation to bite them is less great. Bitter-tasting medicines applied to the nails are of little use, but sometimes putting on nail polish encourages a little girl to feel pride in having her nails look nice.

Nervous habits are not likely to develop to any great extent in a child whose life is serene and happy, whose routine is so planned that he is not put under strains that are too much for him to cope with—like having to play with older children, living in a home where there is quarreling or bad feeling among the adults, or being denied an opportunity for lively outdoor play. An important thing to remember in handling little children is that we tend to manage them too much. A great deal of directing and talking can be avoided if the child is free to carry out his own ideas with the least possible adult interference.

Stuttering and Other Speech Defects

SINCE everyone is dependent on speech for communicating readily with others, anything that interferes with it is in the nature of a handicap. Speech defects that cannot be corrected in the home are rare and parents can do much toward fostering good speech habits and developing ease in the use of language.

Stuttering is fairly frequent in early childhood, so it is worth while for parents to know how to head off this problem and what to do about it if it has already started.

It is popularly supposed that stuttering is outgrown, but many children carry this handicap into their high school and college years. Stuttering is about four or five times as frequent in boys as in girls.

A child is said to stutter when he hesitates at the beginning of a word and tries repeatedly but unsuccessfully to make the right sound come. He may repeat the first letter of a word several times, or the whole word, or he may be so blocked that he cannot get any sound out.

The usual times when stuttering appears are when the child is about two or two and one-half years old and is just beginning to talk freely; when he enters school; and at adolescence. Because these are times of big adjustments that the child has to make, it is only reasonable to suppose that speech difficulty is the result of emotional strain.

The two-year-old is eager to make himself understood and also to learn by asking questions, but as he does not have a large enough vocabulary, he may get into trouble. It bothers him not to be able to put into words what he wants to know or to tell, and stuttering sometimes results. Because young children are so easily influenced by those they are with, associating with a child who stutters or constantly hearing an adult in the family do so may result in a child's unconscious imitation of the habit. Until a child's speech habits are well established, it is not good for him to have as a constant companion a child or an adult who has speech difficulties.

396

Because stuttering has an emotional basis, it is important to remember that efforts to correct it will fail unless the underlying nervous tension that causes it is removed. In a child who is fussed at and corrected, the difficulty may become a very serious one. The child's difficulty should not be mentioned; he should be listened to carefully and patiently, so that he does not feel hurried when he tries to express himself. It is unwise to ask him to talk more slowly or to repeat, nor should you try to help him by filling in the word that you think he is trying to say. Children who stutter do not profit by any special exercises unless given by an expert in speech retraining. Such exercises often merely call their attention to the habit we want them to forget.

When stuttering is slight and only occasional, a careful checking and rearranging of the child's schedule may be all that is necessary. It may be that the excitement in the child's home life can be lessened. If the child seems more inclined to stutter when he is tired, his mother should see that he gets more rest. If the stuttering occurs after he has been playing with several children, it may be helpful to arrange for him to play with only one or two at a time. He should be protected from feeling self-conscious, as he is sure to do if he is expected to "act like a little gentleman" when in company. The strain caused by his parents' expecting too much of him, or by situations in which he is afraid, should be avoided.

Because language ability is vital to a child's success at school, it is important to see that the stutterer is sympathetically handled there. He should not be called upon to read aloud or recite before a group if this is the kind of thing that upsets him. A child who stutters is sensitive, otherwise he would not show this symptom of lack of poise. Many schools have classes for children who stutter, directed by specially trained teachers. It is well worth while to seek out such a school.

THE LEFT-HANDED CHILD

Although authorities differ as to whether or not there is a connection between left-handedness and stuttering, it is generally agreed that it is not wise to encourage the use of the right hand in children who show a tendency to be left-handed. Many children have switched from the use of the left to the right hand with no difficulty. But the very child who, because of his general "nervousness" might be expected to stutter, is also the one who may be excited over an attempted change from left to right. The very slight advantage of being able to use the right hand is not worth the risk of causing trouble. A school in which left-handed children are forced to write with their right hands is very old-fashioned indeed.

SLOW TO TALK—DEFECTIVE SPEECH

If a child who is over two is not talking, the reason may be one of the following:

1. It may be merely that the child is slower in this phase of his development than in others. In such a case he will talk when he is ready to.

2. Occasionally it happens that a child begins to talk and then slows down or even stops talking for a while. It is believed that when he is trying hard to learn a new skill, he may temporarily make no progress in other skills already partly learned. For instance, a child learning to put on a shoe or to handle a spoon might for a time stop using those words he already knew.

3. Sometimes the child's mother attends to his wants so quickly that he does not need to talk. In such a case it is necessary for her to be deliberately unobservant, so that the child will be forced to try to make himself understood. He must not be allowed to depend upon other means of communication, such as gestures and grunts, or he will continue to be slow in learning to talk.

4. Sometimes it is the child's emotional attitude that is preventing the use of language. Occasionally a baby who starts to talk is made so much of, urged to say his new words for visitors, and given so much attention that he becomes very resistant and refuses to open his mouth. Forcing him is likely to make him want to resist even more. Any treatment that results in a child's feeling "contrary" may slow up his interest in being social, or responsive, by means of speech.

Letting a child alone a good deal, being careful not to notice his resistant behavior any more than can be helped, but taking pains to show appreciation whenever he does try to talk is usually helpful in doing away with his stubbornness.

5. Illness or serious malnutrition may slow up a child's speech just as it hinders his development in other ways. Physical care that builds up his health will be the answer here.

6. The possibility of deafness should be considered when a child does not talk at the customary time. Some children are born deaf, but many more have their hearing impaired by complications following one of the acute infectious diseases common in childhood. Deaf children must have special speech training.

7. Just as very bright children usually talk earlier than average children, so children who are born with less mental capacity than average or whose brains have been affected by a birth injury talk late. If a child to whom none of the other explanations of delayed speech applies is not talking by the age of two and one-half years, he should be taken to a doctor or clinic and a thorough physical and psychological study should be made. If failure to learn to talk is due to defective brain development, so that the child will always be slow in whatever he undertakes to learn, his parents should know it, so that he may have careful training suited to his special needs.

8. Cases of speech defect caused by malformation of the speech organs, such as tongue-tie, are exceedingly rare. Children who have had harelips or cleft palates repaired often need special speech training.

A child who is habitually read to acquires a knowledge of words and an opportunity to have his questions answered that is very valuable. Conversation with other children helps him to use language well, if he is not badgered and corrected when he makes mistakes. Little errors should be largely overlooked while a child is learning to express himself. If the speech habits of their parents are good, children will gradually learn to speak correctly.

A Cure For Dawdlers

EVERY child dawdles at some time or other. Some children, of course, dawdle more than others and keep it up for a longer time. If dawdling is permitted to continue, it may readily develop into a habit that will be more difficult to break the longer it remains unchecked.

A dawdler "fools around" on a task far longer than the task itself requires. He is always behind schedule, he keeps others waiting for him, he misses out on a lot of fun, and he begins to doubt his own abilities when people nickname him "Slow Poke" and imply that he is incapable of keeping up with them.

You must not, of course, judge the time a child takes to carry out any task by adult standards. A four- or five-year-old, it has been shown in carefully conducted experiments, takes approximately twenty-five minutes to finish his dinner of meat, potato, vegetable, milk and dessert. You or I could eat the same food in three to five minutes without hurrying.

What is true of eating is likewise true of everything else a child does. He needs and takes more time than we do to put on his clothes, to write a word, to wash his hands and face or to pick up his toys. The reason is that he lacks the muscle coordination to do things quickly. Frequently he does not even know how to go about the task he is trying to carry out.

Dawdling usually begins in connection with some routine activity such as eating or dressing. Unless checked, it then spreads to other activities. Soon the child becomes a chronic dawdler. He fools over everything he undertakes, thus consuming far more time than he needs for simple, everyday living.

The common way of dealing with dawdlers is to penalize them for their slowness. The assumption is that the child's slowness is intentional and that he is just being "ornery" to aggravate his parents. This, however, is unjust and unsympathetic, and shows little understanding of the child's development.

Would you have a kindly feeling toward a person who constantly scolded you for being "as slow as molasses in January"? How would you feel if you were left behind when everyone went out just because it took you longer than it took them to put on your coat, leggings, hat, mittens and galoshes? Do you blame a child for being angry and resentful when his plate is taken away even though he is still hungry?

Treatment of this sort is likely to make dawdling worse rather than better. The dawdler gets his revenge on the adults who have scolded or fussed with him by being slower than ever. The child consciously tries to slow down because he has no incentive to speed up.

The following suggestions, if applied in a sympathetic manner, will cure any child of dawdling. They will likewise prevent dawdling from developing if it is not already present.

1. Show the child efficient methods of doing different tasks. Most children spend far more time and energy on routine tasks than is necessary because they do not know just how to go about these tasks. Left to their own resources they will, in time, learn to cut corners and to eliminate many unnecessary movements. But how much better it is to show them how to go about these activities in an efficient manner than to expect them to work it out for themselves by trial and error.

2. Keep time charts for a child who has a tendency to dawdle or for one who is just learning a new task. Record, each day, the time the child takes for the task and encourage him to try to improve his time scores every day. This soon becomes a game and the child tries to beat his own score. To be able to do this, he is more receptive to suggestions for improving his ways of doing things than if he had no incentive to speed up. The charts should be kept until the activity can be carried out in a reasonable time.

3. Guard the child from all distracting influences until the activity he is attempting to carry out has been so well learned that he does not have to think about what he is doing. It is impossible for a child (or an adult!) to pay attention simultaneously to what is going on around him and to what he is supposed to be doing. Because the former is generally the more interesting, his attention is concentrated on it while his task is neglected.

4. When a child slows down, give him a helping hand rather than a scolding. The task may seem small and easy to an adult, but not to a child. As he becomes tired, he becomes bored. His lagging interest can be revived quickly if someone will step in and help him.

5. Reward the child for doing things in a reasonable time. No matter how small and simple the reward, the child feels that it is worth his while to speed up when his efforts receive favorable recognition. Do you blame him for reacting more favorably to this than to scoldings?

ELIZABETH B. HURLOCK, PH.D.

The First Child Against the Second

L IFE quickly becomes complex for even the very young. By the time he is two, the child is asked to accept some degree of parental authority. This pressure is stepped up gradually. As he becomes three, five, six years old, the screws of parental authority tighten.

The relation between his parents' authority and their greater size and age is not lost upon the child. He soon learns the inestimable value of rank. As his parents seek to teach him habits of eating, of using the toilet, of respecting property, of controlling genital play, he learns the meaning of his low status in relation to theirs. Their ability to reward and to punish him are related, he finds, to their greater age, physical strength, knowledge, and social authority.

To win some of their power is an adventure in which the chances are high and dangerous, but worth the gamble. It is a game which all children at all ages play hard, unless they have been treated so severely that they have become frightened. Some youngsters may attack their parents by cunning, and some by "apple-polishing." Still others do not attack, but succeed by frankness and humor. No normal child *likes* to be subordinated; nor does any normal human being, so far studied. (But child or man may be *taught* "to like it" by systematic intimidation, and by organized suppression.)

Therefore, a child learns this game of striving for extra privil‧ eges, even if he has no brother or sister to prick his jealousy. An "only child" usually is learning, by the age of two, that he can get more of what he wants if he can pit his father against his mother, or the other way around. To weaken their joint authority, to divide their judgments of his behavior and thus to conquer the moral front of parental dominance, he learns to play one parent against the other. He quickly discovers how to use the parent who loves him the more, or indulges him the more—or who is emotionally opposed to routine discipline—as a wedge to split parental authority and super- vision.

When he later gets a brother or sister, he actually gains an ally as well as a competitor. In championing their cause, as children, against the powerful adult parent, they join hands and tricks. It is an ex- cellent kind of skirmishing, in which all the children stand to gain both emotional release of their pent-up resentments, and also a weak- ening of parental dominance by keeping a thin, wavering, but com- mon front of children against adults.

Brothers and sisters, themselves, are divided, however, by their own competition. Whether a child is a first child, who has been re- placed by a new baby, or whether he finds older and therefore more privileged brothers on the scene when he arrives, he certainly will have to come to grips with jealousy and rivalry. To make the situa- tion worse, his parents unconsciously will train him in a contradictory fashion concerning this rivalry. For they will urge him both to *compete* with his brothers and sisters in some ways, and *not* to com- pete with them in other ways.

This rivalry between the children, themselves, is often an insidious, full-scale, and bitter fight. In this battle, the victor gains *more* par- ental care and indulgence than his brothers or sisters. He hopes also to gain, and may actually gain, the one inestimable prize of life, that without which nothing can be wholly satisfying, as the child sees life —namely, the priceless gift of being the "most loved"—by the mother, if possible. If not, to be the best loved of the father is something, a kind of high consolation prize.

In this early game of rivalry, therefore, the stakes are the highest. Each brother or sister thinks he has the most precious thing in the world to defend, or to win. To the outsider, it often may be ironically or tragically clear that the parents have already given their "best love" to one of the children, even *before* the game of rivalry begins!

Many a parent cannot help forming a preference of this kind. No two children are alike even at birth, and it is almost inevitable that the mother and father will form involuntary preferences. For example, a mother who is very much in love with her own image, or who is very sympathetic with her own weaknesses—may love best that baby who, from birth, seems to be a new version of *herself*. And so on.

But these facts learned by the objective, rational analysis of people and their behavior, will never really satisfy the jealous child. Even if he is well-loved, but not the *best* loved, the child (especially in a small, tightly knit, middle-class family) usually will be dissatisfied. Many children, and many adults, in our society cannot bear to be merely well-loved. They must feel themselves the best loved, or even more irreconcilably, the *only* loved one.

This is the real stake in the rivalry between brothers or sisters, then: to be the best loved. To be so means to receive greater care, more attention, and full indulgence from one or both parents, and thus to gain a vantage point from which to dominate the other children in the family. The mother who regards this rivalry as merely one child's jealousy of the other child's toys, clothes, books, or hours of going to bed, etc., will never be able to handle the real causes. For the real fight is over the mother, herself, or the father.

All other privileges—whether they be gifts, personal attention, or fondling by the parents—are important sources of jealousy only because they indicate *which way the wind is blowing;* that is, toward which child the parent's favor and love are veering most strongly. Concerning this matter of preference, which is the most vital stake in life to them, children are not always, nor usually, wrong. They can spot parental preference. Where there is marked jealousy between their children, therefore, a mother and father should analyze first, not their children's behavior, but their own. Honesty and intelligence on the part of the parents will recognize mistaken distinctions which they have made between their children in gifts, bed-hours, punishments, and so on.

Intelligent analysis, instead of guilty feelings, will reveal in time also the irrational, unjust roots of certain prejudices which a parent may hold against one of his children. A father may be irritated because his little son of four years tells untruths, or still acts "like girls" in some respects. These are normal traits of a four-year-old. But the father carries his criticisms of the son to the point of prejudice. Such bias may be the result of the father's knowledge of his own *strong tendency to lie,* or of his own hidden *fear that he was a "sissy"* in boyhood. Or a mother may discern that she has an unaccountable bias against her own daughter, who is only two years old, and a good child. Such a mother may be turning toward her daughter an irrational hostility. Because the little girl happens to *resemble physically* the mother's sister, whom the mother dislikes strongly, the baby may arouse resentment in the mother. Intelligent parents, who are constantly learning, who are alert to the tricks which their emotions will play on them, can and will learn to remedy such injustices to their children. It is not easy. But insight, and the sane handling of *one's own biases* will start one's relationship to the child in the right direction.

One wishes it were as easy to tell how to dull the sting of jealousy in the child, himself; especially in that child who feels he has been replaced in the mother's or father's affection by a baby. First of all, no one who deals with children should wink at the *realistic basis for jealousy* in the child who has "lost" his mother to a new baby. Take the case of a first child, for example. The most "difficult" child in most families is the first child. In middleclass families, he is likely to be the most severely trained and the most conscientious, and therefore the most *anxious* of all the children.

But the most vital single fact about the first child is that once *he was the only child.* In most families, that position means that he is the subject of constant fondling, praise, and attention. Even if he is not "spoiled" in his training, he inevitably is rewarded constantly with flattering attention from adults, because he is the only child in the family. If he was the *only child for four or five years,* he is very likely to be a self-indulgent as well as an anxious child.

Then a new baby appears. The first child discovers suddenly that his mother has taken a strange child, who gets most of her fondling and time. (In the early nineteen-hundreds he was merely shut out by his mother while she was nursing and bathing the new baby. Today he is actually exiled from his mother during the *week or ten days* of her confinement in the hospital.)

The new baby moves into her bedroom, nurses her breast, receives her care day and night. She hugs him, plays with him, and talks lovingly to him. Unless there is a maid to help with the work, the first child usually must be neglected during these early days of the second child's life. The mother has returned from the hospital weak, and usually has all she can manage to run the house and tend the baby. She cannot possibly give the first child his usual care at meals, at playtime, and at bedtime. No one can help this.

To the older child, this neglect comes suddenly and stingingly. No longer is he the most important and the most attended. In the normal middleclass family, where mothers devote themselves to infant-care as if it were a ritual, it is almost inevitable that the older child should feel wronged by his mother, and jealous of the baby. For the time being, certainly for the first week or two, he feels abandoned, tricked, let down. To make affairs worse, the mother, of course, can never tell him that she is sorry, never say he has been wronged! But the child, himself, who has been "over-loved" and overstimulated by his parents, usually feels deeply that he has been wronged.

If he discovers gradually that he is still the better loved, he may be somewhat reassured. But each new skill, each new privilege gained by the second-born probably will frighten the older child and stir up his jealousy again. The blunt truth is that the first child, especially in conventional middleclass families, is often an irreconcilable. *He once had all. He now has only a part.* The jealousy and sense of injustice felt by such a child can never be completely assuaged. No matter how much attention and love he wins from his parents, he can never have their *undivided love* again. The "replaced" first child in middleclass families is the true "irreconcilable." Nothing in life

can ever give him what he once had—the place of the *only loved* in his
parents' hearts. He never really gives up the struggle—irrational as it
is—to be the nonpareil. The sense of injustice, of having been deprived, of having been used and then set a little aside, blown up
and then deflated, remains with him. It spurs him on to regain his
peerless state by attacking the younger child. His behavior may be
irrational, but its cause is real and just from the child's viewpoint.
In a slanting way, he is like a husband whose wife suddenly intro-
duces a second man into the bridal chamber!

There are some types of families, however, in which the sting of
jealousy is assuaged for the first child. In Samoa, where a child is
given affection and care by a large group of women, the 'loss' of the
mother to a new baby arouses little sign of jealousy. In the typical
lowerclass white or Negro-American family, or in the Italian- or
Mexican-American family, where a child has grandmothers and aunts
who often act as his mother (so that he has two or three women who
give him attention and caresses), the first child is more easily reconciled to a new baby. Furthermore, in those middleclass families
where there are several women, or one woman with great emotional
expressiveness and warmth, the first child also will escape the worst
pangs of replacement and jealousy. It may be that, after a second
child is born, the first child becomes a problem in the average middleclass family because there is too little affection *expressed* for anyone in the conventional middleclass home.

The second child, moreover, is also jealous of his parents. That is,
rivalry usually strikes both ways, both from the older against the
younger, and also from the younger. Each child has his stake in the
mother's and father's love and favor. Only the bitter and disillusioned
child refuses to compete for it.

But the second child is fighting for less than the first. He never
has had *all* the stage, nor even the front of it. His fight is *to be as old*
as the older child. This also is an impossible goal, but children are
not logicians. The second child hopes to become as old as the first by
outdoing him in skills, in games, in strength, in possessions. The
second child may eventually succeed in thus becoming *socially older*
and more efficient than the first born. But until he does, he also will
be goaded by jealousy, and irreconcilably stung by his feeling of age-

inferiority. (It is a basic "injustice," from the child's point of view, for his parents to regulate his privileges by his age.)

Do the first and second children usually reveal sharp and typical differences in personality? If so, *why?* These questions often fascinate parents; and are of perennial interest to students of personality. The authors were anxious to see whether their studies threw any light upon this puzzle. Out of the 202 mothers whom we have interviewed, there were *thirty white middleclass mothers who had two-child families.* Each was asked to compare the training and the personalities of her two children.

The average age of the first child in these thirty families was about *six years;* of the second child about *three years.* The mothers agreed overwhelmingly that the *first child was the more jealous and the more selfish,* and that the *second child was the happier and the more generous.*

The answers also suggest that the first child is more likely to be constipated, to be neat, and to suck his thumb than is the second child. The second child is more likely to have a good appetite. He also seems to be the more punished child.

The crux of the difference, however, is that the first child is the more jealous and selfish, and the second the happier. In fact, the first child was regarded as more selfish and jealous *in families of every size,* both white and colored. In most families the first child also was *trained more severely* than the second. He was weaned about two and one-half months before the second child, and he was started in toilet training two months before the age at which the second child was started.

In middleclass homes, the first child usually is reared "according to the book," and probably becomes *more anxious,* therefore. With the second child, the parents grow more relaxed and indulgent.

But the most revealing fact about "two-child" families is this: *No matter what type of training he has received,* no matter whether he was more indulgently or more severely treated than the second child, *the first child is still reported by mothers as being the more jealous and selfish.*

Although the judgments of these mothers concerning their children's selfishness may not have allowed sufficiently for the fact that

one child was about six and the other about three years old, there is
not the same difficulty to meet in choosing the "more *jealous*" child.
Nearly every mother of two children knows definitely which of her
youngsters is the more jealous. *Our findings seem to indicate very
clearly that no type of training (whether severe, moderate, or indulgent) is likely to overcome the first child's sense of having been
replaced by the second child, or to overcome his feeling that he has
lost some of his parents' love.*

Must one expect in our society, then, that rivalry between the first
and second child is almost inevitable? The answer of science and of
common experience seems to be, "Yes!" Whether the children are
of the same sex, or opposite sexes, seems only to make a difference
in the *causes* and *forms* of rivalry, but not to eliminate this competition. Even differences in age, and the attempts of parents to "space"
children so as to avoid rivalry, are shown by observation to be usually of little avail. Brothers or sisters separated by three or four years
are jealous of each other, and so are those separated by only nine
months! The reasons for this universality of rivalry are, first, that the
stakes (love and preference from the parents) are real and precious
to the child. Secondly, as every observant parent will learn, we actually help *teach* our children to compete with (and thus to be jealous
of) each other. We systematically "hold up" one sister as an example
to another sister. This means that in our society a child inevitably is
taught to compete with his brothers and sisters. Parents stimulate
and encourage this rivalry in order to motivate the child, perhaps to
eat a "full meal"; or to learn to keep himself dry, or to keep his room
neat, or to study hard. Usually the mother says explicitly, "You
don't want Henry to clean his plate better than you, do you?" or
"You want to act like a big boy like Henry, don't you, and use the
toilet?" But even if the mother says nothing, rivalry is culturally stimulated by the *age-competition* within the family.

Rivalry appeared in a great many forms in the 202 families whose
training of children we have studied. Mothers do not like to admit
that there is jealousy between their children, however. Indeed, the
most powerful ideal which our society sets up for the parent is that
of "equal love and equal care" for each child. The average mother is
afraid, therefore, to admit that her children are jealous, because she

senses that their jealousy implies some unequal treatment on her part. In addition, there is a powerful code in our society that there should be peace and mutual acceptance between children in the same family. Therefore, a mother fears that, if she admits that her children are jealous, the outsider will conclude that she is a poor mother, with a disorganized family. In spite of these deep-laid taboos, we found that it is normal for rivalry to occur in both middleclass and lowerclass families.

Mothers remembered, for example, that when a new baby appeared, the next older child found opportunities to hit the baby, or to take its bottle, or to try to shove it out of the mother's lap. Other children said they didn't like the baby, or called it a puppy, or said it should be "given back" or "sent back" to whoever sent it!

Some children turned their resentment directly against the *mother*, instead of "displacing" it toward the new baby. This type was sullen, or impudent toward the mother. Such a child pulled on the mother, or hit or kicked her when she was nursing or holding the baby. Such open hostility toward the mother was rare, however; it required a daring and probably somewhat indulged child to attack the mother instead of the baby.

If the older child was being weaned from the bottle, or toilet-trained, or just entering school *at the time of the new baby's appearance*, he frequently began to demand the bottle again, or to soil or to wet his pants, or to rebel against going to school. Still others revived old habits of playing with their genitals. Some clever children began to wake at night, and to "stand watch" over the mother, whenever she nursed or held the new baby! Other children insisted upon returning to their mother's bed.

As the first two children grow older, our studies show, their rivalry often becomes more bitter. In some cases, the younger was bitten by the older, or pushed into a tub of hot water, or shoved down a staircase and badly injured. Such injuries often occurred in situations which the attacker called "play"—or when the older child was "caring for" the younger. The older child usually claimed that there had been an "accident."

The most open forms of rivalry between children at ages three, four, and up are tattling on the other child, taking or breaking or hiding his toys, teasing, and fighting him. All except tattling, which is used by parents as a means of surveillance, are universally disapproved by middleclass families. *Yet they recur in practically all families.* In very lowclass families, however, children of the same sex in the same family are usually allowed to fight each other.

This constant skirmishing—argument, rivalry, discordant play—and the even more irritating "undercover" attacks of one child against another are the most nerve-wracking part of the mother's day. Children's jealousy and competition create a circular, goading relationship, which often seems to become the most constant thing in the child's world.

Yet, what a change immediately occurs if one of the rivals is absent! To the parent, such a moment is a gift of peace; an idyllic half-hour after one child has gone to bed, or perhaps a whole morning when one child visits a friend! At such times, the other child—it usually makes no difference whether it is the older or the younger—seems an entirely different person! Most of his nagging, erratic behavior disappears for the time. He no longer tries either to possess or to irritate the parents. He can relax. So, with a prayer of thankfulness for the incredible peace of the home, can his parents! [1]

This is both a practical and revealing little experiment, which any mother may try. When nothing she says or does to the children seems to go right, when they are full of chronic tattling, complaints, and aggression, let her separate them for an hour. If either child then becomes much more congenial and responsive toward the mother, the answer is clear. His previous caterwauling has been chiefly a form of rivalry and jealousy. Tears, "showing off," playing big, sabotage, impudence—most of them have been spurred on by the children's *competition for prestige and love from their parents.*

This kind of rivalry is basic in the little, restricted family, such as that in America and Europe, in which a child usually has only *one* woman in the role of his "mother," and one man in the social relationship of his "father." But in many folk groups, where the child is passed around from his mother to his grandmother, to his

---

1 But this peace is only specious and temporary, of course. For example, if the child is alone with his parents for *several days or weeks,* he usually becomes overpossessive. He also usually begins to resent his brother's absence, and to hold the parent accountable for it.

aunt, and to his older sister, jealousy of his brothers or sisters is certainly less keen, because each child usually is the *favorite of some of these women who act as his mother*.

Suggestion to Parents

Rivalry between brothers and sisters is a fundamental trait in our kind of family, which has only two persons who act as "parents." There is no chance of doing away with it, but it may be decreased in intensity. Such rivalry will show itself in all degrees, ranging from very mild to very severe. The intensity of the child's rivalry will decline as the forbearance and affection of his mother increase.

Rivalry between children is most apt to be harmful where the parents give too little love and attention to their children generally. Then affection, being scarce, is fought for by the children, and those who lose out in the fight become jealous, anxious, and hostile.

The cure for too much rivalry between children in a family is usually *more affection and attention*, rather than a different distribution of the *same amount*. This increased amount of what the children want may come from the father's giving more of his time to his children, or from the addition of an aunt or a grandparent to the family. Or it may come from the mother's discovery of further resources in herself.

W. Allison Davis and Robert J. Havighurst

Developing Good Posture in the Preschool Child

THERE is usually a close relationship between the child's health and the way he holds his body. This does not mean that every child with good posture will be healthy, nor that every child who is not robust, or who has had some illness, will have bad posture. However, the well-nourished, healthy child is much more likely to hold his body well-poised or balanced than the thin, listless young-ster who is always tired.

Good posture is much more than merely "standing straight"; **it** is the use of all parts of the body with proper balance, with ease and grace. This proper use of the body is called good body mechanics. The body is in some ways like a machine; its parts are accurately adjusted to one another, and if any part is out of correct position the machine does not work perfectly. For example, if the feet are not in good position, the balance of the whole body may be changed.

When the body is out of balance, some part is likely to be pushed or pulled out of its normal place or to work under a strain. When the body is in correct balance, all its parts, including the internal organs, are held in good position.

Parents must not expect the very little child to have the same type of posture as his older brother or sister. As the little child grows up his posture tends to change. For example, a little child who has just learned to walk is at an age when his abdomen is more prominent than it will be after he grows older. By the time he is five or six years old the muscles of the abdomen should be strong enough to keep it nearly flat.

The habit of holding the body in balance—in good posture—is learned gradually as the child learns to control his body. First, as a baby, he learns to sit up, then to creep, then to take a few steps, and finally to walk. Throughout these stages he is learning slowly how to hold his body in balance. All through childhood he con-tinues to learn this lesson. How well he learns it depends largely on the strength of the muscles that hold the body erect, and these muscles should be gradually growing stronger as he grows older and as he uses them more and more actively.

STRENGTHENING THE MUSCLES
THAT GIVE GOOD BODY BALANCE

All-around development, which is gained by strengthening *all* the muscles of the body through active play—climbing, throwing balls, running, jumping, skipping, shouting—lays the foundation for good posture. But if the child is to learn the habit of good posture he must not only gain all-around development but must also strengthen the muscles that have the most to do with holding the body in good balance. These are: (1) The muscles of the abdomen, (2) the muscles of the buttocks, (3) the muscles of the shoulders and of the upper trunk, and (4) certain leg muscles that hold the feet in good position.

The lower abdominal muscles should pull in and flatten the lower part of the abdomen. When a baby first begins to walk, his abdomen extends farther than his chest, but gradually, as he grows older, his abdominal muscles should become stronger and should pull in and flatten his lower abdomen more and more, until finally his abdomen extends no farther than his chest.

When the buttock muscles are well developed, they help to straighten the lower spine and keep the child's back from becoming too hollow. As the child grows older he can learn to use them in this way and to strengthen them.

The muscles of the shoulders and neck and those of the upper trunk help to hold the chest high and the chin in. Many a child who has plenty of opportunity for free play does not use these muscles enough because of the lack of fences and trees to climb and bars to swing on. If these muscles are to be strong enough to hold the child's chest up in good position, they must get plenty of exercise.

Proper use of the feet is necessary if the child's body is to be held in good balance. When the feet are used correctly, the child's weight is on the balls and outer sides of the feet, the toes point straight forward, and the inner sides of the feet are parallel with each other. Wearing the proper kind of shoes and keeping the feet parallel and pointing straight forward will help to throw the weight correctly, but how well the feet do their work depends largely on the strength of certain leg muscles that hold the feet in the proper position. If these muscles are strengthened as the child learns to stand and walk and as he becomes more and more active they will help to keep the whole body in good balance. If the muscles are not strong enough or if the child's weight falls on the inner sides of his feet so that he walks with his toes pointing outward, the ankles may become turned inward and the long arch of the foot flattened and

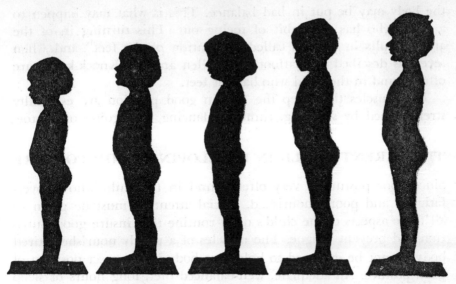

EXAMPLES OF GOOD POSTURE

The healthy children shown above all have good posture. The fact that they do not stand alike is due to their various types of body build.

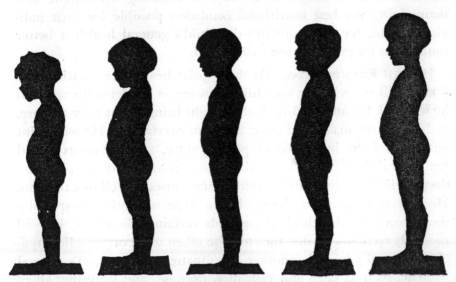

EXAMPLES OF POOR POSTURE

These slouchy, tired-looking children all have poor posture.

the body may be put in bad balance. This is what may happen to a child who has the habit of toeing out. This turning in of the ankle results in what is called "pronation of the feet" and when severe is descibed as "flatfoot" or "fallen arches." Knock-knees are often found in the child who has flat feet.

The muscles that keep the feet in good position are especially strengthened by skipping, running, dancing, and going on tiptoe.

THE PARENT'S ROLE IN DEVELOPING GOOD POSTURE

Since poor posture is very often found in the child who is over-fatigued and poorly nourished, special attention must be given to all those aspects of the child's daily routine that insure good nutrition and prevent fatigue. The muscles of a poorly nourished, tired body cannot be expected to hold that body in the erect position of good posture. An adequate, well-balanced diet, long hours of sleep at night and a rest during the day, outdoor exercise (but not too much) and sunlight are all necessary to restore a poorly nourished, overfatigued child to normal. At the periodic visits to the doctor advice should be sought as to ways of avoiding overfatigue and maintaining the best nutritional condition possible for each individual child, for by improving the child's general health a better foundation for good posture will be laid.

HEALTH EXAMINATIONS. At the regular health examinations the doctor will see whether the child's posture is good for his age and he will look for any conditions that might bring about poor posture, such as rickets, malnutrition, or apparent overfatigue. He will point out signs of the beginning of poor posture, which parents would not be likely to notice. If a habit of poor posture is developing, the doctor will try to find out the underlying causes and eliminate them. He may recommend a change in the type of clothing—especially shoes—worn by the child. If he finds certain deformities, he will probably recommend that the child be taken to an orthopedic physician. He will advise the mother as to matters of the child's general hygiene, such as sleep and rest, diet, exercise, and sunshine, all of which have a direct bearing on posture.

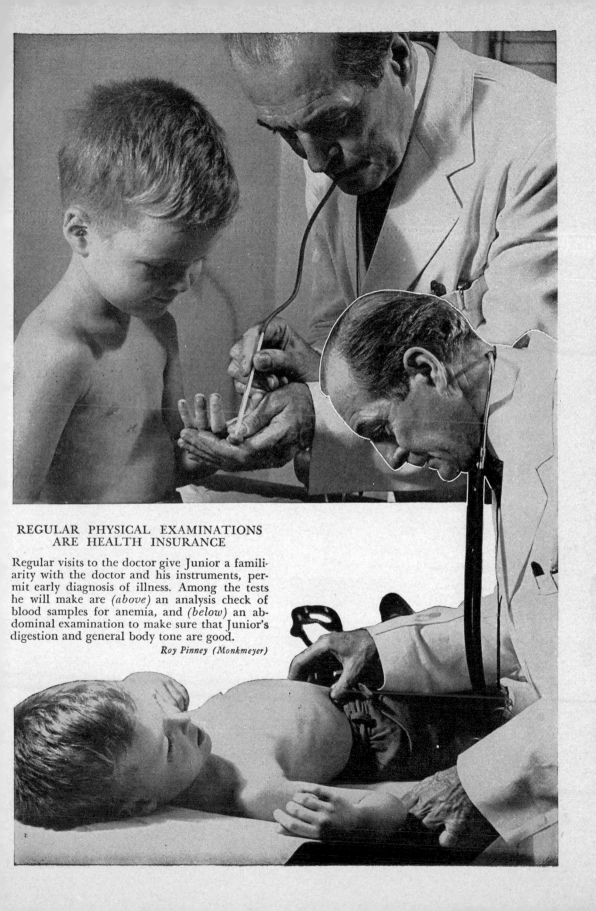

REGULAR PHYSICAL EXAMINATIONS ARE HEALTH INSURANCE

Regular visits to the doctor give Junior a familiarity with the doctor and his instruments, permit early diagnosis of illness. Among the tests he will make are *(above)* an analysis check of blood samples for anemia, and *(below)* an abdominal examination to make sure that Junior's digestion and general body tone are good.

Roy Pinney (Monkmeyer)

YOUR PUBLIC HEALTH AGENCIES

It is wise to find out about and make use of the public health services available in your community. *(Above)* A public health nurse discusses a child's hearing defect with his mother. *(Left)* Youngsters getting their weekly check-up by a community nurse. *(Below)* Calling for check-up at baby clinic.

Clothes and Shoes

A child cannot develop good habits of posture unless his body is free to develop normally without being pressed or pulled into unnatural positions by wrong clothing. Clothing should be planned so as to allow freedom for growth and for muscle activity and should not exert too great pressure on any of the child's bones or soft tissues.

Night clothes should be loose, so as to allow the child to turn and stretch in his sleep.

If a child is to learn to stand well, his shoes and socks must fit properly so as to permit his feet to develop normally. A child's feet are easily injured by poorly fitting or badly shaped shoes and by socks that are too small. Shoes should follow the natural shape of the feet. They should be selected with the advice and guidance of a salesman who is especially qualified in the fitting of children's shoes. Buy your child's shoes at a shop that specializes in children's shoes.

Laced shoes of the "blucher" type (having the tongue and the toe continuous) and straight along the inner side are best. Shoes with the moccasin type of upper are satisfactory if they have soles and are laced. Soles should be firm, flat, moderately flexible, and not slippery. Although heels are not advisable, the sole should be somewhat thicker at the heel and under the arch; a perfectly flat sole is undesirable. The shank of the shoe should be narrow, the heel close fitting, the upper full and soft over the child's toes, and the toe of the shoe broad so that his toes can move easily.

Great care must be taken that when shoes are repaired they are not made shorter or narrower or the shape changed. Careful watch should be kept to see where the wear comes on the child's shoe. A child who wears his shoes down very unevenly should have his feet examined by a doctor.

If a child has flatfoot, he must have his shoes specially adjusted. Ask your doctor about this.

Bed and Bedclothes

The child should sleep in a bed by himself, and the bed should be large enough for him to have plenty of room to turn and move in his sleep. The springs and mattress should be firm and flat, so as to enable the child to lie perfectly flat. A sagging bed throws the body into poor position. No pillow, or a small flat one, should be used, as a large pillow forces the child's neck to bend instead of being straight. The bedclothes should be light in weight and not too tight.

Chairs and Tables

A little child needs a low chair, even if it is made at home out of a soap box. It should be of such a height that his feet can be placed flat on the floor. The seat of the chair should be shallow enough to allow the lower part of the child's back to touch the back of the chair while his feet are flat on the floor; that is, it should not be longer than the child's thighs. A low table at which the child can sit comfortably in his chair should be provided, and he can use this for eating meals and for many kinds of play.

A tricycle suited to the child's size, which he operates by the use of pedals, exercises the feet correctly, for the child must keep his feet in good position in order to put the right pressure on the pedals.

Some kinds of toys and play apparatus, instead of helping to develop the child's body normally and symmetrically, either force him into wrong positions or lead him to use one side of his body while the other is neglected. A toy car that is pushed with one foot may cause one-sided development. A toy car that has too wide a seat may force the child's legs apart and bring about a deformity of the thighs.

GAMES FOR DEVELOPING GOOD POSTURE HABITS

The following games are planned to strengthen the muscles that hold the body in an erect position and to give the child the "feel" of standing and sitting correctly, even though he is not yet conscious of how he does it. The games should help the child to form the habit of using his whole body well when he is doing the ordinary things of life such as sitting, standing, and walking. To teach a young child to use his body well is not difficult if appeal is made to his imagination and love of imitation.

If exercises are presented as games, the little child will take part eagerly, and he will take more interest in the games if several of his playmates—brothers and sisters or other children—join him in the games. Most children like to act a part or to "make believe." Pretending to be a paper doll or a giant is more interesting than doing an exercise. Also it is easy for a little child to understand that to be a paper doll he must flatten his back, and that to be a giant he must stretch himself up to his full height. By means of such imitative games he can learn how to stand well, to pull in his abdomen, to raise his chest, and to stand and walk with his feet parallel and toes pointing forward.

Games that have to do with the posture of the body as a whole and games that strengthen different groups of body muscles are given. Let the children play games of different types so as to use various sets of muscles. The games played standing and those played lying down, which teach the child the "feel" of good posture for the whole body, should be alternated with the more active games, which tend to strengthen special groups of muscles. By such alternation of games the exercises can be kept from being too strenuous.

Do not tire nor bore the child by having him play the games too long. Ten to fifteen minutes of supervised and interesting play is better than a longer period of half-hearted play; and a daily short period is better than an occasional long period.

Games Played Lying Down

(These games teach the children how it feels to pull in their abdomens and flatten their backs while lying on the floor.)

PAPER DOLLS PASTED ON THE FLOOR.   Each child lies flat, with arms stretched outwards and legs held straight, pretending to be a paper doll lying on the floor. By pulling in his abdominal muscles the child can make the lower part of his back touch the floor. He may pretend to need more paste in the hollow of the back to fasten this part to the floor.

THE BOOK. The children lie on the floor with arms at their sides and legs close together, each pretending to be a closed book. Each tries to lie as flat as a book, pulling in the abdomen and pressing the back flat against the floor. The following lines are said:

> Jack laid his book upon the floor.
> He opened the leaves, One, two, three, four.
> He closed the leaves, Four, three, two, one.
> When the book was closed, he said, "That's done."

While the words "One, two" are being said the child raises his arms shoulder high, one at a time. While the words "Three, four" are being said he moves his legs outward, one at a time. When both arms and both legs have been stretched out, the "book" is open.

While the words "Four, three, two, one" are being said, each child returns his legs and arms to their original position, one at a time. When the child's arms are close to his sides and his legs are close together, the "book" is closed. Throughout the game the abdomen should be held in.

THE RUBBER MAN. Lying on the floor with arms raised above his head, chin in, and back flat against the floor, each child pretends he is made of rubber, and stretches himself out so as to be as long as possible. Keeping their backs against the floor, the children expand their chests and stretch their arms and legs while the following lines are being said:

> Watch this funny long rubber man.
> See him stretch as far as he can.
> Up go hands and down go feet.
> Now relax and then repeat.

THE BICYCLE MAN. Each child lies on the floor, his hands over his head and his chin drawn in. The children move their feet as though pedaling a bicycle, while the following lines are said:

> Riding, riding, pushing his feet,
> The bicycle man comes up the street,
> Sometimes fast and sometimes slow,
> It's really a pleasant way to go.
> Sometimes slow and sometimes fast,
> Then he stops to rest at last.

Games Played Standing in Good Posture

(These games help the children to hold their chins in, to raise their chests and stretch their trunk muscles, and to pull in their abdomens and flatten their backs while standing.)

During these games it is easy for the mother to show each child now and then how to pull in his abdomen, by placing one of her hands on the lower part of his abdomen and one on his buttocks and then pressing upward with the hand on his lower abdomen and downward with the hand on his buttocks. The child will respond by pulling his abdomen in and his buttocks downward. Touching the lower part of the abdomen may make the child draw it in and thus show him how to contract these muscles. Little emphasis need be put on this, but if it is repeated from time to time the child will learn to do it by himself.

TREES. Each child tells what tree he would like to be, and then each one plays that he is that tree, standing in the best possible position with his head and chest high, his chin in, the lowest part of his abdomen drawn in, and arms raised to represent the branches. Different kinds of trees may be imitated. All the trees together are a forest. The wind blows and sets the trees swaying. When the wind stops and the branches are quiet, the trees all stand still again in good position.

GIANTS. A giant is very tall and strong and stands very straight. The children all pretend to be giants and walk on tiptoe standing just as well as they know how.

BALLOONS. Each child first blows up his own toy balloon. Then all toss the balloons high overhead. The object of the game is to see how long the balloons can be kept in the air. To keep the balloons up the children must reach and stretch up over and over again, sometimes using the right hand, sometimes the left. Children enjoy playing with balloons and usually can keep them overhead for long periods.

Games That Help to Keep the Shoulders Flat

THE WINDMILL. The children stand very straight, with abdomens in, chests high, and chins in, and play that they are windmills. They rotate both arms toward the right for a few minutes. Then the wind is supposed to change, and the children rotate their arms toward the left for a few minutes. The speed at which the "windmills" move may be varied as the wind blows harder or slackens.

THE DUCK. "Let's play duck." Each child squats down, buttocks resting on heels, head held high with chin drawn in, chest high, fingers touching the tips of the shoulders, elbows held back and close to the sides, "just the way a duck holds his wings." Then the mother calls, "Let's all waddle across the barnyard." While the child is holding the position of a duck his shoulders are very flat.

THE CRAB. The children first lie flat on their backs on the floor. Then they raise themselves up on hands and feet, with abdomens up and backs toward the floor. Last of all, they try to walk sidewise "just like crabs."

Games to Strengthen the Abdominal Muscles

THE RABBIT. To play rabbit, each child gets down on all fours and then hops and leaps forward.

THE MULE. The "mule" lowers his head, and, supporting himself entirely upon his front legs, lashes out with his hind legs.

THE SCISSORS. Each child sits against the wall with his legs straight out in front, keeping his knees straight. His legs are supposed to be the blades of scissors. His hips, back, shoulders, and head all touch the wall. First the child raises the left leg and lowers it. Then he raises the right leg and lowers it. His head and the lower part of his back must touch the wall all through the game.

The following lines are said, at first slowly, later faster and faster:

> Here are great big scissors,
> They go snip, snip, snip.
> Here are great big scissors,
> They go clip, clip, clip.
> I'll cut the cloth before I sew it,
> I'll make a coat before you know it.

Games to Strengthen the Leg and Trunk Muscles

THE ELEPHANT. The children walk on hands and feet, keeping their legs straight, imitating elephants. The knees must not be bent. The head should be held high and the chin in. The head may be swayed from side to side in imitation of the way an elephant swings his trunk.

THE CRANE. The youngster who patterns himself upon the crane faces a chair and stands on one leg, while the heel of the other foot rests upon the seat of the chair. Bending his head forward, he tries to touch the knee of the raised leg with his forehead. He should then stand on his other leg and repeat the game.

Games to Strengthen the Muscles that Support the Feet
(These games should be played barefoot)

THE TIGHT-ROPE WALKER. Use a chalk-line on the floor or a crack between two boards to represent a tight rope. The game is to walk this line with great care and exactness. The "tight-rope walker" walks on tiptoe, with toes turned in and heels turned out, and tries to grasp the floor with his toes.

SAND PILE. The child stands in the sand pile or sand box, dabbles his feet in the sand, and scrapes up piles of sand with his toes.

PICKING UP MARBLES. Sitting in a low chair, each child tries to pick up a marble under his bare toes and put it down again, using first one foot and then the other. Then he tries to pick up two marbles at a time, first with one foot, then with the other, then two marbles with each foot, using both feet at the same time.

A more difficult stunt is walking across the floor holding a marble under the toes. Later the child may try to walk across the floor holding two marbles with each foot.

The Nursery School

TODAY a large number of children are enrolled in nursery schools or child-care centers which, strictly speaking, are play groups. They are not intended to teach academic skills. They provide experiences, which young children need and enjoy, for developing physically and emotionally.

In an established nursery school, there are no set "goals" or "objectives" for each year, as there often are in the elementary grades. Children in these play groups find a variety of materials to use, other children with whom they can play and work, and adults who are friendly, warm, protective people. These adults care for the children physically, see that they do not hurt themselves or others, and try to provide an atmosphere that is relaxed and keyed to the child's slowly developing abilities and skills.

It is important to emphasize this point because sometimes a mother and father, a little upset about their youngster's natural and normal rowdiness, his eating habits, or his lack of manners, will send him to nursery school, hoping he will be taught "how to behave."

This is an erroneous conception of a good nursery school. In playing with other youngsters, in working and living in a group designed and organized for his activities, a child usually benefits, and the results may show in his home life. He may become less destructive of his toys and playthings, more able to use them for happier play; he may be less tense about schedules, meals, going to bed, waking up, and so on. But the behavior changes are slow, and they will depend upon his parents and their attitudes toward him a great deal more than on his nursery-school experiences. Moreover, he will continue to show the normal signs of misbehavior for his age, nursery school or no; he will continue to make demands on his parents and his home that are normal for his age and his needs; and he will continue to need the attention and love of his parents, the familiarity of his own toys, and experiences with his parents that include him—just as he would if he were not a member of a play group.

The nursery school is in no way a substitute for parents and home.

424

It is a supplement and a help—an organized way of offering children rooms to play in, toys and creative materials or tools to work with, outdoor living, other children as companions. Nursery school offers these experiences to a child in an environment that is stable and familiar, where he is certain that they will continue to be there day in and day out, where he becomes an established member of a group, welcomed and made to feel that this is his room, these are his toys, and these, adults and children, are his friends.

WHY DO WE HAVE NURSERY SCHOOLS?

Why do we need nursery schools if children have the familiar atmosphere of the home in which to work and play, where there is at least one parent always on hand to help and protect him? There may be a variety of reasons. Even when both parents do not find it necessary to leave home each day for outside jobs, there may be some inadequacies in the home environment that make a play group or nursery school desirable for the child—perhaps for only part of the day.

The most obvious drawback at home is lack of space for indoor play, or lack of a safe area outdoors where children can safely run, climb, dig, or build. City parks may be a partial answer, especially where playgrounds are available. But even then, unless the play is carefully supervised, some children—the more timid ones, perhaps, or the smaller ones—will have to fight against the odds of more aggressive children or older youngsters, who are more vigorous and who can't be expected to watch out for the smaller ones. Often the younger children find themselves in a group where they have to battle for their possessions and where there is not much cooperative play, but rather a constant childish warfare against one another. Mothers, fearful that their children will hurt others or be hurt, usually appear when there is a squall and carry off the misbehaving youngster, although he may have been defending himself justifiably. The child gets a rather confused idea of social relations and of his own good nature.

At home, even in a house or apartment where there is space and equipment for a child, the routines of housework, cleaning, marketing, and cooking, often prevent mothers from spending all the time they would like with their children. Some of a child's play is messy and requires help and supervision, as with clay, paints, or water-play. Parents sometimes manage to keep their children happy and occupied while they work. Most often, however, spills or breakages occur when mother is distracted with other tasks, and then there are the inevitable scoldings or admonitions of, "Don't touch," "No, no," "Naughty boy," and so on, which, repeated through the day, result in cranky, tired mothers and children.

For young parents who have set up a home and furnished it at a great deal of cost in time and energy, it is extremely hard to be relaxed and pleasant about the accidents that may occur when an energetic child romps. A young child's play needs supervision, and often there just isn't time for Mother and Daddy to stay near by. Toys and materials are limited at home, mainly because most family budgets can't include all the materials a child needs. In cities especially, there is very seldom enough space for a child to play, because apartments are planned mainly for adult living, not for children's growth.

Nursery school, on the other hand, offers a great variety of materials that children take turns in using. The teacher is there to mop up spills, settle quarrels easily, patiently, without hurry—that's her job. She is not distracted by doorbells, telephones, meals to be cooked, visitors to be entertained. The simple furniture of the nursery-school room can always be shifted to make a big, clear space for a game. There are no valuable rugs that might be soiled, no polished wood-work that might be scratched, no precious bric-a-brac that might be knocked down by a hastily tossed beanbag.

Ideally, then, a nursery school is a place where there are fewer limitations on normal child activity. It also provides an opportunity for parents to plan their days so that there is more time to spend with the children when their routine work is done.

In a good nursery school there are many positive things to do. A child is seldom—probably never—called "bad" or "naughty." Moreover, the child learns to meet other children without being afraid that he will be hurt, or that his property will be taken from him. He learns that a few bumps or bruises or quarrels are only temporary hurts, and he gains confidence in playing with other children.

(This will help him also in the primary grades.) He learns that he can "take it," that he can stand up for his rights; this new realization gives him a feeling of competence, which in turn makes him more eager to go on learning and trying out new things.

One of the most important features of a good nursery school is the valuable parent-teacher relationship that is established and the job teachers do in interpreting the methods of the school to the parent. A parent who visits a nursery school (and *all* parents should) sees children learning to play together, to eat their meals happily, to wash themselves and go to the toilet without fighting against it or fussing. A parent who sees that a child's control over himself—social or physical—is gradual and that it need not be forced by physical punishment, feels less pressed to use that punishment. When the child is of nursery-school age, parents may feel anxious about routines, and the innumerable feeding, toileting, "do's" and "don't's"; the school can offer parents ways of handling those routines which are easier for child and parent.

One of the things that always impresses us is the confidence and sureness with which these youngsters of three or four or five meet situations with other children or adults in the nursery school. You realize they are people; you (as a parent) may be much more perturbed than they are by a quarrel or a blow; it helps you to see your child meeting these situations, to feel that he is a person, and that you can be confident he will make the grade if you don't pass on some of your anxiety to him.

HOW DO CHILDREN ACCEPT NURSERY-SCHOOL ROUTINES?

In the established routines of washing, resting, and eating, as well as in play periods, there is a feeling of "we-ness," an easier acceptance of those routines because *all* the children sleep, eat, and wash their hands. While at home a child may feel individually nagged or "picked on" because he must attend to certain regulations and suffer interruptions of his play, here, in his nursery-school group, those interruptions are part of the group life and work. There are, of course, always a few resistant children, but, in general, there is an overall acceptance of routines. Often nobody else naps at home. At school, everyone takes a rest. With very young children, even the teacher may rest on a cot. Young children often relax more easily when the teacher is on a nearby cot.

The teacher knows that these youngsters of three, four, or five are geared to a much slower pace than grownups. There is no "hurry-hurry" about washing hands in the nursery-school room (this process, as most parents know, is absorbing for the child, but time-consuming). The teachers plan the day so that there is no precipitous rush to the bathroom in order to be ready for juice or for outdoors or luncheon. A fair amount of young children's irritability is caused by the conflicts between the adult rush to get things done and their own slow and unskilled ways of meeting situations.

Children in the nursery school also learn to see a certain "cause and effect" relationship between what they do and why they do it. In our complex family life, it is not easy for a young child to understand why he must perform this or that ritual, since those things involve our adult social life with friends or relatives, mother's and father's work, a scheduled appointment which must be met on time, and so on. At nursery school, the child's work and play are the reasons for doing things. Although he may not always accept the suggestion that it is time to put away his blocks in order to go outside and play, he nevertheless understands that "picking-up" is a necessary part of his day. Here again he is not alone in his task; "we" pick up and put away; "we" sing; "we" eat lunch. This identification with the group is the stimulation that a good nursery school can provide, and which, incidentally, a good school can continue to provide later on for a child's whole-hearted participation in work and play.

Here again parents can see how it is possible to help children understand what is to be done without using the "bad" or "naughty" connotation. "We" put away the blocks today because we're going home and we'll take them out again tomorrow. *Also, teachers help the children put their things away.* Remember, parents, it's very hard for a little child (or a big child) to do a thorough job by himself. Company means a lot to a child. Very few children do a complete job of picking up their toys without some help. Although teacher helps in nursery school, the child feels he's doing a job too. "Let's do it" is a good phrase to remember to use at home rather than, "Do it."

WHAT THE CHILD LEARNS IN NURSERY SCHOOL

Group living intensifies and highlights a child's own observations, which might remain vague, confusing impressions unless they were talked out with adults and other children. Here you can observe the child's intellectual development very clearly. If we wished to record and classify the kinds of events and objects a child notices in these early years, the list might include the early stages of physics, biology, geography, the social sciences, and others. The properties of water, the feel of clay, the weight and size of blocks or boxes, the habits of goldfish or the rabbit "we" tend in the screened box, the snow that melted when "we" brought it indoors, the icicles that hang from the sloping toy-shed roof on winter days are all fascinating discoveries for a young child. He wants time and more time to inspect them; he makes up stories about them. This is knowledge, repeated, reinforced, and remembered because all the children are interested and in this laboratory of their room discoveries are immensely important.

THE INDIVIDUAL CHILD IN NURSERY SCHOOL

A child's adjustment to a group must be qualified by a consideration of his own feelings and personality. Every individual child will bring to nursery school and to any other school he is to attend in his future life, the reactions to experiences, happy or unhappy, which he has had at home. These are not isolated attitudes; they give the meaning to all his experience and actually constitute the way in which he will react to a new adult—the teacher—the way he plays with other children, and the amount of sharing and group living he can tolerate happily.

Nursery school will *not* make up to a child for an unhappy or unsatisfactory home and family life. Any problem that is acute for the child at home, that is constantly troublesome, will be reflected in his behavior at school. He may aggressively disturb other children or, anxious and unhappy, he may withdraw from the play materials offered him; his own mixed feelings may be a barrier to easy play.

These statements are not intended to alarm parents. Most children will have ups and downs, show slight changes in behavior from day to day, demonstrate a somewhat hilarious bounciness one day and the next day (as on a "blue Monday") appear subdued and show great indifference to experimentation or games. In nursery school particularly, the cooperation of parents with teachers is essential. The teacher is not a therapist; she cannot effect basic changes in the child's personality or behavior unless parents know what she is trying to do at school and unless they help her in reassuring the child. While their child is in her care, it is the teacher's task to protect him and to try to offer him a happy time. She is genuinely interested in his well-being, not in whether he is "good" or "bad."

Trained to observe children, she knows that their normal behavior is not always even and that the smaller ones are only very slowly learning to become social human beings, that initially they are not always placid or generous or cooperative. She knows that children differ, that there may be temperamentally quiet, excitable, passive, or intense children—all in the same group, all normal children. She does not compare children with one another, but in watching one child over a period of weeks, she learns the way in which he shows that he is unhappy or confused. His repeated hurts to other children, his constant destructiveness, his prolonged silence and withdrawal are signs that something is troubling him that only his parents can help to reach and assuage. When a child cannot find satisfaction in play, when he cannot make use of the materials the teacher offers him, when she cannot find activities he can be interested in, then she has reached her limitations as a teacher. She is not a mother or a therapist, and she must ask for the parents' help, to help the child.

HELPING YOUR CHILD IN NURSERY SCHOOL

Nursery school may be the starting line from which parents can set out in the right direction to gain new insights about their child, learning each step of the way. It can be an extension of the family

environment where, in cooperation with the teacher, parents can
set up a sort of self-correcting system, in which problems can be
faced honestly and cleared up before they become chronic. A child's
difficulties should be viewed not as reflections of a poor home or
mismanagement or uncaring parents, but as an indication of some
undue stress, of which, in many cases, his parents may not be at
all aware. Mistakes are inevitable. They do not affect a child deeply
unless parents refuse to face them and continue to justify their
errors.

Daily contact between parent and teacher at nursery school can
set the stage for an increased understanding of child growth and
development. A parent who knows how his child acts in a group
of other youngsters, who learns to set his standards not according to
romantic notions of how children should act, but according to the
child's own needs and abilities, will be better equipped to help
him face the difficulties that his later school life will present. This
parent really begins to know his own child—his fears, his preoccupa-
tions, the way in which he tackles a job and the kinds of jobs he
can tackle.

In these young years and for a long time to come, a child's play
is a learning experience, and nursery school helps the parent to
see it as such. He shows an interest in the child's questions and
observations, in his "make-believe" and his real friends, and he
learns to value them as expressions of an unfolding personality. During the nursery-school days, more than in any other phase of school
life, the tasks of parent and teacher are remarkably similar and
inseparable; their mutual concern is the child's happiness and
security.

SHOULD YOUR CHILD GO TO NURSERY SCHOOL?

In view of the many benefits of a nursery school, it may seem contradictory to consider whether a child should or should not join
one of these organized play groups. Yet there may be reasons why
some children are not ready to leave the smaller family setting.

Very often parents start thinking about a nursery school for their
older child when a new baby arrives. The difficulties of caring for

two little children are obvious, and mothers may welcome the help that the nursery-school program offers. To the child, however, the idea of being sent away from home at this time may constitute a definite threat. There is a new member in the family who occupies a good deal of his mother's and father's time and attention. This situation, in itself, is disturbing to him since it raises questions in his mind about his own status and importance to his parents. Perhaps the most upsetting question that can worry a child is: "Am I still loved? Did Father and Mother want a new baby because they didn't like me any more?" Then, when he is taken to nursery school, away from mother and the baby, his fears are reinforced. The teacher, however warm she may be, is not mother; the toys and space, however appealing, are no substitute for what he fears he has lost—Mother's and Daddy's admiration and love.

If starting to nursery school and the arrival of a new baby occur at almost the same time, the child may show his anxiety in misbehavior at home. Instead of the beneficial results mother and father expected to see, there may be added problems at home—bed-wetting, loss of sleep, crankiness, loss of appetite. Nursery school can't solve the child's worry about his parents' love. In this case nursery school may add to his anxiety.

Usually psychiatrists and teachers advise that the parent introduce the child to his play group long before the baby is born, or wait a while, several months or a year, until he has adjusted to the new family situation. Later, his adjustment to nursery school will be the cue as to whether he feels content to leave his home for several hours a day.

Other troublesome family situations, worrisome to the child and sometimes not evidently so to parents, may indicate playtime at home rather than in a nursery school. Where there is a family break—even if a parent has gone away only for a while, to return later—young children may feel somewhat shaky about that parent's departure; the absence may threaten the child's own security. He can never fully understand the logical, grown-up reasons for the loss, and he is preoccupied with it. His day at nursery school may then be an anxious rehearsal of doubts as to whether his parent has abandoned him.

A prolonged illness, a hospital experience, moving from one home to another, the severe illness of a parent, may prevent the child's full, happy participation in nursery school. In each case, if the new adult—the teacher—and the new group—the children—present him with new anxiety about himself and his relationships to his parents, then the familiar home environment is the wiser choice for him.

At this point parents might very well comment, "But aren't these ups and downs normal to every family? Will any child ever be ready for nursery school if we consider all the things that might upset him?"

The answer depends largely on the individual child. Some children find a good deal of solace in the company of other children. These may be the energetic children, the outgoing, friendly ones. To other youngsters, who are timid or not so energetic, a group of children may be frightening after or during a worrisome experience at home.

Secondly, it depends on *when* and *how* the child experiences upsets at home. If he is three years old, let's say, just starting nursery school, and if, after one month, his mother goes to the hospital for a while, then perhaps he will suffer a setback at nursery school. Maybe he won't ask any questions at home, but his school behavior may show his worry.

If, on the other hand, he has had one year in a nursery group which he has enjoyed greatly, and then something happens—a family break, a tonsillectomy, the arrival of a new baby—then very often nursery school is just what he needs. It's a known, happy experience, for one thing. It means familiar people who like him, familiar toys, rooms, and a steady schedule.

INTRODUCING YOUR CHILD TO NURSERY SCHOOL

No matter what the family situation, or what the strains and stresses on each individual child, the nursery school is a new environment and the child needs a slow introduction to it. Some play centers include a program for children as young as two years. Obviously, it is difficult for these small children to understand why they are being taken to nursery school, or what it is. Verbal explanations may not be too helpful to these still nonverbal youngsters, so parents must stand by while the child takes his first tentative steps into the new environment. In the early weeks, mother may take the child to school for only an hour or two, stay with him, and then take him home again.

Later, and with some help from the teacher as to appropriate timing, she may stay with the child for the first half-hour and then, assuring the child that she will return, leave him for several hours. "Then," parents may ask, "what happens?" The teacher watches for tears or other signs of dismay. Often there is a piping call for "Mommy," a whimper, a few tears, although after the first day or two alone, children seldom show a reluctance about letting their mommies or daddies go—often less disturbance than they show when Mommy and Daddy go out for the evening! The teacher holds the child's hand or picks him up, takes him to a toy shelf or the table, stays with him to show him how he might use the play materials, and reassures him, if he asks, that "Mommy will come back soon." Mother, in her turn, comes back on time as she has promised, and gradually the child learns to expect that she will come back, and her absence doesn't worry him.

One very common occurrence in the first few weeks of nursery school is this: The little two-and-a-half- or three-year-old skips to school for the first week or more, nods a very vague farewell to his parent (or doesn't nod at all), goes immediately to the toy shelves, and is content for the remainder of the morning. A week later, when the first glow of discovery and novelty wears off, he suddenly catches on to the idea that Mommy leaves him each day. And then he may begin to cling to her hand in the morning, to demand that she stay with him, to refuse to remove his jacket.

Nothing may be wrong at home; there may be no new baby, no operations, no departures. Actually, nothing is wrong except that the child wants to be sure that his Mommy will come back. He's not an "attention-getter" nor an "over-dependent" child. On the contrary, he was ready a week before to play very happily for a while in the company of another adult and other children. His parents may then have to plan a week or more of the slow, careful introduction we spoke of, until the child is able to see that day after day they return to get him, while each day he finds at school a stable routine: the same people, and the toys, chairs, and Jungle-Gyms in their familiar places.

For a child who spends a full day at nursery school, with luncheon and a nap as part of the schedule, this extended introduction to his group is especially important. Going to sleep away from Mommy and his own room is a big step and may be a frightening one. Here again an easy, tentative introduction is best. Teachers help the child to see his rest-time as part of the "we-ness" of nursery school: letting him bring a cuddly animal or a doll from home that he can hold when he is tucked in for nap, singing softly to him, giving him, in short, the reassurance that he is protected.

It is exciting to watch even the little two-and-a-half- or three-year-olds, after the first week or two in the play group. They arrive at school confidently, and as they are greeted by the doctor, then the teacher, then by their friends, they beam with all the satisfaction of a warmly welcomed member with full status in their newly acquired positions. One child may make a face at the doctor as she knows that it will provoke a funny remark or a special word of greeting. Another child holds out a paper bag to her teacher—"Cookies, for juicetime"—enjoying the recognition of playing hostess and provider to her group. Still another youngster bursts into the room, telling in a three-year-old way that he saw a derrick or a truck or a snowplow on the way to school. Although the teacher may smile, she welcomes these overtures with serious attention. They are not laughable or "cute"; they are a child's way of saying: "These words, these things, represent *me;* I am important here, aren't I?"

Parents help their children in nursery school by knowing what it is and why it exists, by understanding the difficulties that the first few days will present, and by giving the teacher all the help and support she needs during this introductory period. For the teacher needs the parent here, in the young years, more than in any other area of school life. In the care of the young child, the physical and emotional are so intimately related that the adults who offer that nurture cannot divide it into assigned parts, nor take independent roles.

HOW TO RECOGNIZE A GOOD NURSERY SCHOOL

Not all play centers are "good" nursery schools. Here are some of the characteristics of a good nursery school that parents might look for.

Check on health practices. Ask (and observe yourself) whether the children's noses and throats are looked at each morning. Find out what the routine is when children sneeze or sniffle at school. There should be a room where children can be isolated who are feverish or starting a cold. Those children who show the first signs of a cold should not be left with the group. Also important—check to see what the room is like where children are isolated. It should not be a bathroom or a cheerless room, and there should always be an adult near the child when he is isolated.

Rooms for nursery-school children should be bright and attractively painted in clear colors, well ventilated, with washrooms easily available. Check to see that there is space for active play, indoors and out, as well as a place for naps and for quiet play for those children who want to be quiet.

For outdoor play there should be climbing apparatus, swings, large blocks and wagons, sand or dirt for digging, large boxes and smaller-sized wooden blocks to challenge the child's interests and vitality. And there should be at least one teacher for every eight or ten children (for three-year-olds, one teacher for every five children is usually a better ratio). Children should use the play apparatus as they are interested, not as the teacher dictates.

Indoors, children should be able to play with materials in their own way. They should not, for example, have to copy a teacher's drawing, nor should they be told what is a "good" drawing to make.

The teacher's attitude toward the children is important. Their ideas and discoveries should be listened to with respect and attention. The teacher who says, "Aren't they cute?" "Aren't they good today?" "My what a sweet little picture," or whose attitude is, "They need to be *trained* to be good," is not helping the children to feel that their work and play and creative products are very important. To children, play is a serious, if exciting, business and they expect adults to treat it as such.

The teacher should see that children are not dressed too warmly in the room and that when they play outdoors they are dressed according to the weather.

Routines should be carried out quietly, without evident fuss, commands, or tense preparations. "Juice is coming—find a good place to sit," is preferable to phrases such as, "Everybody must sit down. We can't have juice until everyone is ready," and then a long wait until the one or two frisky members settle down. In nursery school there is no place for the teacher or adult who takes the attitude, "When I clap my hands, everyone should do as I say."

The teacher should not continually be giving orders. A skilled nursery-school teacher, for example, starts arranging chairs for a "story" rather than calling the group to attention first. Then she may say to a few children who are near her, "Would you like to hear this story?" They may sit down and others join the group. She waits until the children are settled and then proceeds with her story; she knows that an order to be quiet will only provoke a few children to make noise.

In a good nursery school you will see lively children, children absorbed in their work, children talking back and forth to one another. The quiet or timid ones will receive not too pronounced help from the teacher in making social contacts. She may stay near them for a while for reassurance, on the alert that they are not unhappy or hurt. She never uses shame as a device to encourage play, nor does she point out to them that they are "too shy."

The teacher does not call attention to wet or soiled panties. She helps change the underwear with no show of disapproval. If a child is unhappy about a "mistake," she may say, "It's all right. We'll change the panties, then you'll be all fixed up." She shows the child that it is all right. When a parent arrives at the end of the play program, the package of wet clothing should be transferred without "Oh's" or "Ah's" or smiling comments on the child's mistake.

Parent-teacher talks are encouraged in a good nursery school, but not in front of the child. Conferences should take place when both parent and teacher are free, and when the children are not around to hear scraps of conversation.

MARY AND LAWRENCE K. FRANK

When Your Child Does Not Go to Nursery School

Y OUR child may not go to nursery school, but that does not mean that he cannot be a well-adjusted, happy, intelligent child. Home and parents can offer a child excellent opportunities for learning to get along with others, and for meeting the everyday challenges to his vitality and curiosity. Parents whose children do not go to nursery school do, however, have to understand what are some of the child's ways of learning and how to provide for sound learning at home.

THE IMPORTANCE OF CREATIVE PLAY

Play is one of the child's ways of learning and showing you that he is learning. Play is probably a child's most creative form of learning. This is not a sentimental statement. When you watch a young child play, what do you see? You see that he has learned a number of things about people, about what they do and why they do it. He cannot give a list of what he has learned, but he shows you, in his buildings, in his games of "house," in the way he plays Mother or Daddy or baby, nurse or doctor, pilot or fireman. He shows you in his gestures and in the sounds he makes, in imitating the way "Daddy" talks to "baby," or "pilot" to "bombardier."

Not only does he show you how he feels about what he has learned, but he creates. He is an artist; he takes what he knows and gives it his own personal touch. He creates an artistic whole out of pieces of information, observations, his own feelings. The result is his statement in his play about himself and his world. And, alas, often adults look at a picture he may have done and sigh because he has painted what *he* sees and feels, and not what adults see or feel. The child is proud of his production until he sees the critical look or hears the disappointed sigh. "To paint this kind of picture (or build this building)," he thinks, "is not too good." And he may stop showing you what he has learned and what he feels about everything around him.

Play is also his way of finding out. The "house" the child builds at three and the "house" he builds at five may both be made out of blocks, but the five-year-old's building shows that he has discovered how to make windows and doors by leaving spaces between two blocks and bridging the space by putting another block on top of them. Also, he may have added a garage, a road leading to the house, a car on the road. His playmate "drives" a truck to the door of his "house," dumps some "animals" in front of the house, goes away and comes back again with "milk" and "groceries."

The five-year-old has not only discovered more about the way in which people live and work together, but through using the blocks he has also found out that he can balance them to make steady buildings. He has scaled his "garage" to fit the house, the road to fit the car. He has learned to use the various-sized blocks in combination so that the corners of the house fit together neatly.

Play is probably the child's best way of adjusting to his society and his group, to his family and himself. Why? Because in creative play that is not directed or censored he can say what he thinks—he can express his ideas. In creative play (and we must here remember that this includes "messy" play with finger paints, mud, clay, water), he can say how he feels. Remember that very often when he shows you how he feels directly he may be scolded or punished. In creative play he can "say" those things without adult disapproval (except for the lack of understanding mentioned above). Moreover, he says many things about his feelings that can't be put into words, or for which, as a child, he has no words. No one knows exactly why, but children seem to feel better and be more relaxed when they have been allowed to say these things with paints and clay. The child can often "play out" his problems as adults "talk out" their difficulties.

If the child does not go to nursery school, then it is very important for parents to provide some creative play materials.

Don't defeat the purpose of creative play by forcing the child to use materials. If they are left in or near his indoor play space (even if it is a corner of the kitchen), he will find them and use them when he needs them. Don't hide the materials away or tuck them in drawers or on top of closets. There is no more obvious way of telling the child that you really don't care to have them around.

Your child loves to have you near him when he works. Set aside a half-hour for him, tell him it's *his* time. You can paint or crayon or squash and mold clay too. These are not juvenile arts. You will help your child to feel it's good and worth while and plain, honest fun to be creative.

A large sandbox with a generous quantity of sand is an excellent basic piece of equipment. It offers long periods of relaxation for the child and his friends on the occasions when this less vigorous activity "fills in" between other, more active games.

Your child grows up with the sandbox. It is an amazingly effective way of offering an older child and a younger one the same material; both love it and both can use it simultaneously. It has infinite uses and offers infinite variety in play. Sand is an artistic, creative medium that can be given some structure or just scooped and dumped. It can be used with trucks and cars, with water for "mixtures" or "cakes" or tunnels or pools. Sand-play is a soothing activity, especially since adults don't very often demand well-made "cakes" or "tunnels." The sandbox, therefore, is one area where the child can play as he wishes and where there are no standards for achievement. This may be one reason why all ages love the sandbox!

YOUR CHILD NEEDS PLAYMATES

Children who do not go to nursery school need other children as playmates and companions. Even if there are other children in the family, they do not always offer the needed companionship and stimulation. There are always some petty rivalries in the home, some little jealousies, and some competition for parents' attention. There are times in the family when the child strives to catch up with his older brothers or sisters (he can learn from them too, of course). But with his age mates the pre-school child finds common interests and comparable skills. He can be himself, share their jokes, play their games, climb and dig as they do, without feeling incompetent or small and useless.

For the young one in the family, these companionships are the confirmation of his worth and ability. Psychologically they represent a pat on the shoulder which says, "You are not just you, alone. 'We' are friends, 'we' do the same things, 'we' share the same interests, what 'we' do is important."

The shy child, the timid, clinging youngster, will usually loosen up and become less fearful if his parents give him the opportunity to play with friends. But if children enter elementary school without having had friends to play with either at home or in a play group, they may be tense and fearful, not only about the teacher, but also about other children. It is a long, tough pull to become an established member of a group. A child who has to learn how to play with others at six has at least as difficult a task as that of learning to read. For that reason, children need friends at home and the satisfaction of playing and growing with other youngsters. It may mean more work for mother, more time spent in supervision and picking up, and harder wear on the home, but it is immensely important for future years.

On this subject of friends, there is an advantage in a home versus a nursery-school environment for pre-school children. Very often a four- or five-year-old finds in his neighborhood a group of youngsters whose ages range from three to six. He may play sometimes with the older ones and sometimes with the younger ones. The stimulation of the older children and their ideas may be very helpful in his development. Often when parents object to the language or gestures that a pre-schooler learns from slightly older children, they forget that he may also be learning skills and greater independence from a mixed group of this sort. A child also derives a sense of importance from seeing some children younger than he is.

A child who can occasionally invite one or two friends home to play will often choose those youngsters who provide what he needs for stimulation and ideas in play, or for the nice relaxed feeling of being competent when he is with them. It is as unwise to question the little child's choice of friends as it is the older child's. His satisfactions or his needs may not be obvious, nevertheless they are part of him and it is very wise to respect his choice. While the child may enjoy playing with five or six other youngsters, time with one or two friends at home allows more room for each child's ideas and for dramatic and creative play. Outdoor physical activity is important, but *creative play* is a learning process, and as such a very desirable avenue of growth.

MARY AND LAWRENCE K. FRANK

Part Four

THE CHILD OF SCHOOL AGE

Is Your Child Ready for School?

BECAUSE boys and girls are sent to school when they turn five or six, we are tempted to assume that all are going to be ready for that first big step away from home. Experienced teachers know well the problems which the first days at school bring. Some children come willingly, eager for this new experience; some find it difficult to take their place in this strange new world; and others among the beginning pupils would definitely prefer to turn back to the familiar rather than try to take this step. To know why some children cross over the threshold into school eager and unabashed while others hesitate and stumble is important to parents and teachers alike.

Most parents are anxious to know how they can pave the way to school entrance so their child can take this new experience in his stride. Many seek help in guiding their child's learning to help him take his place proudly in his group, to find pleasure in standing on his own feet. As parents and teachers together approach this problem of starting children successfully in school, there will undoubtedly be fewer children who will begin school life with unhappy experiences.

A child's experiences on first entering school often influence his whole later attitude toward schools and learning. For this reason, it is well to plan carefully for him to have success and satisfaction in his first days and weeks at school. Findings on child development now throw much light on ways both home and school can help children be ready for this important experience when it comes.

When is a child ready for school? To answer this question it is well to look at the child's development thus far and size up his strong and weak points. It is not fair to decide this by comparing him with neighbors' or friends' children as the yard stick. A child's readiness to do a job successfully depends, first, upon his own ability, and, second, on his past experiences. Since children are born with different body structure and personalities and they grow up in widely

445

differing homes, their ways of responding to schoolroom situations are bound to differ.

It is the differences in children, the fact that no two are alike, which must be taken into account in deciding when a child is ready to start to school. Some children will have been away from home a great deal, be used to being alone, and have developed independence. Others have never been separated from their parents but for a few hours. Some are robust, others have been ill much of their lives. Some have grown up in families with several children, thereby learning to hold their own in a group of children. Others may be only children, who have spent most of their lives with adults. Even within a family group each child's experiences differ from those of his brothers and sisters. It is no wonder then, that in beginning school, no two children present the same background and personality characteristics.

Not only is it important to take into account the kinds of experiences a child has had before he goes off to school, but to know what kind of a child he is, that is, how he has been growing. While at each age level children have certain characteristics in common, some phases of their development are often uneven. For instance, a child may have a well-developed body, in outward appearance be a large child for his age, yet be quite immature in getting along with other children. A six-year-old child may be as advanced as a seven-year-old in his use of language, yet be so clumsy with his hands in using tools or drawing that a four-year-old could surpass his performance. It is difficult to explain these uneven patterns in the growth of children, but certain studies point to growth needs which may not have been met by the child's environment.

As a teacher gets acquainted with her children during the first weeks of school, each child's behavior is the cue which reveals many things about the ways he has been growing. As she observes children alone, in a group, or with their parents, it is possible to pick up some of the threads of their past from the things they do in the beginning weeks of school.

One teacher observed three children who were having some difficulties adjusting during the first week of school. There was John, whose mother in parting from him the first morning in kindergarten said, "Good-by, John, you must be a big boy *now*." Had she realized that it takes more time than a day to build his confidence in staying alone? Five years had elapsed and John's mother had kept him a baby, but on this day she was asking him to be "a big boy." Wasn't it natural for him to be awestruck and frightened? There was Mary, who had been kept away from children for fear she might catch something. She seemed to feel strange and lonely, and wanted to be near the teacher. And Timmy, very much in the foreground, was always stirring up trouble with the children or ready for a showdown with his teacher. He was the youngest of his family. He had always had his own way; the whole family had turned about to keep Timmy happy. They had not foreseen the price he would have to pay later on for being allowed to dominate the family.

John, Mary, and Timmy were all starting school with some rather serious handicaps. Their difficulties might have been prevented had opportunities been provided for the children to have experiences similar to the kind of situations now confronting them. The learning could have been gradual then, without the sudden strain they now faced of finding themselves in a very difficult situation. It was expecting too much of the children to change their behavior overnight. Parents and teacher would need to work together to help these children over their first unpleasant impressions of school.

When the time comes for a child to go to school it is important to remember that this is not only a step for *him* to take, but a step for his parents to take as well. It is natural for parents to want their child to make a good start and to enjoy this new adventure. But there is a fear which often lurks in their minds of wondering how well their child can face the great big world alone. Some parents come to school with the child and continue to shelter him. The danger when this happens is that then the child may begin to doubt whether he can get along without Mother or Father at his side. And there are some parents who deep down want their child to stay with them.

As one watched Sally, just turned five, she appeared a confident little girl. She could not only manage her coat and hat perfectly, but also her rubbers and leggings, and she enjoyed the responsibility, too. However, her mother, with whom she had spent much time, loved to do things for her. It had become a habit to wait on Sally for many things she could do herself. When Mother came to call for Sally at kindergarten she was so delighted to see her she would take over the dressing before they departed. The teacher, who chanced to be near, one day remarked casually, "Well, Sally, can't you put on your coat and leggings? It is a long time since you were a baby."

"Of course, I can put them on," she said; and she did.

But her mother felt that something had been taken away from her; something which she enjoyed. Her face revealed her desire to have the child depend on her. Long ago she had overlooked those wonderful words her child had spoken as confidence began to blossom: "I can," and "Let me!"

Growing up is a two-way process demanding adjustments on the part of the child and his parents all along the way. Parents need to be watchful of the things they can do to let the child try out his powers to be a person. Long before the time arrives to send the child to school there will be opportunities for him to have experiences through which he will gradually learn to guide his own actions. He may go to a playmate's home for an afternoon, to Grandmother's for a little vacation, or stay with a friend while Daddy and Mother are away on a trip. These and similar experiences, meeting new people, being in strange places, and learning to get along without his parents are important to his growing before his fifth or sixth birthday has rolled around.

It will be less difficult for the child starting school if he has learned to be sufficiently independent to be away from Father and Mother for reasonably long periods of time. As a child plays alone in his room or in the yard while Mother is busy with the household duties, he is learning to be on his own. Between four and five years it is desirable for the child to have his boundary expanded so that he may move safely about his immediate neighborhood. If he lives within reasonable distance of the school, providing the traffic dangers are not too great, he may even be able to get to school alone after the preliminaries of registration and introductions to persons at school have been made.

Readiness for school is not measured precisely on a scale of growth and maturity for school entrance. Only one factor is common for children in beginning school—the age at which they enter. Just as a

THE FIRST DAY AT SCHOOL

Children react differently at the prospect of going to school. This break with home can prove a frightening experience, but a sensible mother and an understanding teacher can make the first day at school an exciting and a memorable adventure.

(*Above*) Having accompanied son to school, mother leaves him with promise she will return when session is over.

(*Left*) His wise teacher quickly makes him feel a member of the group and he is soon joining in blackboard and other activities (*below*).

Three Lions

CHILDREN OF HIGH INTELLIGENCE

The bright child presents a special problem to educators. Unless properly trained, he may grow up to be a social misfit. At experimental school where these pictures were taken, youngsters have average I. Q. of 150 — unusual for children ranging in age from three to eleven.

(Top) While these boys may enjoy many of the activities normal for their years, chess provides a mental stimulus more in keeping with their mental age. *(Above)* Calculating machine replaces more time-consuming methods of study. *(Left)* This seven-year-old child drawing rings around Saturn can discuss light years and solar time.

Three Lions

parent should not judge the child's performance by comparing him with other children, the school does not expect all children to have a similar pattern of development. Individual differences in children and various rates of growing must be considered in organizing the school program to meet children's needs.

WHAT THE SCHOOL EXPECTS OF THE CHILD

Schools differ in what they expect of children who are entering kindergarten or first grade. Some of them plan the beginning of school so as to allow time for children to make the adjustment to this new life gradually. Others may provide less time for the child's transition from home to school. Some schools take into account the various experiences children have had in being away from their parents either in a nursery school or play group. Others may plan the first school days ignoring the child's preparation for becoming a member of a group. This is why parents will need to know something about the school which their child will enter.

By school entrance age he will be expected to have made a beginning in getting along with others in a group. His social growth should be such that he can play happily with others and make friends with children in the group. He will have learned to respect them as persons as well as to recognize their property rights.

Most children by five or six have developed sufficient skill to take care of their dressing. They can put on and take off their clothing, attend to toileting needs, wash their hands and face alone, and be responsible for putting their playthings away.

Children of this age should have acquired a number of health habits to protect themselves and others as well. It should have become a matter of routine to use a handkerchief, to cover the mouth when coughing, and to keep objects out of the mouth. They learn these things from adults who set a good example more than they learn them by being told.

There has been rapid growth in the development of language during the early years. In learning to talk a child takes tremendous strides during babyhood. The child who on his first birthday had only two or three words at his command now at five years has a vocabulary of 2,500 words if he comes from an average American home. He is very much interested in words, enjoys trying new ones, invents some of his own, and learns their different shades of meaning. A child entering school will have sufficient language to express himself in sentences, ask for things, and make himself understood. Home background and the types of experiences a child has had play an important part in the child's facility with language. The ease with which he expresses himself influences his school adjustment.

As a child is learning to use language, he needs to hear words spoken clearly and in correct grammatical construction. Sometimes adults make the mistake of using baby talk with the child or talking down to him. Laughing about the child's mispronunciation of words or repeating these errors after him is often a stumbling block to a child's language development. Since language is difficult to master even under favorable circumstances, parents need to give the child every opportunity to practice correct speech and ease in expression. Talking to him, telling stories, going on trips, and listening to him when he talks are avenues for helping the child acquire and use the "mother tongue" well.

Now that the child enters into a group situation, he will be expected to share with others the teacher's attention. He will be able to play alone for definite periods of time, and follow simple directions, such as putting the blocks away or joining the group, listening to a story or music. These situations require some sustained attention on the part of the child as he participates in a group.

Most children of five or six years will be able to handle the usual play materials children have at this age—blocks, puzzles, paints, crayons, scissors, or simple tools. They will also have picked up information about colors and numbers, and will recognize differences in size and shape. Their muscle coordination will have developed so that they can go up and down steps, climb, and use their bodies with poise and good balance. Children at this age are very active. They are constantly experimenting and exploring the world about them.

From this brief outline and discussion of achievements of five- and six-year-olds, it may be noted that a new entrance ticket has been added to beginning school. Today there is no expectation on the part of schools that children will know their ABC's or be able to count to ten. There was a time when parents had a child learn these without meanings attached to them. He might even have been given some introduction to reading. Knowledge about the way children grow and learn has helped us to be wiser now and to lay the foundation stone on good social and emotional adjustment first. After these, learning proceeds steadily, the skills are acquired, and there are fewer failures along the way.

Some children come to school with strange impressions as to what their parents expect of them. They want more than anything else to measure up. Sometimes a child may reveal this worry on beginning school. A teacher told about a child who expressed some anxiety during the first day of school. The first-grade room was filled with the buzz of children. Suddenly the noise was shattered by the heartbreaking sobs of a little girl. "Take me home, I've got to go home," she cried. The teacher bent down, put her arms around the trembling child. The child, feeling comforted, quieted perceptibly. The teacher asked, "Mary, why do you feel that you have to go home?"

"Because," sobbed Mary, "I don't know how to read."

"Why, that's all right," replied the teacher. "You don't need to know how to read. You came to school to learn how."

Comments dropped by parents about school may be quickly absorbed by a child and weigh heavily upon her mind. Sometimes a child takes seriously a remark made jokingly by an adult. Or hearing parents tell of their school experiences, a child gets an erroneous impression as to what school days will be like.

It is possible that parents may need to brush-up on school methods and programs. To give children a picture of things in school as they will find them, it is well for parents to visit the school and ask questions.

Parents will doubtless find that things have changed since they went to school. For example, parents will want to become familiar with the recent findings on reading readiness. They may learn that there is great variation found in the time at which children are ready to learn to read. Occasionally a child may learn to read before entering school as a result of his interest in books, his individual development, and other experiences he has had in the home. There may be a few children who are ready for reading early in the first grade, but the majority need to have experiences of many kinds to build sufficient background with words and their meanings. If children are forced to try to read before they are ready, they may even develop a distaste for reading, which may affect their desire to learn and retard other progress throughout school.

They will learn, too, that reading is a very complicated activity which involves many other skills in preparation for this accomplishment. Many of these skills do not develop until after the child is at least six or older. Such things as eye, hand, and finger coordination must be developed to the point where the child can use these skills together. He needs also to have had direct contact with many objects, to have first-hand experiences so that the things he reads about in his new books have meaning for him. Parents and teachers are wise to work together and not press the child before he is ready for this step in his learning.

Getting ready for school is a gradual process which requires preparation through the important experiences home and parents' guidance provide. It is not possible for parents to cram their children with learning in the weeks before school and have them ready to make a good start. Learning is a step-by-step process according to the child's own readiness to mature and organize his impressions of the world. The experiences which the child is offered all the way from birth to his fifth or sixth year and his relationships with others are tremendously important in determining the progress he makes. Good sound preparation for school is found in repeated chances to grow up in body and spirit under parental guidance. Parents need have no fear that their child will do poorly in school if the planning for growth allows opportunities to explore, grow in independence, and learn about the world.

HOW THE HOME CAN HELP IN ADJUSTING
THE CHILD TO SCHOOL

It is really "at a parent's knee" that children begin to get ready for school. Parents may have no conscious thought of school as they gradually drop off doing for the child so that he may do more for himself. Nevertheless, they are encouraging the child to learn by what they do or do not do for him.

How does the child learn to be self-reliant? By his very nature he starts out feeling that dressing himself, brushing his teeth, and putting things away are exciting and grown-up things to do. Small children can learn to be a real help around the house. Putting away the silver, setting the table, helping mother wash the vegetables are all delightful occupations for the young child and give him a great sense of independence and responsibility. And the child who takes an active part in family life is more likely to cope with situations outside the family than is one who has never helped.

With praise and encouragement from his parents he delights in a chance to embark on even more difficult things, such as going on errands, clearing the table, and tidying his room. He wants to have a part in important jobs and please his mother and father. He has a sense of satisfaction when he has been able to do things which are needed by the family. Through the completion of simple tasks in the home the child grows in independence and acquires skills which carry over into school life.

Sometimes adults are in so much of a hurry they fail to let children have a chance to share and carry responsibilities. This was what was happening in one home where four-year-old Alice, an active, alert child, was eager to help her mother with the cleaning, baking, and house work. "Let me help, Mother," was her constant plea. But the mother found Alice in the way and preferred to do her work by herself.

"Go and play with your toys, Alice, and stop hindering me," she would say. "No, I don't want you fussing around while I am baking. I'll give you one of the cookies when they are done."

Thus, the desire to be helpful and to satisfy normal curiosity is often nipped in the bud when children are deprived of entering into the household chores.

Children learn how to take care of their things largely through the example set by their family. Given a place for their toys and some help in putting them away, they will learn to be orderly, and to carry their part in the family group. They need time, of course, to do this, and they need adults who recognize when fatigue may interfere with their cooperation.

Parents can help a child grow in independence through allowing time and opportunity for him to carry responsibility for such simple things as:

> Dressing and undressing himself
> Hanging up his clothes
> Caring for his toileting needs
> Putting his toys and personal possessions away
> Helping in simple family chores
> Going on errands
> Answering the telephone
> Meeting visitors in the home
> Entering into the table conversation

Very early it is possible to allow children to have choices and to make decisions within their range of experience and development. A little three-year-old girl was delighted when her mother said she might choose the dress she would wear each day. There are many matters on which young children may be asked to express an opinion, such as deciding whom they will invite to their parties, the kind of present they will buy for Daddy, or the way they would like their room arranged. Simple problems put before the child will help him learn to make more difficult choices and decisions, and his willingness to take the responsibility for his own acts will grow with each experience.

The years before school are the time to lay the foundation for good health. In this period much can be done to pave the way against future illness, build a sturdy straight body, and develop a happy frame of mind to meet each day's tasks. During these formative years children establish their routine health habits, such as eating the right kind of foods, getting sufficient sleep, having regular habits of elimination, and getting exercise and fresh air through play out-of-doors. If children are dressed for different kinds of weather when they play out-of-doors, they learn to adjust to changes in temperature and to build resistance to illness before entering school.

Early establishment of a routine in living helps a child to devote full attention to new experiences as he faces them. Fortunate is the child whose parents assist him in carrying out a schedule where routine habits fall into their proper relationship with the rest of his daily program.

So important is active play to the child's growth needs in the years before six that it cannot be overemphasized. A wise parent fits up the backyard, if he has one, or finds a play area for his child in a neighborhood playground to provide the space he requires for using his body. Swings, ladders, sandboxes, planks, and boxes are the tools of play, wonderful aids for muscle building, too. Inevitably this equipment will attract other children to the yard, and the result will be to provide lessons in sharing, exchanging ideas, leading, and following, all of which are necessary experiences for a child in learning to get along well with others.

Health and Safety

Certain precautions need to be taken to protect the child's health. An annual health check-up with the doctor should be arranged to make sure that any physical defects are discovered early and corrected. Most pediatricians advise that children be vaccinated and immunized for certain childhood diseases in their preschool years. A visit to the dentist is also a matter not to be overlooked. Since all of these health matters require time and preparation of the child for them, they should not be left until school begins. Planning for them at intervals will eliminate strain on the child and enlist his cooperation.

Children living in cities learn much about safety in their day-to-day living. Very early they are intrigued by the traffic lights and the police as they travel with their parents on shopping tours or other trips. This is an excellent time to answer questions concerning the safety regulations of the city. Much incidental learning needs to take place and a background of information should be acquired before the child begins to travel alone to school or do small errands for his parents. A four-year-old son was guided by his father, who allowed him to give the signal when he should go and stop as they crossed the downtown street. By the time he was five he had learned to be cautious and dependable in those decisions affecting his safety. He knew why he should walk on the sidewalk, cross streets at corners, watch the lights, and obey traffic controls.

Social Adjustments

Getting along with others is more or less expected as children begin to live as members of a group. Perhaps the surest way to success in school is to help children learn to make friends. Early experiences with different people who do not force themselves on a child but let him make the overtures, will start him on the way to enjoying others. The stage is set for children when parents show an interest in other people and are friendly in their contacts with them.

A certain amount of experimentation, however, must go into the life of every child before he finds his place in a group. Through play with other children his own age he learns the rules of give and take and of making friends. In the beginning years children need to experience fair play, learn to recognize the property of others, share, ask for turns, and get over the first hurdles of learning cooperation. When children are left to their own devices to work out difficulties in their early years, often the stronger and more aggressive child will try to dominate. For this reason children need supervision in their play until the rules of fair play have been learned.

Parents may notice that children with interesting play ideas naturally attract followers. As children are taken on excursions to the airport, the railroad station, the zoo, a dairy, a farm, or other places of interest, they come back to relive these experiences in their play. Not only is their play stimulated, but such trips increase the child's vocabulary and add to his information and understanding of the world in which he lives. He begins to reach out to encompass a new horizon as he gradually masters the immediate surroundings. Stretching his sights into the unknown by trips challenges and provides important experiences for him before he starts to school.

After a child has been on a trip he can be observed reliving the experience at home in various ways. His impressions of what he saw may come out in his block building or as he paints or draws. Time may elapse before he talks much about the trip, but when he does, parents will be interested to listen to what he saw and learned from the experience. Sometimes he will have questions which have come up after he has thought about the trip. If so, another visit may need to be taken to help him check on what he saw or some help be given to enable him to get answers to his questions. Finding the answers is so much more fun than being told by adults.

Books and Music

Books provide another avenue for reliving the experiences a child has had. They also help him to satisfy his longing and hunger for new words, new ideas, or more about the familiar. It is possible to develop in children a feeling of delight and love for books which will greatly influence their success in school. Much depends on the parents' approach even from the first picture books. Fortunate is a child whose parents see that he has some well-chosen books of his own, who take time to read to him, to tell him stories, and listen while he retells experiences or stories of his own. These are ways to help the child acquire skill and ease in self-expression. An appreciation of books fostered in the early years will also become a treasure to cherish throughout his entire life.

The child's response to sounds and movements finds a natural outlet in rhythms and songs during the years before school. Music brings so much pleasure that it should never be omitted in the life of any child. Singing, listening to music, and playing on simple musical instruments develop a feeling for music which may provide a background for musical study or personal enjoyment in the later years. Parents need not be musical themselves to give children these experiences. The stage can be set if he has among his play materials, possibly, a drum, xylophone, glass tumblers, and other rhythm instruments.

Emotional Well-Being

Taking into account the many phases of child growth perhaps none is more basic to school success than emotional well-being. As judged by teachers, readiness in this aspect of development rests heavily upon the child's assurance that he is loved by his parents. A child needs, more than anything else, a happy home where mutual love and respect abound and where he feels he has a place in his parents' affection. This means parents who love and enjoy each other as well as loving and enjoying him.

Parents give a child security in his home through the many things which happen to him. For example, he needs to know that his parents love him whether or not he is a good child. There may be days when he is uncooperative, when he throws his toys, gets into mischief, and destroys valuable things. As a parent meets this behavior he will not condemn the child, but focus on the act when handling these situations.

There are many ways of showing that children are loved besides displaying affection. One way is to see that the things they do well are rewarded through praise and approval by the parent. A child will strive to repeat the good things which bring him satisfaction. Recognizing when a child has done a job well, not by an adult's yardstick, but by what the child is able to do, is the fairest way in measuring his achievement. The relationships which are established between a child and his parents do more to build his sense of values than anything else.

In watching the adjustment of hundreds of school children, the observation has been made that a child who knows there is no place like home is a child who finds school a good place, too. He can leave his parents and go into the new experience confidently; he can put his full attention on the tasks ahead. The child who is uncertain of the love of his parents, who is unhappy at home, is torn within and can give only a part of his attention to his school work.

GETTING ACQUAINTED WITH THE SCHOOL

Before a child is ready to start school, parents should get acquainted with the school their child will attend. Some schools invite parents and children to visit during the spring of the year to plan for school entrance. Often this is done by having small groups of parents and children come to school at intervals so as to see the kindergarten or first grade in session. After the classroom visit the school may arrange for parents and teachers to meet together to discuss the school's program. At this time information may be given concerning the steps to be taken in registering a child, preparation of the child for this event, and some of the ways in which the home and school can cooperate for the best interests of the child.

Schools will, of course, plan their introductory meetings with parents in different ways. Conferences, trips, meetings, observations may all provide opportunities for parents to ask questions and to get to know the school and its staff. Among the subjects which might be discussed in such a series of contacts, the following will be of interest to parents:

Meeting the school staff
Getting acquainted with the school building
Getting acquainted with the school program
Clothing and materials the child needs
Planning for safety
Home attitudes
Parent-child relations

The School Staff

Parents welcome an opportunity to meet the school staff in advance of their child's entrance to school. And it is just as important for the school staff to get acquainted with the parents of children coming to school. In addition to the members of the teaching staff there will often be persons who serve as special consultants to teachers and parents. It will be helpful for parents to know of the services the school provides in the event that some problem is presented as the child progresses in school. Schools will differ, of course, in the number and types of specialists on their staff, but these are some of the people you will meet who will help your child when he is in school:

THE PRINCIPAL. Your first contacts with the school will usually be with the principal. The principal is the person in charge of the school who works with the teachers to provide a good program for children. He or she is also interested to know the community and how the school may best serve the needs of all families who live there. The principal knows all the children and will help you use the services the school offers.

THE TEACHER. Your child will feel safe and happier about school if he realizes that you and his teacher know each other and are friends. Information about your child will help the teacher to know him. She will be glad to exchange information with you later when she has become acquainted with him, too. Try to remember that the teacher has many children in her group and that she is trying to help each child to profit from his school experience. She will welcome your interest in the school. She will understand your child better if she has a chance to get acquainted with each child's home.

THE NURSE. The nurse is concerned with the health of all children in the school. Children visit the nurse's office often. Their height-weight measurements are checked regularly. Minor accidents are treated, and parents are notified if a child becomes ill. The nurse keeps in touch with sick children and issues a permit to return to school when all danger is passed. If you have any problems concerning your child's health she will be glad to talk with you. She may also call on you at home.

THE SCHOOL DOCTOR. Although the school doctor is not at the school daily he and the nurse work together to see that the school is a safe place for the children. In some schools it is the plan for the doctor to give a physical examination to all new children. This may be done during the summer round-up. In other schools the parent may bring a report of the child's physical examination from the family physician.

THE SCHOOL CUSTODIAN. Because schools must be kept at an even temperature, be well ventilated, be clean and orderly to be good places for children to live, the school custodian is an important person. Your child will get to know him and may tell you of the ways in which he helps this person on the school staff.

OTHER SCHOOL PERSONNEL. Parents may not need to call upon the services of all the specialists on the school staff, but they should know what service is available and how it can be obtained. This is only a part of getting acquainted with the school. For example, it is well to know whether your school has a visiting teacher, a psychologist, a speech teacher, an oral hygienist, a librarian, a parent consultant, to mention a few of the specialists a school may have. These persons have had training in a specific field, and are on the staff to help parents, teachers, and children.

The School Building

How big and strange the school building seems to boys and girls when they first enter. The change from living in a small house or apartment to living in a large school is likely to overawe them. So much about the school is different from home. There are different chairs, tables, places for wraps, and so many children all together. The toys must be shared with everyone. There are drinking fountains and big toilet rooms. Mother is no longer within calling distance. The teacher shares her attention with all the children. This new world is quite strange at first, but if the child is introduced in advance of his entrance to school he will make the transition from home to school quite happily.

A tour of the school building made by the child with his parents helps dispel any fear of getting lost and being all alone in this strange place. After school has started, the teacher will no doubt plan for some walks around the building with the children to help them feel at home in their new environment.

The School Program

Children often want to know from their parents what school will be like; what they will do at school. A visit to see the kindergarten or first grade in session will enable parents to give a description to the child of the activities at school. Telling him about the play materials he will have to use, the music, games, stories, and trips he will take help him to anticipate this experience pleasantly. Parents will also want to discuss with the teacher her methods and educational views, to reach certain common ground on what the objectives of the school are. An exchange of ideas on these matters helps the teacher and parents to understand each other better and to work together for the child's best all-round development.

REGISTRATION. When the day for enrolling your child in school arrives, parents should have certain information ready. It is well to be prepared to take to the school all the reports and papers which are needed as required by law or as background on the child's development. The following information may be requested:

Child's birth certificate

Immunization record—most schools require children to be vaccinated for smallpox before school entrance. Doctors also recommend that children be immunized for diphtheria.

A recent physical examination report—this should include a checkup on the child's teeth, hearing, and eyes.

Illnesses the child has had and any serious accidents.

Members of the child's family and family background.

Any unusual tendencies.

Names, addresses, and telephone numbers of two or three persons to be called if parents cannot be reached.

REGULAR ATTENDANCE. Coming to school every day on time is important for a child to make steady progress in his school work. When children are absent, they miss important experiences which may cause them to lose interest or to become discouraged.

Good health habits established before school and a routine schedule for the day's activities help to assure regular attendance at school. Arriving at school on time will not be difficult for the child if the home has helped him to be prompt at meals, to go to bed on time, and to follow a plan for his day.

Parents know well the effect on children of being hurried. To avoid these difficulties, ample time should be allowed the child to get up in the morning, to dress, and to have a leisurely, adequate breakfast. A child starts his day badly if he arrives at school in an upset, unhappy mood.

Adequate sleep at night and periods of relaxation during the day are essential in this period of adjusting to new surroundings. As more energy is required for a child to live with a group of children, his hours after school should be planned so he will not be overstimulated. Parties or trips scheduled in the late afternoon are often too fatiguing for young children. Remember the child has been with other people at school and may need time to be alone.

Clothing and Materials the Child Needs

Getting along away from mother and father is not nearly so difficult if children have clothing they can manage. Some parents and teachers have found these suggestions useful to give the child the assurance he needs in taking care of himself:

Clothing which is appropriate and simple in style.

Clothing to allow for freedom of bodily movements, large enough for active play, such as jumping, running, climbing, or stretching.

Clothing which is comfortable and long enough in the crotch. There should be no binding portions around legs, arms, or waist.

Clothing to allow for independence in toilet and dressing habits. Openings should be long and wide enough for head or feet. Buttons and buttonholes should be large enough to be easily fastened, and as near the front as possible to be easily managed. Loops on the clothing aid the child in hanging it up.

Clothing that is easily laundered. Cleanliness is important.

A smock or apron to cover his clothing while painting, carpentering, or working with clay.

Clothing appropriate to weather conditions and temperature. Try to send him to school with necessary wraps.

Shoes and rubbers amply large so a child can put them on alone.

Mittens and rubbers or other possessions brought to school properly marked so as to prevent loss.

SAFETY MEASURES TO BE LEARNED AT HOME

If you live in the city, older school children will act as safety patrols at street crossings to help younger children observe the safety rules. At busy corners school police usually direct traffic during the hours children are arriving at or leaving school. Parents who live in the neighborhood will not need to accompany their children to and from school after the first days, for children will have ample protection during the school hours.

In preparation for coming to school alone the child should have been taught certain things about safety. A child can be on his own if he can be trusted to do the following things:

Come and go by the route parents have taught him.
Walk on sidewalks.
Cross only at street corners.
Look both ways before crossing.
Walk straight across the street.
Obey the traffic patrols.
Come directly home.
Know his full name, home address, and parents' names.
Know how to walk up and down stairs carefully.

It will take time for the young child to learn all these things, hence these safety precautions will need to be learned over a period of time. They can be grasped more easily if the child understands why it is important to follow these instructions. Variations in such learning are to be expected in line with children's development and the guidance they receive at home.

PARENT ATTITUDES

All efforts on the part of parents to help a child forestall fear and upsets at school are well worth while. Parents can help do this by commenting favorably about a visit to the school, calling the teacher by name, and speaking about the school as a pleasant place to be. They can help the child look forward to having many children as his playmates. They can create an interest in the things he will be doing, the new games, songs, stories he will learn and enjoy. They can speak of the teacher as a friendly, helpful person whom he will like. Before and during the first year a child's future attitude toward school is being formed. He needs to know that his parents believe that he will get along well, and find school to be a place where he wants to go.

PARENT-CHILD-TEACHER RELATIONS

Parents will be better able to understand the program of the school if they keep in close touch with the teacher. The teacher also needs the help of parents to give the best guidance to the child. Success of a child in school is dependent in large measure on close cooperation between home and school.

As parents indicate their interest, the teacher will be glad to arrange conferences to talk about the child's progress. A visit to the school after the beginning weeks are over and the children are settled will give parents a chance to see how their child is getting along in the group. It will also add to their familiarity with the school and strengthen the child's feeling of being "at home" there.

Watch the child's adjustment in school, but try not to expect too much of him. Give him time to find himself. He needs the backing of his family. If comparisons are made between his achievements and those of other children he begins to feel the lack of faith of his parents in his ability. Since each child's growth is an individual matter, any prediction on the part of the parents as to how much he should have learned or how far he should have developed may fall far afield. Encouragement should always be given when successes are reported; try ignoring the failures.

Children are pleased to have their parents take notice and talk about the work they bring home. A bulletin board where drawings and paintings can be posted or a shelf for wood and clay products is often used by parents to let the child feel his achievements are important. Parents who listen to the spontaneous reports the child gives of the happenings at school will find the way open for confidences to continue when he needs to talk things over with them.

Many schools have active parent-teacher associations with programs to interest all parents. New parents in the school will be invited to join this organization and to participate in its activities. There is much to give and to be gained by affiliating with such a group. Taking part in a study group or a special project with the other parents will help you to feel that you belong to the school. It will also broaden your vision concerning the needs of the community and what can be done to improve the opportunities for all children. In all probability your child will take pride in knowing that his parents are members of the parent association.

Just as parents have planned and guided the child during the years before school, they will go right on providing experiences which tie up with the child's activities after his entrance. Each age brings different phases of growth and requires understanding adults to help a child over the bumps. As children grow, parents also grow in planning for and guiding their offspring.

Your Child and His Education

WHAT do we mean by education? Do we think of it as reading, writing, geography, music, and history, something confined to the school building, or do we think of education as a process that has been going on ever since the child was born, and that will continue all his life?

If we consider it in this larger way it is an exciting thing to have a hand in. No matter how active we have been in a child's informal education at home, we all lean heavily on the help of the school, where his more formal learning will take place. Some parents seem to wash their hands of all responsibility once they have waved their children good-by at the school door; but more thoughtful ones want to know what's happening in the school, what the aims of educators are, and how they can help their children get all they can out of their school experience.

Dividing the school day into subjects to which twenty or forty minutes are assigned is of little help to a child's understanding of how to get along with people, or of assuring him happy learning experiences. School is life, nowadays, and the education that a child is getting at home is an inseparable part of that life. As subject-matter boundaries are broken down, so the dividing line between home and school should be broken, too.

WHEN HOME AND SCHOOL WORK TOGETHER

Parents certainly can't content themselves with hustling their children off in the morning, rested, well-fed, and clean. They've got to go along with them in spirit, every day; and in person often enough to learn how they can reinforce what the school is doing. Younger school-age children love to have their parents visit school, yet some parents never put their heads inside the school door unless they are sent for because their child is in trouble.

What are some of the things we gain by school visits?

1. Even a very limited acquaintance with a child's teacher helps to throw light on his behavior in school, and it is an advantage to his teacher to get a glimpse of what the child's family and home life is like—which she can get some notion of even in a brief talk with his mother or father.

2. By visiting the schoolroom we get a chance to see our child in relation to others. We sense something of how he is accepted by the group; whether the behavior we have noticed at home is common among children of this age; and why he either likes or dislikes school.

3. For his parents to demonstrate their interest by taking the time to visit school, to go to parent-teacher meetings or open house, bolsters up a child's feeling of the importance of school. How can we expect children to keep on having the glowing belief that school is a wonderful place—almost invariably their attitude when they start out—if we groan and grumble over giving only one night a month to school affairs? By our attitude we do a great deal to prompt our children's. "Timothy just hates school, and I don't blame him. I always felt that way myself," says Tim's mother—in his hearing, too. She has never taken the trouble to see whether there's really something hateful about the school, or whether he's echoing her because he thinks it's the thing to do. Tim's school may be as good as his mother's was poor, but he is not getting the support he needs at home.

4. Parents may find by keeping in touch with school that they can very capably supplement what goes on there. Hearing a social-studies discussion may remind Mrs. White of a map or pictures that she can send to school by Jack. Or discussion of a certain locality may bring up the question in the family, "Why don't we drive there some

Sunday, and learn more about it?" Parents need to be on the alert to foster children's interests and abilities, any one of which may have an influence on vocational choice.

Parents can be used in schools, too. They can work in the lunch-room, help on projects, display their hobbies, and arrange for reading rooms and parents' meetings there.

5. Parents need to visit school to break down the barriers that sometimes exist between them and the teacher.

A good many parents are afraid of teachers. They feel that teach-ers will be contemptuous of them because they are not so well edu-cated, and can't talk the teacher's language. They can't talk the plumber's or the electrician's language, either. All of us have our special fields of knowledge, and it's absurd to be stand-offish with each other. Sometimes teachers are even more afraid of parents, because they get so much criticism from them. They tremble at the thought of home visits, especially at the beginning of their career. And often, teachers thoughtlessly blame parents for things they don't understand, things that can be remedied by mutual respect and trust.

Instead of being suspicious and fearful, parents and teachers need to get together. It should be easy when they have the common ground of interest in children to stand on. The trend nowadays toward replacing report cards by individual conferences with parents should do a lot toward bringing together the two institutions that are the most powerful influences in children's lives.

Schools have changed so much in the last few years that even com-paratively young parents should be very careful not to criticize a child's school on the basis of their own experience. Even though we are not able to understand what the school is trying to accomplish by a certain procedure, we had better withhold our judgment until we can find out. Parents weaken a child's morale when they divide his allegiance by scoffing at things the school is trying to do. The school needs our backing.

If we are really convinced, after study, that something is wrong, we can voice our opinion through an organization set up to serve our needs, such as the parent-teacher association. This is a much more effective way of bringing about changes than by acting individually.

To "take sides" with a child against his teacher, or some school rule, without getting the facts is to undermine the school's authority unfairly. Naturally parents feel protective toward their children. But there is a difference between the hasty, violent reaction that we all feel when we imagine our "young" are threatened, and the more mature approach that refuses to let blind mother- or father-love or pride get in the way of a sensible study of the question involved. Whether it's a matter of believing that Pat is being bullied on the playground; that Irene isn't being taught to read soon enough; or that Marcia's report of her teacher's sarcasm is true, a calm approach rather than an immediate taking of the child's part will give better results—and save us from possible shame-facedness, later.

We are unreasonable if we expect the teachers to whom we entrust our children to be superior human beings, unless at the same time we pay them adequately. We ought to make sure that people of good ability will enter this field. When we hand over to schools and teachers the most precious things in the world to us—our children— we ought to do everything possible to provide emotionally mature, broadminded, intelligent, and alert teachers who are capable of taking on one of the biggest jobs in the world today.

In many communities, teachers are bound by rules of behavior parents wouldn't want imposed on themselves. Often a teacher is expected to devote her spare time to supervising clubs or other activities. In many places there is still discrimination against married teachers, whose experience with children of their own may give them sympathetic insight into other children's needs. A teacher should be allowed to be a real person.

One of the matters parents often need to talk over with the school is that of promotions. Most children move along from grade to grade in the group they entered school with. A great many schools now automatically "pass" all children in the lower grades. But there are many circumstances such as prolonged absence, due to illness, or irregularity for some other cause, which make it best for a child to repeat a grade. It is far better for a child to do this than it is for him to go on and hopelessly flounder later because of poor preparation, or immaturity in relation to his group.

Occasionally a child finds his class work so easy that he is not challenged to work up to his capacity. Schools used to promote such a child to a higher grade. This sometimes resulted in his being thrown in with children who were physically larger and more able. In order not to create this second problem schools now usually attempt to enrich his experience at the more suitable grade level. Giving him special projects or letting him read when the class is busy with things in which he does not need day-to-day practice sometimes eases the situation. Often parents can be of great assistance in giving such a child stimulating outside interests that will keep him on his toes. Music, handicrafts, or classes at a good art school may be better ways of encouraging in him habits of application and effort than urging that he be pushed ahead a grade at school. Being free to visit the library, to go on trips with his father, or to take advantage of other ways of using his abilities is exhilarating to a child of superior mental gifts.

Whatever the problem, the interests of the child will be best served only when his home and school get together on a plan for solving it.

LEARNING TO READ

To most of us, going to school means, first of all, learning to read. And this skill is, perhaps, the most important single one a child has to acquire, for without a firm grasp of reading he is helpless when he comes up against other things he wants to know about.

Because parents recognize how very closely the ability to read ties up with their child's school progress they often try to help him get a start before he goes to school. Odd as it seems, these efforts sometimes hinder him more than they help him. Direct teaching of the alphabet at home, for example, is unnecessary; but it will be very helpful indeed if a child is given plenty of experience in solving his own problems. For the business of learning to read is full of problems, from learning to recognize the "shape" of different words, and concentrating on one's "place" on the page, to meeting the competition of someone quicker than oneself. It matters very little whether a child is able to print his name when he goes to school (though many five-year-olds do pick this up), but it is a great advantage if he has been read to and talked with a lot, so that he understands what many words mean, and can connect them with experiences he has had and explanations he has been given.

Parents should let their children lead the way in any before-school reading practice. Many a bright child gets a good start at reading from signs, headlines, and advertisements. But it serves no good purpose to *urge* the printed word on children before they go to school.

Another thing that matters is that a child shall be *ready* to learn to read. This does not suddenly become true just because he becomes six years old. Some children will be ready earlier, some much later. A child's mental age counts much more than his calendar age in years. Some of the children in a first-grade room will be all set to go ahead quickly, others will need a much more gradual approach.

The teacher must be alert to see the different needs of different children, some of whom will demand much more of her time and effort than others. If individual workbooks are provided for the children to use, she may be able to put her finger on the special difficulties of any certain child. With such materials, the one who catches on quickly can go ahead at his own rate of speed; the teacher can spend more of her time on those who need more help. Parents' interest in cooperating with the teacher is far more important than any coaching they may give their child, for few of them are familiar with the highly developed techniques the teacher uses in opening up the world of books to children.

Some parents do not realize the tremendous advantage with which a child starts out if he has a good first-grade teacher. When he is taking his first steps in school adjustment and his future habits of learning, it is vital that his teacher be well-trained. Great numbers of children are not only slowed down by a poor start, but more or less permanent damage is done to their self-esteem and confidence in their ability in general. They may acquire feelings of timidity and self-distrust that are very hard indeed to shake off. One child, although slow to start in reading, may pick up fast at seven, eight, or nine. Another may find reading hard for a long time. Each child needs to be allowed to travel at his own pace.

THE PARENTS' PLACE AS TEACHERS

Parents cannot usually determine whether their six-year-old is ready to learn to read, but they can do much to prepare him for reading experience. Their pleasantly stimulating companionship is far more important to a child than being taught any particular skill.

Poised, happy children attack any new adventure with more spirit than children who have worries and fears; so those parents who have succeeded in keeping their children easy and relaxed can feel they have taken a long step toward preparing them for *all* their school experiences. Children who already know how to play with other children will not find it hard to work with them. Having an orderly life at home, and doing things in a regular and systematic way, will help them to fit into the routine that has to be observed at school. Joe, who has learned to dress himself without help, who is accustomed to coming to meals when he is called, will find taking responsibility at school natural. Ray, who has always had attention at home the moment he demanded it, will find it harder to settle down to work at school without constantly seeking help from the teacher than Kenneth, whose parents have taught him not to interrupt them rudely with clamorous demands.

Another way of getting children ready for learning to read goes on quietly and pleasurably in some homes from the time they learn to talk. In such homes interesting and varied experiences, like trips to the zoo, or to farms, are almost as much a part of the children's life as eating and sleeping. Picture and story books have whetted their curiosity and imagination. Parents have taken their questions seriously.

Fathers and mothers who take pains to show their children how to recognize different kinds of trees or insects; to explain to them things like where coal, wood, butter, paper, or bread comes from, will be rewarded not only by their children's having a wide general fund of information, but also by their ability to listen attentively. This will be very useful to them when in school they have to listen to, remember, and follow directions. Giving children a chance to express their observations and imaginings fosters clear thinking. Encouraging them to tell about their experiences will help them talk before an audience, a matter of growing importance at school.

If jingles and rhymes and games involving word sounds and meanings have been a part of the child's play experience at home he will have an interest in words that will help him in learning to read. Hearing clear and correct pronunciation rather than the slovenly speech we all fall into so easily will help children to recognize words when they meet them in print. It's all very well to be amused by a three-year-old's calling "window" "windle" or "basket" "bastick," but it is unfair to him to let him enter school with such mispronunciations.

Finally, readiness for reading means *interest* in learning to read. A child who has been introduced to the world about him by means of trips and excursions, who has heard many stories and has had access to picture books, who appreciates something of how reading will be the "open, sesame" that will unlock a whole new wonderful world to him, will look forward to learning to read with eagerness and enjoyment.

IF LEARNING TO READ PROVES DIFFICULT

If a child has trouble learning to read, there are several explanations that may not occur at once to his parents. The sooner the difficulty is located the better.

A child's eyesight is among the first things to think of. School tests of children's eyes often pick up only very noticeable defects, so they cannot be relied on completely. Whether a child needs glasses or not should be determined by a competent eye specialist.

Sometimes difficulty in learning to read can be traced to poor hearing. A child who does not hear clearly will have trouble with reading. What he hears and the words for which it stands may have no relation. If the loss of hearing is serious, the child may need to be placed in a special class. If the loss is very slight, having a seat near the teacher may be about all that is needed to avoid difficulty in learning to read.

Right- Or Left-Handed?

A good many children go through a period of confusion before they
learn to read from left to right across the page. A child's experience
in following the comic strips may help him a bit to gain this sense
of direction, which should make parents less impatient about reading them to him. For the left-handed child a right-to-left direction
is the natural one. When such a child is given paper to write or draw
on, it should be placed on a slant opposite to that in which right-
handed people place paper. If this is not done, the left-handed child
will be forced to twist his wrist around and write or draw in an
awkward, back-handed way.

Long before children go to school their handedness has been
established. No attempt should be made either by parents or teachers
to force a left-handed child to write with his right hand.

Children who are just starting to learn to read often reverse letters
and words; that is, they confuse "b's" and "d's," read "saw" for
"was," and write letters and figures backwards. When this confusion
persists beyond what seem natural limits, that is, when a child does
not gradually "see" words and letters as they are, he will need patient
individual help if he is not to become discouraged.

Is He Cooperative?

Few parents realize that a child's slowness in learning to read may
have little or nothing to do with reading itself. Instead it may be the
result of an unhappy frame of mind that interferes with his giving
close attention to his reading. The first adult relationship he enters
into outside his home is usually with his teacher, who takes the place
of his mother while he is at school. If he has done things willingly
and gladly for his mother, the chances are he will try hard to do what
the teacher wants him to. But if he is not on good terms with his
mother, this attitude may be transferred to his teacher, and he will
not make any effort to learn to read.

When a child is sullen and resistant about reading, when he
refuses to put forth the necessary effort, we are apt to think this
results from his struggles with reading. Actually, it may be the other

way round; his difficulty with reading may come from his inability to get rid of some burden he carries which keeps him from entering into a cooperative relationship with his teacher. Perhaps the child's and the teacher's dispositions may clash. Teachers, like parents and everybody else, may have problems of personality, of family life, that handicap them in their relations with children.

When emotional problems resist the earnest efforts of teachers and parents alike, the help of mental-health experts should be sought. If there is no local child-guidance clinic, the State Department of Education will know where such services may be found.

The fact that more boys than girls have trouble learning to read suggests the possibility that there may be less understanding of boys' needs than of girls' on the part of mothers; that women are too apt to demand behavior of their sons that fits into their own scheme of life. Because girls are not naturally quite so aggressive as boys, they may find conformance easier. In this connection, too, it should be remembered that girls are slightly ahead in their general development, and for this reason they may find learning to read easier than boys do.

Certainly a child's emotional resistance toward reading must not be dismissed with the easy, surface explanation that it is a result of his finding reading hard. The reason reading is the thing around which emotional attitudes grow up is probably because it is so much stressed in the early grades, and so much prized by parents as evidence of a child's brightness.

Once a child has developed a feeling of hatred toward reading, his sense of failure and discouragement will almost surely hamper him no matter how much he tries to improve. Patience and sympathetic understanding are absolutely essential. Occasionally parents become so baffled or fretted by what seems to them to be laziness, or stubbornness, or lack of effort that they do not use good judgment. "Why don't you do as well as your cousin Helen?" "You could read if you'd only try!" are the kind of reproaches thrown at the helpless child all too often. They only confuse him, worry him, and increase his difficulty.

DON'T MAKE COMPARISONS

Children should not be expected to live up to the achievement of an older brother or sister, of a twin, or of a friend's or relative's child. Discouragement is sure to mount when unfavorable comparisons are constantly dinned into his ears. It is surprising, though, how hard it is for us grown-ups not to push and nag with the mistaken idea that this kind of treatment will stimulate a child to try harder.

Getting together with the school is the very first step in helping a child who has a reading difficulty. In some places reading clinics, with experts trained in reading difficulties, are available. We are not likely to have more such centers unless we are interested enough to work for them. Parents need to educate each other, as taxpayers, to the realization that such investments are economical in the long run.

LEARNING TO WRITE AND USE NUMBERS

There is as much difference between children in the time they are ready for writing as for reading, because each child's muscular adjustment is an individual matter.

Because the movements involved in handwriting require the working together of very small and fine muscles, a great many schools now encourage children to begin with printing, or manuscript writing. In this type of writing each letter is formed separately, with simple, short strokes, which are much easier for young children.

There is much to be said for encouraging children to begin using a typewriter early. Children in the lower grades have been found to have more to say on paper, and to use a larger vocabulary when they can use a typewriter than when they must write by hand. The results, too, even with mistakes, look like more of an accomplishment than handwriting.

By the time a child is in first grade, he is not only interested in numbers, but there are many times when he needs to use them. Perhaps his room is the third from the door in the second hall; he needs to be able to count to find his seat. Perhaps the teacher asks him to choose three other children to play a game with him.

If in his everyday experience at home he has learned to use numbers he will enjoy this practice, instead of being confused and puzzled. But sometimes parents have paid more attention to teaching children to count than to helping them learn the meaning of numbers. Many a five- or six-year-old can glibly count up to ten without having any idea of the relationships between the words he repeats.

There are a thousand and one ways in which a mother can help her children really understand what numbers mean. She may ask her four-year-old to bring her two spools of thread, or to get three spoons when he is helping her set the table. When he is playing with blocks he will enjoy following suggestions to make towers of two and four blocks.

We are so casual in our conversation with children that we deprive them of a great deal of information that might come in handy. For example, both wool and butter are known to children from their earliest years, yet less than half of our five-year-olds probably have any idea as to where they come from. Both in connection with general information and with specific needs (like the requirements for good progress in reading and arithmetic) parents can be very helpful indeed. Letting a child figure out which is a one-pound and which is a two-pound box of crackers at the store gives him the beginning of discrimination that may be followed up in numerous ways like dividing an apple in halves or counting out three of his weekly ten pennies to put in his bank.

On the other hand, children can go through their early school years reciting their "tables" without really understanding what they are doing, because only rote memory is involved. Parents can help greatly in making numbers meaningful to children by playing parchesi, dominoes, and simple card games with them.

How to distinguish between "larger" and "smaller," "longer" and "shorter," "lighter" and "heavier" can be learned by playing games that involve guessing weights, distances, sizes. Some six-year-olds will be able to tell what time it is when the clock hands show the hour, but they will probably be unable to grasp any finer divisions of time.

THE VALUE OF SOCIAL STUDIES

Parents who went to school before "social studies" were an important part of the school day may be puzzled as to what the term means.

A child's school life should provide experiences that prepare him in every possible way for life after he leaves school. Unless a person understands something of the world in which he lives he can't be expected to act very intelligently in it. And now that we are all so close to and dependent on people all over the world, it is immensely important that we understand *how* we are related.

When most families had their own cow, there were no problems of milk distribution. But nowadays, when a family's milk supply may come from hundreds of miles away, children need to learn how a strike or a blizzard may interfere with their having a glass of milk at each meal. Children who live where wheat is grown must get an understanding of how a drought affects not only them and their neighbors, but children in far-off lands to which we export wheat. The city boy must learn how our natural resources can be conserved —why forests should be protected, how great rivers can be harnessed, or saved from pollution by industrial plants.

Why is it any better to have "social studies" than to have geography, history, and civics as separate and disconnected subjects? Such a change grew out of the realization that our world has changed. If our children are to understand other human beings' needs, they must know the conditions under which they live, how the way they are governed came about, and how our lives are affected by what happens to other people. It is impossible to split human relations and the problems connected with them up into little separate pieces called "subjects."

If it takes a lot of understanding and skill to gain mastery over the physical world it takes even more to handle relations between people. What can we do to build friendly relations with people in other countries? How do roads, telephones, and automobiles encourage good neighborliness among ourselves? Why do we have rules for the games we play? When many city people don't have jobs, does that make any difference to farmers?

These are the kinds of questions that social studies try, not always to answer, but to awaken children's minds to.

Children show their interest in the kind of information they get in social studies by the kind of spontaneous questions they ask. Third- to sixth-grade children want to know things like this:

How did people get divided up? How were countries formed? How did people learn to use oil? Where does the lead in a pencil come from? Do the people of India dress the same as we do? Why do some people have jobs, others not?

This interest in origins, and causes, this desire to have real explanations, points out how necessary it is for teachers to be well informed in the natural sciences, and in those that deal with the way people live and get along with each other.

The school gives children experience in friendly living together and in taking responsibility in dozens of ways. They learn to think of others' rights when they are taught to keep their voices low and their heels from clattering in the halls. They learn to conserve materials by taking good care of their books, and paint brushes, by saving paper and crayons. They begin to appreciate the meaning and value of family life when they learn how our family way of living grew up in answer to the need of the helpless baby for protection.

Social studies try to bind together all the different kinds of learning that used to be scattered about in hit-or-miss fashion under many different subject headings. Life is more meaningful when it is studied as a whole.

INTRODUCTION TO SCIENCE

Parents who know something of the load of superstition and ignorance many people carry around with them will be delighted to find their children studying science in grade school. The earlier children begin to get the scientific attitude, the better. The objectives of science and social studies are the same: To help children understand their world, and have some idea about how men go about getting useful knowledge of that world.

A child in the grades can get a "head start" toward more direct and detailed study by having problems to work on (like learning how water evaporates, how frost acts or how a magnet works). He learns by real experiences the need of planning how to go about finding out things. He learns to keep an open mind, how to avoid accepting easy explanations not based on facts. Learning to work with others on a problem, and how to go about getting information from reference books are other valuable contributions of simple science experimentation and observation, planned to suit the children's growing ability to think and reason.

ENCOURAGING SELF-EXPRESSION

We would all like to see our children learn to express what they have to say clearly, whether in speech or in writing. Until a child can write easily he must depend on the spoken word to get across his ideas. This is why it is important that a child have a chance to talk freely and spontaneously in many situations, before he gets to the point of putting his ideas down on paper.

Children who have not been repressed at home are seldom timid about expressing themselves when they enter school. Of course it takes any child some time to learn how to act as a member of the large group he is a part of when he goes into first grade, but within a few weeks he should feel comfortable enough to tell his group about something that interests him, or take part in discussions.

Much of a child's later ease and naturalness in speaking before a group, or his reticence and fear of doing so, depends upon the skill with which his first teachers encourage him to take part. The informal atmosphere of the early grades seems strange to many parents whose school life was in the stiffer, "reciting" type of classroom. But such an atmosphere is one of the best signs that the teacher is not old-fashioned or dictatorial.

Parents can have a share in helping their children get a good start at self-expression. The richer a child's experiences, the greater his vocabulary and his ability to put his ideas into words. The person who is tongue-tied before a social group is not always the one who has nothing to say. But the child, or even the adult for that matter, who has variety in his life is better prepared to make a contribution to a discussion.

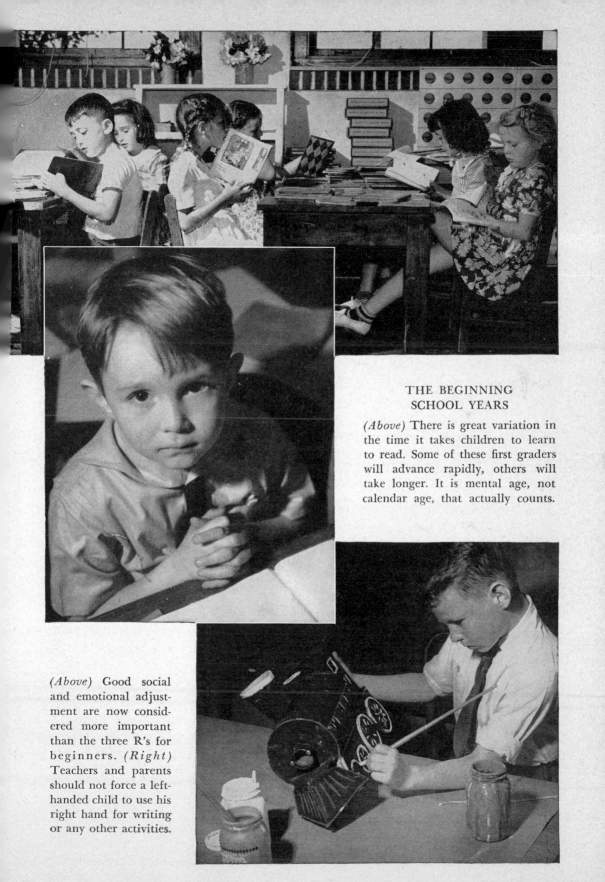

THE BEGINNING SCHOOL YEARS

(*Above*) There is great variation in the time it takes children to learn to read. Some of these first graders will advance rapidly, others will take longer. It is mental age, not calendar age, that actually counts.

(*Above*) Good social and emotional adjustment are now considered more important than the three R's for beginners. (*Right*) Teachers and parents should not force a left-handed child to use his right hand for writing or any other activities.

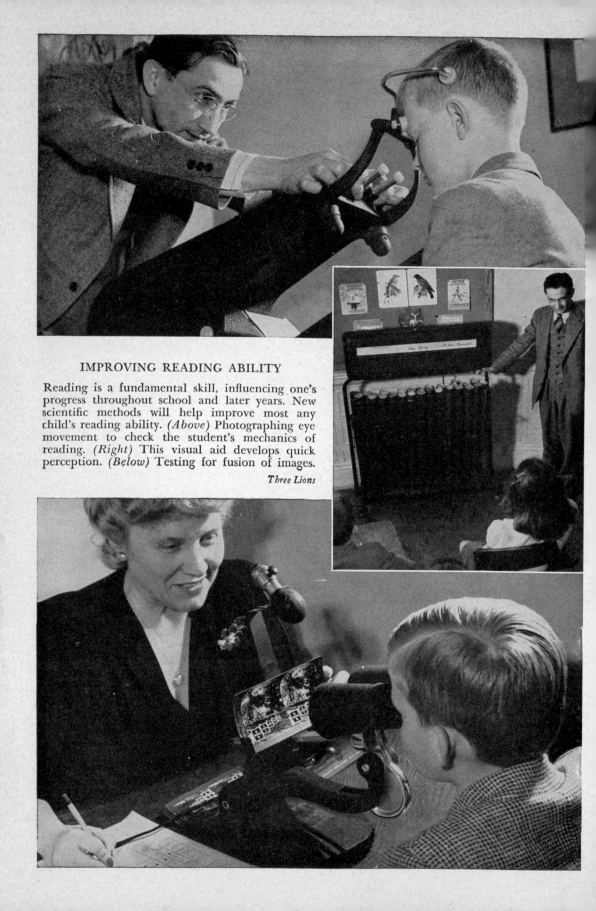

IMPROVING READING ABILITY

Reading is a fundamental skill, influencing one's progress throughout school and later years. New scientific methods will help improve most any child's reading ability. *(Above)* Photographing eye movement to check the student's mechanics of reading. *(Right)* This visual aid develops quick perception. *(Below)* Testing for fusion of images.

Three Lions

Before children write easily enough to put their ideas on paper, they often express themselves in language that is more fresh and charming than any of the written work they will labor over in school later. Teachers and those parents who have time to take down at children's dictation, stories, rhymes, and accounts of experiences they have, are making it easy for these children to transfer their thoughts to paper later.

Spelling is closely connected with a child's self-expression in writing. One of the reasons why children so often find writing letters or school papers irksome may be because misspelled words are invariably called to their attention.

To encourage children to learn to spell we should make use of their natural activities that call upon them to use words. Children making signs for a circus or a fair they are planning, or printing tickets or placards for a play, will go to a lot of pains to see that they get the words right. Parents should use everyday, natural situations that come up to make children word-conscious in an enjoyable way. Words that sound alike but are spelled differently can be made the basis for games in which the different meanings are brought out.

There seems to be great variations in children's natural ability to spell. It would seem that a child who reads a lot would tend to be a good speller, but such is not the case. Such a child may be too deep in what he's reading to watch the details of words.

Parents who try to help a child learn how to spell should be careful to see that their methods are not too unlike those in use in school. For example, learning to spell according to certain rules, which many grown-ups did, is not practiced today as much as is drill on words that contain pitfalls.

Dramatizing what they read about or experience is one of children's great pleasures from the time they are very little. The child's ability to lose himself in the character he is portraying is a wonderful way he has of freeing himself from self-consciousness. It is a form of expression of deep-lying urges that can be a help to the expansion of a child's personality. It is one that parents can aid and abet by providing stage properties and a variety of clothing to be used as costume material. The old trunk dedicated to cast-off finery, old hats, ribbons, lace curtains, and discarded jewelry will be a gold mine for children who carry on dramatic activities.

HOMEWORK

Although most educators no longer stress homework as much as they used to, some grade-school children still have assignments to be done outside of school. When this is so, the time and conditions for study should be carefully planned to keep it from being a hateful chore. Preferably homework should be of the voluntary sort, should grow out of the child's interest in getting further information, pictures, or other material to illustrate and expand what is being discussed at school. Home assignments should allow a child to pursue interests that are truly his own and give scope to his originality. One boy may spend thoroughly pleasurable hours on a map; a girl may take great delight in making her notebook expressive of her taste and love of color.

Unfortunately, too often homework is purely routine—so many problems to work, so many spelling words to learn. When this is true, it certainly taxes a parent's cleverness to make homework anything but irksome.

Children need freedom for active, outdoor play after being confined in school for hours. For this reason, the study period should not come right after school. Just before or soon after dinner may be a good time. Most children like to have a little relaxation before going to bed, so to leave home study until the last thing at night is questionable. The conditions surrounding homework should be such that the child isn't interrupted or distracted. A comfortable chair, and a desk or table where the light is good, are essential. Some children like to study in the family group, but the chances are they will settle down to business and get their work over much quicker in a separate room. If they study in the same place every night they will get more done, because they don't have to spend time adjusting to an unfamiliar situation. Only children sometimes do slightly better work at school than those with brothers and sisters. This may be connected with the fact that they can study undisturbed. On the other hand, some adults have very pleasant memories of working with a group of brothers and sisters.

Oftentimes a child will get his homework out of the way more promptly if it is sandwiched in between radio or television programs. This has the advantage of discouraging dawdling; many times a child *thinks* he is studying when he is really aimlessly reading words over and over.

Because of the feeling some older people have that homework is desirable, some of the things educators have found out about it are worth knowing:

1. Children who spend a lot of time on homework often do little or no better than others. A dull but conscientious child may plod away endlessly at homework, but lack the ability to make a better showing at school on that account.

2. Many teachers find that homework doesn't seem to be much of a factor in raising a child's marks at school. This is a good point for parents to keep in mind who are very ambitious for their child's school success.

3. On the positive side, there is some small likelihood that a child who has formed the habit of home study in the grades will do better in high school, where homework seems necessary.

4. There are many times when parents ought to help with homework, and would build up a closer relationship with their children by doing so. The school has a responsibility for letting parents know when and how they can help. Their interest in what their children are doing encourages a favorable attitude toward learning.

Study outside of school by young children is useful, apparently, when it is something freely and naturally entered into because of a child's interest in learning. One who begins to make a collection of railway maps, enthusiastically enlisting his father's help, and talking over with him the reasons for different routes, time of laying rails, and so on, is learning something about our country's history, and also about its resources, trade, contours, and settling by people from other lands. But it is the self-initiated enjoyment that makes this valuable.

The home can contribute by helping a child form the habit of putting his time to good use. This does not mean pushing, prodding, keeping children busy every minute, but rather surrounding them with the ways and means of using leisure time productively, such as books, pictures, materials, and—above all—an atmosphere of enthusiasm and ideas.

In discussing children's activities we always come back to how absolutely necessary it is to know children. Because a great part of a child's life is spent in school, it is necessary for parents to know the school, too. Parents and schools should be partners. Too often parents are silent partners, or if not silent, they voice complaints. Why not be constructive? When parents get back of a plan for hot lunches at school, for including family life courses in the curriculum, things begin to happen in their communities.

ON STAYING HOME FROM SCHOOL

Even though a child shows only slight signs of being under the weather, home is the place for him if he has any of the symptoms listed below.

A running nose, red or running eyes, sneezing or coughing, a rash or a sore throat are signals that tell us a child is coming down with a cold, or with one of the infectious diseases such as measles or whooping cough. And yet where school funds are paid on a basis of average daily attendance children with seemingly slight ailments are not encouraged to stay at home!

A cold or any of the so-called children's diseases is highly contagious during the early stages; so keeping a child at home safeguards both himself and others. If the early symptoms are not neglected, the time a child has to be away from school may be short. If the child turns out to have an infectious disease, rest in bed from the very start may prevent complications which are more serious than the disease itself.

Sometimes symptoms are less noticeable than those given above, but are equally important. Listlessness, tiredness, irritability, or any departure from a child's usual behavior; paleness; a feverish appearance; swelling about the neck, are all causes for keeping a child at home.

Painful symptoms like earache or running ears, vomiting, diarrhea, or headache are so obvious that they can hardly fail to be thought of as good reasons for a child's being put to bed instead of being sent to school. It should be kept in mind that vomiting, often thought of as being due to something a child has eaten, is even more often connected with disease, such as scarlet fever or influenza.

Using Illness As An Excuse

Occasionally minor illnesses are made so pleasant by the extra attentions his mother gives—special foods, special toys trotted out for the occasion—that a child pleads sick when he wants to escape something he dreads at school. If there is any suspicion that such an attempt is being made, a child's stay in bed should not be the occasion of a lot of fussing and attention. A few hours will tell whether something is really the matter, or whether he is trying to get his mother's sympathy because he couldn't get any elsewhere.

"If you're sick enough to stay at home you're sick enough to be in bed," can be the attitude, and this will give us time to observe whether the illness is real or feigned. A well child seldom wants to stay in bed long if it is not made attractive.

Self-Understanding

A First Step to Understanding Children

Do you ever lose your temper with your children for no good reason?

Do you sometimes make excessive demands on them—knowing that you are being unreasonable and will regret your behavior later on?

Do you ever use bad judgment in guiding your children when you really "know better"?

In short, are there many things about yourself and your relationships with your children that you don't understand?

If you are like most parents, there probably are. Human behavior is complex. No one really understands himself completely. But everyone can understand himself better. It's a difficult job but an important one.

WE CREATE AN ENVIRONMENT

Self-understanding is especially important for those of us who are parents. Our behavior not only determines *our* successes and failures, happiness or unhappiness, *but it gravely affects our children's development.*

Children are the product not only of the chromosomes and genes they inherit from us; they are the product, too, of the environment we create for them. This environment includes physical things, like food, clothing, housing, comforts, and toys. This environment also includes people and the way they behave. And our behavior, the behavior of parents and teachers, gives children their earliest, strongest, and most lasting impressions of the world.

The way we frown or smile; our laughter and scoldings; our expressions and gestures when we are sad or gay, pleased or angry, satisfied or frustrated—all our behavior molds the personality of the child. He absorbs our emotional tones even before he understands the words we use. Very early in life he takes on expressions and gestures and moods from the people in his environment. As he grows, the ways in which we behave determine his behavior habits —his personality pattern. Our ideals, our values, our pettiness and prejudices, our strong points—perhaps even our neurotic symptoms —may become his.

Improving the Emotional Environment

As parents, it is easy to see what we can do about the *physical* environment of our children. We can improve our homes, the food and clothing we provide our children. We can see that they get better medical care and have better schools and classrooms. It is more difficult to see what to do about their *emotional* environment —the environment we create by our behavior, our attitudes, and our actions. Improving that environment is a more difficult task.

But the first step is clear. It lies in self-understanding. Before we can improve the emotional environment we set for our children, we must better understand ourselves, our own emotions and feelings, in short, our personalities. If we know why we behave and feel as we do, it is easier for us to do something about that behavior and those feelings.

But how much do most people actually know about themselves? Usually they have some idea about their physical anatomy—the way their body is made and how its parts operate. But when it comes to the how and why of their feelings, actions, thoughts, and beliefs, they rather vaguely attribute these to their "personality" and let it go at that.

What Is Personality?

What is this thing called personality? What is this unknown "something" that has such a great effect on our children? Actually, it's a very complex thing.

First of all, your personality is the *total* you. It includes all your physical equipment—brains, bones, skin, organs, muscles, blood vessels, as well as your winning smile, Roman nose, and jutting chin. In addition, personality also includes your ideas, feelings, hopes, longings, loves, hates, friendships, interests. It's the way you use your body to express yourself, to transport yourself, to perceive, to feel.

Most people find it hard to think in terms of a "total" personality. They're used to thinking of themselves as made up of distinct and separate parts—a mind and a body. Actually, what we call our mind and body are really one.

These two are so closely related that they cannot operate, or even be considered, separately. Your mind affects your body. Your physical condition affects your mental state. For example, when you get angry with your child (that's mental), your blood pressure (that's physical) goes up, and other changes occur in your body. When you're embarrassed (mental) by a friend's remarks, you blush (physical). And when you have a toothache or headache (both physical) you can't feel gay or interested (both mental) no matter how happy other circumstances around you may be. In other words, your physical condition has affected your "frame of mind."

Now You See It—Now You Don't

We can easily see and locate the parts of our physical anatomy and describe their functions. But we can't point to any one organ of the body and say it is responsible for any one emotion. We can only understand the operation of our "personality anatomy" by describing it in terms of forces or energy drives that can neither be seen nor located in any one part of the body. Psychiatrists and psychologists describe these forces as arising from three parts of the personality: the *conscious,* the *unconscious,* and the *conscience.* A knowledge of these parts and forces provides the basis for understanding human behavior—your own and your children's.

STAYING MENTALLY HEALTHY

There are no sure-fire instructions for the prevention of personality maladjustment as there are for the prevention of many diseases. Malaria, for example, can be controlled by eliminating pools of stagnant water in which the disease-carrying mosquitoes breed. But it's not possible to prevent all the unhealthy incidents that affect a child's developing personality.

No person is immune to tragedy, illness, or injury. Even with the best planning, economic problems can become too big for an individual to weather emotionally. Floods or droughts can wreck our life's plans—and upset our emotional balance. No one, in fact, can be absolutely free of emotional difficulties—they are an inseparable part of our lives.

Five Areas of Mental Health

Despite the problems, most people can maintain good mental health. Strong personalities weather unbelievable stresses. With support and assistance, even people with weak personalities can function effectively under stress. Mental health depends not on being free of problems but on facing them and finding ways of solving them. Knowing how your personality is made and how it functions can help a lot. And although there are no simple rules for handling or preventing difficulties, there are some general principles which, if followed, can help everyone maintain and improve their mental health.

In general, your mental health depends on: (1) your relationships with other people; (2) your codes of behavior; (3) your sources of satisfaction; (4) your ways of obtaining security; and (5) the value of your goals in life.

Perhaps in the discussion of these areas, you will be able to pick up further clues to understanding your own problems—and improving yourself in the areas where you are weak.

1. Your Relationships

By all odds the most important factor in your personal happiness and effectiveness is your ability to get along well with other people. This ability really depends on whether you *can love* and *are loved* more than you hate. And by love we mean family affection, friendship, courtesy to acquaintances, as well as love of husband or wife. Difficulties and unhappiness almost always are related to the fact that one does not give and receive enough love to balance hating and being hated. Everyone hates—to some degree—the person or thing that prevents him from doing what he wishes. If hate is to be overcome it must be balanced with love and affection.

Your ability to overcome your impulse to hate depends largely on your early experiences with your family. To love is a lesson that one must learn in infancy through being loved by parents and then learning to love them in return. When this initial learning fails to take place, the child grows up in a kind of emotional vacuum. He never had the occasion as a small child to give love. So he learns very early to get along without doing so. People who never learn to love sometimes are impressively self-sufficient. They may attain success in business or a profession, but usually they are flops as parents, teachers, husbands and wives. In their personal relations they are loveless—lone wolves.

Some people love themselves so much that they have very little to give to anyone else. They idealize themselves, attract attention to themselves, are conceited and cocksure. Others expect an un-reasonable amount of love. These are the folks who like to talk about their operations, who seem to enjoy ill health. They demand sym-pathy, attention, and constant reassurance. People in this category are excessively dependent on another person. Someone else has to decide for them, lead them, show them how, encourage. Much the same type get their love through being extremely passive; they must be waited on, looked after—they are the clinging violets.

Some people can't get along with members of their own sex. A woman who never learned to love her mother often can't like any woman. She is the kind who constantly backbites and gossips; she is apt to have a hard time even with her own daughters. Men who have had unhappy relationships with their fathers may show the same hostility toward other men—and toward their sons. On the other hand, some adults have particular difficulty in forming happy relationships with members of the opposite sex.

Mismanagement of Hate

Unhappy relationships also result when the drive to hate is mis-managed. There are people who are always attacking others. Their aggressiveness is destructive rather than constructive. They are not only critical but hyper-critical. It seems that their purpose is to obstruct and thwart whatever and whenever they can.

Such people, who usually weren't loved by their parents, grow up fearing to make any attempts at being loved or accepted. They fear that they will meet rejection again. It is as if each one were saying, "I know you won't love me, so I'll reject you before you have a chance to reject me."

Another mismanagement of the hate drive shows up in the person who automatically hates anyone who has authority over him. He is following his childhood pattern of being unable to form a satis-factory relationship with anyone who stands in the way of his wishes. His parents probably stood in the way of so many of his wishes that he has come to resent everyone who exercises control— teachers, foremen, policemen, army officers, and even his own chil-dren when they won't obey him.

The capacity to love and the ability to manage hostile feelings are essential to good mental health. Your capacity to love can be measured by your tolerance and understanding of others; by your loyalty and steadfast devotion to your relatives, friends, and associates; and by how you express these qualities.

Since patterns of loving and hating are formed in childhood, what can you, as a parent do about them now?

First, investigate the management of your own emotional drives toward love and hate. How well do you get along in your relationships with other people? Are you giving the children in your care enough love and acceptance? Equally important, are you helping them learn to accept their obligations as members of school, community, and family groups?

Second, correct your own attitudes and behavior that are interfering with your relationships with others. You don't necessarily have to know just what happened in your early childhood to change your present approaches to people. You can do a lot simply by seeing the situation as it really is and then working at the changes you know will make your relationships better.

2. Codes of Behavior

Your code of behavior—ways of acting toward others—results from the way three forces in your personality, the unconscious, the conscious, and the conscience, combine and react to one another.

The drives to love what pleases and to hate what interferes originate in the unconscious. These drives motivate you to satisfy selfish desires—to remain on the receiving end of the line as you were as an infant. Your conscious, which is constantly in touch with your environment, urges you to act in an unselfish, social manner—to play your part as a member of your family, your school, your community, your club. Your conscience, a sort of inner policeman, urges you to act in accordance with the ethics and standards you absorbed from your parents.

Because of these different drives operating in your personality, you sometimes find it difficult to decide whether your decisions are good or bad, whether a particular feeling is right or wrong. Some things that seem right to you will seem wrong to someone else, and vice

versa. How do you know whose judgment to follow? A good yardstick by which to judge your decisions is to ask yourself these three
questions:

Will this action or behavior harm me in the long run?

Will it harm anyone else?

*Is there a better way to achieve the same result or to find the same
satisfaction?*

If you are going to hurt yourself or unnecessarily cause distress or
pain for someone else, then by any standard the act is wrong. It
is particularly important to act on the basis of these questions in
your relationships with your children. Your actions contribute
greatly to their present happiness or unhappiness. And they learn
how to behave toward others from the way you behave toward
them. The child who does not learn to consider others, to act in
an unselfish manner most of the time, is sure to fail in his relationships with others; and he will always be closer to babyhood than
adulthood.

3. Sources of Satisfaction

To be mentally healthy, and to help children attain good mental
health, you must get satisfactions from life. Satisfactions come from
filling your personal needs, from making wishes come true. You
can get satisfaction from creating a beautiful product, from carrying out a plan, from doing a worthwhile job. And that satisfaction
is increased through the appreciation by others of what you've done.

Satisfaction isn't to be expected from everything you do. You
must do a lot of jobs that are monotonous, routine, dull and distasteful. Even these can eventually lead to satisfactions. They can be a
means of reaching an important goal. But if sight of the goal is lost,
then any none-too-pleasurable activity becomes drudgery.

The amount of satisfaction you get from life depends largely on
your own ingenuity, self-sufficiency, and resourcefulness. People who
wait around for life to supply their satisfaction usually find boredom
instead. Here are some suggestions for achieving greater satisfaction:

a. *Stand aside and look at how you contribute to your own unhappiness.* You may be too dependent, too passive, waiting for a sym-

bolic mother to attend you. You may, on the other hand, be too aggressive, so demanding and sharp that others are afraid of or hostile toward you. Are you so changeable that people wonder if they can catch you in the right mood when they need or want your interest and support? Much of your unhappiness may come from not forming relationships with others who would include you in their fun and adventure—and this may include your children.

h. *Do something out of the ordinary now and then.* Right in your own home, school, or community you can have fun and adventure if you make the effort. Use your imagination and explore new ideas and activities. Include your children in your adventures.

c. *Make a serious effort to find ways and means of doing your main job better.* Do you let your good intentions of reading or studying go by the board? The home is always something of an experimental laboratory, and you ought to be constantly seeking new and better ways of dealing with children. There is great satisfaction to be derived from learning to do your job better.

d. *Re-create and refresh yourself.* No matter how busy you are, you should include in your weekly schedule some time for play, for creative activity, for doing what you want to do purely for the fun of doing it. A hobby isn't merely a matter of filling spare time; it is an important support for your personality. The more fun you have in your leisure time, the better it is for you. Everyone should have some time for doing what he wants to do, the way he likes to do it, with full freedom of conscience to be happy in his own way.

e. *Make and keep friends.* Friends can be a great source of help and satisfaction. They can be the strongest of all supports in time of trouble. Real friendship has to be a give-and-take relationship, although one of the pair may have to take the initiative now and then. The parent always has to take the full initiative in cultivating the friendship of a child. Are you mature enough to take the initiative? Are you willing to go the extra mile? Too many people are afraid to take the initiative for fear they will be turned down.

Friendliness is an art. You can't neglect it, and you can't abuse it. You can't expect to build a friendship if you demand from it more than you give; nor is it healthy to do all the giving.

4. Emotional Security

The ways in which you attain security and the degree to which you are secure is very important to your happiness and effectiveness—and to your children's. Emotional security depends on self-confidence; a knowledge that you are loved; freedom from a sense of guilt; and a firm and certain relationship to family, job, and friends.

A sense of security is essential to happiness and good adjustment. When you feel insecure, you are likely to be upset, tense, or worried. Insecurity is closely related to fear.

It is difficult to give children a sense of security unless you have it yourself. If you have it, they catch it from you. You know where you stand with them and they know where they stand with you. Parents, more than anyone, have the responsibility of providing emotional security for their children. Home should be a retreat where each member of the family can find sure understanding and support when life gets difficult.

The lack of emotional security, the uncertainty about where one stands with family and friends, is a major threat to mental health. To be welcomed, to be recognized, and to be in good standing are terribly important. And secure realtionships don't just happen; they must be built and kept alive through loving care. Parents have the special obligation of teaching children how to contribute to their own sense of security by investing love and interest in other people.

5. The Value of Your Goals

Finally, take a look at the goals you have in life. You can't go very far in life without a goal. Even though it may be one that is impossible to reach fully, it gives you purpose and direction. Parents share a common goal—the development of a healthy, happy new generation.

Unfortunately, there are too many people who drift through life like ships without rudders. On the job they work along in a humdrum way, interested only in their wages. They have no goals. When anyone crosses them, they pick up their marbles, walk out, and try something else. Others are only a little better off—they make a good living but they don't make a good life.

Emotional Maturity—The Prize Goal

If you have a goal that is high enough and worthy enough, your achievement will come with your emotional growth. For that reason a universal goal in life for all of us is to approach as closely as possible to that ideal state: Emotional Maturity.

You are emotionally mature to the extent that you:

Find greater satisfaction in giving than in receiving.

Form satisfying and permanent loyalties in give-and-take relationships.

Use your leisure time creatively.

Contribute to the improvement of your home, school, community, nation and world.

Learn to profit from your mistakes and successes.

Are relatively free from fears, anxieties, and tensions.

It is possible to come close to ideal maturity, and many people do. For no one is this a more important goal than for parents. We can hardly expect our children to be more mature adults than we ourselves. If we hope to have a healthy, happier, more effective—*more mature*—next generation, we must come closer to maturity ourselves.

WILLIAM C. MENNINGER, M. D.

Striving Toward Successful Parenthood

THE kind of people we are impresses itself so deeply on our children that the best of efforts don't amount to much if our own personalities get in the way. In other words, we must understand ourselves, our own longings, frustrations, and good points before we can hope to do a bang-up job as parents.

Children will overlook a lot in a mother and father who really love them. They can stand being scolded, or even punished, by a mother who is warmhearted, and enjoys her children. They will thrive better under her care than under that of a patient, out-wardly devoted mother who is inwardly cold, selfish, and resentful, or of one who is constantly afraid of doing the wrong thing.

Family jokes are one of the finest means of enabling children to feel comradeship with their parents. Laughter eases strain and apprehension. Even a rebuke, given in a way that causes a child to laugh at himself, contributes to his sense of security since he feels bigger than his mistake. Laughing together provides many of the warmest memories of home life.

It's a good thing parenthood comes fairly early in life. Young people haven't had time to get quite so hard and set in their ways. A parent whose personality is very masterful sometimes overawes his children into socially acceptable behavior. We may not have the faintest idea that we are "dominating"; we may be only uncon-sciously adopting toward our children ways that were used by our own parents. It seems natural to give orders, to have our opinions respected, to have John and Ann jump when we call. If we were used to the same kind of father- or mother-behavior we may not see that we are making our children afraid to express themselves, and more yielding and submissive than will be good for their rela-tions with other people. We all need to take stock once in a while, and to keep in mind that allowing children to develop into fine human beings is as important as directing them.

Of course there are mild, gentle, submissive parents, too. Their lack of strength may result in their children's acting stubborn and balky when they try to get their way with others as they have with their yielding parents. Ordinarily, these tendencies are somewhat evened up by the fact that children have two parents; they learn to balance their behavior in relation to two different temperaments. Johnny's father may be easygoing, his mother somewhat dictatorial. The boy adjusts to and is influenced by both. And, luckily, he influences them, too.

UNDERSTANDING AND ENJOYING OUR CHILDREN

Most important of all to a child's future personality is a feeling of being approved of, accepted, and enjoyed by his parents. Children who grow up in an atmosphere of security have confidence in themselves. They can face both the present and the future without the perplexing doubts that trouble children who don't feel this sureness. How can Barbara feel accepted if her mother constantly laments her daughter's straight hair or her freckles? Won't Leo's belief in himself be less sturdy if his father is impatient over his difficulties with arithmetic?

Children need the assurance of feeling that their parents are proud of them; of knowing that no matter what scrapes they get into, Father and Mother are the ones they can turn to for understanding and help, and that though their behavior may be disapproved as unwise or unsuitable, their parents will not stop loving them because of it.

Among the studies that give us hints about how to be of help to our children are some that show how valuable are opportunities for using initiative. Having such opportunities means, first of all, the absence of rigid, repressive discipline. To be able to do things on his own, without being criticized for lack of expertness, gives a child a sense of personal dignity. Tom is likely to do a better job of cleaning the basement if his father says, "Make your own plan of how you're going to rearrange these shelves after you've washed them," than if he stands over him and directs every move. Of *course* Tom's father thinks his plan would be better! But he knows Tom thinks *his* plan is best, too, and he wants Tom to get the job done and enjoy doing it. He'll be readier to take on the next job!

We want children who are lively and original, not just carbon copies of the "average" child! What we have is at least partly up to us—to our way of handling our children. If we put them on their own a lot and allow them to use their initiative, we're likely to see the results in their original ideas.

Your face will probably be red sometimes, when your children's ingenuity takes the form of freer activities than your neighbors allow their boys and girls; when their investigations lead the neighbor's children to come home with wet feet (from boating experiments) or torn clothes (from tree climbing), acquired while very willingly following the leader.

But take heart. Though you may be looked upon dubiously for

a time by people who want children to conform, to do everything exactly as they are told, your courage will be rewarded. Your children will develop judgment, along with height and weight. Always presuming, of course, that they have been taught such basic things as property rights.

If stability is one of our goals, then opportunities for experiences that encourage some freedom of action must be part of our parental plan. The values of different experiences are hard to measure when we are close up to them, especially if they are annoying or embarrassing to adults. The mother who is very dependent on what other people do or think wants her children to wear the "right" clothes, do the "proper" things. But if overalls are what Jerry wants to wear, who are we to deny the possible values of his decision?

The opposite of giving children chances to use initiative, that is, being too watchful and solicitous, may keep children so immature that their school adjustment is affected. It will pay, though, to keep in mind what have been called children's natural powers of recovery from adults' well-meant misdirection.

Each child will be "himself," no matter what we do. Our part is to observe early and try to understand what special innate tendencies each one has. When we *know* Johnny we can tell better how to help him develop some of his natural inclinations, and soften others that seems less useful.

Sometimes, of course, a child's decisions, while not made in deliberate disobedience, are so hasty and based on so little experience that trouble results. Often that trouble is enough to make the child think twice before doing a similar thing. Isn't this one of the purposes of punishment? But in this case we are relieved of having to inflict it ourselves!

However, consequences can't always be relied on to bring the regret that will prevent an act's being repeated, or to make a child more thoughtful. An eight-year-old who eats more candy than we have said he should have won't always have a stomach ache. For the ten-year-old who "forgets" to come home after school to change to old clothes there are no sure-fire consequences. If Ann tears her good dress, and has to wear it patched for months, she may learn to be more careful to follow family rules. But we can't count on that sort of thing happening, so sensible parents try to build a *desire* in their children to behave in ways that work out well for them and everyone else.

ESTABLISH A FEW COMMONSENSE RULES

Children need to have some rules to guide them. Not dozens, which restrict their activities in all direction, but a few clear ones, such as the times when they are expected to show up at home, the boundaries within which they should play, the home duties that are theirs. It is more comfortable to know what one can and can't do than to be uncertain.

If our plan is to work, our children must understand the rules. If we punish hastily and thoughtlessly we may only make a child sulky, instead of sorry. Scolding Ann for having stayed too long when she went to play with Mary, without even giving her a chance to say whether she tried to phone home, may make her resentful. Denying her the privilege of going next time, if she's late after having been warned, is more logical; it may make her try to be more co-operative in the future.

Denial of privileges can be done in such a way that a child sees he is being treated according to the immature way he has acted. He can be helped to understand why he has to forfeit the right to decide for himself this time. Unfortunately, we can also do it harshly, leaving a child thinking we are mean and vindictive.

SHOWING PARENTAL DISAPPROVAL

We often punish without knowing it. Our displeasure is so plain that words are unnecessary; a look is enough to let a child know that this is something about which his mother or father feels keenly. Psychological punishment, in which we show our disappointment or disapproval, is pretty generally practiced. It can be helpful, or it can be terribly damaging, depending on the way it is done. To show our disapproval of a child's disregard of the rights of others is not only legitimate but necessary. To cloud his happiness all day by overblaming him and harking back to the incident is another matter. To be denied his parents' esteem is strong medicine, and should be used accordingly, in tiny doses. Not too close together, either. When disapproval is shown, a child needs to be taken back very promptly into the warmth of his parents' regard.

It is often remarked that we should make it clear to a child that we disapprove of his *misdeed,* not of *him.* We can say, and mean it, "You are a fine person. This thing you did was not worthy of you. Be yourself and you'll be O.K." We can show that we think he'll do better next time. The point is to strengthen his belief in himself.

Believing in a child, and constantly loving him, will do away with the need for much punishment. If a child hasn't his parents' backing he has to hunt up some kind of safe retreat from the hurt of disbelief. Study of children indicates that much punishment may tend to make them turn away from reality to a world of dreams, where they can find comfort in pretending these cruel parents aren't really their own.

If withdrawal of approval serves as a punishment, so does giving of approval become a reward. People sometimes talk disapprovingly of rewards for good behavior, meaning, of course, material rewards like presents or money. Children who are really in harmony with their parents don't need such rewards, and it is too bad to introduce them.

It's quite a different matter to say, "You've been such a help at home all week that there's extra time. Let's go to the movies together," or, "You picked out the vegetables you bought so carefully you can have what you saved to put in your bank." Unexpected, unplanned rewards in the form of pleasant surprises help to keep a child's morale high.

There is one form of reward none of us can get along without— sincere appreciation. We mothers get it in the form of cries of delight when we bake a chocolate cake, or the look in the eye of a husband who finds his pet tie freshly pressed. Rewards are what we make them. A parent who doesn't dare step in the door after being down town without an offering of candy or a toy has made something bad of them.

Promises to reward are a risky business. "A dollar, if your report card is better next month" may bring results, but not always the kind we want. It may bring cheating; it may bring dismay to a child already doing his level best; it may even bring a slump in the marks because the child gets tense and frightened trying for the reward that for him has to take the place of real encouragement.

Physicians judge that about one-third of all the people who consult them have nothing actually wrong with their bodies as far as the physicians can tell. There is no doubt, though, that these people suffer. They have all kinds of things the matter with them, but they are not definite *physical* ailments. Rather, their trouble is in their emotional life.

How did they get that way? Somehow, somewhere along the road of their experience they have picked up a load of fear and worry and anxiety that has finally grown so big as to be unbearably heavy. The person is ill in spirit no matter how husky his frame. Sometimes these anxieties are associated with things that happened away back in childhood, with situations that could have been straightened out if the parents had only known what was bothering the child. If we more often passed over little things in a child's behavior we wouldn't run the risk of having him worry unnecessarily about whether he is respected and accepted.

Sometimes, of course, what children worry about are things their parents have had no hand in. Such happenings can be counterbalanced by the gaiety, humor, and atmosphere of happiness that prevails at home.

An example of the way in which a parent can unconsciously contribute to a child's tendency to be overly concerned about himself may occasionally be seen in reactions toward illness. Mrs. A, for example, may lay great stress on illness. She is constantly worrying over the slightest symptom, popping her child into bed, and calling the doctor needlessly. This may make *him* all through life use illness as a way of getting attention. Sensing but not understanding his mother's feelings, he uses a device, sickness, to get her to make a great fuss over him.

Another example of how a parent's perfection-seeking attitudes sometimes hamper a child is in connection with social pressures that we take too seriously. We overimpress upon children how necessary it is to be clean and presentable, how some things are or are not "done" ("don't belch"; "say 'thank you'"), losing sight of the child's immaturity, and need to pick up these bits of learning gradually.

OVERZEALOUS PARENTS

It is very easy, in our zeal for giving good training, to attach too much importance to some things, or to the wrong ones. Just as our frowning on belching would seem queer to those Orientals for whom this is socially acceptable, so it would seem absurd to us, if we stopped to think, to encourage a child to think of his genital organs with disgust. And yet that is what many a mother risks doing when she expresses disgust over a little child's dabbling in his urine or bowel movements.

What has this to do with a six-year-old or a twelve-year-old? Just this. The "forgotten" happenings of childhood have been stored up, not in his memory, where they may easily be brought to light, but deeper, in his feelings. If he has been made to feel guilty over this, or any other idea that his parents imparted forcibly, he may feel unnatural and unnecessary restraint throughout his life. In many women who are frigid, to whom sexual intercourse is distasteful, this feeling may have had its start in the emphasis placed upon the disagreeable nature of the body's waste products. Because of the location of the genital organs, the feeling has come to be associated with them.

A child may become oversensitive to dirt and germs. He takes so seriously chance remarks about them that he can scarcely enjoy a meal away from home. He must in adult life scrub the restaurant silver before eating, and search his plate or glass for thumb marks. Another child, hearing that milk is a frequent carrier of infection, becomes so disgusted that he declares, and believes always, that he "doesn't like" milk.

We call people who have such aversions "fussy," a term that doesn't go below the surface. Really, their fear or distaste is deep-seated and unhealthy.

A child whose parents make too many demands is likely himself to become conscious of and ready to criticize the mistakes and shortcomings of others. Overanxiety about whether one is living up to the expectations of parents may result in odd behavior that seems to have little or no relation to the underlying trouble. If we want our children to accept and enjoy other people we ourselves should accept them as children. To try to make our children over into something they are not, to urge on them an ideal pattern of behavior that we have somehow set up in our minds is unfair. Fortunately, most parents like their children too much to try any such tactics.

LETTING CHILDREN BE CHILDREN

There would be little point in trying to describe an ideal home, because such widely different kinds of environment produce splendid results. One thing we are pretty sure of, though, is that what children need for happiness (aside from the kind of parents they have) is a place where children can be *children*. This at once rules out a house that caters only to grown-ups. If great importance is attached to polished furniture, then the child must be limited so much in his actions that he misses much of the fun of being a child. The exchange of the old-fashioned chilly parlor for the living room of today is a symbol of our altered feeling about family needs.

Actually, the *atmosphere* of a home matters quite as much as the size. There are happy families living in trailers, and there are keenly unhappy ones with more rooms than they know what to do with.

Our society has paid little attention to the need for privacy for individual family members. Houses and apartments have grown steadily smaller. They're easier to care for, but people have to rub up against each other too much. A good deal of ingenuity has to be used to see that children, as they grow older, can retire from the family group when they want to. When space is very limited it becomes extra important for each child to have some place of his own, even though it's only a desk in a corner, or some shelves or drawers beside his bed. If there is no basement work room, the kitchen will often have to be set aside for such use. It takes a lot of patience and self-control to live squeezed up together like seeds in a pod.

Housing is one of our really desperate problems. It is ironical even to say that each child needs a room of his own when millions of families are living in wretched conditions of overcrowding, are barely existing in shacks and trailers, and in miserable old houses that should long since have been pulled down. How can we expect to raise mentally healthy children when whole families have to live in a single room, sharing toilet facilities with perhaps twenty other families?

However, there are brighter sides to the picture. More and more families, when they build, buy, or rent a home of their own, move to the edge of town, or outside, because they recognize children's needs of space and air and freedom. Housing developments are providing playgrounds. The family car has made possible a great increase in family enjoyment through jaunts and trips. Such shared pleasures may help to take the place in children's memories of a family home, lived in for many years.

Parents can do a lot toward inspiring traditions that will endure, like family celebrations of holidays, birthdays, and other special occasions. These may help to substitute for the security built up by long-continued life in one community.

Because of the earlier exposure of children today to outside influences like radio and pictures that come into their homes from the very earliest years, some ways must be found of emphasizing the values that can come only through family life. The emotional satisfactions of home must be great if they are to compete with the forces that are pulling families apart.

Only the family can give children what they need as a start toward becoming fine human beings. The responses a child learns in his family set the tone of his feelings towards people. Even when he is reproved or punished it will not be in the coldly impersonal way of the outside world. He senses that it is because his parents *care* about him, that it is because his welfare means so much to them that they correct his mistakes and wrong-doing. If he is wanted and cherished here he can face life with greater confidence, even when his skin color or his name is "different."

When you see the eagerness with which children set out for a Sunday hike with their father you wish it could happen oftener. When he plays games with them, whether baseball or rummy, a man has a chance to learn what his children are like. Working with them shows him one side of them, playing with them another. The more, and the earlier, a father enters into the life of his boys and girls, the better he is able to understand them, and contribute to their growth. What he gives them by his companionship is specially welcomed because feminine influences so largely prevail in American homes and schools. What they give *him* is beyond measure, as fathers will agree. A man who is bringing up a family of children is constantly being surprised at the way they are influencing his personality.

PUTTING DOWN FAMILY ROOTS

Some of us can remember a time when family life was more stable than it is today. To the millions of children and young people who have no chance to put down roots in any one place we owe a great debt. Somehow we must create for them something to take the place of more permanent and secure ways of life.

Nowadays, even in a neighborhood in which many families own their own homes, only one child out of fifteen or twenty may have lived in the same house ever since he was born. In a great city, many families move every year, or even oftener. With increasing numbers of tenant farmers, farm families, too, are on the move.

Under these conditions family treasures and heirlooms — what H. L. Mencken calls "the sacred rubbish" of the family—are largely lacking. How can we give children a sense of "belonging," a sense of the enduring nature of family life? If there are few familiar, cherished possessions, symbols of his family's life in the past, does a child miss some stimulus that comes to him through pride in his ancestors? American families have come here from all over the world. But to become Americans does not mean that we should let our family traditions fade out of mind any more than we would let the precious strip of embroidery made by a great-grandmother fade.

Perhaps the fact that there are more grandfathers and grandmothers alive today is one thing that helps children feel the on-going nature of family life. Grandparents should be encouraged in story-telling about their youth, and in recreating the past for children through old songs.

Parents who have to move from place to place can make a whole-hearted effort to be warmly friendly to their children's new acquaintances. Boys and girls whose ties are frequently broken need to have a home that invites the making of new ones.

But new ties can't be formed unless new neighbors are generous and friendly. Those who are secure and established in a community may thoughtlessly fail to accept newcomers. Epecially when migration means a mixing of people who have very different backgrounds and customs, the more settled community members may turn up their noses at ways with which they are unfamiliar. Their children can easily develop feelings of being "better" than their neighbors. The children of both groups are hurt by such unfriendliness, but the bruises show more on those who are inspected critically, on the children who are made to feel that they don't fit in.

Who can ease such hurts or prevent them? Those families that have been less buffeted about have an obligation to do something constructive in their neighborhoods. Such parents can do a lot to back up the efforts of schools, which are finding many ways of encouraging real brotherhood. All groups have much with which to enrich the lives of other groups. By sharing with each other our music, art, dancing, special foods, and other traditional folkways we add to our enjoyment and understanding.

Most of our schools are trying their level best to dig out the ugly prejudices that are the result of narrowness and ignorance. We parents need to find out more about how we can help. For one thing, we can guard our words. Expressions that belittle others, used because we hear them so commonly rather than because we believe them, should be kept strictly out of our speech. Love of our neighbors should be shown in our everyday living, in our acts—such as the way we vote—as well as in our words. Because harmful fears and suspicions of peoples, races, religions, and political ideas are harder to get rid of than poison ivy, we need to give our help to all the agencies that are working out methods of fighting evil forces. Each individual family that does all in its power, even though the visible results seem small, is having a hand in the education that may help to save us from disaster.

Many of us suffer from a false notion about "the good old days." In the first place, they were not good—for enough people. In the second place, they are not going to return. Let's not try to escape our obligation to our children:

We must bring up our children so that they expect and like to work out their own problems, instead of yielding to others who may try to force them into accepting ready-made solutions. We must at the same time help them to see the need of being able to work with others toward common ends, and not to be too stiff-necked to accept new ideas and ways of living.

Most of us parents can hear echoes out of our childhood urging us to "be good." We even make those echoes ring over again, without thinking, when we say to our children, "Be a good boy!" or, "Have you been a good girl?"

If we stopped to ask ourselves what we mean by such cautions, we'd have to admit that they are tinged with a dread of *bad* behavior! They are really a sort of warning to a child not to do anything we might be ashamed of or blamed for! Parents are only human; they dislike to have anything happen that will reflect on them. When their Louis or Paul breaks a neighbor's window or scratches his car fender, they feel that it's not to their credit as parents, so it hurts their pride.

It's not strange that we look on our children as extensions of ourselves, and want their doings to make us show up well. But it *is* strange that we are so blind about it, always fooling ourselves into thinking that what we do is for our children's good, when really, deep down, it's as much, or more, for our satisfaction or our reputation.

Actually, children turn out better if less weight is placed upon "goodness" than on seeing to it that conditions under which they live are such that "goodness," happiness, and all-around fine adjustment will be the natural results. Strain and tension come in when our attitudes show distrust of a child's good intent.

If we're too eager for our children to be "good" we easily fall into habits of being critical. Because obedience used to be so much stressed, we unconsciously follow along, forgetting that what we *really* want is for children to develop standards of their own that will stay with them, rather than to be little puppets that are jerked on a string in tune with someone else's ideas. Children who are brought up to respond like clockwork to rules we have laid down have little chance to gain the strength that comes from self-handling of problems.

Besides the absence of training in self-reliance that goes with too much pressure on "obedience" there is the possibility that a strong-willed, bright child may be tempted into an outer show of submission while inwardly he rebels. This is almost bound to cause unhappiness later. For when such a child reaches an age when stirrings toward independence are very urgent he may suddenly break down the fence of his parents' restraint. His father and mother are puzzled and hurt. He has kept his feelings to himself; they have had no notion of the inner conflict under his hitherto submissive behavior.

What seems like sudden rebellion is really the breaking out of a fire that has been smouldering a long time.

It can happen that parents, with the best of intentions, make a child become deceitful in efforts to escape domination.

Parents need to be aware of the changes that are bound to come with development, and of how absurd it is to expect to rule all their children's doings. We need to remember that some sort of "protest" behavior is necessary during the growing-up period. Even youngsters who are thoroughly happy in their home life, who need not struggle for independence, "feel their oats" on occasion, and kick up their heels accordingly.

THERE IS NO MAGIC FORMULA

We all want our children to grow up law-abiding and honest, with high moral standards and character. But to believe that there is any special training magic that will produce "character" is to be disappointed. We can't bring up a child of whom we will be proud by following any set of hard-and-fast rules.

What we *can* do is to make it more satisfying to our children to do right than wrong, we can give them plenty of enjoyable practice in doing acceptable things. We can try to keep from shaping their attitudes by pressures coming from our own sometimes very set ways of thinking or acting, like social or political prejudices. We can be so fair in our treatment of them that they will not be pushed into doing wrong through fear.

Take cheating in school, for example. Why do children cheat? For a great variety of reasons. Because they think their teacher is unfair; because they want to make as good a showing as some other child; because they are afraid of punishment for failure, among others. A child may cheat in spelling, because spelling is hard for him, and yet have no inclination at all to cheat in arithmetic, because that comes easy to him. One may cheat in a game who would not think of doing so when money was involved. Honesty, or dishonesty, appears in specific situations. It is not a large, general way of behaving applying to everything a child does.

A child's home is the first influence on the moral development, and the one that never lets up. There he is exposed to four different kinds of help: the example of his parents; their preaching and urging; reproof and punishment when he does wrong; and the pleasant and stimulating effects of actions that result in his getting warm approval. There, in the home, the underlying capacities of the child need a chance to develop. We must be as careful not to get in the way of character development as we are about directing it.

LEARNING MORAL VALUES

Learning to be honest and upright follows the same pattern as other kinds of learning: it takes place when children find satisfaction in doing right (whether through the happiness their parents show, or their own joy at having lived up to what was expected of them) ; when they find that poor behavior brings sorrow or pain (but this can be carried too far, as when a child lies because he has suffered severe punishment and fears it will be repeated); or when the consequences of desirable behavior are pleasant.

When parents are careless and lax and have no consistent plan of guidance, conditions are right for children to "get by" with things they know are wrong. The importance of our own personal moral habits and attitudes can't be overlooked. Because we get at the child first, and he unconsciously accepts our ways as "the" ways, we parents have an enormous advantage over any future influences.

Also a very grave responsibility. We have to be careful that the things we stress are the really important ones. A boy may grow into manhood with perfect table manners, but with very little sense of keeping his obligations to the very same people he is polite to. If his mother has emphasized the one and neglected the other, can he be blamed for acting as if it were more important to jump from his chair every time his mother comes into a room than to keep his word to her?

By the time children are passing through the elementary grades they are being deluged, of course, with all manner of other influences. Other children are probably next most important to parents in helping to form a child's character. Because they want to be liked and admired, children follow the leader a good deal; the influence of friends on conduct is very marked in the schoolroom and in group play. But what one does when influenced by the spirit of the group may not match up with his behavior when away from the crowd. Jim may join his neighborhood gang in throwing stones at street lights when he would never think of doing such a thing by himself.

That the effect of such follow-the-leader behavior is often short-lived may be a comfort to parents who may, temporarily perhaps, have to live in a neighborhood where the children's morale is not high. It has been found that as the group changes, standards change, too; so temporary contacts need not necessarily be a cause for great alarm provided a child's home background is good. Natalie is not going to turn into a pickpocket because the little girls she plays with in the second grade give her the idea of taking home colored chalk from school. Jack's parents may be taken by surprise when he is reported as one of a group that has been scrawling filthy words on the school lavatory walls, but it doesn't mean that he's going to be a sex pervert.

If some of Jack's and some of Natalie's companions keep on doing wrong things it will be largely because of the way their acts are looked on at home. Her mistake is an isolated one for Natalie, because her ideas about honesty are clearer after her parents' discussion of how careful we must be not to take things that do not belong to us. Another child's mother may smooth over the dishonesty, saying, 'The school has lots of chalk, anyway we're taxpayers." Jack's escapade may be used well, or poorly, as a ground for home teaching. His father can explain to him how natural boys' curiosity about sex is and how smutty words or stories, used in the hope of impressing others, are often a confession of ignorance, thus making the whole thing seem silly and "young" rather than "bad." Or, he can punish his son harshly, leaving him with the feeling that sex is dirty and disgraceful.

We come back over and over to the home as the most important influence in a child's life. The home interprets what a child picks up outside, solidly backing up his outside learning when it is good. When family standards and ideals are high, the child is more likely to question ways that don't measure up to them.

Parents who demand special favors, who use roundabout methods of getting what they want, such as accepting "rake-offs" or seeking out the "right people" who can save them money by outwitting the law, are doing their children great harm. The children may, because of this experience, sink into the habit of excusing themselves for sharp or crooked practices, with the idea that *their* needs are special, that favors are their natural right.

Attitudes, once absorbed, are as hard to remove as it is to get ink out of a blotter. Because we parents are largely unaware of our prejudices and special slants of thinking, we pass them on in ignorance of what we are doing. When they disagree with what a child is learning outside, he becomes confused; like the child who said, "When I'm at school, I believe the way my teacher says we should. But when I go home, what my parents say seems right."

LEARNING TOLERANCE

We have to be especially careful about our very human tendency to build ourselves up at the expense of others, which, if we are insecure, we are sometimes betrayed into doing. If any group in a

CHART OF CHILD NEEDS

NEEDS	FROM PARENTS	FROM TEACHERS	FROM PLAYMATES	FROM COMMUNITY
EMOTIONAL AFFECTION (feeling of being loved)	Comradeship. Playing no favorites. Serenity in home.	Evident fondness for child. Happy cooperative atmosphere in classroom. Kindness, fairness.	Friendships. Interest in child's achievements.	Understanding teachers. Active child welfare agencies and kind foster parents when home supervision breaks down.
BELONGING (feeling of being wanted by the group)	Significant share in family work and play. Proud of child as member of family.	Welcoming child in school and giving real share in activities of classroom and playground.	Full acceptance of child. Genuine share in group's activities.	Inspiring child's cooperation to contribute to the beauty, health and welfare of community.
INDEPENDENCE (feeling of managing and directing own life)	Child helped to stand on own feet. Given opportunities to make decisions and choose friends with reasonable guidance.	Initiative encouraged. Participation in class discussions. Training in self-control and self-direction.	Child given his turn in doing things and being leader.	Opportunities for older children and youth to participate in community councils.
ACHIEVEMENT (satisfaction from making things and doing jobs)	Encouragement in school work. Opportunities for worthwhile tasks; hobbies and adventure.	Work at which child can succeed. Opportunities for success in sports, hobbies, dramatics, etc.	Child included in school projects, sports, dramatics, musical and other activities.	Vocational guidance. Share in community enterprises—church activities, etc.
SOCIAL APPROVAL (feeling that others ap-	Praise for good behavior, honest effort in work and	Commendation for good behavior, diligence in	Generous admiration for child's accomplishments in	Credit for constructive activities, patriotic work, etc.

	...prove of conduct and efforts)	...other accomplishments (sports, making friends, etc.).	school work, success in sports, dramatics, music, etc.	
SELF-ESTEEM (feeling of being worth-while)	Confidence in child and his future.	Making child feel a worth-while person. Helping child understand and accept his strengths and weaknesses.	Appreciation of child's good qualities.	Making child feel he matters to community. Giving him share in community enterprises.
INTELLECTUAL (for training in ability to think clearly and solve problems wisely)	Encouraging children to find out the facts before coming to conclusions.	Training children to think in an orderly fashion, to acquire sound study habits, and to read wisely.	Participation in group projects planned and carried out by children themselves.	Compulsory education. Inviting partnership of children in helping solve community problems. Developing partnership between home and school.
CHARACTER AND SOCIAL (for developing ability to live with others in a co-operative and worthy way)	Good standards of behavior at home, encouraging honesty, sincerity, social service and spiritual development. Sex education.	Training child to cooperate with others in work and play and to complete difficult tasks for worthwhile ends.	Approval of child when a good sport (good loser, good winner, etc.).	Good character-building agencies—schools, churches, playgrounds, day nurseries, recreation centres, etc.
PHYSICAL (for developing a healthy body and good health habits)	Nutritious food, adequate sleep, suitable clothing, sanitary living quarters, medical and dental care, training in good health habits, outdoor activities.	Health education, physical training, cooperation with medical authorities in health inspection and immunization against disease.	Consideration by child of health and handicaps of associates. Full cooperation in preventing spread of contagious diseases.	Adequate medical and dental services. Immunization against diseases. Sanitary living conditions. Full social security.

Prepared by the National Committee for Mental Hygiene (Canada) at the request of the Canadian Broadcasting Corporation for use in connection with network programs directed by the women's interest department. Used by permission of the Canadian Broadcasting Corporation.

community is very much in the minority, those who belong to the larger groups sometimes belittle the few as "different." Whether the group be newcomers to America, people of an unfamiliar religious faith, are "capitalists" or "labor groups" or belong to another race, the damage to our children of accepting hasty, ignorant opinions about them is the same.

"Helping children to enter imaginatively into the lives and feelings of others is at the basis of all good character-education in both home and school," says S. R. Laycock. "To come to treat all other human beings as one's brothers involves the keen realization that other human beings have the same needs and the same capacity for feelings as oneself."

If we can bring about in our children such feelings of well-being and such a sense of perspective and fairness that they are not always having to measure themselves against others, we shall have gone a long way toward strengthening their moral fibre. What we want is for them to hate injustice and wrong, and to love truth and honor. We cannot expect to keep illogical emotional reactions entirely out of their lives, but we can help them at least to be flexible in their thinking.

Our children will have courage to lift up their voices for causes that are good and just—but that may be unpopular—only if we imprint on their minds clear images of what "good" is. Such images will largely be reflections of our own behavior.

The School-Age Child's
Stages of Growth

How simple it would be if parents had a definite set of rules to follow that assured developing to the full their children's inborn abilities. And yet, one of the most intriguing things about being a parent can be the mystery and unpredictability surrounding these youngsters entrusted to our care for a few years. Viewed in that light, perhaps it is just as well we don't have a magic formula by which to direct their lives.

In many ways the school-age period of the child's development may prove more interesting than the appealing years of early childhood. Boys and girls are trying out their own abilities and interests, and are gaining in self-confidence and self-reliance. While they still need and count on the friendly care and backing of their parents and others in the family, they manage more and more of their own affairs. The feeling that the loyalty and service they give their family is appreciated is highly enjoyable to them.

During this period, while a child's personality is becoming increasingly complex, it becomes more of a challenge to understand him. His growing independence and ability to think and reason for himself are sometimes disconcerting. It upsets our notions of our superiority just a bit when our children begin to question our opinions, and to have very definite ideas of their own.

While a child is very young and also very ignorant, we older people feel secure in our bigness and power. We feel important in contrast to the child's smallness and helplessness. We enjoy his naive way of looking at life because we can say to ourselves, "Oh, we know all about that!" But as children grow out of complete dependence, they begin to think and reason for themselves.

We tend to be less observant of school-age children because their development is far less spectacular, in many ways, than that of the young child. Physical growth has slowed down greatly. Mental growth goes on so quietly we take it for granted. While a child is learning to talk, everything he says is novel and arresting. Once he gets into middle childhood his ability to understand things and to express himself has progressed so much that what he says no longer seems so remarkable. His reasoning is much better; he no longer argues amusingly that butter is made from butterflies because the two words sound alike; he stops believing that trees make the wind blow.

Nor is his health a cause for quite such vigilance as earlier. Once a child has passed through the preschool years, the time of greatest danger from childhood diseases, his parents become a little less watchful and anxious. He can take care of himself much of the time; they no longer feel worried every minute he's out of their sight.

In short, he is on the way to becoming a self-contained, self-directing, self-motivated person. Still close to his parents, still appreciating attention, love, and sympathy, he is striking out for himself, making friends, showing individual tastes, exploring many fields— a lively, eager, able, light-hearted, and often maddening creature. He is tremendously interested in the things and life about him. His thoughts are mostly turned outwards toward the practical, material world.

Does this sound as if all children are alike? Of course they're not. They're as different and varied and surprising in their individuality as in their looks, but there are ideas, feelings, ways of acting and looking at things which they all go through at certain stages in their growth.

MUSCULAR CONTROL AND BODY SKILLS

Once a child has acquired good control over his body, he has a great deal of energy to expend on learning skills and adding to all manner of abilities that were only partially perfected before.

Little girls of six to ten, for example, delight in hop-scotch and jacks, which call for more precise muscular adjustment than the large-muscle activities of their early childhood. The intricate rhythm of skipping rope, fancy stunts on a bicycle or on roller-skates all involve bodily control that was not possible at four or five. Learning to whistle, to turn handsprings, to balance a pole on the open hand, to bounce a ball in time to a special pattern of bodily movements—all these kinds of skills delight the boy and girl who are coming to have more and more control over their muscles. Learning to write requires very exact adjustments and coordination between hand and eye. (Remember your struggles not to get the tail of the "y" too far below the line, and to keep the "e's" from looking like "l's"?) Increasing ability to use the fingers makes later childhood a time in which such things as playing a musical instrument or typing should be getting under way if they are to become highly developed.

Children can't get enough of games that emphasize physical alertness. Chasing, climbing, dodging are a never-ending joy. Swinging, on a proper swing if that's all that's handy, better on a grapevine discovered in the woods, frees them from being earth-bound clods. Tag, run-sheep-run, "cops and robbers"—anything in which there's the thrill and excitement of avoiding capture appeals to the "wild Indian" stage of the early school years.

EXPLORING NATURE

Caves and tree-houses, dams and pools, fires to roast potatoes in, trees to climb and swamps to explore—nature's resources seem made to be exploited by children. Imagination is at a high peak; the early school-age child becomes what he has read about or heard of or listened to. He re-creates the life about him; boys build houses, girls set up housekeeping in them.

A boy and his dog are attached to each other by invisible, unbreakable ties. The tenderness with which an injured bird or a motherless lamb is cared for shows us what wonderfully responsive creatures our children are.

Children's joy in the world of nature is matched by their delight in putting their hands to work.

The school-age child constructs things with initiative and fervor. Carts, kites, airplanes, boats are undertaken with varying degrees of success according to the skill present at different ages and individual cleverness in the use of the hands. Girls cut out paper dolls by the dozen, make dresses for them by the score. Weaving, knot-tying, carving, all have their devotees.

Not only is this when children prove and improve their physical skill, it is a time for trying out everything under the sun. Eight- or nine-year-olds have a greater variety of play interests than children of any other age. Later on, after a child has explored a great many possibilities it becomes necessary to spend more time on well-liked ones if he is to become good at them. But now—now there's time for everything.

Experimentation leads children everywhere. It urges them into using every one of their senses. They discover the sweet taste of the growing ends of grass blades, and sample pungent, tangy pine needles. They make leaves squawk, tear apart paper-thin birch-bark layers. They rub the leaves of mint and sniff its fragrance, and say "phew!" to the "cow-pie" they almost stepped in.

They burrow into the haystack, climb on top and come hurtling down with dust in their hair. They run, panting, after the fire engine, hoping the fire will be a big one. When the plumber comes to the house, they're right under foot, watching. And when a street is being paved, every operation is followed by fascinated eyes. They can't wait for it to come time to go barefoot, when they can "squdge" mud between their toes, or feel the cold tingle of dew-wet grass. They like to bite and suck and chew on anything, from slippery elm to bubble gum and pencils.

A rain-filled gutter cries out to be stepped in, rubbers or no rubbers. Soap is something to work up a lather with, rather than something to get clean with. They love the rites and rhymes and tricks that are handed down perennially by older children, like "wire, brier, limber lock" and "Adam and Eve and pinch-me." They like to believe that without question they'll get their wish on the "first star."

Guessing games, riddles, conundrums and jokes all have their day. Code language is rattled off by two nine-year-olds as fast as they can talk. Charades are a gold mine of fun. Dressed up in Mother's cast-off dresses and high-heeled shoes, little girls pay very formal calls, or have baby parades with their doll carriages. Table games consume lots of time; although there's a painful period until children understand that someone must be the loser. Hard to take at first, this is an important kind of learning, and paves the way for team play later. Sending away for samples, saving box tops or coupons, making collections of anything and everything, and jealously hoarding these nondescript treasures; following the iceman for pieces of ice to suck; haunting the back premises of grocery stores in the hope of getting boxes to build with; pouncing on the evening paper so as not to lose a minute in looking at the funnies—these are almost as characteristic as eating is.

Sleep is something made for babies or aged parents, a terrible waste of time for those whose days are far too short to get everything in. Energetic children hate to be inactive, unless they've an absorbing book, a piece of string to play cat's cradle with, or some other way to occupy their fingers.

Sleeping may be a bore, but eating is a joy forever. Preferably, children think, eating should be done in a hurry. If food tastes extra good, why, naturally it should be gobbled; if it's something you don't like but have to eat—gulp it down fast, after you've left it on your plate till the very last. And as for the folly of eating at set times—who ever invented such nonsense? Meals are all very well, but how are children going to last between them, when they're tearing all over the neighborhood, doing important things like riding bicycles, climbing trees, or planning a show? A ten-year-old is absolutely empty, caved in, after school.

The school-age child has quite a different attitude toward clothes than he did when younger. He is much more conscious of what other children wear, and wants to look like them. To be different is as hard on a child of this age as it is on a man who feels too short or a woman who thinks she is too fat. Shoes, caps, dresses, or hair-do's unlike those worn by most children can cause acute humiliation.

As for older and younger children in the same family—what a gulf exists between them at school and at play! "We don't want you tagging along! Scram!" is the attitude of the older ones who like to think of themselves as far more grown up than their little sisters and brothers.

But older brothers and sisters often display a tenderly protective care over little ones that is beautiful to see. It gives us intimations of their boundless possibilities for consideration and gentleness, which will be developed to the full when they themselves are parents.

Along about nine or ten, boys begin to be intolerant of girls, and girls to turn up their noses at boys. Oh, each sex is all right when it comes to games that need a number of players. But girls are scary things, say the boys, who like to make them shriek by holding dead mice under their noses, or grabbing their ankles under water. And boys are rough, and careless, according to girls. Do they ever comb their hair? But underneath this exaggerated contempt for each other lurks an attraction that before very many years will become strong.

Brothers and sisters are allies one minute, scrappy as alley cats the next. There are times when each seems to get delight out of tormenting the other: Ned gets Polly at his mercy and tickles her. She in turn tattles on him in a most disagreeable way. But let an outsider pick on one or the other and right away, Ned or Polly is up in arms defending the other.

At this stage either one of them is probably quite willing to skip the daily bath in order to have more time to play. Or, they both claim the bathroom at the same time when they *do* decide to bathe!

Charting the Development of the School-Age Child

YOUR CHILD BETWEEN SIX AND SEVEN

PHYSICAL GROWTH AND SKILLS. Has six or seven wrist bones. Has one or two permanent teeth. "Knock-knees" of preschool period have disappeared. Very active; sitting still is an effort; wriggling especially noticeable at table. Absorbed in running, jumping, chasing, and dodging games. Enjoys any sort of wheel toys. Likes to bathe self, with help on ears, neck, and back. Can dress self without help, even to tying shoe laces, but is inclined to dawdle.

SOCIAL PROGRESS. Thoroughly enjoys group play, but groups tend to be small. Boys and girls play together. Boys begin to wrestle, have fist fights, often with good friends; must prove their masculinity. Parties greatly in favor, but behavior is unlikely to be decorous. Able to use telephone competently. Teacher's opinions and ideas very important. Rapid alternation between "good" and "bad" behavior.

INTELLECTUAL GROWTH AND ACTIVITIES. Commonly uses upward of 2,500 words. Delights in imaginative dramatic play; may carry on long conversations with imaginary person after going to bed. May believe radio characters are real. Knows comparative value of the common coins. Knows own address, parents' names, how to cross street. From now up to the teens, adventure programs on radio and television much liked. Name-calling, vulgar talk common. Belief in Santa Claus may be fading. Knows number combinations making up to 10. The beginning steps in learning to read greatly delight the child.

YOUR CHILD BETWEEN SEVEN AND EIGHT

PHYSICAL GROWTH AND SKILLS. Adds from three to five pounds weight yearly. Slow, regular growth in height. "Nervous habits" like nail-biting, tongue-sucking, scratching, pulling at ear common, but show no increase from six to twelve; more frequent in girls than in boys. Less impulsive and boisterous in actions than at six. Jumping rope, hop-scotch, and jacks popular with girls.

SOCIAL PROGRESS. Recognition of property rights sketchy. Competition in school, at play, begins to be present. From now on becomes more interested in dressing and acting like his friends. Choice of friends uninfluenced by social or economic status. Demands of the environment make learning to use money desirable. When angry at parents may toy with idea he is not their child. Awareness of differences between his home and those of others increasing.

INTELLECTUAL GROWTH AND ACTIVITIES.   Child's ability to make things is not up to his ideas of what he would like to do. Can count by 1's, 2's, 5's, and 10's. Can grasp the basic ideas of addition and sub-traction. Can tell time; sometimes knows what month it is. Ability to run errands, make purchases, take responsibility generally on the increase from now on. Often argues about what he is expected to do. Curiosity about differences between the sexes and how babies come indicates increasing interest in reality, and suggests importance of giving truthful information.

YOUR CHILD BETWEEN EIGHT AND NINE

PHYSICAL GROWTH AND SKILLS.   Ten or eleven permanent teeth. Growing interest in games requiring co-ordination of small muscles (hitting moving target, shooting marbles, catching with one hand, etc.) . Ability to write progressing, but fine muscle work is still diffi-cult and taxing. Can swim well, if there has been opportunity for learning. Can bicycle and roller skate expertly. Bathes self, but sketchily.

SOCIAL PROGRESS.   Evidence of modesty may be increasing, due probably to social pressures. Group projects become absorbing, but child is not yet entirely capable of team play. Recognition of prop-erty rights well established if training has been sound. Manners often better away from home than at home. Is becoming more selec-tive in choice of friends. Doll and paper-doll play mimics family life.

INTELLECTUAL GROWTH AND ACTIVITIES.   Begins to be interested in what happened in the distant past (likes to make Indian costumes, utensils, etc.) . Fairy tales are great favorites with both boys and girls. Can tell day of month and year. Can make change for small amounts. Begins to read the funnies, a favorite occupation from now on. Listening to radio one of main interests, but begins to be skeptical of "realness" of programs. Sense of humor marked, especially in bright children. Experience has opened the door to interest in the world at large. Far-off places, ways of communication now have real meaning.

YOUR CHILD BETWEEN NINE AND TEN

PHYSICAL GROWTH AND SKILLS.   Slow growth in height. Last wrist bone appears in girls. Teeth straightening, if needed, can be begun. Can care for physical needs like baths, hair combing, etc. Uses tools increasingly well. Many children at this time and later need more rest and sleep than they get, because constantly "on the go," and interested in so many different kinds of play. Disdainful of danger, but gets into plenty of it.

SOCIAL PROGRESS.   Sex differences in play interests begin to be marked. More different kinds of play engaged in than ever again. Antagonism between sexes noticeable for next several years; longer for boys than girls. "Gang" and club enthusiasm noticeable, with hostility toward other groups; exclusion an important feature of clubs, which are short-lived. Visits alone away from home; may go to camp. Some of spontaneity of relations with adults may be giving place to reticence, even to hostility, shown by having secrets.

INTELLECTUAL GROWTH AND ACTIVITIES.   Can grasp easier multiplication and division facts. Differences in boys' and girls' reading interests begin to be noticeable. Bright children begin to use card indexes at library and read full-length books. Begins to have friends outside immediate neighborhood. Interest in fantasy and make-believe on the decline. Comedians, news broadcasters, drama in general more and more appreciated on radio; boys like programs of greater violence than girls. Interest in how things are made, produced, etc., is increasing. If interest in a special field—science, nature, or mechanics—has developed this may begin to crowd out some other play activities.

YOUR CHILD BETWEEN TEN AND ELEVEN

PHYSICAL GROWTH AND SKILLS.   Rapid increase in weight may begin in girls. Has fourteen or sixteen permanent teeth. Willing to work hard at acquiring physical skills; emphasis is on excellence of performance of physical feats. Interest in hazardous activities points up the need for safe places to play. Boys more active and rough in games than girls.

SOCIAL PROGRESS. Organized and competitive games more and more prominent. Team-work, submission to fixed rules in play now possible. Occasional privacy becomes important; a room of one's own, secret caches for personal property are greatly desired.

INTELLECTUAL GROWTH AND ACTIVITIES. Ability to plan ahead is increasing. Gathering factual information important, especially among boys. Uses numbers beyond 100 with understanding. Begins to understand and use simple fractions. Able to discuss problems, to see different sides of questions. Interested in other people's ideas. Likes to set up rules and bylaws for clubs. Steadily growing capacity for thought and reasoning makes creative companionship with parents ever more desirable.

YOUR CHILD BETWEEN ELEVEN AND TWELVE

PHYSICAL GROWTH AND SKILLS. Last wrist bone appears in boys. Girls falling behind boys somewhat in physical strength and endurance; can no longer compete with them on equal terms. Menstruation occurs in a few girls. May be strongly individual in liking for different games and play involving motor skills.

SOCIAL PROGRESS. Membership in clubs and groups increasing in importance. Enjoy taking part in school, neighborhood, and community affairs, like "drives." Team games are very popular. Shyness, if present, may be becoming more noticeable.

INTELLECTUAL GROWTH AND ACTIVITIES. Begins to be critical of own artistic products. Can understand human reproduction. Understands need of care in using towels, glasses, public toilets; also importance of using handkerchief to cover coughs and sneezes. May for some time have been interested in earning money. Small earnings will allow him some independence in spending in connection with hobbies.

YOUR CHILD BETWEEN TWELVE AND THIRTEEN

PHYSICAL GROWTH AND SKILLS. Games involving whole body activity, like run-sheep-run, on the decline. Capable of carrying out good personal hygiene habits. Muscles have grown to represent 40 to 45 per cent of body weight. Parts of the hip bone unite in girls, Has twenty-four or twenty-six permanent teeth. May show self-consciousness about trying to learn new feats of physical skill. If too unlike mates in size or maturity, boy or girl may be conscious of awkwardness; girls may be quite conscious of their maturing figures. Choice of activities more and more influenced by individual preferences. Many, from now on, tend to be spectators at many games and sports.

SOCIAL PROGRESS. Social contacts constantly widening; independence in choice of friends more noticeable. If conditions surrounding child are unfavorable, beginnings of juvenile delinquency may occur. Lack of experience and practice in motor skills may have resulted in child's becoming an onlooker instead of an active participant in games. As puberty approaches, child may crave periods of being alone. Boys admire other boys who are skillful, bold, and daring. Girls, to be looked up to, must "conform," be feminine and ladylike.

INTELLECTUAL GROWTH AND ACTIVITIES. Can add and subtract decimals. Ability to reason is markedly on the increase. Understands abstract ideas like "justice," "honesty," etc. Can postpone satisfactions; emotional outbursts when his desires are thwarted are becoming infrequent. Similarity of interests and mental age increasingly influence the choice of friends. Interest constantly growing in the culture in which they live—the contributions of the past, how science affects it, etc. Awareness of moral codes (shown by interest in living up to those embodied in Camp Fire or Scout work). Religious interests prominent in many children, but religious ideas usually still accepted uncritically. As adolescence approaches, sympathetic understanding by parents is of prime importance to successful adjustment.

Physical Developments During Middle Childhood

BETWEEN early childhood and adolescence comes middle childhood, a time when physical growth jogs along at a pretty even pace, without the rapid gains that came earlier and will come again later. It is a period when parents can breathe a sigh of relief, too, for it is a relatively safe and healthy period. The time when the childhood diseases are most dangerous is past. Colds, broken arms and legs, and infections are bothersome, but parents put in fewer anxious days and nights over sickness than they did when their children were younger. Even the accident rate for this age group is strikingly lower than for others. It is less than half as high as for the under-five's and those between the ages of fifteen and twenty-four. This "breathing spell" between the rapid growth periods of childhood and adolescence enables parents to get off on the right foot before the coming of the teens brings a whole new range of concerns.

It is a time when a child is all set for a great deal of learning. His mind is on the stretch. He can grasp many kinds of new ideas. He is very able physically. His muscles are well controlled, so that he can become skilled in a great variety of physical activities, such as swimming, milking a cow, playing a musical instrument, or batting a ball.

What is going on with respect to growth and how does it affect our handling of the child? For one thing, body build differences that may have been hidden by chubbiness while children were little begin to show up. Characteristic family tendencies toward broadness and stockiness or slenderness with accompanying long bones now become apparent.

GROWTH IN HEIGHT AND WEIGHT

In judging children's growth we must consider the great differences in children's types. So much depends upon biological and family background that it is useless to compare a child with another of his age, to see if he is growing properly. Instead, we need to compare

526

him with himself, at an earlier period, or with other chilldren who resemble him in general body type. There are slender, narrowly built children, and broader, thicker children; children who are small-boned and children who are large-boned. There are those who will always be "big for their age," others will always seem small, though this lack of conformity is right for them. Children who are tall when young keep right on being tall for their age, with temporary exceptions.

Growth in weight does not follow as regular a pattern as in height, because of the many things that influence it, such as illnesses, the presence or absence of nourishing foods, and of emotional conditions that affect a child's well-being. Because these are things over which his parents have a good deal of control, a child's gains in weight should be watched more closely than his gains in height. What he eats while he is growing will be used first for his immediate energy needs, and next for growth in length, for his bony development. What he adds in flesh will be an individual matter of his having the right foods and other conditions, like happiness, that contribute to good nutrition. The kind of weight a child puts on is important; a child may look comparatively thin, but have excellently developed muscles. Another may be fat without being well-nourished. In general, children add about five pounds a year in weight during this period.

Girls are, from birth up to about the age of nine or ten, both shorter and lighter than boys. From about ten to fourteen or fifteen, however, this is reversed, as girls begin their preadolescent spurt in height and weight earlier than boys. Then the boys get ahead again, and stay there.

At every age girls are more mature than boys. Their teeth appear earlier, their organs mature more rapidly, and the endocrine changes that make them into adolescents start earlier. By age twelve they are about two years ahead of boys in general development.

DIFFERENCES IN THE BODY'S GROWTH

The parts of the body do not grow evenly and regularly. Each has its own growth pattern. Some parts are much larger in proportion than others, from the earliest years. At six, the head is about as large as it ever will be. At this time it makes up about one-sixth of the entire body length, while in adulthood its proportion is one eighth of the body length, the difference in proportion being made up mostly by the greater growth of the legs. The trunk of the body is long in proportion to the arms and legs. The latter, especially the legs, have a lot of growing to do, as they are relatively short in early life.

The nervous system, of which the brain makes up the largest part, grows very rapidly at first, slows down decidedly by the age of six, and is about completed by the end of the period we are concerned with. Just the opposite is true of the genital organs, which grow very little during the years from six to twelve, but begin to speed up rapidly during the teens. Only one part of the body is strikingly more developed now than later, the lymph glands, which gradually subside during adolescense. This partly explains the great frequency of enlarged tonsils and adenoids in early and middle childhood.

GROWTH OF MUSCLES, BONES AND TEETH

Children's muscles are developing rapidly during the school years. Evidence of this is the popularity of strength-testing feats, and the skills that take bodily endurance. By the age of twelve, well over a third of the body weight is due to muscle tissue.

The bony growth of children is very interesting, although it is so well hidden that we seldom give much thought to it. The development of bones that underlies changes in size is brought about by a gradual shift from soft, cartilaginous tissues to firm and hard, or ossified, structures. The bones both support and protect. They form the framework of the body ,and are bound together by the muscles. Bones grow both in thickness and at the ends, where cartilage is being gradually added and calcification, or hardening, goes on. A child's body contains more separate bones than an adult's, for bones fuse together as growth proceeds.

The greater softness of children's bones means that their bodies are more flexible than adults', which has both advantages and disadvantages. Children can make movements impossible to grown-ups, but the lack of firmness in their bones means that care must be taken to see that pressure does not cause deformed bones. The reason we hear so much about providing well-shaped shoes that are large enough to allow room for the growth of the feet is because a child's foot bones may be permanently harmed by being crowded into short or narrow shoes that distort the bones. Even the pressure due to socks that do not fit properly is bad. Those children are fortunate who live where they can go barefoot safely.

For the same reason, good posture is of immense importance. Children and young adolescents should not do manual work that means using the same set of muscles for long periods. Many of the jobs that children do, like transplanting and weeding, cramp and strain the body. They prevent its free use as a whole, so necessary while bone growth is going on.

Poor habits of sitting while reading or studying, with the shoulders bent; bad ways of standing, so that one hip or shoulder is higher than the other; sleeping slumped into awkward positions because of a poor mattress or bedspring, all these things should be prevented. Children's beds should be selected with great care. They should have firm mattresses and good springs. Children should never sleep on make-shift beds, or use old ones relegated to the children's rooms because they are not good enough for adults.

Extreme fatigue has a very bad effect on body posture; a child's need of frequent rest, change of position, and exercise of the whole body is plain to be seen. The "activity program" in modern schools is an attempt to meet these needs among others.

To understand what is going on in the child's bones we need only look at X-ray pictures of the way the bones change from year to year. From having in infancy no bones in the wrist hard enough to show up by X-ray, a child develops a large number of bones by the age of nine, and these will harden and fuse together as he becomes more mature. The same process is going on in other parts of the body, as well.

The development of the bony part of the child's body is closely connected with his general physiological maturity, which means that of all his organs. Not until children reach the "right" age of skeletal development do they become sexually mature. Thus, a girl who menstruates early, by eleven or twelve, will also be found to have reached a greater "skeletal age" than the majority of girls of her chronological age. Children who are large and well-developed are likely also to be well-advanced in their bony development.

The teeth are, of course, part of the bony structure of the body, and are important both to a child's health and his appearance. We need a great deal more knowledge about the teeth, and how to keep them from decaying. However, if we did as well as we know how to do, at the present stage of our knowledge, we would be able to boast of progress far beyond what we are making.

We have long known the importance of the sixth-year molars, but we still let these four teeth become diseased or decayed in the mouths of thousands upon thousands of children because we have not all realized that these are not "baby" but permanent teeth. They often come in before any of the baby teeth fall out, and their importance in the jaw as the guides that determine the position of the later-coming teeth goes unnoticed. Even the teeth that drop out, and so are called "deciduous," are important enough to warrant being carefully cared for and filled. If they decay and are pulled long before the new teeth push to the surface of the jaw, these latter teeth may not come in straight because the shape of the jaw has been affected.

As the permanent teeth are forming in the jaw long before they erupt, the child's diet must contain plenty of good building material, especially phosphorus and calcium, and the vitamins. Because the phosphorus and calcium in foods cannot be utilized by the body unless vitamin D is also present, the use of fish liver oil should be continued during the growing years. Foods that give much exercise to the jaws, that have to be well chewed, are helpful to jaw development. It is almost impossible to find tooth decay among the older natives on the Pribilof Islands, and very easy to find it among their children, who have been introduced to our soft, ready-prepared foods and sweets.

There are great individual differences in children as to the age when their permanent teeth erupt. Also, girls' come earlier than boys'. By the age of eight or nine, most children have ten or eleven permanent teeth. By the time they are ten and eleven they acquire fourteen to sixteen of their second teeth. But by the age of twelve, most children have their full set of teeth, with the exception of the wisdom teeth that appear in very late adolescence. If there is a tendency for the teeth to be crowded (impacted) the wisdom teeth may cause trouble when they come in.

When the upper and lower jaws do not grow evenly, so-called "malocclusion" or poor fitting together of the upper and lower teeth may happen. There are occasional cases where the teeth are so irregular that chewing is interfered with, which in turn affects nutrition. If either the lower or upper jaw tends to stick out because the lower teeth overlap the upper in front or the upper teeth protrude too far beyond the lower, the child should be examined frequently by a dentist specially trained in this field, known as orthodontia. Sometimes the condition will correct itself as the child grows; in other cases it may be necessary to have special treatment in order that a child's appearance may be improved. Before the jaw has become completely calcified this is a fairly easy procedure; later on, little or nothing can be done.

The contours of the face change quite appreciably during adolescence, when the features take on their adult proportions. Then the nose may not be so prominent or the forehead so rounded. Many a child who has disapproved of his profile finds it changing for the better. But when a child between six and twelve has a chin that recedes noticeably, or lips that cannot be closed because of protruding teeth, no pains should be spared to make him feel happier about his appearance, even though this may mean rather long-drawn-out orthodontia. If it is an expense his family can't afford, effort should be made to find a clinic that does such work free. The discomfort and the conspicuousness of braces are in many cases offset by the child's feeling that the end results will be worth while.

Although some children with the best of diets have poor teeth, it is still worth while to provide foods that are known tooth-builders. To some extent, good and poor teeth seem to run in families. Until more is known, we cannot insure a child's having good teeth by feeding him the "right" foods, having him brush his teeth, and go to a dentist regularly. But these things undoubtedly help.

VARYING ASPECTS OF BOYS' AND GIRLS' GROWTH

Because girls go through their preadolescent spurt in growth earlier than boys, many of the girls begin to approach their full height by the age of twelve or thirteen, the twelfth year being the period during which most girls gain the most in both weight and height. Among the first parts of the body to reach adult size are the hands and feet. The girl of thirteen may be startled to find herself having to buy shoes that are as large as or even larger than her mother's. She will take comfort in knowing that her body will "grow up" to her hands and feet. Many an older boy and girl would have been saved a lot of distress if someone had taken pains to explain to them the unevenness of growth that makes them feel awkward and conspicuous. A twelve-year-old girl who is taller than any of the boys in her room at school needs to be reassured that in two or three years' time she will not seem so tall because they will have caught up to her. Boys and girls who go through a stage of being extra plump need to be told that this will pass, and that a few years hence they may be among the more slender of their age group.

When a child is unusually tall and promises always to be so, he may be made to feel pride in his height by a tactful build-up of the advantages of being tall. The father of one very tall girl always took pains to point out any tall woman they saw who dressed tastefully and carried herself well. The girl, impressed by her father's admiration for tall women, was glad she was going to be one.

Of course many a girl who reaches her full height early will not seem tall later on, when the slower-maturing girls catch up to her. It is well to remember this, and reassure the girl who for a while outstrips her classmates, who are near her in age.

Although smallness goes with the femininity often thought of as an asset in women, girls who are short hate to have their smallness remarked on. It would be a good idea for both parents and teachers to keep from making personal remarks about children's variations in either height or weight.

THE SHORT BOY

The small-for-his-age boy may be worried for fear he will always be short. This is not likely to be a matter of much concern in the six to twelve group, because so few boys will yet have begun to grow fast. But there will be an occasional small boy who, judging by family tendencies, will probably remain relatively small, whatever his age. In view of the many ways in which some short men try to make up for being decidedly below the average in height, it is just as well to think about this boy's problem well ahead of time, and try to see that he has many sources of satisfaction to offset the limiting feature.

Just as it makes a child self-conscious to have constant comments made on how much he has grown, so it brings on worry and feelings of inadequacy to be reminded of his small size. If he has skills or gifts that he can be proud of, he will have less time to spend bemoaning his shortness. In most cases, of course, even boys who have been small through their elementary school years make such quick strides in growth in the teens that by the time they are sixteen or seventeen they have forgotten that they ever were worried about their height. However, this is one of the big secret fears of many young boys.

APPROACHING PUBERTY

Few boys show signs of approaching puberty by the age of twelve, but quite a number of girls will give evidence of coming sexual maturity. The development of the breasts and calves of the legs is one of the more obvious evidences. A widening of the pelvis is going on, too, preparing the girl for child-bearing later.

The tendency toward a slightly earlier age of menstruation, observed nowadays, is presumed to be related to the better nutrition of children in recent years.

Sex differences in strength, endurance, and motor ability are less marked from six to twelve than later, but girls are already beginning to show that they are less adapted to athletic types of activity. The physical endurance of girls is less than that of boys. They tire more easily, and take longer to recover from the effects of physical exertion like running. By the age of fourteen or fifteen, girls have reached the limit of their gains in motor performance, although there are great differences, of course, between individual girls. A "boyish" type of build has some influence on a girl's physical prowess.

The amount of encouragement and practice children have strongly affects their use of their bodies in activity. A girl who is not urged to learn bodily skills during middle childhood is less and less likely to learn them as she gets older. Not only does motor performance begin to decline in the teens but social attitudes do not stress athletic games and feats for girls. But girls who have early become enthusiastic about sports often go on to remarkable achievement. Learning to figure-skate, to play tennis or volley ball, to ride or to swim must come at a time when enthusiasm for physical activity is high if girls are to make full use of their physical powers.

Boys Will Be Boys – 'Sissy,' 'Bully,' or 'Good Sport'

NOTHING is worse, in a boy's mind, than to be called a "sissy." A child's urge to grow up is sometimes at war with his parents' urge to keep him under their thumb. His efforts to establish himself may be in part rebellion at this.

What an inescapable stage that of fist fights seems to be! And how parents deplore it! But fighting is a way of proving that you are no longer a baby, no longer dependent on "Mama." Strength and toughness are traditional possessions of boys and men. Tommy has probably been told dozens of times that "boys don't cry, they are brave."

How better can he show his toughness than by having fights? He has to impress himself on other boys in *some* way. The ones who can run fastest, climb highest, throw a ball the farthest are likely to be the most admired. The one who shows he can "take it" in a fight is respected by his companions.

Then there is the fact that some bigger boys "pick on" small ones in order to show they are smarter and tougher, and in general prove their superiority. The small ones pick on each other. The more secure and sure of himself a child feels, the less his need of asserting himself in this way; but most boys, even those who have little or no impulse to boast of physical supremacy, will be called upon sooner or later to hold their own, and show that they are unafraid physically.

A child who has been forbidden by his parents to fight is in a dilemma. If he obeys his parents he will be considered a coward; if he disregards them he will be scolded at home.

If we can remember that this primitive way of settling disputes is a phase that passes quickly, and that it takes stout courage to stand up to physical pain, we shall be less likely to set up conflict in our child's mind by showing that we are disturbed by fighting.

Only occasionally does it seem wise for parents to step in. If they constantly put their oar in they may make their child suffer much more than he would from any physical hurt. It will not be to his advantage to learn to lean on someone else's help in settling matters, he should take care of himself. Even in handling the case of the typical "bully" who habitually lords it over children younger or weaker than himself, it is as necessary to find the reasons for the offending child's behavior as it is to protect the others. To stop him puts only a temporary end to the trouble. To probe into the reasons why he wants this kind of relationship is more constructive; for by uncovering the roots of the bully's problem it may be possible to do away with the *cause* of his behavior.

The child who is popular in school is one who is somewhat aggressive, in the socially approved sense of the word. This implies parents who aren't so dominating that they have flattened all the life out of their child. Those who are popular in a group have been found to be the ones who are enthusiastic and lively. They stand out because they have strong personalities.

But in child-to-child relations other things count, as well. Children in the middle grades who are good looking, who look neat, who are happy, friendly, and smiling are apt to be well liked. The latter qualities probably make more difference than looks.

Children who play fair, who are "good sports," are welcomed and liked by other children. Parents have a lot to do with developing this kind of behavior. If we take a child's part on every occasion we deny him the chance to learn to take small defeats and unfairness as a part of life. Sooner or later he is going to run up against situations beyond his control where he will have to accept unfair treatment. He should be able to do so without sulking or self-pity.

Parents can build up a child's belief in himself. Each time he becomes good at something his ability to succeed at other things is strengthened.

"THE GANG"

By the age of nine or ten, children want something more than to be accepted as a member of the herd. They begin to band together in small clubs or gangs or packs. It adds to a child's fun and safety and prestige to have a bunch to back him up. The Boy Scout movement recognizes this impulse; their program makes something wholesome and constructive out of it. But the fact that there is a need for Cub Scout Packs suggests that the twelve-year-old age of entrance into scouting was set too late—later than the appearance of the strong desire to belong to an intimate group.

The word "gang" has come to have such a sinister meaning that we hesitate to use it in speaking of the activities of children. But it does convey a sense of solidarity that such a word as "group" or "club" doesn't quite carry; also, this stage of wanting to run together in a pack is something so normal that the term "gang age" has been used to describe it.

Neighborhood gangs fall into hoodlumism only when their natural desire for joint activity has nothing wholesome to feed on. The spirit back of the gang can be used to promote team play, good sportsmanship, and forgetfulness of self. It is up to parents to see that there are opportunities for safe and sane and legitimate activities. To go on hikes with a knapsack lunch, to scoop out a dugout in the back yard, or fence off a corner of the attic or basement that children can call their own, satisfies some craving so deep that we had better go along with it rather than to try to thwart it.

There should be some sort of medal for those mothers who, never having been boys themselves, still have enough imagination to allow their boys to use their own rooms pretty much as they like. Boys need a place where their friends feel free to gather, where no one will interfere with the radio parts that are so precious, even if they are strewn in what seems hit-or-miss fashion. A father who sacrifices his chance to sleep late on a holiday in order to drive his son's gang up-river for a night's camping trip is going to have that son rise up and call him blessed.

Girls do not feel the urge toward strenuous athletic activities quite as strongly as boys. They are more likely to be interested in putting on plays, in painting, or in other things that take highly skilled hands. They like to bicycle, and hike, play baseball, and take part in swimming matches. But they are apt to be more interested in the social than in the competitive side of sports.

Of course, there are wide individual variations in the play interests of children. Some girls may go in for strenuous activity almost entirely and some boys may prefer quieter games. Individual differences in play activities are often greater than the differences between boys and girls.

Play Prepares the Child for Life

PLAY is the stuff of which a child's life is made. It uses every ounce of his energy. It encourages his imagination. It develops skills of both body and mind. It brings about understanding, warmth, and sympathy toward others.

How to compete, how to take hard knocks, how to win gracefully; when to assert oneself and when to forget self-interest are all learned through play. Perseverance, how to struggle through to a desired end, is as much a part of play as it is of work.

Play offers healing for hurts and sadness. It breaks down tension and releases pent-up urges toward self-expression. Play is the working partner of growth, for activity is as vital to growth as food and sleep.

The far-reaching significance of children's play has only lately been understood. Unless the deep-lying impulses satisfied by play are allowed to express themselves in childhood, adult life suffers. Some men and women are never able to take part freely in the life around them; they are stiff and lonely because they don't know how to mix with others. They can't lose themselves in spontaneous fun. Somehow or other their urges toward expression in play were denied the chance to come to the surface in childhood.

THE CHILD'S PLAY HAS MEANING

The attitudes and feelings that children reveal in their play are full of meaning. A boy who plays unfairly may be reflecting his feeling of having been treated so. A child playing with dolls may act out undercurrents of jealousy of another child shown in no other way; or such play may offer a mother lightning flashes of insight into her methods of discipline. The scoldings a child receives are often passed on to dolls or toy animals. Unsuspected feelings about parents sometimes come to light in this way, too.

A child's play is his occupation, just as surely as keeping a store or driving an engine is his father's. If he is able to use all of himself in his play, the change-over to whole-souled enjoyment of work happens without his having to cross any bridge. Tommy, the boy, intent on building with his blocks or perfecting his batting, turns into Thomas, the man, deep in blueprints for a building, or training a track-team.

ADEQUATE SPACE FOR PLAY

A "must" for play is space. There must be room for running games like tag and kick-the-can, hide and seek, and pom-pom-pullaway; the more children the more room they need. Up to the age of nine, children do not—nor should they—go more than a few blocks to a playground, but the community is rare that plans with this in mind. If we had built our cities with the idea of thwarting children's play we could not have done a more thorough job. No wonder children of school age have many accidents, when the streets are their only playgrounds.

The far greater freedom country children have for play is some-what offset by the lack of outside companionship that so often goes with it. But there are incomparable advantages in being able to "whoop" and "holler" and make use of what nature so lavishly pro-vides in the way of play materials—brooks, and woods, rocks, caves, and wild creatures.

Up to school age, children are content with one or two playmates, but from then on they play in larger groups. There must be chasers and chased when you play cowboy, Indians, cops and robbers. To be able to be a leader one must have a group to lead.

HOW PLAY INTERESTS CHANGE

Mostly, the activities of the first school years are activities of the whole body; but as control of arm and leg and back muscles is gained, play that makes use of finer coordination becomes more com-mon—marbles, jacks, handicraft of all sorts. With growth of the mind comes interest in games that involve quick-wittedness and memory—card games, word games, and checkers. Parents who play such games with their children are doing more than add to family jollity and harmony; they are broadening their children's vocabularies, help-ing them get a "head start" in arithmetic, and giving them practice in the art of good sportsmanship.

Children become more and more interested in turning out finished products. The model airplane, the home-made boat that really "works," the doll clothes, all put together clumsily at first, become gradually more skilled and handsome. If children are to become clever and versatile in the use of their hands, they must have tools and materials to work with, a place to work, and "how to do it" books to refer to. One mother, in a small apartment, for weeks clambered over her son's pushmobile as it was being put together in the kitchen and counted her inconvenience well worth while.

INTERESTS OF BOYS AND GIRLS

Differences in play interests between boys and girls need more study. Up to about eight or nine interests seem to be fairly similar, but after that time there is less play involving both sexes.

But no boy is *all* "boy," any more than any girl is all "girl." There is a good deal of overlapping of so-called masculine and feminine traits in the sexes. This shows up early in such things as play interests, and later in preferences as to school subjects and vocational choices.

The generally known tendency toward superiority in males in such things as size, strength, and motor ability leads us to expect of boys the kind of activities that go with these physical characteristics, and to expect different behavior in girls. Our social customs tend to encourage patterns of behavior in each sex that conform to our knowledge of physical differences. But it is important to keep in mind the mixture of femaleness and maleness in each child, and not to allow ourselves to have preconceived notions of what boys and girls are like.

The "tomboy" girl, who used to be disapproved of, is no longer frowned on; we recognize now that the value of lively activity and bodily freedom is as great for girls as for boys. For girls to play what used to be called "boys' games" encourages good feeling and understanding between the two sexes. But when an older girl seems to be making a protest against her feminine role in life by insisting on always wearing overalls, having a very short haircut, or turning up her nose at mixed parties, it should be a signal to us of the need of discovering why she is not following the more natural and usual course; for with the approach of puberty, most girls look forward to their feminine privileges of fripperies and cosmetics.

If her experiences with girls have not been happy, we must somehow fill in the gap between her interests and those of other girls. If she is trying to live up to what she thinks will please her father, who, having no son, calls her "my boy," and is proud of her masculine behavior, we must try to get him to see daylight. When sexual maturity is reached, girls' play interests change very decidedly. Dolls are forgotten. In place of the earlier interests, whatever they were, comes an interest in parties and boys. Girls are maturing earlier than they used to, so parents should be prepared for their daughters' possible menstruation while they still tend to think of them as little girls. We can't, and don't want to, hold back growth, so we had better take in our stride the changes that make girls interested in boys, in movie stars, in lipstick—and in the privilege of shutting the family out of their room on occasion.

Girls quite often go through a time of wishing they were boys— few boys return the compliment. Mothers whose daughters grow up feeling that being a woman is a privilege thereby proclaim their own good adjustment. Some girls develop a belligerent feeling that the world is against women. There are inequalities, it is true. But if a girl has such a happy childhood that she never stops to think of wanting to be anyone but herself she is likely to be more contented in adult life than one who is full of protest.

GROUP SPORTS AND TEAM PLAY

More and more, as children approach the teens, they enjoy organized team play. This means, of course, that they are becoming "socialized"; that they can think of the good of the group, and not merely of themselves. Earlier, they wanted to win personally; now having their "side" or team win looms large. Hockey, basketball, swimming, and football all give a chance for the development of this desirable spirit. Being exposed to physical pain, undergoing disappointment and, sometimes, unfair treatment are accepted as all a part of the game.

Children differ widely in the degree of their interest in group sports—or in sports at all, for that matter. A boy or girl who doesn't care much for team play is not necessarily a "poor sport" on that account. He or she may be developing the same quality of being able to "take it" by competing with a single partner, as at tennis, or by pushing himself to the limit in high-jumping or on skis.

There is no reason for urging a child into something we think he *ought* to be interested in provided he has enough variety in his play to be gaining from it physically, and isn't staying out of things on account of some hidden fear or feeling of inadequacy. Each child should be his own judge of what and how he wants to play—again provided he does not retreat from the everyday contacts that seem necessary to getting along with people. But it must not be forgotten that many children, left to their own devices, without a good example, are very limited and cramped in their interests. Parents and other adults can do a lot toward stimulating enjoyable interests by providing companionship and equipment.

SPECIAL INTERESTS THAT SATISFY A CRAVING FOR NEW EXPERIENCES

From the age of about nine on, children engage in fewer different play activities. As they begin to have special interests, each thing that absorbs them will have to be given more time, so some things will drop out. Swimming, making a collection of butterflies, drawing cartoons—anything that becomes a hobby—will crowd out other forms of play.

This means that if we want children to have a rich, full life we will see to it that they have chances early for all sorts of experimentation. They are notorious for sudden enthusiasms, for scattering their energies over many activities that to adults often seem to have little or no value.

Back of these spurts of interest, many of which vanish as unexpectedly as they arise, is, of course, the child's intense curiosity and eagerness to learn about a great many different things. He wants to try things for himself, to explore, to experiment. He is no longer satisfied merely by pretending and imagining, he wants the real thing: the model plane a boy makes must really fly; the stove a girl cooks on must really bake.

In his craving for experience with the real, his "hunger for hardpan," he comes to grief fairly often, or makes trouble. In her curiosity to see what will happen when the mercury in a thermometer reaches the top, Jean holds a lighted match under it. Tom wants to try out walking a plank fifteen feet above the ground, and his mother suddenly looks out of the window to see him teetering on the beam of a new house next door.

Every mother can give dozens of illustrations of the folly and mischief this curiosity for real experience has led her children into. Fathers tend to take a lighter view: they don't have to clean up the mess as often, perhaps! They more often, too, take a longer view. Through having other interests, they have gained perspective, and are not quite so apt to be overanxious as mothers.

Nothing takes the place of real experiences, whether it be with mud (making dams), wind (flying kites), height (climbing trees), machinery (repairing a bicycle), stoves (cooking a meal), or paint (see Tom Sawyer).

All of these experiences should be as freely open to girls as to boys. Healthy comradeship now lays the foundation for future understanding. Douglas is not going to turn up his nose at Debbie as a "silly" girl because she plays with paper dolls if she also shares his passionate interest in raising puppies. Patty is not going to dismiss boys as "rough" if she has learned to admire and hold her own with them on the neighborhood baseball nine, or if Peter has helped her fly a kite.

Parents are often unnecessarily bothered because their children plunge into something hastily, only to drop it just as suddenly. This usually happens just about the time their father and mother have begun to take the new interest seriously. Jackie spends every spare minute wood carving with a paring knife, only to lose his enthusiasm by the time his father gets around to buying him a set of carving tools. Mildred is all excitement over tap dancing, but her interest peters out when Joan moves away and she has to go to take her lessons alone.

These are typical of situations that could be multiplied endlessly. The parent is disappointed because the child "doesn't stick to what he undertakes," especially if money and effort have been put into the project. The child is unable to say why his interest has melted away. Conflict results.

There are a number of things to be considered. First of all, perhaps the child has got what he needed out of the experience. A child who has clamored for a chemistry set and who, after the first few weeks of feverish interest seems to have forgotten its existence may have got, in his added fame among the neighborhood boys, something of far greater value to him than further smelly experiments.

It is not to be expected that every path that entices a child will be followed to its end. In the course of exploring it, some more attractive bypath may open up. A girl who is in the seventh heaven over her chance to take part in a play may come to see that designing scenery is more to her liking. A boy who pleads for a printing press for the neighborhood gang's newspaper may wind up by being **interested** only in writing stories for it.

Childhood is a time for trying out many activities. Some of them will be only a flash in the pan. But what does that matter if the child is busy, interested, and learning? The variety of interests he has is even some measure of his intelligence. Only intense curiosity is going to make it possible for children to persist and insist enough to explore a wide range of interests. Instead of being willing to take up the first leisure occupation at hand, such intelligent children are going to be all set to put their own ideas to work when they have spare moments.

"But," some thoughtful parents say, "isn't it bad for a child not to finish what he sets out to do? Won't he learn habits of fickleness if he drifts from one thing to another? It's only by persevering, even if our enthusiasm has flagged, that we learn to be stable."

IS PERSISTENCE ALWAYS TO BE DESIRED?

Of course children must learn persistence at hard and sometimes uninteresting things. But don't their school work and home duties afford them plenty of practice in this? Perhaps in leisure-time projects we ought not to limit them too much; we don't want them to lose interest in taking flyers in may kinds of venture. Surely an adult needn't feel guilty if after taking up bowling as a hobby he decides it doesn't appeal to him, and tries golf instead. How are children, with much less basis for judgment than adults, going to hit upon those things that are to have lasting interest unless they have chances to experiment and dabble?

An eight-year-old, fired by the skill of a friend, wants to take piano lessons. How can we tell without a few try-out lessons whether it is worth while to go on? If, after conscientious effort, a child who seems to lack the musical interest or dexterity of the hands necessary to real progress wants to stop, who can say that what she has learned hasn't been worth the time and money? If nothing else, she has learned to respect the musician, because she now has a notion as to the tremendous number of hours and concentrated effort that are back of good performance. She has also learned something about how to read music, and some musical terms that add to her vocabulary. Most important of all, she knows her own lack of interest in it and can move to something else.

A child who tends to scatter his energies so much that none of his efforts come to anything certainly needs help. One way of curbing such waste is to let the child feel the result of his too-hasty and short-lived enthusiasms, by bearing the expense himself. Such a plan works out better if based on an allowance. Jim's craze for collecting comic books suddenly vanishes in favor of making a glider. That the money he's been squandering would have gone a long way toward buying the materials for the glider will be all too evident even to Jim.

Letting a child learn by experience is very hard to do. From our vantage point we see farther ahead than can the child, so we tend to decide abruptly—"No, that's nonsense!" or "We know best," instead of letting the consequences of a child's decision come home, as it occasionally must, to roost.

CHILDREN SHOULD HAVE PETS

Few of us look back on our childhood without tender memories of some pet. It may have been anything from a crow to a raccoon, if you lived in the country; if a city apartment cramped your style it may have had to be a canary, or a turtle that lived in a box.

Having close friendships with a living creature kindles sympathy and tenderness in the child. It also makes it possible for him to express affection without fear of embarrassment. A boy of eight would be laughed at if he were always hugging his father or mother, but no one criticizes the caresses he showers on his dog. Pets often show their love, and seldom, if at all, their disapproval. This is one of the great things a pet does for a child—it accepts him and doesn't find fault with him.

Finding suitable reading material about all those lovely, wiggly things that children bring home in cans and jars and pockets, should be our cue, instead of saying, "Don't bring that slimy thing into the kitchen!"

How much responsibility can and should children take for the care of pets? Parents are often disappointed because a child's fondness for animals doesn't make him invariably remember their needs. From six or so on, a child can be entrusted with feeding a pet, and gradually with the other demands they make for care.

But they need reminding. Habits are established much easier in some children than others, and are of course set up faster when there are pleasant associations. But just as we may have to remind a boy to wash before coming to the table, even though we have encouraged this practice from early childhood, so we will probably have to remind him occasionally about feeding his goldfish, or putting out fresh water for his chickens. Let's make it reminding, though, not nagging.

WHEN PETS DIE. Some parents hesitate to get their children pets because they remember the sorrow they felt when a pet died. This is not really a good reason; sooner or later every child comes up against death, and while we would not deliberately expose a child to grief, the benefits he gets from having close association with animals probably outweigh the shock when he has to part with them. Getting another dog or cat soon means that the new attachment will gradually dull the pain of loss. A child may protest that he will never feel the same about any other; but this merely means he doesn't know his capacity for love.

Learning About Sex From Pets

Pets that have offspring do a lot of explaining. They illustrate better than pictures or words can how birth takes place, how mothers care for their young. Instead of surrounding birth with mystery, as we so often do, we can bring it into the open through a mother dog or cat, and in the simplest, most natural way. The pig-tailed eight-year-old is ecstatic because the cat chose her bed to have her kittens on. Nine-year-old Peter gets up in the middle of the night to make sure the new puppies are all right. And lucky indeed are children on the farm, who intimately live with lambs, and baby chicks, and calves; who hear the coming events talked about in a casual, normal way.

And how better can the spiritual side of sex be shown than through the mother-love and parental care given young creatures? Even though a child doesn't have a pet that "belongs" to him, he can observe this in one of its most marked developments among birds.

But when they can, children should have that intimate understanding of animals that comes from living with them. We should think pretty carefully before we say "no" to a child's plea for a dog or a cat, or to his desire to raise rabbits.

SEX PLAY

Many a mother of six- or seven-year-olds has been needlessly upset by finding that a group of neighborhood children have been carrying on sex play. Though of a quite innocent nature, probably such play has been secretly rather than openly engaged in because one of the children, at least, has had his natural curiosity about his body poorly handled, and thinks of such an interest as a forbidden one. We should not get panicky over such occurrences. As it is, the mothers involved often make something serious out of what should not be so regarded. In the present state of our ignorance and lack of understanding, there are almost always some mothers in a neighborhood who are so shocked that they withdraw their children from the group. This is unwise. Any action that causes children to feel guilty, or any punishment, should be avoided. It is often better to say nothing whatever to the children, for fear of saying too much, or the wrong thing. Instead, divert their minds, give them new interests. Get together and plan for more satisfying and constructive play activities. Often it falls to the lot of one or two women to take the responsibility for providing stimulating play materials, and a place for play.

To make such incidents stand out unhappily in a child's mind is exactly what we do not want to do. Wholesome attitudes toward sex are not built up by making a child feel that his interest in his body is something dirty or bad.

The Summer Camp

EVERY child should have the experience of attending a summer camp at least once. Camping is not only fun; it offers recreation different from any a child can possibly have if he spends his vacation with the family.

A good camp offers possibly a child's best opportunity for "psychological weaning," for freeing himself of dependence on his parents. This process is an essential and difficult part of growing up, perhaps most difficult for the parents. They can help by giving him the warmth, guidance and protection he needs—for he is still a child—plus a willingness to keep hands off when he wants to do something on his own. With this sort of help, he will be ready to assume the new responsibilities that come each year as he grows older, and he can grow into a mature human being.

In the few short weeks at camp your child can make great strides toward independence and enjoy it, but the opportunity can be marred by homesickness. You can guard him against it by letting him visit friends or relatives for part of a day, a whole day and finally the night.

Preparation should begin several months before time to start to camp. It will include helping him to learn how to take care of his clothes, make his bed, sweep, dust and put away his treasures. You will doubtless find that swimming, ball games of all sorts and manual skills such as carpentry, modeling and painting are part of the camp routine. Familiarity with a few of them—he needn't do them well— will help him make a speedier and more satisfactory adjustment to camp.

When the time for departure arrives, there are likely to be tears and the beginnings of homesickness. To avoid a situation which may start the whole experience off on the wrong foot, it is a good policy to have a small farewell party for his closest friends, with all the gaiety that accompanies such events. Tearful farewells can be avoided if the guests accompany him to the train.

Sending him to camp with a group of other children is far better than having the family take him. This gives him an opportunity to become acquainted with some of his fellow campers before he arrives. It avoids the feeling of strangeness that is likely to develop if he arrives when the camp is already in action and the other children are acquainted with one another.

Letters from home may be a source of homesickness for a camper. Too frequent letters or those dwelling overmuch on the familiar happenings at home are bound to give rise to tension.

Visits from parents should be kept to a minimum, preferably to one during the camp season. The more he is on his own, the better he will get along in camp and the more independent he will become. The visit should be short, so as to avoid as much as possible disrupting the camp schedule. It should be an occasion for entertaining the child's campmates and counselors rather than a private family reunion. For your departure, choose a time when the camp is ready for some important activity or your child is surrounded by a group of his friends.

Parents are often upset by homesick letters from their children and give in to their pleas to be allowed to return home. Often letter-writing is accompanied by homesickness because it focuses the child's attention on home. When the letter is finished and the child turns his attention elsewhere, the homesickness usually passes. That's one reason for not being upset if your child is not a "good" correspondent.

Unless there is a constant bombardment of homesick letters with heart-breaking pleas, the wisest policy is to ignore them. Only when every attempt fails should parents take a child out of camp before his scheduled stay is over. Of course, you must first of all have chosen a good camp.

Bringing a child home is an indication of defeat that will undermine his confidence in his ability to make future adjustments away from home. Instead of bringing new independence, such an experience is likely to make him regress to a less mature state, of greater dependency than before he went to camp. But with sensible parents, a well chosen camp and a little preparation, the experience is rare.

ELIZABETH B. HURLOCK, PH.D.

THINGS TO CONSIDER WHEN CHOOSING
A SUMMER CAMP

1. Are buildings and sanitary arrangements planned so as to protect children from danger and disease?

2. Is a health report required before entrance? Is there a physician within easy reach, if not resident in the camp? Is there a registered nurse on the staff? Are there good arrangements for isolation of ill children until it can be determined whether they are coming down with an infectious disease? Has the camp's record in regard to health been good in the past?

3. Where does the milk come from? Is it pasteurized? Are a variety of foods available? Are the meals planned by someone who knows how to provide a well-balanced diet? Have those in the kitchen been given physical examinations to make sure that they are safe persons to handle foods?

4. Are the swimming arrangements safe? Are older persons with lifesaving training always in charge when the children go into the water? Are enough adults assigned to supervise so that each child is under observation all the time?

5. Are the camp directors well trained, responsible, and mature? Are they interested in children, or in making money? What are the ages and background experience of the counsellors? What opportunities are there for them to spend their free time in wholesome ways?

6. Is there enough variety of projects and activities available so that each child can find things to do that he thoroughly enjoys? Does the camp follow such a crowded routine that the children never have a free moment, or is there plenty of leeway for them to carry on individual interests? Is there planning for both large-group and small-group activities? Do children who enjoy doing things alone get some chance to?

7. Is the camp in question one in which great emphasis is placed on working for awards and prizes, or is there freedom from competition? Do the children feel that their attainments are being compared with those of others or does a more constructive attitude prevail, in which children are judged by their own efforts and perseverance?

The School Child's Health

NUTRITION is more than a matter of food. It involves every part of a child's life; his sleep, his activity, and his state of mind as well. A child cannot really be said to be well-nourished unless all these things are taken care of.

Malnutrition is one of the most common and often one of the least easily recognized obstacles to health. People rarely think of irritability as being a symptom of a poorly balanced or inadequate diet. Because fatigue is a feeling everyone knows, we tend to pass it over as of little consequence, when it may point to a nutritional lack that could be remedied.

Again, malnutrition is often thought of as something that refers to food lacks alone, because we associate "nourishment" with food. Actually, a child who is malnourished may be getting plenty of good food, but not the active outdoor play, or the sunlight, or the fun out of life that puts his food to work for him.

Infection somewhere in his body may be dragging a child down. Irregularity of meals, so that a child "pieces" in between, may be responsible in families which are careless about when mealtimes come. Late hours, or too little sleep, may play a part in malnourishment. A child whose life is on a hit-or-miss basis may never be very hungry. Poor sleeping conditions may mean that although a child is spending enough time in bed, he is not getting a good quality of sleep, because of poor ventilation, overcrowding, or noise. A school-age child may have extremely poor eating habits because too much attention is paid to his food whims; perhaps he eats too much of certain things, like cookies or crackers, to the exclusion of other very necessary ones.

Surveys of the breakfasts eaten by school children reveal that a large number of them start off to school very poorly fortified to begin the day's activities. A good many eat no breakfast at all. Often these same children have very poor lunches. Whether lunch is carried from home, or provided at school, the child seldom gets enough of the foods of which two or three servings a day are desirable, such as vegetables and fruits.

Because so many children eat lunch away from home, dinner is often the only really good meal of their day. They can hardly make up in one meal, even if very well planned, for the lacks of two others.

AVOID EARLY-MORNING HURRY AND WORRY

Many failures to eat a good breakfast can be blamed on hurry. Haste to get off to school implies the child stayed in bed until the very last minute, which pushes the blame back on the time he got to bed the night before.

Sometimes the child's anxiety about getting off to school on time points to pressure that is put on him in school. When a child must catch a bus, or meet a car-pool, his mother must see that he is up in time so that he does not feel too hurried to eat a good breakfast.

Children in the early grades do not have a clear idea of time. It will not help to keep saying "Hurry, hurry!" but it will help to have a schedule laid out for getting off to school on time. Planning the night before what is to be worn, fixing lost buttons or rips, being sure that caps, mittens, and school materials are in their proper places will be a big help. Scheduling turns at the bathroom or sink, having breakfast ready on the table, and remembering to allow time for tooth-brushing and a bowel movement after breakfast are seemingly trivial but important steps in the morning activities.

If, when care is taken to see that plenty of time is allowed for all the necessary details, the child still seems nervous and ill at ease, his mother ought to consult with his teacher to make sure that too much emphasis is not being placed on his not being tardy. Worry has no place in the life of a child.

The habits of the older members of the family have much to do with children's attitudes about meals. If late-rising makes the whole family feel rushed, so that everyone eats breakfast on the run, children will follow this same pattern.

Many children of the grade-school group spend the whole school day away from home. Even where there is a well-planned school lunch, and this is an essential, many children may spend part of their lunch money foolishly at a corner grocery or drug store. Candy and soft drinks, if indulged in at the expense of more desirable foods, can do much to upset a carefully planned home diet. This is not to say that all buying of such things need be forbidden; school children are so active that they can take care of some extra energy-producing material.

Not until children are in their teens do they begin to feel any real interest in health, and then it is because it affects their appearance rather than for its own sake. But, much earlier, *habit* can begin to play a part, and this is where parents come in. They have the very best opportunity to set up good health habits in their children by always providing suitable foods. Few habits are stronger than those connected with food. Parents have a pretty free hand in setting up eating patterns in their own families; they mostly have themselves to blame if they fail to bring about wholesome eating habits.

When lunch is provided at school, some attention must be paid to guiding children's choice of foods. They can be encouraged to take the plate lunch, if one is provided; or if not, to take a vegetable, as well as a main dish and dessert. Mothers who take an interest in the school lunch can often make changes for the better in the type of foods provided; by observing children's choices they can learn how color, texture, and the attractiveness with which food is served influence children's selection. By asking a child what he had at noon we can avoid serving the same vegetable that night, and, at the same time, keep track unobtrusively of whether he is eating wisely at school.

One way to prevent children from craving sweets at unsuitable times is to make sure that they are supplied at home at mealtimes with raisins, figs, dates, apples, fruit juices, and other things that renew their energy.

A WHOLESOME, BALANCED DIET

While school-age children can eat the general family diet, with the exception of tea and coffee, their mothers need to keep an eye out to see that they do not eat too much of some kinds of food, and too little of others.

Most children like the foods that are good for them: bread and butter, milk, fruit, vegetables, and meat. But in case a child has become finicky about his eating, school entrance is a good time to make a fresh start. His school, in its health teaching, will reinforce our efforts—in the beginning grades children are very much impressed by what the teacher says. One little boy came home accusing his mother of not serving as many vegetables daily as his teacher said were necessary. For days he suspiciously counted to make sure his mother was living up to what he had learned she ought to provide.

If at this period desirable eating habits don't get to be a matter of course, it will be harder and harder to establish them. As time goes on the child will eat away from home more often, so it is essential that we know he can be depended on to eat a sufficient variety and suitable amounts of food for both energy and body building.

If a period of rapid growth sets in before the age of twelve, as it so often does in the case of girls, it may be necessary to check up to see that added growth needs are being taken care of. A girl at this age is prone to eat extra cookies, candy, or ice-cream sodas when she's hungry. As these take care of extra energy needs only, they must not crowd out those more necessary foods for which the need goes up sharply at this time.

Following are foods that contribute to children's needs by supplying energy and providing materials for body building and maintenance. They are called "The Basic Seven Food Groups."

DAILY FOOD NEEDS

Each of the seven should be included in every day's meals.

GROUP ONE. Dark green, leafy, and deep yellow vegetables, such as broccoli, kale, green peppers, turnip and other greens, carrots, sweetpotatoes, winter squash—these may be raw, cooked, frozen, canned. There should be one or more servings daily.

GROUP TWO. Citrus fruit, tomatoes, raw cabbage and other high vitamin C foods, such as oranges, grapefruit, lemons, limes, musk-melons, pineapples, strawberries; green peppers, and turnips. (If fruits are hard to get, use more, especially raw, from groups one and three.) There should be one or more servings daily.

GROUP THREE. Potatoes and other vegetables and fruit, such as beets, celery, corn, eggplant, lettuce, mushrooms, rutabagas, summer squash; apples, apricots, peaches, pears, rhubarb, prunes, raisins, dates, figs, and other fruits and berries—may be served raw, cooked, frozen, canned, dried. Two or more servings daily.

GROUP FOUR. Milk, cheese, ice cream—the milk may be whole, skim, evaporated, condensed, dried, or buttermilk—three to four cups daily.

The following portions contain as much calcium as a cup of milk: one ounce cheddar cheese, four ounces cream cheese, twelve ounces cottage cheese, two or three large dips of ice cream.

GROUP FIVE. Meat, poultry, fish, eggs, dried beans and peas, nuts—one serving of meat or fish daily if possible; four or more eggs a week; two or more servings a week of nuts, peanut butter, or dried beans or peas.

GROUP SIX. Bread and cereals—whole grain or enriched and restored—should be served every day.

GROUP SEVEN. Butter or fortified margarine should be served daily. Energy foods (such as rice, jams and jellies, cakes, bacon and salad oils) may be used in addition to the seven basic foods, but should not be used in place of them.

School-age children are constantly on the go. They often need extra food between meals. If a child's appetite for his meals is hearty, and he eats the necessary variety, he should be his own judge of the amount of extra food he needs.

The main point to remember about between-meal eating is that it should be regular, not just "piecing" any time a child feels like it. A lunch of sandwiches and milk or fruit eaten right after school, or in the middle of the morning should not keep a child from being hungry for his next meal. Without a reminder from his mother, a child may wait until too close to the next meal hour to make lunching desirable.

THE UNDERWEIGHT CHILD

The child whose parents have been told by their doctor that he needs to put on weight may not be able to eat any larger amounts of food than he has been eating. He needs more of the highly concentrated foods, such as eggs (if he tolerates them well), cream, and butter. Evaporated milk, used in cooking without being diluted, adds to the nourishment in soups or puddings. More butter or margarine on his bread, more cream on his cereal may be used.

The fats, starches, and milk in his diet can be increased only if they agree with him; they should not be added too rapidly, nor should they crowd out valuable foods like vegetables and fruits.

Often the underweight child needs extra rest just as much as he needs extra food. He may be a child who is overactive and easily overstimulated. More careful supervision of his play may help. Providing interesting, quiet occupations will keep him from feeling so thwarted if he must cut down on active, romping play. If he must rest before meals and go to bed earlier than his playmates, he may be furnished with books or quiet table games or a radio in his room.

The long, lean type of child is sometimes assumed to be underweight when he is really in good physical condition.

THE OVERWEIGHT CHILD

No attempt should be made to reduce the weight of a child except upon the advice of a competent physician. If a diet is suggested, great care should be taken to see that it includes enough bulk (supplied by vegetables and fruits) and the essential vitamins and minerals that keep the body in good repair. Unlike the underweight child, who needs more fats and starchy foods, the overweight child may need careful supervision to see that he does not overdo such items as butter, cream, cake, and candy.

A fat child's problem will not always be solved by attention to his diet. Some children overeat because, in the absence of other satisfactions, they have a craving for pleasure, and eating is an easy way to get it. A child who is ignored by other children, whose home life is unhappy, or who for any other reason feels wretched may turn to greedy gobbling of food, as another turns to daydreams.

Overweight caused by lack of glandular balance is another matter. The physician who takes care of the child will try to determine whether the cause is physical or psychological.

MEALTIMES SHOULD BE PLEASANT

To get the most benefit from their food children need to eat under pleasant conditions. They need to be relaxed and at ease if digestion is to be good. Because the school-age child is typically in a rush, it is often a good idea to set a definite length of time which must be spent at the table, say fifteen or twenty minutes at least. If this is a rule, the urge to bolt his food and run back to play or school will be less, and nagging can be avoided.

The conscientious child is often worried for fear he may be late to school, which makes it important to have lunch, as well as breakfast, served in time so that the child will not feel hurried.

Since excitement of any kind—anger, fear, or any intense emotion —hinders digestion, parents should strive for a pleasant atmosphere at meals. *Meals are not the time to talk about a child's faults or to bring up disagreeable topics.* Harping on table manners may have an opposite effect to the desired one. If the table is neatly prepared, the food appetizingly served, and the parents' own table manners good, children will gradually, by imitation, learn a great deal about pleasing manners.

A few families still consider that the adults' conversation is all that matters at the family meals; others go to the extreme of letting children be the center of attention. If children are to learn to talk well, they need to have a part in what goes on; but they need also to learn how to listen, and not to continually interrupt. They will be helped in learning how to be hospitable, and they will enjoy their meals more if their friends occasionally share them.

CARE OF THE TEETH

The state of a child's teeth is easier to determine than that of his nutrition, for defects in teeth can be seen.

The percentage of school-age children having dental caries or decay goes up steadily through the elementary-school years, running up into 80 and 90 percent in different communities by age twelve. The provision of a well-balanced diet, with plenty of the so-called protective foods, is probably the best means of prevention within parents' control. Fluorides are now known to retard decay in children's teeth, if applied early enough. Your dentist can paint your child's teeth with them.

Even when school examinations show that children's teeth are in poor condition, parents are often slow to have defects taken care of. Some of this failure is because parents are unable to pay for dental work, but a large share of it is simply neglect. It reflects the ignorance among parents themselves of the importance of a healthy mouth to over-all good health.

The sixth-year molars (so-called because they usually appear in that year) are especially liable to decay, and need very carful watching. Few adults have perfect sixth-year molars which is silent evidence of neglect during childhood. This neglect is often the result of very early food lacks, due to parents' failure to know that these four molars are permanent teeth, and have been present in the child's jaw since before birth.

Since perhaps only one out of ten school children pays any attention at all to the connection between health and good habits of eating, exercise, and rest, it is up to parents to supervise closely their children's habits in this period. Even though children may *know* that eating candy between meals is undesirable, they can't be depended on not to indulge. Health teaching in school needs to be bolstered up by whatever means parents can devise at home. Visual education seems to work better than talking about health needs, and parents might very well make more use of pictures, charts, and any other way they can to let their children *see* for themselves why healthy teeth are so important.

Parents would think a long while before they would deliberately do anything to prevent their children from having the best of health in adult life. And yet that is almost exactly what they do when they don't make two visits a year to the dentist or a dental clinic.

PREVENTING LOSS OF HEARING

The kind of hearing a child will have in adult life depends to some extent upon the care his ears get in childhood. It is not possible later on to make up for any neglect that occurred while the child was little, and early recognition of any existing trouble may help to keep hearing from becoming steadily worse.

Almost every kind of deafness seen in adults is found in children between eight and fourteen years old, with this difference: in children the impairment of hearing is just beginning, and it may be possible to prevent its progress.

Prevention of any hearing loss, of course, is better still. This means that great care should be taken when children have diseases such as measles, one very frequently associated with ear infections. Running ears, which if neglected may result in deafness, are often caused by chronic, or long continuing, infection in the tonsils and adenoids. Pain in the ear should never be "home treated" but a doctor or clinic should be visited.

Colds—the main cause of absences from grade school—are one of the worst offenders in bringing about earache and the ear trouble that follows. The pity of it is that we take "colds" so casually. "It's just a cold" will never be the attitude of the mother who is truly interested in promoting her child's health, with special thought for his hearing.

One of the serious and immediate results of impaired hearing can be a slowing up in school. One study showed that half of those children who are hard-of-hearing may be expected to be a grade behind, if they have not learned lip reading. Early discovery of any loss of hearing can keep this from happening.

BE ON THE LOOKOUT FOR DEFECTIVE VISION

Even though a child has had regular care by a physician up to the time he enters school, the chances are great that he has not had his hearing or his vision tested; relatively few physicians make a practice of doing this. Many schools now routinely test children's eyes, but with so many children to examine it is not always possible to do more than pick out those children whose eyes have rather obvious defects.

If a child holds his book close to his face; if he tips his head to odd angles when working; if he has sties frequently, or any discharge or redness about the eyes; if he squints; if he seems to have difficulty seeing things at any distance, his parents should have his eyes examined by a competent ophthalmologist—a physician who is an eye specialist.

Children sometimes are well along in the grades before anyone notices that their eyesight is poor. The child himself, of course, has no way of knowing that his eyes are not like other people's, and so may struggle along, though very much handicapped. His parents are the ones who should be on the alert to rule out any such happening. They should give special thought to this when their child goes to school, and begins to use his eyes for close work more than he has before. Being on the lookout will make possible the early finding and correction of such things as near- or far-sightedness, astigmatism, or crossed eyes.

When study of a child's eyes reveals that he must wear glasses, parents should follow the eye doctor's recommendations closely as to how often follow-up examinations and change of glasses are needed. Because children's eyes are changing and developing rapidly, often new glasses are needed every year.

GETTING ADEQUATE SLEEP AND REST

By the time children go to school they are usually sleeping about eleven hours out of the twenty-four. From this time on, their constant cry is to be allowed to stay up later.

While there can be a very gradual decrease for the next few years in the length of time a child sleeps, no hard-and-fast rules can be given as to the exact amount needed at any given age, because each child's requirements are different. Just as some children thrive on less food than others, so children differ very decidedly in the amount of sleep necessary to their best health. A good general rule is to see to it that a school-age child goes to sleep early enough to awaken naturally in the morning. A little experimentation will determine whether being allowed up an extra fifteen or twenty minutes at night means irritability in the morning.

The older children grow, the more varied and demanding interests they have, and the more independent they like to feel. If they have a hand in working out plans, they feel much less thwarted than when rules are laid down—with no back-talk, no discussion. But the last word must remain with the parents in matters of health. Twelve-year-old Mary may be so conscientious about homework that she wants to keep on with it after the agreed-upon hour for bedtime. Better than allowing her to talk us into letting her stay up till ten "just this once" (which it never turns out to be) is a firm but sympathetic "no," and then later a conference with the teacher or teachers (after consulting with Mary) to find out just how much time she is expected to spend on homework. If a junior high-school child is overburdened with homework because teachers are making assignments without consulting each other, as occasionally happens, parent-school sifting out of the matter is the answer.

Whenever the prepubescent growth spurt sets in, which may very well happen before the teens in the case of girls, more rest and sleep are necessary. Growth makes great demands upon the body, which can be met only by ample sleep and food that contributes to body building. The easy tears and fits of temper that mothers frequently complain of in their daughters at the approach of adolescence are just as likely to be connected with unsatisfied sleep or food needs, as with glandular changes.

DISTURBERS OF SLEEP

Radio, television, and the movies give us and our children much pleasure nowadays but also cause some of our biggest headaches. They contribute immensely to our lives, but they also offer some perplexing health problems.

We know that children should have a chance to calm down at the end of the day, and yet that is just the time that they want to listen to the radio or go to a movie. Is it harmful to let them?

Careful study has shown that even after very mildly exciting movies, children's sleep is disturbed. The more thrilling the movie the greater the effect on the sleep. The disturbance is not just for a single night, but can be noted for two or three weeks. Children of grade-school age are more affected by scenes of danger, and as they like hair-raising movies rather than romantic ones, these are the ones they'll pick out, if given a choice.

Television is harder to deal with than the movies. The parent who says, "It can always be turned off!" is forgetting that for a school-age child, to be doing, hearing, and seeing the same things his friends are is very important. His carefully protected health is of little use to him if he is "different" from his mates.

However, children whose parents have been firm and consistent from the beginning of their training come to accept a sensible bedtime matter-of-factly. Letting a child stay up a little later occasionally for a program he very much wants to hear, or when "special" company comes, will keep him from feeling that his parents enjoy putting obstales between him and his pleasures.

The School Lunch Box

LUNCH-BOX meals for the school child should be appetizing and satisfying, wholesome and adequate. A carried lunch is as much a part of the day's meals as breakfast and dinner. Thus it should supply its share, or about one-third of the day's food essentials.

The lunch-box meal should contain protein foods for growth and repair of body tissues. It should have fats and carbohydrates for fuel and energy. There should be vitamins and minerals to keep the body fit. Milk, cheese, eggs, meat, poultry and fish are excellent sources of high-quality protein. These foods also furnish minerals and vitamins. Fruits and vegetables are other good sources of minerals and vitamins. Moreover, they contain sugar and some protein, and provide bulk as well. Fats, starches and sugars are most economical for energy.

Milk should not be neglected in the lunch box. It furnishes

calcium and phosphorus for building and maintaining good bones and teeth. It also furnishes protein for growth.

There are many nourishing foods which are easy to pack in the lunch box. If properly prepared, these foods remain appetizing and attractive until the noon hour. A hot dish or a hot drink gives variety and tastiness to the well-planned lunch. Hot or cold drinks, as well as hot foods, such as soup, may be carried in a vacuum bottle. Many schools today, not equipped with a cafeteria, are serving drinks and a nourishing hot dish to supplement the lunch brought from home. Take these into consideration when you plan the child's lunch.

Breads for sandwiches should always be 100 per cent whole-grain or vitamin-enriched. Get acquainted with black Russian bread and sweet Swedish rye as well as Jewish pumpernickel. Lettuce should be added to all sandwiches, and as much butter and mayonnaise as weight permits.

Sandwich filling may be made of almost any food valuable to health, such as meats and fresh green pepper, liver paste, chopped egg and celery, tuna salad, bacon and tomato, avocado, banana and peanut butter, and peanut butter alone.

If a sweet is desired, an excellent sandwich spread may be made by stirring wheat germ into black molasses or honey until a solid paste is achieved; nuts and raisins may be added. Cookies which contain wheat germ, black molasses, powdered milk, raisins and nuts are delicious and are valuable in any lunch.

Dried fruits should be the main candy substitute; enough should be carried to allow some to be eaten at the mid-morning recess and also in mid-afternoon. Other health-building tidbits are unsweetened chocolate, salted peanuts or soy beans, chocolate-covered peanuts, and crackerjack made with molasses.

With careful planning it is possible to pack in the lunch box not only sandwiches well wrapped, but also some fresh fruit or a closed jar of stewed fruit or a custard, as well as the thermos of hot drink or hot soup and an appetizer. Variety should be the watchword and each food should be carefully wrapped so as to remain fresh and free from the flavors of adjoining foods.

Always plan well in advance the lunches you are going to prepare. In your working space, arrange the slicing knives, mixing spoons, and the other necessities where you need them in those early morning hours which so seldom are tranquil and easy-paced. Have the other supplies at hand, the essential box of waxed paper, folded clean waxed paper taken from bread, cake, and other bought foods, the packages of paper cups and napkins, the washed and aired vacuum bottle, the clean and aired lunch box. Always have the important small things ready in advance, little waxed-paper packages of salt, and sugar or lumps of sugar, if they are needed for the box. Have the butter or margarine standing at room temperature to soften for spreading the sandwich bread.

SUGGESTIONS FOR BOX LUNCHES

FOR THE VACUUM BOTTLE:

Milk, cocoa, soup, fruit or vegetable juice

BREAD FOR SANDWICHES:

Whole-wheat, enriched white, rye, raisin, brown, cracked wheat, oatmeal

FILLINGS FOR SANDWICHES:

Vegetable

1. Chopped raw vegetables, as cabbage, carrot, celery, onion and pepper, plain or with chopped peanuts added
2. Tomato, lettuce and bacon, salad dressing
3. Chopped celery, lettuce and salad dressing

Cheese

1. American cheese, grated or finely cut and mixed with chopped onion, relish or pickle and salad dressing or mixed with seeded raisins and nuts
2. Cottage cheese, salted and mixed with any of the following: onion, parsley, celery, chopped nuts, green peppers, dill pickle, chili sauce
3. American or swiss cheese, sliced and seasoned

Egg

1. Scrambled or fried—plain, or with lettuce and dressing
2. Hard-cooked mixed with chopped olives, pickles, bacon, green pepper or dried beef and salad dressing
3. Hard-cooked, sardines, mustard
4. Hard-cooked, sliced tomato

Fish

1. Flaked—salmon, tuna or crabmeat
2. Sardines with lemon juice or hard-cooked egg yolks

Meat

1. Cooked liver (ground or chopped) mixed with chili sauce or mayonnaise
2. Chopped roast meat with pickles or raw onion
3. Chopped ham and egg
4. Dried beef slices
5. Liverwurst and tomato

Peanut Butter

1. Peanut butter and chopped raisins moistened with fruit juice
2. Peanut butter on one slice of bread and tart jelly on the other
3. Peanut butter and chopped sweet pickle or relish
4. Peanut butter with crisp bacon crumbled on top
5. Banana, peanut butter and salad dressing. Lemon juice on the banana will prevent its turning dark
6. Peanut butter, shredded or chopped carrots and lemon juice
7. Peanut butter and prunes, chopped

Sweet Sandwiches

1. Chopped dates, figs, raisins or a mixture of these with lemon or orange
2. Prune filling—1 cup cooked, chopped prunes, 1 teaspoon lemon juice, 1 tablespoon orange marmalade
3. Coconut, chopped dates, chopped nuts and orange juice
4. Jelly or marmalade—nuts may be added

5. Graham crackers spread with peanut butter mixed with lemon juice

APPETIZERS:

Raw carrots or turnip sticks, celery, whole tomatoes, scallions, pickles, radishes, or vegetable salads (in jar)

DESSERTS:

Cookies, cake, tarts, turnovers, custards, or puddings

FRUIT:

Apples, oranges, bananas, pears, dates, figs, apricots or any in season

LUNCH-BOX MENUS FOR CHILDREN

(Age 6 to 12 years)

Milk, orange juice or hot soup may be bought at the school lunch counter; or a chilled or hot drink can be carried in a vacuum bottle.

Peanut Butter Whole Wheat Bread Sandwich
Chopped Leftover Meat and Catchup Rye Bread Sandwich
Milk, Two Oatmeal Cookies
Apple

* * *

Chopped Cheese and Relish Boston Brown Bread Sandwich
Leftover Cold Baked Beans and Catchup Rye Bread Sandwich
Chocolate Milk
Whole Orange (peeled and sections loosened)
Two Brownies

* * *

Cup of Creamed Asparagus Soup
Three Whole Wheat Crackers
Minced Leftover Meat and Mustard Enriched White Bread Sandwich
Celery or Carrot Sticks, Salt
Apple Tart

* * *

Container of Macaroni and Cheese
Container of Green Salad
(Carrots, Cabbage, Apple, French Dressing)

Buttered Boston Brown Bread (two pieces)
Chocolate Cup Cake
Milk

* * *

Container of Baked Beans
Buttered Enriched White Bread Sandwich
Fresh Fruit (Apple, Peach, Pear)
Cup Custard   Cooky
Chocolate Milk

* * *

Cup Rice Pudding and Raisins
Small Container of Cream
Cream Cheese and Jelly Graham Bread Sandwich
Minced Chicken and Vegetable Enriched White Bread Sandwich
Gingerbread
Milk or Orange Juice

LUNCH-BOX MENUS FOR ADOLESCENTS

(Age 13 to 17)

Milk, orange juice or hot soup may be bought at the school lunch counter; or a chilled or hot drink can be carried in a vacuum bottle.

Swiss Cheese and Bacon Enriched White Bread Sandwich
Cream Cheese Date-and-Nut-Bread Sandwich
Whole Tomato, Salt
Peach Tart
Milk

* * *

Liverwurst Rye Bread Sandwich
Deviled Egg
Enriched White Bread-and-Butter Sandwich
Gherkins
Apple Turnover with Piece of Cheddar Cheese
Hot Cocoa

* * *

American Cheese with Mustard Whole Wheat Bread Sandwich
Meat Loaf and Chili Sauce Rye Bread Sandwich
Fruit and Nut Salad   Soft Frosted Molasses Cookies
Chocolate Milk

* * *

Two Sliced Tongue and Swiss Cheese Whole Wheat Bread
Sandwiches
Vegetable Salad, with Soya Crackers
Chocolate-Nut Candy Bar, or Two Dates and Two Figs
Milk or Fruit Juice

* * *

Peanut Butter and Jelly Whole Wheat Bread Sandwich
Cream Cheese and Olive Enriched White Bread Sandwich
Carrot Sticks and Celery Heart
Devil's Food Layer Cake
Milk or Fruit Juice

* * *

Cream Cheese and Date Whole Wheat Bread Sandwich
Sliced Chicken Enriched White Bread Sandwich
Stuffed Olives
Fresh Pear or Banana
Two Pieces of Chocolate Fudge or Four Dates
Milk or Cocoa

A Natural and Wholesome Attitude Toward Sex

MORE and more, thoughtful parents are undertaking whole-heartedly their obligation to make the matter of sex behavior, feelings, and understanding a part of their planned guidance of their children from the earliest years. They realize that failure to weave in this thread may weaken the whole fabric of their child's future life. By school age, a child's curiosity about his body, and about where babies come from has either been answered satisfactorily enough for the moment, or it has been crammed down into the realm of tabooed subjects.

Let's hope the first is true; but, in either case, the widening interests of the school-age child give us a good chance to do a quiet, natural job of satisfying his present needs and preparing him for the big changes of the teen age. If we are ourselves unsure or emotionally tense, our first step is to free ourselves of foolish fears or inhibitions. This can be done. Parents have the strongest possible motive for learning to do so—their children's welfare.

We may need information about what is going on in the child, who on the surface seems fairly indifferent to sex during these years. We may not see much evidence of sex interest, or activity that can be called sex activity, except as boys and girls tend to draw apart, and mingle less than before with the opposite sex. If very little interest is displayed, it is partly because children are quick to see that some things are not freely and openly discussed or done. For example, the practice of having separate toilets for boys and girls makes it obvious even to beginning school children that excretion is not only something private, but something each sex excludes the other from observing. By the time children go to school, their parents usually have begun to have boys and girls dress in different rooms, and the earlier habit of letting them take their baths together has been dropped. These, and dozens of other ways of behaving, so commonplace that we accept them without a thought, are such a part of a child's training in his home and his particular cultural group that he builds up sex awareness as he does a general feeling about sunshine and rain. His awareness can be wholesome and natural, like his enjoyment of sunshine, or tinged with disagreeable meaning. A "gloomy day feeling" about sex is not anything we want to encourage.

HOW PARENTS INFLUENCE ATTITUDES

We must not make the mistake of thinking that information is all a child needs. Really, that is probably the lesser part of our job. Although accurate and definite knowledge is highly desirable, the feelings a child builds up, the interpretation of the information he gets, will determine how he puts that information to use. Children get a good deal of sex-related information at school in all kinds of subjects. Our job is to see that their attitudes toward this whole matter remain wholesome.

We inject our feelings into our children, willy-nilly. If we hated and feared arithmetic in childhood, we'll have a different attitude toward Joan's struggles with long division than if we enjoyed it. So with sex. If we have feelings of disgust or fear about sex, we'll find those feelings creeping into our children's lives. This makes it of first importance for us to be sure that sex is a wholesome, constructive force in our own lives.

If a child's two parents have a good relationship based on real sympathy and understanding of each other's needs—sexual and otherwise—their unconscious influence will be the main food on which the child's adjustment feeds. Their frankness, their naturalness, their love for each other, will be the soil from which his attitudes and feelings spring.

Of course there are some basic facts that a child needs to be acquainted with, that we parents must give him, if he is to avoid being confused and troubled by misinformation such as we ourselves probably met with in childhood.

He needs to know how his body works, to understand the marvelous mechanism of his muscles, lungs, and heart and what happens to the food he eats. If he's given facts about how his body is nourished he can take the body wastes for granted and without disgust as being the unused elements of the food he eats and the water he drinks. He needs to know the names of the various parts of his body, their purpose, and a little bit about how they perform, from his intricate brain, through his digestive organs and genital system, down to the bony structure of his feet. He needs to know that there are hidden glands in his body, glands that don't open to the outside like his tear ducts, but manufacture and pass on their secretions inside the body at appropriate times, bringing about changes not only in his appearance but in his feelings, too.

He needs to know the reasons back of both the written and unwritten rules governing sex behavior: why marriage and family life are necessary for the protection and welfare of each oncoming generation; how and why it has come about that in our way of life, mating taking place as soon as sexual maturity is reached in the teens is considered undesirable; that only by putting off mating until the parents have become well enough established to give proper care to their children can children's safety and well-being be assured. When he understands all these things he can better accept the restraints that society imposes on him. A strong, harmonious relationship between his parents unconsciously influences a child to regard marriage with respect.

He needs to have the powerfulness of the sex urge that arises in adolescence explained; to understand how this strong drive is in itself neither good nor bad, but simply a necessity to the continuance of the race. Boys and girls need to learn how primitive sex behavior, from being originally a purely physical manifestation, has come to be associated in successful marriage with all that is highest and best in us. It is important for them to know that this has come about through the development of family life, and the devotion which the partners, first drawn together, perhaps, through the awakening of sex interest, come to feel for each other. Only by the building up of affection and shared interests and experiences has this become possible.

Especially as the time draws near when they will become mature sexually, at puberty, boys and girls need a clear, straightforward explanation of the ways they are going to change physically, and of how those bodily changes are going to be accompanied by emotional changes. Thousands of youngsters suffer every year from not being given even the vaguest sort of help: the girl who is not prepared for menstruation, or for the changed interests she begins to feel; the boy whose voice begins to change, who surreptitiously tries his hand at shaving, and who worries needlessly about nocturnal emissions.

AS BOYS AND GIRLS MATURE

Girls need explanations even earlier than boys for they mature earlier. Often this doubles their puzzlement: they feel out of step, because they seem older than the boys of their age, and yet they are probably being surrounded by an increased amount of protection by their parents. Unless they are given an understanding of the meaning of menstruation they may be shocked and frightened at its first appearance. They need to know beforehand that menstruation is merely a device by which their body discards the blood, disintegrating tissue, and other materials the uterus stores up in its lining to nourish the egg which is released each month by the ovaries. That when, during the child-bearing years this egg is not fertilized by meeting with a sperm cell, it passes out of the body along with the blood that has lined the uterus in preparation for the possible nesting there of the egg. When this plain and commonsense explanation of menstruation is given, it can be accepted as a natural and normal function.

Girls need an explanation of the changes that are to come about in boys, too—just as boys need to know how girls mature. To learn of their own earlier maturation helps girls to see why they are often attracted to older boys, rather than to those of their own age. It helps to make plain to them their part in social life between the sexes, to know that the male is more aggressive in sex behavior than the female, and that their behavior will have a lot to do with what they may expect from boys.

Once a boy has reached school age, it is often assumed that his father is a more suitable person to turn to for help than his mother. Fathers should be on such friendly terms with their sons as to make embarrassment or reserve unnecessary at any age. But some men seek to escape the responsibility for giving their sons sex information. Unless, or until, a father feels prepared to do so in an easy, natural way he probably should not attempt to handle his son's questions .

Because, in our way of life, mothers are usually closer to their young children through their day-in and day-out contacts, a boy's mother is perhaps more often the person who has given him answers all along, and to whom he has turned first for everything from a skinned knee to an explanation of death.

But she, never having been a boy, cannot possibly enter into his feelings the way his father can. Also if a child comes to rely solely on his mother, a valuable chance is lost for father-and-son contacts, and understanding. Boys need more, not fewer such bonds. The ideal thing, of course, is for mother and father to be so in tune with each other and with their children that they can share this responsibility like any other; that whenever the occasion arises, discussion of this subject is as natural as talk about where coal comes from, or what causes the frost on a window.

As the physical and psychological changes associated with puberty begin to come about, though, there is a very real reason why a boy's father can handle questions better than his mother.

One of the most noticeable things about the youngster at such a time, boy or girl, is the new awareness of sex. The first way this may impress itself upon us is by our children's increasing modesty. They begin to insist on more privacy. The boy no longer wants his mother to come in and scrub his back when he takes a bath. The whole matter of sex is becoming infused with emotion. A boy's mother is no longer just his mother—she is a woman, too. There is a rising consciousness that the old love relationship between mother and son must alter, now that he is on his way to becoming a man.

Does it seem unnecessary to discuss here a situation that will not force its way into our attention until the teens? Though we are discussing children of twelve and under, what we will be up against later really has a very important bearing now. We don't need to put a stumbling block in our path. We can avoid doing so if we give children adequate preparation before the stage is reached when sex takes on a highly personal and emotional color. When such confidence and understanding exist in the preadolescent years, a child expects and is readier to meet the coming of puberty.

THE SCHOOL CAN HELP

Of course, parents have the primary responsibility for the sex education of their children. There are some parents, though, who hate to face the fact that their children are going to grow up; who try to get out of hearing of the approaching sound of teen-age problems. But help must come from somewhere if the adolescent years are to be the pleasant time they should be.

If parents feel unable to do the job as it should be done, then they may want to see that the school (the only other agency that reaches all children) takes over some of this responsibility, and handles it according to the most approved methods. "A talk" to boys or girls by a physician, or someone pulled in because a serious need is suddenly felt, won't answer the purpose. Little can be said for such a separate and isolated "talk," even with the best of intentions on the part of all concerned. It lifts the subject out of its context of everyday life, and spotlights it, with resulting over-emphasis. Both too little, and too much, is said. For one child, such an approach may be mildly amusing; another may have his curiosity stimulated. It is next to impossible to give in a single lecture information that will be useful to children from the great variety of backgrounds and of the degrees of maturity found in a single school grade.

If parents feel that sex education should be included in school guidance, they should find out what the most desirable methods are. To insert a course into the curriculum is not the whole answer. But with the cooperation of intelligent and personally well-adjusted teachers, the school can carry on a broad and pervasive program, where every single subject, from mathematics to art, contributes to an all-around interpretation of what sex means in our lives.

Does it sound farfetched to say that mathematics can make a contribution? The right teacher can make it clear as daylight that figures and money are a part of family relations; that the conflicting needs of different family members, sometimes based on sex attitudes, are often responsible for misunderstandings about family budgeting and the fair distribution of money.

English classes can contribute through discussion of characters in stories and novels; social studies, by talking over the reasons for laws relating to children and marriage; biology can give background physical facts.

When both parents and schools arrive at the point where they are prepared to help children on their way to the goal of mental and emotional health through building wholesome sex attitudes we will have fewer tragedies in adult life.

Comics, Radio, Movies and Television

COMICS, radio, movies, and television—these are a part of our children's world today. They are among the ways by which words and ideas, our culture and our thinking, are being passed along to our children. Yet many view these new developments with misgivings, and yearn for the good old days when a child could sit down with a book without being distracted by the voice of the radio and the ever-present lure of a comics magazine.

This wish might astonish parents of not so many generations ago who looked upon books themselves as breeders of idleness and day-dreaming. When the invention of printing made books available to everyone, pleasure reading was first forbidden, then restricted. Not so many years ago *Gulliver's Travels* and *Huckleberry Finn* were forbidden reading for the young. Today we not only accept books, we hope and sometimes insist that our children read them. Indeed, many parents now resist comics, radio, and movies on the ground that they take time which might otherwise be spent with "a good book." Sooner or later, however, we shall probably accept these new developments, too, and learn to use them as we have learned to use books.

THE COMICS

What is in these magazines? The greater portion of them still fall, roughly, into about the same groups that children's reading always has: adventure, fantasy and magic, crime and detective, westerns, humor and nonsense, humanized animals, adolescent jitterbug capers, stories about real people, and history and current events.

Along with these however, are an increasing number of highly unsavory crime and horror stories, many of them sadistic and full of sex excitement, whose covers scream with lurid pictures, often promising more murder or more sex interest than their inside pages offer. At present, there is no way to distinguish—without reading them—the comics that are suitable for children from these unsavory ones. In general, the latter are not among the high favorites with younger readers, but are more apt to attract adolescents and adults.

Why Do Children Love Comics?

What is the fascination of the comics? Probably the greatest common ingredient is *action*. Children like things to happen, and in the comics they do, fast and furiously. The very first page, even the cover, offers a sort of preview of things to come. And from the very outset there is never a dull moment. Even the gentler types of comics never let the reader down, but maintain a swift pace from beginning to end.

The action is easy to follow; the relation of cause and effect clear and immediate. As one child put it: "You know by the pictures what the people are doing, and you know by the balloons which person is saying what." You also know by the pictures which are the "good" people and which the "bad," and you know more or less what to expect of them. The young reader gets a lot for his money—and with very little effort. Since reading is, for most children, a difficult skill to master to the point of enjoyment, this is no small factor in the popularity of the comics.

The fact that all the action is of the biff bang variety, with everybody and everything being battered about, is especially pleasing to youngsters, to whom physical encounters are always fascinating and forbidden. They can hardly take all this very seriously since they take it quite for granted that the battered victims will get up in the very next picture and go into action again, just as, in their own games, the "dead" soldiers or cops or robbers are expected to pick themselves up after the fight and join the play.

Very satisfying to the youngsters, too, is the pattern of the comics. To many of us they seem stereotyped, with endless repetition of theme and character. But for children this offers a certain security: They can count on everything turning out as they would have it, for it always does. There is reassurance in knowing that the "good guys" will defeat the "bad guys," no matter what the odds. Just as in the classic fairy tale, the hero will be in danger many times, almost outdone, but always triumphant, thus satisfying children's need for a "moral ending."

For many children the comics provide a reflection of their own fantasies. Identifying themselves with the hero or the villain, they are in there punching. They fancy themselves strong and invincible, able to overcome the limitations of time and space, defending the weak and routing evil. Or they are clever and wicked, but authority steps in (in the form of the law) and their guilt feelings are resolved by punishment of the villain. Perhaps they find in these fancied roles some escape from the frustrations that go with being "small fry" in a world full of people bigger and stronger than they are. Here, too, as in the classic folk tales, children may find release for pent-up feelings of hate, anger, fear, and aggression. Civilized living demands that they speak softly and behave nicely. But along with the fabulous characters in the comics they can fight their enemies, rescue their friends, rough-handle the people who stand between them and their goals, and generally break through the painful restrictions that go with learning to be civilized.

What Is Their Effect?

So much controversy has raged about the comics that it is hard to separate the facts from the feelings that run so high. The emotional atmosphere that seems to surround this whole question will not help solve the very real problems that are raised, not so much by the comics as such, as by their quantity, their availability, and the abuses to which they have been subject. Many of the recent attacks on the comics have made parents anxious as a result of the scare headlines. This is unfortunate, because anxious parents may do more damage to their children than comics reading! The critics are apt to point to the "horrible examples," without reassuring parents that comics are not all like this and children are not all like this. It is deplorable that sordid and vulgar picture magazines, of any kind, by any name, should be displayed and sold to children. But it should be possible to eliminate these abuses without depriving millions of children of their pleasure in *Donald Duck,* and without terrifying parents into battling with their children over comics reading.

The question whether reading about violence provides safe release for children's aggressive impulses or may, in some instances, stimulate them to aggressive behavior, cannot be answered readily except in terms of the individual child's reactions. Psychiatrists point out that many children find deep satisfaction in sharing the daring deeds of their heroes, that those few children who are driven to experiment with danger would be as likely to respond to any other stimuli, Anything they see or hear may suggest the pattern if the drive is there. There is no substitute for parental vigilance!

Do Comics Create Fears?

All children, even the hardiest, should be protected from the type of comics magazines whose pages drip with horror and blood. No good can be served by pictures or stories which exploit the appetites of a horror-loving public. While crime stories seem to hold a fascination for many children, as they do for many adults, the point at which this enjoyment becomes unwholesome for the young reader is one which must be carefully watched. A child too preoccupied with crime or horror is showing up plainly that he needs help. *Excessive* comics reading, too, may be a symptom of disturbance.

Parents and Comics Reading

Perhaps the most frequent complaint about comics magazines is that they are so many, so available, and so persistent. Even the parent who raises objections to them on any or all of the counts mentioned would tolerate an occasional comic book. But hordes of them! Not only does a child amass them for rereading, but he clings to his hoard, guarding it against housecleaning mothers and borrowing playmates. Not only at home, but everywhere he goes there are comics. One cannot shut them out for they are everywhere. Forbidding is worse than useless—even if it were desirable—for it only drives their reading underground.

A child reading a comic is lost to all else. He hears not, neither does he see. This can be pretty irritating in a household when chores and routines have to be done. And in the classroom, how can arithmetic or grammar compete with the surreptitious comics magazine?

The answer to many of these problems seems to lie in the same kind of wise and understanding management we use in all our relationships with our children. There is a time for reading and a time for other things. There are limits beyond which anything may be harmful. These limits cannot be fixed for all children and all times, but are governed rather by the needs of the moment and the needs of the child. We cannot count on rules and dictums: one comics magazine a week, one comic for every "good" book read, one old one discarded for every new one bought. Such devices are meaningless and arbitrary and lead to endless bargaining and bickering. On the other hand, a child can, if he feels his parent is sympathetic, accept the reasonableness of a suggestion to postpone the comics until after his homework is done, or his practicing, or the dishwashing. He can understand why he should not bring comics to school where more urgent matters demand his attention. Such suggestions or directives, however unwelcome, are reasonable and understandable—and most children will respond to them, especially if they are free at other times to read as they choose.

The guidance we give to his selection will depend upon our understanding of the particular child's needs and interests. His choices will often give us clues to the needs he is trying to meet through his reading. Does he prefer the less exciting Disney animals or the sheer lunacy of Popeye? Does he like true stories and real heroes, or prefer fantasy and magic? Young children prefer the gentler animal fables and cartoons. At seven or eight or nine they turn to the more fantastic and magical, and thence to the more realistic "could be possible" tales.

Within each of these categories there are good and bad comics among which we may help children select those which are better edited, better printed, and better drawn. We need to know what is in these magazines and what are the differences among them. We can help children arrive at standards of their own for selecting the best and recognizing the unsuitable. As with everything else within the child's reach—his play, his sports, even his food—he needs parental guidance, and he will accept it if it is based on parental understanding that he also has reasons for his choices, and tastes of his own. These will change and develop and grow as his interests and experiences expand.

RADIO COMES IN

Radio attracts children for many of the same reasons as do the comics. And it raises most of the same objections from parents and teachers: that radio listening interferes with other activities, wastes time which might better be spent in reading, athletics, outdoor fun, or creative activity; that what the children hear dulls their tastes; that listening to crime programs may inspire them to crime; and, above all, that the horror and mystery programs induce nightmares.

Radio listening is in certain respects more difficult for parents to manage than the comics reading. It cannot be confined to a particular listener—it reaches everyone within earshot, young and old, sensitive and robust, receptive and unwilling. It demands even less effort than comics. Parents complain that the children sit for hours, letting the waves of sound pour into their ears. They even do their homework with their ears slanted to the loudspeaker. "Ear-massage," one mother calls it. Yet children can do more than listen. They can and often do participate. For radio is, in a very true sense, a people's art.

In radio listening, just as in comics, movies, and other interests, children's tastes differ. Some boys and girls avoid the thrillers, preferring the milder entertainment of music or comedy, or the more thoughtful quiz or forum discussions. There can be no doubt, however, that the largest audience is attracted to the blood-and-thunder adventure serials. These are the programs which are the time-clock for great numbers of school-age children.

While these adventure serials seem to follow a formula or pattern, they are not really "all alike," as casual listeners think, but differ widely, not only in their content and characters, but also in the skill and care of their script writing and production. Some of them are hackneyed, lacking integrity in plot and background. Others are imaginative and sincere, with honest characterization and carefully authenticated background. Thus, some of these programs serve our children, much as books do, offering entertainment, information, and background. Some of them offer little beyond suspense and excitement, though the children seem to enjoy them nevertheless.

It is these programs which have drawn the greatest criticism from parents, who complain that they are full of violence, suspenseful, and overstimulating. Almost always the program that is most heartily disapproved of in any poll of parental opinion turns out to be the one enjoying the highest rating with the young audience. The children, on the other hand, often reject parentally "approved" programs as dull and unexciting, no matter how desirable they may be from other points of view. One committee of parents which issued a carefully selected list of "recommended" juvenile programs, rechecked a year later and discovered that all but one of the "approved" programs had disappeared from the air, though most of the programs not so listed were kept on the air, presumably by audience demand.

Chills and Thrills

What are they finding in this listening that keeps them coming back daily for more? Like the comics, adventure programs provide for many children escape from the humdrum of ordinary living. Where in their daily routines will most of our children today find opportunities for adventure? Certainly not on city or even suburban streets, in communities hedged around with restrictions. Not in our shrinking homes, crowded and ill-planned for childhood. Not even in the routines of school and the supervised playground. Small wonder that so many children search for it in radio listening, movies, and comics. Along with their favorite hero they can fly through the air, travel to remote corners of the earth in search of buried treasure, or zoom by airplane to the deepest jungles. They can live dangerously yet remain within the reassuring safety of home.

Great numbers of children seem to take in their stride an amazing amount of blood and thunder and remain seemingly undamaged by it. Their hero's perpetual state of jeopardy they take quite casually, having long since discovered that the hero always survives these threats—else the program could not continue tomorrow. They seem to prefer programs with plenty of action, sound effects, suspense, and violent happenings. Do we have to give them what they want? The answer again seems to be that we need to determine for each child how much is enough, how much is too much.

Whether or not such programs are overstimulating or frightening will depend on the particular child who listens, and somewhat, too, on the quantity of such listening. This has already been discussed in relation to comics. That these programs sometimes provide the stuff from which nightmares are made is not surprising, since everything in the child's experience is grist to the mill of his fantasies. The fact that a particular experience—whether radio or television program, comics, or movies—gives form to his dreams does not necessarily make it harmful. It may possibly be helpful in providing a pattern for working out problems of his own. We do not know, with certainty, how far such experiences provide release or how far they increase tension. Psychiatrists suggest, however, that where a child seems to be unduly disturbed by radio, movies, or comics, he may need to be protected from such experiences. But beyond that, parents will want to examine other factors which may be contributing to his fears. Talking over his fears with him may give us the key to his problems—and only by understanding these can we really protect him from experiences which may be too much for him. Just prohibiting a particular program won't solve the problem. And general prohibitions against listening will, in the long run, not work. We want to enrich the child's life, rather than restrict it, by providing attractive activities, new interests, real adventures that may supply those things which he lacks and for which he is seeking.

Responding to pressure from parents, the networks and some producers of children's adventure serials have made efforts to tone down the excitement in their programs, and especially the suspense of the "cliff-hanger," by which they hope to carry over the child's listening interest from one day to the next.

Children and Adult Programs

One disconcerting result of some of the efforts to "reform" children's programs has been to divert young listeners to adult programs which are not subject to censorship as "juvenile" entertainment. It is not hard to see why. Even the most daring juvenile adventure serial would be hard put to it to compete with the violence, the pace, and the grueling suspense of adult crime and mystery programs. Evidently children like it rough, and when they don't get what they want in their own programs, they take it where they find it.

A surprising number of children, girls more than boys, listen to daytime dramas—the so-called "soap operas." Parents are often amazed to find their youngsters listening breathlessly to a medley of intrigue, romance, divorce, jealousy, blackmail, love, and hate in melodramatic scenes never intended for young ears. Much of this would seem to be far out of range of their childish understanding and experience. Why do they listen? Perhaps for the very reason that such emotional matters in adult affairs are usually carefully veiled from our children. Yet they have already sensed that more goes on in the adult world than meets the eye—or ear—and they want to know. Unfortunately, the distorted pictures they get from these heart-throb dramas will hardly clarify these dark matters for them. At six or seven or eight (they listen as young as that!) they will get only the emotional overtones and a sense of satisfaction from just being included. But the nine- or ten- or eleven-year-old may find the soap opera's standard of human relationship mystifying or even disturbing. Here again it is not by forbidding such listening but by listening with them and then by talking over and interpreting what we hear together that we can best help our children. Many a good family discussion has been inspired by a bad radio program!

Learning to Discriminate

Along with all the sound and fury—adventure, crime, and mystery— the young people are also listening to quiz programs, educational and informational discussion, dramas, comedy, music, sports, and news. Some of it is first-rate radio; some of it is pure corn. Some boys and girls are highly selective in their listening; some listen indiscriminately. This sampling, of movies and comics as well as radio, is one of the ways in which children learn not only what there is in the world to choose from, but also what they like and what they don't. It is one of the ways of learning to discriminate. Our job is to keep them in touch with a variety of things that are being offered, to offer them a balanced diet, and to help them arrive at their own standards of selection.

Listening Together

Our wisest course is to listen with the children to the programs they most enjoy, not with a view to criticizing their choices or ridiculing their tastes, but rather to keeping informed about what they are hearing and being prepared to discuss the programs with them. Listening together is a sharing of experience which can replace the fast disappearing practice of family reading together.

If we are patient and tolerant, we can watch the evolution of our children's tastes and interests, watch them discard one program and go on to others, as they grow in discrimination and judgment. We can invite them to listen with us to the programs we enjoy, and find a common ground of fun and interest in comedy, drama, music, or sports. We need not expect them to desert their childish delights and to accept ours overnight. But in homes where the adults habitually listen to good programs ("good" in its widest sense, covering many interests) the children will grow eventually in appreciation and discernment. In families, taste is contagious.

Time for Listening

When radio listening cuts too heavily into a child's time-schedule, parents can help him budget his time to include the things that must be done: a time for homework, music practice, outdoor play, household chores, etc. Usually these "musts" can be fitted in with due regard for certain favorite program hours. Talking it over with the child will determine in a friendly way which programs may have to be dropped, and which can, perhaps, accompany some of the chores. Doing homework to the accompaniment of radio seems to be almost universal, and parents as well as teachers are concerned about this. Where a child's school marks show plainly that the homework is suffering, this should be a convincing argument even to him. He should be willing to experiment for a while with homework unaccompanied by radio, and if his marks improve, he may concede that homework and radio do not mix happily, at least for him. Teachers report, however, that many students combine radio with their homework with no apparent damage to their marks. They seem to have developed a technique for listening with one ear!

GOING TO THE MOVIES

None of the movies shown in motion-picture houses in this country are made especially for children. This is despite the fact that children are heavy movie-goers. Even the shorts and animated cartoons, which children have taken unto themselves, are designed to interest the whole movie audience. Many of these are amusing and child-like, but some are sophisticated, vulgar, or frightening, and highly unsuitable for children. Serials and westerns, usually offered as Saturday afternoon children's specials, certainly have a strong appeal for the young audience, though these are also aimed at adults. Feature pictures from Dickens to Disney, are primarily intended for adults. Many are excellent for children, or for the whole family to see together; others range from the merely unsuitable to the downright undesirable.

The motion picture industry contends that motion pictures for children would be unprofitable, since this would automatically limit their audience. This is probably so. It says, too, that youngsters prefer adult entertainment.

Too Young for Movies

For young children, movie going is much more manageable than radio listening. They can be kept away from the movies. There is little in the motion picture theater that is at all suitable for children under six. Furthermore, just sitting still and keeping quiet for the duration of a full-length movie is more than should be expected of children of this age. Some of the best efforts of parents to organize special matinee movies for children have been hampered by the attendance of large numbers of two-, three-, and four-year-olds who are not yet ready for movie going of any kind. The Motion Picture Association suggests eight as a minimum age, and even then the child's first movie going should be in the company of an adult, preferably a parent, for the impact of this experience, alone and in the dark, may be devastating or, at the least, confusing.

Parental Responsibility

Parents should know what their children are seeing and be ready and willing to interpret for them the conflicting standards of behavior they find on today's screen. Talking over with children the many ideas presented, helping them to discuss their reactions and clear up their confusions about what they see and hear, is our best safeguard against the danger that they will get "false ideas" from the movies. Whether movies incite young people to crime raises the same questions which have already been discussed earlier in the chapter in connection with comics and radio.

As has already been said, too, in connection with comics and radio, some children, more sensitive than others, may need to be protected from overexciting or frightening screen showings. Sensitive children are apt to know their own limitations and will cooperate with sympathetic and reasonable parental guidance. We do not always know, however, what to protect them from. Several psychiatrists have expressed the belief that children may be more disturbed by childlike film stories, such as *Snow White, Dumbo,* and *Bambi,* which come close to the child's own fantasies than by the more remote adult dramas. Yet the former are the very films parents feel are most suitable for children, and many boys and girls do enjoy them seemingly without harmful effects.

Excessive movie going, like excessive radio listening or comics reading, suggests that something is amiss in the child's life. Too great reliance on this escape into a world of unreality, or too little else to do, or will to do it, are equally signals of distress.

Psychiatrists agree that the movies—because they provide visual experiences—are likely to have a greater and more lasting impact on children than comics or radio. It would seem important, therefore, that all children, and especially those already under tension, should be safeguarded in their movie going. By the same token it would also seem that motion pictures have high potential value for education and instruction.

AND NOW—TELEVISION

Like radio, television cannot select its audience, and children are not easily pried from their seats after the "kiddie show" is over. Revivals of the old-time western thrillers, intended for adults, are lapped up by the same young audience that has loved the radio adventure serials. But there is a difference: in television the action is much more graphic. Shooting frays and cafe brawls are vivid, with victims "biting the dust," "dead" riders falling from their horses, guns "pouring lead," murdered corpses being tossed about and frisked—all in the day's work for a ranger. There is nothing new about this type of entertainment, or about the fact that children love it. What is new is that it now becomes available to any three- or four- or five-year-old who happens to be within range.

The problems television raises for parents are twice as compelling. Young children will have to have their television sessions time-scheduled, with other activities to take them away from the screen when their show is over. School-age children who have developed a technique for listening to radio along with other activities—homework, for example, or washing dishes—will find that they cannot similarly watch television "out of one eye." Yet essentially the parent's job will be the same, calling for sympathy with children's interests, wise management of time, and sane guidance in selection.

For older children and young people, television offers really thrilling fare: *sports*—they can actually watch the World Series, play-by-play, in some distant city; *news*—they can meet face-to-face the personalities who are making world history; *politics*—they can sit in on party conventions and actually watch the wheels go round; *travel*—they can see the native life, as it is lived day by day, in India, China, Mexico, and Palestine; *drama*—they can see the best plays, modern and classical, adapted and beautifully presented with talented acting. What opportunities for expanding young people's experiences and range of vision!

If we are wise, we shall make this fascinating new medium serve our children more fully than radio has. Visual images, it has been said, make deeper and more lasting impressions than auditory ones. Now is the time, while it is still in its early stage, for educators and parents to explore television's possibilities. Skillfully used, at home and at school, television can widen cultural and educational horizons for our children to an extent never before attained by textbooks, movies, or radio.

WHAT TO DO?

In evaluating these different media, we must take into account not only what each has to offer but the combined impact of all of them upon the children. While we have no way to measure the effects of any one program or movie or comics magazine, yet we must consider the sum total of this barrage of sound and fury to which all our children are subjected from all sides. Our task is to find a balance.

What Can Parents Do?

1. *Try to understand the basic needs of children—and of your own children in particular.*

2. *Know what your children are reading, seeing, hearing.* Listen with them to their preferred programs, or go with them to movies of their own choosing. Introduce them (not too insistently) to other reading, other programs, other movies which you think they will enjoy. Invite them to listen with you to certain of your favorite programs, or go with you to a movie of your choice.

3. *Discuss their favorite programs, comics, movies, with them.* Such discussions (if they are without censure or condescension) often help break down barriers and create mutual understanding.

4. *Respect their rights and feelings*—don't throw away their comics without their consent, don't shut off their radio or interrupt their programs needlessly, don't drag them out of a movie in the middle.

5. *Help them develop critical standards by pointing out values;* good drawing or good content in a comics magazine, good production or good writing in movies or radio programs. Help them to recognize these differences.

6. *Help them budget their time,* for homework, music practice, outdoor play, necessary chores, allowing for their favorite radio programs, some comics and other reading, and occasional movies.

7. *If you find that certain programs or movies upset them, suggest that they skip these for a while.* If they are really disturbed they will probably be glad to cooperate in this. But if they still seem to want these disturbing programs or movies, you may find that just sitting with them while they are listening or watching will be reassuring. If radio listening or movie going absorbs the children to the exclusion of other interests and activities, talk this over with them, too. Together you may arrive at a sensible plan for cutting down or selecting more wisely.

8. *See that they have plenty of enjoyable things to do, places to go, wholesome friendships, varied experiences, and real adventures.* Encourage their hobbies and help them get the needed "makings." (Puppet making has been greatly stimulated by television.) Include them, too, in your own fun and interests.

JOSETTE FRANK

Learning the Uses of Money

MONEY is a modern tool which all children must learn to use. In the family of but a few generations ago very little money was handled in the course of a year and managing that little was usually the business of the head of the household. But today, more and more the family's activities take place outside the home—especially the earning and the spending—and each member of the family must handle some part of the family's cash.

The child has to learn how to use money for modern living just as he has to learn how to cross the street in a maze of modern traffic or how to tune in a radio. Parents and teachers, however, find it more difficult to teach the child about money than about most other common things. We have certain traditions about money which make it impossible to approach this subject in an objective mood. For reasons that stretch back past the memories and the intentions of those living, money is to all of us a beloved enemy. It is a symbol of power, of which we never have enough, and of which most other people seem to have more. When it is being spent, money becomes a means of self-assertion but because of our limited resources, it is a constant reminder of our frustration. In community life, money becomes a measure of worth and for most of us self-esteem suffers.

It is no wonder then that we suffer from what we might call a special "money mood" and that we separate money from the rest of the child's education, sensing in it potential danger and attaching to it peculiar moral significance.

SPENDING BEFORE EARNING

The first stumbling block in approaching the educational task is our tradition that one must not spend money until he has earned it. Yet obviously such a maxim cannot hold for children in our society as it is constituted today. We have already brought up a whole generation of boys and girls who had to be educated as buyers, who had to learn to spend, without ever having had any genuine experience in earning. Whether or not we believe that this is desirable, we must accept the actual situation and proceed to educate our children on that basis.

We would not think of withholding from a child the necessities of life until he has earned them: food and shelter, clothes and education, toys and books. We have always granted the child his needs as a matter of course. Why, then should money be made an exception? Parents and teachers must recognize that today money is very much the same kind of necessity and they must help the child learn to use this modern tool objectively.

It may be argued that the child does not *need* money, since all the necessities of life are supplied him. But this argument ignores the important fact that money is a part of the environment in which the modern child lives and breathes. In most homes today the child sees money early and often. Even a three-year-old will have noticed that the adults around him are very much concerned with certain pieces of green paper and certain round discs of various sizes and weights. He sees these precious pieces exchanged between them with solemn faces. Later he becomes aware that desirable goods may be obtained in such exchanges—a round disc is exchanged for an ice-cream cone, a ride on the bus, or a toy. He learns very early that money is important.

CONTACTS WITH MONEY INEVITABLE

Even if we could protect our children from our preoccupation and concern with money, we could not keep them in ignorance. There are, for example, visitors who, with the best intentions but with little ingenuity in entertaining the young, offer the child odd pennies—for being cute, of for not being a nuisance. They give him coins and he finds it fun to jingle them or just to handle them. Soon he discovers—again from the attitudes of adults—that certain of these coins are more important — more valued — than others. And so, whether we will it so or not, he comes to an acquaintance with money.

At first he will probably handle the coins much as he does any other toy. He will arrange them in piles or in rows. He will scatter them about. He will even lose them. Then he will discover that these shiny bits are different—to us, at least—from other shiny bits. We are not overly upset when he loses his ball or his toy fireman's badge. But when he loses coins we scold him roundly for being "careless with money."

Sooner or later we shall expect him to use money with understanding and not merely play with the symbols—just as we gradually accustom him to speak on a real telephone instead of on a toy replica. For this there is no fixed date; there is no set age for beginning; nor can any standard ritual be prescribed. We can only say that at about five or six most children will have become sufficiently interested in money to handle it themselves and sufficiently aware of one-two-three to know the difference between a few and many.

There are, however, great differences in this regard both among children and among homes. The city child obviously comes into contact with money more often and at an earlier age than the country child. The younger children in a family will want money in hand at an earlier age than did the eldest child; his possession of "spending money" now sets an example of power to be emulated. Perhaps it is safe to say that the time to give children money-in-hand is when they can count and when they seem to understand what these transactions mean.

THE ALLOWANCE

Since the child learns to do by doing, we can help him toward a practical acquaintance with money and its working by seeing that he has a regular supply. This "allowance" we must think of as an educational device, just as we think of other tools placed in the hands of the child before he is entirely capable of using them—pencils and hammers, needles and rakes. But many of us feel differently about money and money *is* different. The other things which the child gets may, indeed, be misused but after all there is a limit to what can be done with a toy or even with a small hammer. With money, what there is of it, the child has unlimited choices. This very fact is alarming. He may choose not only foolishly, but injuriously. We are afraid to trust him with this slight degree of freedom, this bit of discretion, for the outcome is beyond our own control. We are not ourselves altogether clear as to the place of money in life and we attach to it many conflicting emotions. Money, for most people, is hard to get, at least in sufficient amounts, therefore it should be used respectfully. Money confers power in a way that is quite peculiar and so much power in young hands may be dangerous.

In striking contrast with the old attitude that children should earn their own spending money, thus teaching them the rewards of labor and the benefits of accumulation, today we believe that the child's allowance, like his supper or underwear, is his by virtue of being a member of the family. It is given him neither as largess nor as a reward for good behavior. It represents merely a small part of the cash that is ordinarily expended on him—a separable part which he is free to manipulate to suit himself, with the goal that in time he will manage all the cash items that concern him and that are separable from the general family expenses.

HOW MUCH?

How much is a fair allowance? Parents often ask this question and nobody can tell them the answer. It depends on too many factors that only the parents can know or judge or control. How old is the child? How much experience has he had in handling money? What are the opportunities or needs to spend? What are other children in the family getting? What is the level of the family's regular expenditures? What are his companions spending? All of these factors may have a bearing upon the amount of the allowance for a particular child. There is no mathematical formula that will yield a universal answer. The amount has to be arbitrary to begin with, and it has to be adjusted from time to time by experimental groping. A boy at high school may need much more spending money than his sister who is still in grade school. A child in the country may have less need for money than his city cousin of the same age. There are also such variables as carfare and lunches and contributions and membership dues. What is important is that whatever portion of the allowance a child receives over and above any fixed or prescribed expenditures must be his very own—free and clear—to spend, to save, to give away, even to lose. That is the essence of the allowance.

LEARNING TO SAVE

Our whole civilization does of course depend upon "saving" in a broad sense. The individual also needs to learn how to live on less than the total income so as to build up reserves for various contingencies and emergencies. That is the nature of our kind of world. But parents hardly help the child in such learning if they make "saving" a ritual in which a portion of the income or receipts is mechanically set aside. For the child on an allowance, saving that is not in terms of the needs and purposes which he discovers for himself means either that he is getting more money than he can spend to good effect or that he is missing the education which the allowance is intended to help him acquire.

Too little money leaves no chance ever to save or to plan. Too much money may result in great "savings" but it gives no chance ever to discriminate, to defer purchases, to sacrifice a present for a later satisfaction—to learn the saving aspect of money-handling.

In learning to handle money, as in all learning, individual differences are apparent and here, as elsewhere, no procedure will guarantee the desired results in all children. We do not always know what it is that makes one child a spendthrift, another—perhaps in the same family—a thrifty hoarder. One child won't spend because nothing appeals to him enough to make him part with his money. Another cannot save because everything appeals to him too much. To some boys and girls everything seen in the store or in the possession of a companion gives rise to an aching want. These children never seem to have enough money. There are others who find in money a useful means to popularity. Sometimes these differences, or rather extreme forms of meeting situations, are indicative of the child's temperamental needs or difficulties; sometimes they are symptomatic of deep-seated problems. It is usually more important to know *why* the child spends or saves than to count up how much money is involved. Excessive spending and excessive saving may be equally suggestive of some anxiety or insecurity for, in the traditional meaning of money, hoarding spells a reserve of power, whereas spending it is, in itself, a display of power.

PAY FOR HOME WORK

The question is often asked, should children be paid for work they do in the home? Helping with the housework — washing dishes, sweeping and dusting, making up beds, removing snow or ashes, or looking after the furnace—presents itself as the most obvious, and it is in fact the most frequent, means of earning money among children not placed in industrial or commercial jobs. Selling or delivering newspapers at fixed hours, helping in shops, looking after younger children, mowing lawns and doing occasional errands of one sort or another, constitute the range of most opportunities available outside the home. Within recent years "baby sitting," covering the care of children of a wide range of ages, opened up a lucrative field for teen-agers. This can be valuable experience, if young people are properly prepared and guided.

This raises, however, another issue that is quite as important as the need to experience earning. Within the home it is necessary to carry on a great variety of activities for the comfort and convenience and well-being of all the members. Many of the tasks fall upon the mother because she is, in most homes, the houseworker as well as the household manager and homemaker. Whatever part of the household work can be done by other members of the family is not merely a relief for the mother, but a contribution to the welfare of the entire group. To place the odd jobs that the children can do on a pay basis sets up a false relation between the members of the cooperative enterprise that homemaking represents. We expect children to wash dishes or dust the furniture because they are able and willing to share in the work of keeping the plant going. There is no thought of bargaining here any more than in the distribution of the benefits. The child gets his food, his shelter, his clothing, his recreation, his school and his social opportunities on a basis unrelated to his contributions—the strong child and the weak, the industrious one and the lazy one, all share benefits in terms of their respective needs.

The one possible rule that seems applicable is this: *children may be paid for doing only that for which somebody else would otherwise be hired*. This leaves the child free to take the job or to leave it, without needing to apologize or to defend his action. If we pay him for doing work that we consider part of his duty, we place the transaction upon a false basis: for in the first place, people must not expect material compensation for doing their duty; and in the second place, when work is done for pay, the worker should be free to abandon it if the conditions no longer suit him.

VALUES MONEY CANNOT BUY

If, through his allowance, the child gets his education in relative values among things that can be purchased, he has to learn also that there are some values which money can neither measure nor buy. To pay a child a quarter for doing his arithmetic will teach him neither arithmetic nor the purchasing power of the quarter. To fine him for forgetting to put away his coat will accomplish little for his sense of order but it may seriously impair his management of an allowance subjected to such incalculable—and unwarranted—fluctuations.

Too many parents use the allowance not primarily as an instrument for educating the child with regard to money, but as an instrument of discipline, to purchase the child's obedience, or affection, or goodness. "If you don't bring in a better report card next time you will not get your allowance," or, "If you are late again I will fine you ten cents," and so on, in infinite variations.

Conversely, many parents—often the same parents—attempt to manipulate the allowance at the other end for purposes unrelated to the basic problem. "If you bring a better report I will add ten cents," or "Every time you take a nap you will get a nickel." There are endless temptations to use money rewards, in contrast to money penalties, for deeds or services or efforts that, within the family, should be without money and without price.

Still more confusing are those situations in which money does, indeed, play a role but in which it is difficult for the parents and practically impossible for the children to see just what that role is.

SHARING IN FAMILY COUNCIL

Whether the family's income be large or small, we must recognize that for the children, at least, it is almost impossible to reconcile the many unavoidable inconsistencies in our handling of money. It is a necessary part of the children's education to learn the grounds on which discriminations are made and the methods by which decisions are reached. It is, therefore, helpful to take them into council when budget problems are discussed, even if you know and they know that the final decision will not rest with them.

The various talents or handicaps of the different members of the family obviously call for adjustments. One child needs special schooling, braces for his teeth, or a particularly expensive diet. One is harder on his clothes than another. It is impossible to provide for every individual all that he wants, but it is possible to consider the best for all concerned—in view of the available funds. This is possible, that is, if the individuals have at heart their common welfare, if they are actuated by mutual consideration and affection.

Perhaps even younger children can understand that each individual's claim rests upon his membership in a joint enterprise. We can help them see the family principle operating in the community. Even out there, among strangers, people in distress or in want have to be cared for, whether they have been good, bad, or indifferent; while there are any resources, all will have something.

Children often ask questions about money. They are curious to know how the family derives its income, to know its financial status and the significance of money in society at large. They need this orientation and we must try to answer their questions, but most of the information and most of the attitudes which they gather about money will come from observing and from living, rather than from being told. Not all that children learn about money can be taught through conversation or even by giving them a chance to handle money for themselves. They learn also from observing the financial affairs and attitudes of grown-ups. Here, as elsewhere, the fundamental attitudes are caught, not taught.

SIDONIE GRUENBERG

Part Five

APPROACHING ADULTHOOD

Approaching Adulthood

THE years between childhood and adulthood—from twelve through the teens—are generally regarded as the period of adolescence.

If parents in increasing numbers have come to look upon these years as the most perplexing, trying and disquieting period of parenthood, there is good reason. First, with modern life becoming increasingly complex, the process of growing up in turn presents more problems. Second, not only is the child approaching physical maturity—he must also become intellectually, emotionally and socially mature. As these various forms of growing up may not all take place at the same time, adolescence stretches out over an increasingly longer period. A girl who reaches puberty at the age of twelve or thirteen years may find herself at a loss for a time because her intimate associates are still immature, while she is experiencing feelings that make her seek wider social contacts; or a boy, growing up with adults and spending much of his time in reading and adult conversation, may reach sixteen with an intellectual maturity far beyond that of the average adult, while physically and emotionally he is still immature.

But other periods in the life of the child are similarly complex in present-day civilization. During early childhood, boys and girls must not only learn to care for such simple physical needs as keeping clean, but they must also learn to read and write, to be polite, to get along with others, and to control their tempers and their impulse to cry over every injury.

Not until the child begins to grow up is he, however, likely to be troubled by, or even conscious of, the fact that there are many sides to his nature; that these sides do not always keep pace with one another; and that, although he is "too big" to do some things, he is not old enough to do others. He may find that although he is too grown up to play "Indians" or to be "tucked in," he is not yet considered old enough to go to late parties; or although he is wearing long trousers he is not yet considered old enough to smoke. Nor does the law help by setting any one age as the end of childhood and the beginning of adulthood. On the contrary, it fixes one age as the minimum for driving an automobile, another for required school attendance, another for entering industry, another for culpability for unlawful conduct, another for marrying without parental consent, another for making valid contracts, and another for voting; and, although some of these may coincide, they are more likely to vary, not only from state to state but even within one state and one community.

Thus the growing up which takes place very simply in primitive children, who are often initiated into their adult responsibilities as soon as they have reached puberty, is so gradual and complex in our children that it requires approximately eight years; and these eight years have come to be regarded as a special period with peculiar qualities and characteristics of its own, known as adolescence.

"Problems of Adolescence"

Within the last few years the "problems of adolescence" have been the subject of so many investigations, books, articles, and speeches that many people have come to think of adolescence as necessarily a period of problems. Every period of life has its problems. But the problems occurring in early childhood or in late adult life are likely to bother only the members of the immediate family who, in one way or another, must adjust themselves to the undesirable personality traits and behavior manifestations of their offspring, their sisters and brothers, or the husband or wife, as the case may be. The problems occurring during adolescence, however, are likely to be noticed in the boarding school, the high school, and the college, or in recreational groups, such as clubs and camps; and they may come to the attention of such an agency as the juvenile court. As these institutions and agencies have looked to the fields of psychology and psychiatry for help in dealing with their young people, the problems occurring during adolescence have doubtless been scrutinized more extensively and more specifically than those occurring, for example, during the twenties or the thirties.

It is not to be denied that the teen years present very definite problems of a physical, mental, and social nature which youth must necessarily meet in its adjustment to present needs and preparation for life's future demands. These problems are sufficiently well recognizd, and the most common causes for failure in meeting them sufficiently well understood to justify discussion. Yet to assume that every adolescent boy or girl is drifting about in an emotional whirlpool or may be dashed on the shores of failure because of some hidden conflict, is nothing more than an indulgence in phantasy.

HOW YOUNGSTERS GROW AND DEVELOP

A sudden and perhaps surprising increase in height and weight, and in the size of arms, legs, hands, feet, and any other part of the anatomy is typical at the onset of adolescence. Within one year the child may gain twenty-five or thirty pounds in weight and four or five inches in height. This period of rapid growth usually occurs anywhere between the ages of eight and fourteen in girls and between eleven and sixteen in boys. On the average, twelve-year-old girls are going through their most rapid period of growth, while for boys the year between fourteen and fifteen will frequently be the one in which the greatest spurt in height takes place.

This sudden increase, however, rarely changes the nature of the child's physique. In other words, both the short and the tall child grow noticeably during adolescence, the short child growing into a short adult, and the tall child into a tall adult. A short child may outstrip a taller one for awhile if the latter happens to be a late-maturing individual. If puberty takes place early, the full growth is also likely to be reached early.

There are, of course, exceptions; a child who has had long and serious illness interfering with normal growth before adolescence may, on recovery, suddenly make up for this during adolescence; and a child suffering from a glandular disturbance may have an abnormal rate of growth. For the average child, however, nothing but continuous growth should be expected.

Girls grow much more slowly after fourteen years and usually stop growing entirely before they are twenty. Boys may continue to grow slightly until they are twenty-two or even twenty-three years of age, but their rate of growth is slower after the fifteenth or the sixteenth year.

Strength also increases rapidly from the seventh year on, and more rapidly during the early teens.

THE REPRODUCTIVE ORGANS MATURE

The most outstanding physiological development during adolescence is the maturing of the reproductive organs. When these organs become capable of functioning as in the adult—when the ovaries in the girl begin to release the egg cells, or ova, essential to child-bearing, and the testicles in the boy begin to release the sperm cells essential to fertilization—puberty has been reached.

It is not easy to know just when the reproductive organs begin to function. A girl is said to be "mature" when she has had her first menstrual flow, or "monthly period." Although there is no similar process in the boy, the discharge of semen during sleep, known as a "nocturnal emission," is often considered evidence that he is approaching maturity. It may be some time, however, before the maturing of egg cells in the case of the girl, and of spermatozoa in the case of the boy, makes reproduction possible.

The age at which these signs of maturity occur varies considerably. In this country puberty is likely to occur between the ages of twelve and fifteen years in girls and a year or two later in boys. But race, climate, living conditions, and the child's own physical condition all play a part in the maturing process and make even further variations in age possible.

Accompanying and preceding puberty itself, noticeable physical changes take place in the child. There is a growth of hair in the arm-pits and pubic regions, and further development of the genitals; the voice becomes fuller and, in the boy, is likely to "break" as it changes from a childish to a more masculine pitch. As the girl's breasts develop and her hips broaden, her body begins to appear womanly, while the boy, with his broadening shoulders and the growth of hair on his face, begins to take on a more manly aspect.

THE FUNDAMENTALS OF PHYSICAL HYGIENE

With all these changes taking place in the child's body, some thought must be given to his physical hygiene. Rapid growth is likely to cause either a tremendous increase in the child's appetite, or, particularly in the girl, a tendency to finickiness with loss of appetite at some times and strong, special cravings—as, for example, for particularly sweet or sour dishes—at other times. Attention must therefore be given not only to the child's diet but also to his eating habits. Sudden increase in the rate of growth is likely to cause fatigue, making long hours of sleep essential. Rapid growth of the larger muscles, gain in strength, and the possible awakening of a disturbing sex-consciousness make out-of-door exercise highly desirable. As all the increased body activities are likely to increase the body wastes, good habits of elimination, including freedom from constipation without the use of drugs, and a healthy, active skin condition are of primary importance.

In other words, the rules for the adolescent are much the same as those for the younger child. Parents scarcely need to be reminded that an abundance of milk, wholegrain bread and cereals, and fresh fruits and vegetables are essential; that a diet too rich in pastries, sweets, and other carbohydrates is undesirable; and that tea and coffee are unsuitable. They know from experience that regular meals and a minimum of eating between meals keep the small child's digestive system in good order; and that plenty of out-of-door play, regular toilet habits, and a clean body are essential to keeping him comfortable, healthy, and cheerful. By the time adolescence is reached, they should be able to depend on their boys and girls to follow a hygienic routine with little assistance.

Certain modifications may have to be introduced; e.g., increase in the amounts of food, gradual decrease in the hours of sleep, changes in the type of out-of-door activity, and perhaps greater conscientiousness about internal and external body cleanliness. But there are no special rules for the hygiene of the adolescent; puberty is, after all, but the continuation of a development which began before birth and for which the normal human being is as well equipped as he is for any other natural physical change. The parent who has helped his child establish good habits of eating, sleeping, elimination, cleanliness, posture, and exercise in early childhood needs only to impress upon the adolescent the importance of continuing to observe the fundamental principles of physical hygiene in order to maintain a healthy and efficient body during this or any other period of his life.

ADOLESCENT BEHAVIOR

Much of the behavior which parents consider unusual, disturbing, irritating, or alarming is actually but a normal reaction to the processes of physical development and the general business of growing up. One of the trying difficulties for both parents and child may be the self-consciousness that comes to a child who has his attention constantly called to his rapid growth. He may become diffident and sensitive, developing an awkwardness that is the result of a feeling of social ineptness rather than of growth changes in themselves. So, too, the self-consciousness and unhappiness resulting from the poor complexion with which many adolescents are afflicted may lead to such lack of self-confidence that the boy or girl prefers solitude to participation in activities with others, and may wander about friendless and forlorn. One of the things an adolescent fears most is to be considered different from others. This makes him more aware of changes in his body and more sensitive to criticism and comparison with others.

The importance of good posture habits in maintaining the various organs of the body in their proper position and in enabling them to work to the best advantage has been so much stressed by physicians in recent years that posture charts, posture exercises, and posture clinics have been made available for great numbers of children. Posture training is something which should be begun in early childhood and under the supervision of someone familiar with the anatomy and "mechanics" of the human body. The subject is called to the attention of parents of teen-age children for two reasons only:

(1) Rapidly growing children may have difficulty in learning how to carry themselves or may feel tired and inclined to slump, so that special attention to posture is advisable at this time; and (2) many adolescents, particularly girls, assume unhealthy posture because of self-consciousness over their sudden growth. The former may need more rest, other forms of exercise, and possibly the advice of the physician, but the latter need chiefly a change of mental attitude.

Round-shoulderedness is not an easy habit to overcome. Although it is difficult to convince the twelve- or thirteen-year-old girl that she will come to be proud of her height and her good figure as she grows older, it is far easier to prevent poor posture habits than to correct them once they are formed.

Parents can accomplish a great deal in this direction merely by helping the girl choose clothes suitable to her type, and, so far as possible, sufficiently attractive to make her confident that she looks well. They can also help greatly by softening some of the inevitable jibes of thoughtless brothers and sisters (or, indeed, by encouraging these members of the family to be more considerate) and, most of all, by helping the girl to see her good points and gain enough self-confidence not only to take criticism good-naturedly but to make the best of her figure as it is.

Self-consciousness over an unhealthy and unsightly complexion is even more likely to give parents cause for anxiety. Skin eruptions are fairly common during early adolescence. The small ducts through which oil is carried to the skin apparently do not grow fast enough to take care of the increased activity of the glands supplying this secretion, and, as a result, they become stopped up and a comedo, or "blackhead," forms at the opening of the duct. As the glands continue to function even though drainage is blocked, the ducts become overfilled and little raised places, or "pimples," begin to appear on the surface of the skin.

It is unfortunate that just at the time when the growing child's skin is perhaps in need of a little added care he is most tempted by chocolates, candy bars, cookies, ice-cream sundaes, and soda-fountain drinks, and possibly most careless about keeping his digestive system in healthy order. Skin specialists have found that proper attention to the fundamental principles of physical hygiene already referred to, wholesome diet, free elimination, plenty of sunshine and out-of-door exercise, and thorough daily or twice-daily washing with warm water and soap (which is not nearly so harmful to the complexion as many adolescents believe) will keep most young complexions in good condition. When the skin fails to respond well to this routine, more specific measures under the direction of a physician are advisable. It is well known, however, that proper attention to the skin in the early stages of these afflictions can prevent development of the unsightly later stages for which medical treatment may be necessary.

But in spite of our best efforts we cannot eliminate all the sources of unhappy self-consciousness during adolescence, and therefore we might well spend some of our effort in helping young people acquire a philosophy of life which will make their burdens bearable.

We must accept the fact that the world has its share of unfeeling individuals, who derive some compensatory satisfaction from calling attention to the defects and weaknesses of others. There are always some who, being insecure themselves, seek reassurance by pointing out directly or indirectly the physical, mental, or social imperfections and inferiorities of others. To meet these attacks requires courage and a greater indifference to pain than most adolescents possess. For it is through the experience of pain that individuals develop a philosophy of life which permits them to endure suffering, and in early adolescence most boys and girls have not yet had sufficient experience to endure pain easily.

Discoursing on the injustices of life adds little sweetness to the adolescent's own suffering. Perhaps the most that can be done to help him is to encourage him to see his strong points and build his philosophy of life which permits them to endure suffering, and in and then to help him gain a little perspective, so that even though the tribulations of today loom largest, he will not completely lose sight of the fact that tomorrow and the next day and the next still hold promise of brightness.

Preparing Your Daughter for Womanhood

THE majority of girls reach puberty and begin to menstruate between the ages of twelve and fourteen years; but menstruation may start in the tenth or eleventh year (occasionally even younger), or the first menstruation may not take place until fifteen or sixteen or older. Thus there is no specific age for the beginning of the menstrual cycle, but a wide range of individual variation.

How Menstruation Varies in Different Girls

There are also individual differences with regard to regularity or irregularity of the menstrual periods, the amount of blood, and the length of time for the period. Some girls menstruate regularly (once every four weeks) from the start; others menstruate irregularly for a while before the monthly rhythm is established, with perhaps a little longer than four weeks between periods or skipping of the menses for a month or more. However, if there is a prolonged cessation of menstrual periods after they have once occurred, it is advisable to consult a physician.

Some girls have a scanty flow of blood compared to others, while the period may last from two or three to five or six days. The amount of blood and length of the period may be more or less at various times for the same individual, as well as for different persons. Thus there is a fairly wide range for these aspects of menstruation within the limits of normal functioning.

HOW THE BODY DEVELOPS

The establishment of the menstrual periods is not the only striking physical change during adolescence. Concurrently, there is a spurt in body growth and a development of the secondary sexual characteristics. Accelerated growth in height and weight is usually very noticeable. Less visible, but equally important, is an increase in size of internal organs such as heart, lungs, uterus, digestive organs, etc. The breasts round out, the pubic hair appears, the hips widen and the figure acquires more mature feminine curves. Both the accelerated general growth and the development of these secondary sexual characteristics are stimulated by glandular secretions (hormones) produced by the ovaries from the time of their maturing at puberty.

The Growing Girl Needs Plenty of Rest and Food

The rates of growth are not identical for different parts and organs of the body, which means that the organism is in a continuous state of somewhat uneven development for a few years after puberty. As a result of this uneven developmental process, the girl is apt to be under more or less physical strain during early adolescence until the rate of growth has become slower. She needs sufficient rest (nine or more hours nightly) and an ample amount of nutritious food to offset this physical stress and protect her health.

It appears that nature affords some protection of health, during the adolescent stage of rapid growth, through a coincidental tendency to refrain from excessive physical exercise. Comparing the attitudes and interests of a fairly large group of girls who had begun to menstruate, with girls of similar age not yet menstruating, Stone and Barker found a definite trend toward avoidance of vigorous physical activity among the girls who had recently matured.

The menstrual periods are often accompanied by even more distaste for physical exertion than exists between the periods. The healthy girl should not, however, suffer very much pain during menstruation. Any considerable amount of pain indicates that a doctor should be consulted, for painful menstruation may be associated with thyroid overactivity or some other physical condition requiring medical treatment.

HOW GIRLS REACT TO MENSTRUATION

Long before adolescence, most girls have some hazy knowledge of menstruation, obtained through glimpses of stained clothing of their mothers or older sisters or by overhearing conversations. These chance observations may be misinterpreted by a child, and menstruation conceived as due to injury or illness rather than to a natural biological process. Such mistaken ideas probably are only partially corrected later on when the girl is given information to prepare her for menstruating. Traces of earlier childish misunderstanding appear, for instance, in the fact that girls and women often speak of menstruation as an illness.

Fears of Menstruation

During the preadolescent years just before puberty, the girl usually secures considerable information about menstruation from her mother or older sisters or friends. She then becomes expectant of this phenomenon in her own experience. Usually she regards the prospect of starting to menstruate with a mixture of hope and fear. On the one hand, she wishes for it because it will mean that she is no longer a child but is mature sexually and closer to fulfillment of normal desires to marry and have children. On the other hand, she is fearful because she does not know exactly what will happen or where she will be when her first period occurs.

One of the girl's principal apprehensions is that she may be in school or somewhere else away from the protection of mother and older sisters, with no one to help her through her novitiate into womanhood. She may expect a gushing forth of blood instead of the actual slow bleeding, and believe that there is danger of her condition being revealed by wet, stained clothing. If she has heard that girls sometimes faint when menstruating, she may be afraid that she will do so. Thus her anticipation of the badge of womanhood is marred by her anxiety.

PREPARING THE GIRL FOR MENSTRUATION. Adequate explanations and reassurances as to what she may expect can relieve the girl's apprehensions to some extent, but her state of expectancy will continue. She may be so eager to have her first period, either because she wishes for it so ardently or dreads it so greatly, that she may imagine she has begun to menstruate some time before this really happens. If she makes such a mistake, she will suffer from some chagrin and will need tactful reactions from her mother and older sisters.

The Beginning of Menstruation

The girl's expectant, anxious state of mind is relieved once she has begun to menstruate and lived through the initial experience. Her immediate reaction is likely to be one of disappointment, however. There is a letdown from the feeling of tension and expectancy, but she does not feel as grownup as she anticipated, nor do others treat her much differently than during her childhood. The girl is usually quite unconscious of this disappointment, and is aware only of vague irritability and depression. Often her family does not appreciate the cause of her moods of irritation and unhappiness, any more than she does; they find them annoying and hope that she will soon outgrow these unaccountable adolescent traits. If older relatives do have some insight into the situation, they will of course be more patient and tolerant.

WHY THE GIRL IS SELF-CONSCIOUS.   Another immediate reaction to the establishment of the menstrual function is self-consciousness, for the girl is concerned about keeping her periods secret from members of the opposite sex. There is a whole body of folklore about menstruation which is passed on from generation to generation and from one girl to another. This includes ideas that boys can judge when a girl is menstruating because she is pale, has dark circles under her eyes, appears fatigued, stays away from gym, etc. The girl may try to conceal such possible betrayals of her condition by all sorts of devices, using more makeup, pretending to be very lively, going to gym in spite of having a period, and so on.

Disposal of soiled articles, used to protect clothing, presents a problem because of the need to do it secretly so that brothers and their boy friends will not suspect anything. Because menstruation at first seems so extraordinary and important to the girl, it is hard for her to believe that boys are less interested than she assumes, that they are not observing her for signs of whether she has yet matured, and that they could not tell in any of the ways that she imagines if they did covertly inspect her looks and behavior.

Once accustomed to having menstrual periods, the normal attitude is acceptance of them as a natural biological function, and satisfaction in this concrete evidence of the capacity to bear children.

This attitude is so logically to be expected that it is necessary to consider why girls frequently seem to have an aversion for menstruation, as suggested even by some of the terms used in speaking of it; for example, referring to it as "the curse," which hardly indicates that it is looked upon as a blessing.

Why Some Girls Have an Aversion to Menstruation

Misconceptions left over from childhood—notions of menstruation as resulting from illness or injury—probably influence adolescent girls against acceptance of it as a natural physiological process. Another source of repulsion is an over-fastidious standard of cleanliness, originally acquired during early toilet training and later carried over into associating the stickiness of the menstrual blood with excreta from the bladder or rectum. This confusion between the blood and other excretory matter leads to thinking of menstruation as dirty.

Sometimes girls have been told that it is dangerous to health to bathe while menstruating, and they dare not alleviate the sense of uncleanliness by taking a bath. A tendency to think of menstruation as something unclean is exaggerated if a girl has had weak bladder control when a child, for the moisture from the blood then reminds her of the shamed feeling she once had because of wetting her pants.

RESISTING THE FEMININE ROLE. Aversion to menstruation may have a more serious significance when it arises from the resistance that girls and women sometimes have toward the feminine role in life. In early childhood, girls often go through a phase of wishing to be boys; this early phantasy-wish and rebellion against the reality of sex differences sometimes lingers on after puberty. If so, there is dislike of menstruating because it is the final proof of being female instead of male.

Long before adolescence, girls should have become reconciled to their sex through the knowledge that it enables them to bear children while the male can never have this experience. But mothers, and other women with whom a girl has had contact, may have robbed the prospects of marriage and motherhood of attractiveness if they have dwelt upon the problems of the marital relationship and the pain and danger of childbirth. If things she has heard from women have caused a girl to become frightened of marriage, and to associate childbirth with pain and the possibility of death, she may revert to childish wishes to be a boy instead of a girl as a means of protecting herself from fear. She may then hate menstruating because it negates her wishes to be masculine and to escape the troubles and dangers that she has learned to ascribe to the feminine lot.

The girl rarely knows that dislike of menstruation may have this origin, for if a wish to be a boy still exists at adolescence, it has been repressed and has become quite unconscious. She rationalizes her annoyance on the basis that the menstrual period interferes with athletic pursuits or social pleasures, or on other similar grounds. She does not connect her resentment of the menstrual function with a rejection of femininity, because she is unaware of such an attitude. There is conclusive evidence of the fact that girls do want to change their sex, however, for in clinical work we encounter cases where, at the age of five or six, phantasies of being a boy are very prominent, and in the psychoanalytic treatment of adult women, unconscious wishes to be masculine are often revealed.

ASSUMING A WOMAN'S RESPONSIBILILTIES. It must be remembered that there is a persistent cultural tradition that women suffer more and make greater personal sacrifices as wives and mothers than men need to do as husbands and fathers. Since menstruation is unique to females, it may become the symbol of this traditional view of woman's unhappy destiny, and an adolescent dislike of it may express the girl's reluctance to give up the carefree existence of childhood and assume the responsibilities of womanhood that growth is forcing upon her, if as yet only symbolically.

The girl who has adjusted to her feminine status during childhood does not object to menstruation, but accepts it as a step toward fulfillment of her womanhood. If she feels a little depressed at the menstrual period, it is because of some unconscious disappointment that the longing to have children is not yet to be gratified—just as married women who are trying to become pregnant are consciously disappointed when another period proves that they have not yet been successful.

Why Irregular Menstruation Occurs

Extreme irregularity, or prolonged cessation of the menses, may be of mental origin, resulting from attitudes of intense aversion and difficulty in adjusting to the feminine role. In such instances, psychological therapy may be more effective than medical treatment in restoring normal menstrual functions. The first step, however, should be a thorough medical study, since endocrine disturbances, ovarian tumors or other physical conditions may also cause interruption of the periods.

PSYCHOLOGICAL PREPARATION FOR WOMANHOOD

Regardless of age and of attitudes toward menstruation, the emotional life of the girl is still that of a child, prior to maturing of the reproductive system and the start of the menstrual cycle. At puberty, the same glandular secretions that stimulate accelerated physical growth also furnish a strong impetus toward emotional development. As the organism matures physiologically, the instinctive and emotional drives become more intense, less childlike and more womanly. It is indeed only natural that with the development of the capacity for bearing children, and for full sexual experience, there should simultaneously be an increase in sexual interests and desires.

The Adolescent Girl Is Curious About Boys

The preadolescent girl often has little interest in boys, though she probably has had a good deal of curiosity about sex matters, and during childhood normally has passed through a stage of wanting to have babies of her own. The girl who has become adolescent finds boys more attractive than she ever did before, and her thoughts and daydreams are concerned with marrying and having babies. She imagines what sexual intercourse and childbirth will be like; she sometimes has dreams of boys making love to her and of giving birth to a baby, although these sexual and childbirth motifs in dreams tend to be represented in disguised and symbolic form rather than so openly.

These ideas, phantasies, and dreams on the theme of sexual relationships and giving birth to children are the psychological counterparts of the physiological processes going on within the organism at adolescence. It is not as common for girls to turn to masturbation in the form of manual stimulation of the genitals, under the impulsion of sexual drives, as for boys, although girls occasionally masturbate when under extreme sexual tensions, so that it should not be taken as a symptom of abnormality if it does happen.

The Girl's Anxieties About Sex

The sudden influx of strong and sexually colored emotions at and directly after puberty is often frightening to the girl. Intense feelings urge her to impulsive action without stopping to think of the consequences of her acts, and she fears these impulsive tendencies because they threaten to overrule her judgment and self-contol. Her ego—her central sense of self—feels in danger of being overwhelmed by the drives arising from her instincts and emotions. The age-old feminine dread of loving not wisely but too well, of becoming involved in sexual relationships and having a child without being married, stirs in the girl's mind, if only nebulously and as a vague anxiety rather than something specifically recognized.

THE EMOTIONAL CONFLICT WITHIN THE GIRL. Besides the ego-anxiety, evoked by fear of losing control over behavior because of the strength of the instinctive and emotional impulses, ethical and moral ideals often cause girls to look upon their sexual longings as sinful, adding to anxiety and producing guilty feelings.

The ego speaks realistically, in effect saying: "I must control sexual desires, for social customs make it inexpedient to have sexual relationships or give birth to a child before marriage." The voice of conscience gives sterner warning: "It is wicked to think about sexual matters or to wish for a baby before you are married." Thus the girl may have to endure severe and prolonged emotional conflict, as biological sexual drives assert themselves while the ego and conscience struggle to keep them under control. In short, the young adolescent finds herself in possession of—or as it sometimes seems to her, possessed by—womanly instincts and emotions while still inexperienced in managing them, and before society considers her old enough to enter into actual sexual experiences.

WHY REPRESSIONS MAY BE DANGEROUS.   It is unfortunate if the ego is so panic-stricken and the conscience frowns so severely upon an interest in sex and childbearing that the girl has to repress thoughts and wishes concerning them. Strict repression of sexual feelings during adolescence may lead to continued repression after marriage, and rob the mature woman of pleasure in its sexual activities. Again, the repressed sexuality may find expression in the form of neurotic illness symptoms, as for example in nausea, vomiting, abdominal distention and pains, for which no physical basis exists. In clinical practice, these neurotic symptoms, which so obviously simulate those of pregnancy, are seen in adolescent girls who are trying to suppress conscious wishes to have babies, for fear of yielding to sexual temptations.

UNDERSTANDING THE GIRL'S SEX LONGINGS.   It should be frankly recognized that the sexual longings of adolescence are a normal preparation for wifehood and motherhood, even if sexual impulses cannot be permitted to outweigh social considerations in governing behavior. There is a tendency to confusion in both adolescent and adult thinking, when it is assumed that if certain types of behavior are socially undesirable, the instincts and emotions that motivate such acts must also be disapproved. While ethical ideals and social considerations may require conformity to certain rules with respect to sexual conduct, it does not follow that sexual desires themselves are against the cultural and ethical code.

If, at first, sexual stirrings are provocative of anxiety for the girl, there may be consolation in the realization that this state of affairs probably will not continue indefinitely. The adolescent gradually becomes accustomed to both the physiological and psychological changes that have accompanied sexual maturation; the ego learns that control over instinctive impulses can be maintained; partial (sublimated) satisfactions for sexual desires are discovered and relieve some of the tension during the years when marriage and motherhood must be postponed (the sublimated satisfactions will be discussed later in this chapter). Moreover, girls have some compensation for their emotional conflicts in that their heightened sensitivity enables them to be more keenly responsive to stimuli and to feel more fully alive than ever before. If the capacity for anxiety and unhappiness is enhanced in adolescence, so, too, is that for pleasure and joy in living.

The Adolescent Strives for Independence

In addition to the emergence of full-fledged sexual instincts during adolescence, self-assertion and strivings for personal independence are similarly reinforced. In a sense, all childhood development has been in this direction.

With the maturing of body and mind at puberty, there comes anticipation of complete release from adult control, and readiness to move much faster toward the goal of independence of parental authority. The move away from the considerable degree of dependency upon parents, characteristic of the individual before adolescence, to the wholly independent position of adult life cannot be made in a single step. The girl does not feel able to take over entire responsibility for her actions and decisions during early adolescence. For a considerable time, she is likely to vacillate between feeling grown up (and competent to think and act for herself), and reverting to childlike wishes for advice and authoritative decisions from her parents. Especially, whenever she is in acute conflict between her impulses and ethical standards, or whenever she feels too inexperienced to make a wise decision, the girl tends to fall back upon her earlier childhood security in reliance upon her parents for guidance.

MOVING AWAY FROM THE PARENTS' CONTROL. As she becomes more practiced in adjusting to the counter-demands of her emotional impulses and her judgment, and in meeting new social situations, the adolescent girl's need to fall back upon parental authority is less. Her alternations of self-assertiveness and dependent attitudes gradually decrease in frequency, and by late adolescence she should be ready to undertake the management of her own life. She may still talk over her problems with her parents and other adults, but now chiefly to compare their viewpoints with her own and to clarify her thinking thereby, rather than to let them decide what she should do. After careful consideration, she is capable of making her own plans and should be permitted to do so.

Physical adolescence ends when the body has reached its full growth, about five or six years after puberty. By then, too, the psychological development normally should be completed; the girl should have learned to manage her sexual impulses and should have acquired confidence and responsibility for making her own decisions. If the girl has so developed, she will have a mature integration of personality and will be well prepared emotionally for womanhood when she has become physically a woman. If, however, the girl has lived during childhood and adolescence under circumstances unfavorable for her emotional development, her psychological preparation for adult sexual relationships and responsibilities may lag behind her physiological readiness for wifehood and motherhood.

How Parents Influence the Girl's Emotional Life

There is a period in early childhood when girls normally develop an intense attachment to the father and feeling of rivalry with the mother. Hence it need not be surprising that one of the manifestations of increased sexual stimuli at the beginning of adolescence is a renewal (more or less) of these earlier feelings toward the parents. This revival of a former developmental phase should last for a short time only. To some extent, this situation will again be solved by identification with the mother. However, a new kind of solution is now available because the girl has grown mature enough to think of marriage as not too far off, while in childhood it still seemed in a distant future. Thus, at adolescence, the girl normally gives up her old attachment to her father in favor of new love relationships with boys, one of whom she can hope to marry eventually.

WHY SOME GIRLS ARE ATTRACTED TO OLDER MEN. If her attachment to her father has been exceptionally great, a girl may become interested in some older man outside the family circle instead of feeling an immediate interest in boys only slightly older than herself. Ordinarily the love for an older man, who serves as a father substitute, does not last long and merely represents a transition stage between leaving the love relationship with the father for one with boys. However, there are some girls who cannot take this final step, who can love only men much older than themselves, and marry a man nearer to the father's age than their own. If, for instance, a girl's father has died during her childhood or early adolescence, she may remain so in need of paternal affection that she is impelled to marry an older man.

Again, if a father's attitude toward his daughter has been more loverlike than paternal, she may feel the necessity of breaking away from their relationship and yet be able to do so only by forming a new relation with an older man who will offer her a continued father-lover combination. Moreover, girls sometimes become involved in sexual relations without being married, to fulfill their need for a father-substitute to replace their own father who has died, or to free themselves from a strong attachment to their own father.

THE POSSESSIVE MOTHER HARMS HER CHILD. The mother-daughter relationship is equally important for adolescent psychosexual development. Excessive love for the mother and too little for the father may interfere with normal sexual tendencies, since an attachment to the father serves the purpose of preparation for normal sexuality in adolescence and adult life. In spite of the biological urge toward normal sexuality that accompanies pubertal maturing, girls who have been too close to their mothers may seek homosexual love in adolescence and even in womanhood, hoping thus to recreate the relationship with the mother which satisfied them during childhood.

Occasionally a mother loves her daughter so possessively that she cannot tolerate her forming an attachment to her father. Sometimes, too, a mother cannot endure a daughter's turning to her father, because of jealousy and rivalry with the daughter. In either case, the girl may be kept too tied to the mother emotionally, and therefore be unable to establish love relationships with men. If she does partially love a man and marry him, the girl who is still too bound to her mother may not find happiness in marriage. Wives who tend to leave their husbands at the least difficulty and return to their mothers are very often women who had too much attachment to their mothers, and too little to their fathers, during childhood and adolescence.

SOCIAL PREPARATION FOR WOMANHOOD

The social experiences during adolescence are important factors in determining whether the psychological maturing processes are accomplished successfully. In particular, family attitudes may foster or hinder the girl's emotional adjustments. For example, if parents are seriously worried about a girl's sexual behavior, their fears may reinforce her own anxiety, or she may resent their suspicious, distrustful attitudes. Furthermore, if parents, because of undue concern over possible sexual dangers, stringently restrict a girl's social contacts with boys and continually warn her against them, she may turn toward homosexual relationships.

Since the physiological changes at adolescence furnish a powerful force toward normal sexuality, the girl is not easily influenced away from it. But it is possible for parental attitudes to operate as inhibiting factors of normal sexual drives, when a girl has been kept overdependent during childhood or when her concept of marital relations, based upon observations of those between her parents, is not a happy one. Rather than becoming homosexual, however, a girl is more likely to rebel against parental restrictions, seeking boy friends regardless of disapproval, and even if her course of action provokes family quarrels. She may, however, feel guilty about going with boys in defiance of her parents' wishes instead of being able to enjoy these social contacts.

Why Girls Have Conflicts with Their Parents

Parental attitudes such as those described above fail to afford support to the girl's ego when it is beset by anxiety lest it be overcome by the sexual impulses. Indeed, a girl may behave less circumspectly than she otherwise would, for to feel that if one has the name one may as well have the game is a natural human reaction.

On the other hand, parents who look upon the girl's sexual interests as normal, help her to see them in that light, reduce her fear and ego-anxiety, and thus give her confidence in her ability to preserve self-control. Moreover, if parental views on sexual matters have always been realistic and honest, the girl's sexual adjustments are less likely to be complicated by a conscience that considers sex bad or shameful. In short, the girl who is provided with a stable family environment probably will pass through the transition from childhood to womanhood with a minimum of emotional conflict, and with the best chance of maturing psychologically as well as physically.

While the adolescent girl has a healthy desire to achieve independence of her parents, she is, in most instances, still economically dependent upon them during adolescence, and also, as previously stated, she cannot abruptly give up all dependence upon them. She needs their help in making the change from a dependent relationship to a self-reliant one. Some parents cannot bear the prospect of a daughter's terminating the close relationship that she has had to them during childhood, and try to prolong it by opposing her tentative moves toward being more independent. More often, parents' attitudes are less clear-cut; they are at the same time eager to foster a daughter's growth toward self-responsibility, and reluctant to lose their intimate relationship with her.

Since the girl is, like her parents, involved in conflict between strivings for independence and wishes to retain the comforting security of parental care, it will be only by lucky coincidence that parents and daughter will simultaneously be in a mood favoring her taking responsibility for her own decisions. Usually, the girl will be manifesting her desire for independence just when her parents are nostalgically longing for her to remain dependent upon them; and when she most wants their advice, they will be saying that she is old enough to decide things for herself.

When a girl's parents are fully reconciled to her growing up and gradually turning away from them, so that she can alternately try herself out independently and turn to them for counsel, as prompted by her own needs, she is in a fortunate position. Actually, most parents realize that this is the kind of relationship they should have with an adolescent daughter, but emotional attitudes of which they may be quite unaware sometimes prevent them from acting according to this knowledge.

The Girl Turns to Adults Outside the Family

Partly because of the discrepancies between her own emotional needs and those of her parents, the adolescent girl often turns to adults outside the family for help in solving her problems. At the same time, this is partly a step in the direction of attaining independence, for it enables her to emancipate herself from the close family ties of childhood without foregoing entirely the protective guidance of older persons.

Friendships with older people outside the family are valuable to the girl in still another respect. As a child, she has considered her parents as ideals of what she would like to be. Through wider social contacts in adolescence, she has opportunity to observe admirable traits in others, and can thus enlarge her ideals for herself and become more than a mere replica of her parents. Sometimes parents are jealous of a daughter's admiration for other adults, not realizing that she will eventually turn from these far more finally than she will ever break off relationships with her parents, to whom she will still have affectional ties even after she no longer lives in their home but has one of her own.

Beginning to Date

In the two or three years just preceding puberty, known as the preadolescent stage of development, girls and boys have little mutual social life; they do not enjoy the same activities and prefer to be with companions of the same sex. At this age, boys often form gangs, while girls tend more toward pairing off into devoted couples. A pair of preadolescent girls will go everywhere together, share all their secrets and exchange mutual confidences, particularly those concerning information about menstruation (which they are beginning to expect) and about sexual matters.

At puberty, the girl begins to find boys far more attractive than other girls. However, she continues to go with girl friends in order to experiment with social contacts with boys. In the personal anonymity afforded by being one of a small group of girls, flirtatious advances to boys can be made which would not be dared as an individual. It is only after a period of this kind of group social experimentation, and gaining some familiarity with boys, that a girl feels competent to essay individualized social relationships with the opposite sex.

WHY GIRLS SMOKE AND USE COSMETICS. After she begins to date with boys, the girl is still somewhat unsure of herself socially for a while. In order to feel more at ease, she copies the styles and manners prevalent in her age group. Typically, the high school girl wants to dress and act like the majority of her classmates; if most of them use cosmetics and smoke, she will want to do so, too; if they are permitted to stay out until midnight on dates or at parties, she will demand similar privileges. She fears that she will not continue to be dated if she cannot stay out as late as other girls; she lacks the social grace to extricate herself from a party before it is beginning to break up.

This need to conform to the social behavior of her group may lead to differences of opinion with her parents; they may consider the girl disobedient or regardless of her health if she smokes or keeps late hours, while she considers them old-fashioned or unreasonable. At the same time, she probably will feel guilty for her angry, critical attitude toward her parents and for failing to meet their requirements for her conduct.

How Early Love Affairs Affect the Girl

Adolescent love affairs are frequently more disturbing to parents than other aspects of a daughter's social life, yet they are almost inevitable in view of the fact that the girl is biologically ready for love. The girl's parents dislike her having love affairs for fear she will marry too young, or become involved in sexual experiences before marriage. This parental anxiety is somewhat unrealistic in that it does not take into account the fact that the girl is well aware that she cannot marry young, for economic reasons, and knows the disadvantages of secret sexual relationships. She, too, would prefer not to fall in love during her early teens for she knows that a love relationship of that age cannot last and carries with it the prospect of grief when it must end.

In spite of both her parents' and her own misgivings, the adolescent girl usually does love some boy, or more frequently several boys, successively, before she is old enough to marry. It would be difficult to say whether the emotional coloring to these early love affairs is predominantly pleasant or painful. If the boy in the situation happens to prefer someone else for his sweetheart, the girl is unhappy. If he returns her love, she may be happy for a while, only to be unhappy when they must separate to go to different schools or to work in different places. While some high school lovers are never separated, and the love of others survives fairly long periods of separation, this is not true for the majority.

UNDERSTANDING THE GIRL'S GRIEFS.   A girl says goodbye to an adolescent sweetheart with the conviction that she can never love again and will be miserable and lonely the rest of her life. She may be depressed for a time after their parting and wish that she might die. Suicidal phantasies are not likely to be carried over into action, however, for if youth can suffer deeply, so, too, it has remarkable recuperative powers. Before long, the girl is likely to find herself in love with a new boy and her cycle of intense emotions will be repeated. While still grieving for a lost love, however, she may worry her parents considerably. Knowing that adolescent love affairs are not taken seriously by adults, or else are taken too seriously, she does not confide in her parents, as a rule. Hence they are unable to understand her depression and moodiness and may be concerned about her health when she is only manifesting signs of grief.

EARLY LOVE AFFAIRS—PREPARATION FOR MARRIAGE.   Whatever the difficulties the girl encounters in establishing social relationships with boys, either because of her own inexperience or restrictive attitudes of parents, and whatever the painful aspects of her youthful love affairs, one of the important preparations for womanhood lies in just this area. A normal social life with boys during adolescence is a girl's right in the interests of her normal sexual development and her chance for a happy married life later on. The other important preparation for being a woman is the achievement of self-reliance and emancipation from dependency upon parents. Only when this has been accomplished is a girl mature enough for successful marriage and adequate motherhood.

MENTAL HYGIENE OF ADOLESCENCE

Sex Education—Wise and Unwise

It seems unnecessary to refer more than briefly to the mental hygiene advantages of sex education, for it is generally accepted that correct information about the reproductive system, menstruation, sexual intercourse, conception and birth is advisable to prevent worries due to lack of knowledge or to misinformation. Perhaps it is less well known that a purely educational approach cannot afford protection against anxiety arising from the ego's fear of losing control over instinctive impulses, nor alleviate guilt produced by the pangs of a too severe conscience. As previously implied, wholesome attitudes toward sex on the part of parents, during both childhood and adolescence, are more influential in supporting the ego or modifying the conscience, and consequently in saving the girl from too much emotional conflict.

Sometimes there is an improper use of sex education, when it is given in a hope that it will reduce the strength of the instinctive drives or perhaps do away altogether with sexual desires. Since these are biologically determined, it is strange that such a notion should exist; it would be, for instance, quite as logical to anticipate that sex education might prove sexually stimulating. Perhaps there is indeed a fear that it might be a source of excitation, for frequently emphasis is placed upon the purpose of sexual instincts for continuation of the race, with little or no reference to sexual activities as pleasurable in themselves. Occasionally there also is more than necessary stress upon the dangers of contracting venereal diseases, as if in unconscious effort to frighten adolescents away from yielding to sexual temptations.

Needless to say, the purpose of sex education should be to furnish accurate information, and it should not be utilized as a method of controlling behavior. An unrealistic, prohibitive type of sex education adds to adolescent maladjustments by instilling fear of disease, or of impregnation by casual contacts (kissing, etc.) , and thus discourages normal social relationships with the opposite sex. As a mental hygiene measure, its objectives are to reduce worries, not to increase them, and to foster normal sexual development, not to act as a force toward repression.

Artistic Outlets Are Emotional Outlets

Further mental hygiene principles can best be formulated through considering certain characteristics of adolescence. The richness of the emotional life at this age often stimulates creative activities, so that children who have shown some talent for artistic or literary work usually become more productive along these lines during adolescence.

The advantage of this tendency lies in the ease with which creative activities lend themselves to the expression of emotions and afford sublimated satisfactions. For example, a girl's desires for motherhood may be partially gratified by drawing or painting pictures of babies and children such as she hopes to have someday. Her wish to be attractive to boys may be represented in sketches of glamorous faces or seductive figures indicating how she would like to appear in her own person, or in designing fashions that she thinks would promote her attractiveness. The girl is more or less unconscious of the personal feelings involved in her artistic productions, but the emotional associations are often revealed when she talks while working on them, if she is speaking to someone with whom she is not too shy and from whom she does not fear ridicule or disapproval.

The girl with literary gifts can console herself for delayed satisfaction of desires to marry by writing romantic stories; she can identify herself with the heroine and feel as if she were living through the events that she describes. If she is in love but cannot look forward to the culmination of her love affair in the sexual relationships of married life, because of her youth, she can at least write poetry expressing her passionate feelings; if depressed because she has lost a sweetheart, she can find some relief for her grief by putting it into poetic words.

How Adults Can Help. The connection between the girl's emotional life and her absorption in artistic or literary work is not always as plainly revealed as in the comparatively simple illustrations just given. Since creative activities are an expression of repressed, unconscious wishes and feelings, this connection may be disguised. The girl does not undertake to sketch or write something with a conscious realization that she is sublimating instinctive drives and releasing emotional tensions. She does not know that there is greater motivation than the sense of achievement and the aesthetic pleasure enjoyed in viewing the results of her efforts. It may be as well that her insight goes no further, lest self-consciousness inhibit her spontaneous ways of sublimation. But the adults in the girl's environment need to understand the mental hygiene values of her creative interests, so that they will not discourage her from continuing with them by criticizing the products of her labors or by reproving her for wasting time on worthless pursuits.

There are, of course, other means of sublimation available to adolescents; singing, playing a musical instrument, composing music, dancing, etc., serve similar purposes of expressing emotion and satisfying instinctive drives. If a girl possesses no gifts for any kind of creative activity, she still can find some sublimations in listening to music, reading books, or going to the theatre or the movies. She can identify herself with characters in stories, on the stage or screen, just as the more talented adolescent lives through the adventures which she imagines happening to the characters of whom she writes.

Why the Adolescent Is an Arguer

Another adolescent trait, is a new intellectual preoccupation with abstract or social problems. This increased use of intellectual capacities, like the stimulation of creative activity, is a reaction to the emotional conflicts that have arisen in the girl's experience. Discussions of such questions as free love versus marriage reflect the conflict between sexual impulses and moral ideas, as well as represent the efforts of the ego to maintain control over behavior. Debates about revolution versus slower evolutionary processes as a method of securing social progress, parallel adolescent conflicts between the urge to rebel against parental authority, in order to be freed quickly from it, and the need to retain some dependency upon parents, with release from their control coming more gradually. Consideration of the advantages of economic independence compared to those of marriage is likely to mean that the girl is not fully reconciled to her feminine role in life and is trying to overcome fears of marrying and bearing children. More abstract intellectual discussions may be disguised expressions of emotional conflicts, or may be a way of seeking at least temporary rest from conflict by thinking of things that are far removed from personal feelings—indeed, are quite impersonal.

Since they are so frequently an attempt to resolve emotional conflicts, the sometimes lengthy and boring dissertations indulged in by adolescents should be endured in spite of their confused, inconsistent presentation of the pros and cons of the argument. Impatience with lack of logic should be tempered by the recognition of the mental hygiene value of the effort to work out a solution for conflicts and make a better adaptation to reality.

SECURING PROFESSIONAL HELP FOR THE GIRL'S PROBLEMS

It has been intimated that the natural processes of development during adolescence afford a favorable opportunity for overcoming emotional conflicts and reaching a more mature personality. Hence it is questionable whether it is wise to suggest psychiatric help at this stage of growth except when difficulties of adjustment are so severe that a normal outcome seems unlikely. The situations in which psychotherapy is most clearly indicated are those where a girl suffers from illness symptoms without physical basis, is subject to extreme anxiety or moods of depression that are more than temporary, or is quite unable to make social contacts.

PHYLLIS BLANCHARD, PH.D.

Preparing Your Son for Manhood

JUST as training in the habits of physical hygiene for adolescence should be a continuation of the training of early childhood, so instruction in the nature and function of the reproductive organs and the part that sex plays in the life of the growing human being should be a continuation of earlier sex instruction. In other words, the parent should not think of adolescence as the time for a campaign in physical hygiene and sex instruction. For just as habits of physical hygiene, either good or bad, are formed long before adolescence, so sex information, either good or bad, is picked up by most children before puberty. The parent who thinks that a boy who does not discuss these things is ignorant of them should be warned that his son's very silence may indicate a greater knowledge than he cares to share with his parents.

Nowadays, parents try from the early years to build wholesome attitudes toward sex, as well as to give clear, frank answers suited to the child's intelligence and development on all questions of sex. When this practice is followed, it may well happen that by the time a boy reaches adolescence, particularly if he is brought up intimately with older children, he has asked for all the information he needs. But the parents should by no means feel obliged to wait for his questions when they see that rapid development is taking place. They can easily notice the body changes already described and remind or point out to him that these are signs that he is passing from childhood to adulthood.

The father can, perhaps, discuss these matters most helpfully with a boy. He should prepare him to expect an occasional discharge of semen, likely to occur during sleep, explaining that this is nature's way of taking care of his sex activity until he should be physically, economically, and socially ready to assume the responsibility of mating, and assuring him that these nocturnal emissions, as well as the involuntary erections he may experience either in sleep or in sexually exciting situations, are perfectly natural occurrences about which he should feel no alarm. He should also advise

the boy that he is less likely to be disturbed by these experiences
if he leads a vigorous life, finding pleasure and perhaps a certain
pride in hard work and play, cool and regular sleep, cold baths,
and wholesome interests.

Boys should be told not only about the organs and processes
of reproduction in their own sex, but also about those of the other
sex. Above all, they should be made to feel free to ask any questions
or consult their parents about any feelings or experiences which
they find puzzling or disturbing.

Parents who feel that they do not know enough about these
matters to explain them to their sons may find it well to discuss
them first with each other and with their family physician. If for
any reason they still feel unable to tackle the subject, they should
arrange to have the school or family-guidance counselor or the
family physician confer with the child or recommend something
to be read by the child himself. Although by this method they
will probably lose the rather precious experiences that come to
the parent who is on an intimate, confidential level with his child,
they will at least not fail the child as they would by neglecting
this matter entirely.

Some parents are inclined to feel that the importance of sex
instruction—and, indeed, of all aspects of child care and guidance—
is greatly exaggerated. They believe that they, and many of their
friends, grew up to be competent men and women without any
so-called habit training or careful sex instruction. But even if they
can recall no anxieties, doubts, shocks, or unhappy experiences
which they might have been spared with wise guidance, they will
surely be able to see that the very changes which they and their
generation have made in the world are creating the need for
changing methods of bringing up the next generation.

Parents should expect, and accept, that it may be a bit disturbing to themselves and their children to discuss this subject. It is
wiser to talk about sex in relation to a lead given by the child,
through remarks or questions, than to bring the subject up "out of
the blue," when the child is not prepared to consider it. But a
parent who is sensitive to children's needs will find opportunities

arising when explanations (as of reasons for social customs, perhaps) make the transition to discussion of sex behavior natural.

OBSCENE LANGUAGE AND "SMUTTY" JOKES

Parents, as well as teachers and recreation leaders, are frequently alarmed at the sexual precociousness shown in the conversations of some of their worldly-wise children, or concerned, and possibly offended, by what they consider "smutty" or "dirty" talk. Their concern increases when they discover that these conversations are traveling far and wide and that indignant parents are complaining of having their children contaminated.

The child's motive in such talk may be merely a response to a lively, healthy curiosity and a desire for information. If he is already well supplied with information and has not been made to feel that it is particularly private or personal, he may have a generous inclination to pass it along or to show off his superior knowledge to companions who are less well informed. Children will often use vulgar words or phrases in each other's company. Characteristically they mention the word or phrase and then giggle or nervously laugh. Every normal child experiments with these words or phrases which are taboo. Parents who recognize this, and who don't censure a child when they overhear such talk, will be helping to prevent unhealthy feelings of guilt.

Even after boys reach puberty, and long after they have acquired an intellectual understanding of sex and its relation to much of their social activity, they may still utilize sex talk, obscene words, smutty stories, and recitals of personal experiences (often without a foundation in fact) as a means of "putting themselves across." But there seem to be other, more fundamental reasons why not only adolescents but many adults in this country joke about sex. Everyone feels that sexual adjustment is very important in his life. Many people feel uncertain and insecure about sexual problems and feelings because they sense that they don't know as much about the subject as they need to. Joking about sex often helps them in two ways. They seek additional sex knowledge through listening to jokes; and second, when one can laugh at

what one is a bit afraid of, one feels easier and more assured—
false though this feeling may be. Sometimes they begin to derive
from their conversations a vicarious sex thrill—first through the
visual and verbal stimulation of an imagined experience, and
secondly through the excitement of participating in a conversation
that would be frowned upon, if not actually forbidden, by their
elders.

The method of handling these problems depends on the type of
individual concerned. It is useless in any case to appear shocked
and horrified, or to resort to tears or anger. It is far better to let
the immature youngster know that we understand just what this
activity means to him and why he is seeking to gain recognition
in this particular way. The fact that people in general consider
this line of conversation vulgar and offensive, just as they would
bad manners, may be pointed out to him, and at the same time
other ways of getting recognition may be suggested. With the
younger group a frank talk on the subject of sex, making it interesting and unemotional, does more good than anything else. It
gives them a new and more responsible attitude toward keeping
the whole subject of sex clean.

Most children do pass through this phase of using more or less
obscene language, just as they pass through phases of making grimaces
or tiresome noises. It requires considerable patience to live through
all these various phases with equanimity. An unemotional attitude
and a certain amount of understanding of what the child is driving
at are more helpful than either wrath or sorrow.

Much of the discussion concerning sex talk applies also to the
reading of erotic literature. The danger in this type of lurid literature lies in the fact that much of it portrays situations which are
overdrawn and not actually representative of reality. There is
always a sufficient amount of literature available which serves the
purpose of diverting sex interests into other channels without stim-
uating sex phantasies and creating further problems, and both the
schools and the public libraries should offer every assistance to
parents and to the adolescents themselves in finding books that
are worth while.

ADOLESCENT MASTURBATION

The practice of masturbation is encountered so frequently in normal, healthy boys, as well as girls, from the preschool age through adolescence, that everything possible should be done to help the parent understand its occurrence. The real harm results from the treatment of the habit which is likely to be instituted when parents become emotionally upset. The parent is likely to think only in terms of the possible dire physical effects the habit may have upon the human organism, quite unmindful that the real danger lies in making the child feel self-conscious and inferior, and in leading him to turn all his thoughts upon his supposed wickedness and abnormality. This tendency to introspective self-examination and self-condemnation in turn affects his attitude toward the world at large; he avoids mingling with others, feeling unworthy of their society and perhaps fearing lest they suspect and discover his weakness. In this way the child's normal, healthy outlook on life may become distorted.

There is probably no surer way of perpetuating such a habit than that of making the individual feel that he is sinful, different, queer, and wicked, or will become physically degenerate, an object to be avoided, and a candidate for a mental hospital through his indiscretions. What he needs is relief from anxiety, not more anxiety; a feeling of strength and superiority, not of weakness and inferiority; truth, not lies. The adolescent already feels that he is a victim of an undesirable habit. He knows that any habit which makes him think less well of himself is something to be fought and mastered. He is already carrying a heavy burden. A panicky parent should not add to it by injecting fears which have no basis in fact merely because this seems to be the easiest way to meet the situation.

Undesirable sex behavior need not be either ignored or condemned. When it comes to the parents' attention as a problem of one of their own children, they should seize the opportunity for a frank discussion of the whole subject of sex and the varied healthy activities that may be utilized as substitutes in this intellectual and unemotional way, they should delegate the task to the family physician, a wise teacher, a friend, or some other suitable person who will help rather than hinder the adolescent in his attempt to get a mature outlook on sex conduct. This is not the time for evasion, prudery, or deceit; it is the time for a frank, honest approach to one of the most common problems adolescents have to face.

It is unwise for parents to pry into the sex activity of their children and get confessions of these secret indulgences. The whole sex problem can be discussed quite as frankly in an impersonal way and often more helpfully than the individual problem. It is wise for parents to let children appreciate that these situations are common to practically everyone, that most boys have to meet them, and that it is everyone's responsibility to learn to control them. At the same time they do well to stress the fact that solitary preoccupation with one's own body for the purpose of obtaining pleasurable sensations is an immature form of behavior, that immature sex habits tend to interfere with one's normal adjustment to other people, and that any habit which tends to lessen one's self-esteem should be discarded. Then ways and means of meeting the situation can be outlined, and there will be a much better chance of the plan being carried through by the boy whose self-esteem has been restored than by the boy who is in the grip of fear.

Sex behavior of the adolescent boy or girl is determined to a large extent by their whole adjustment to life. If their relations with their parents and their friends are satisfactory and happy, and they have adequate outlets for their various energies and interests, they are likely to meet their maturing sex drives adequately. It is the emotionally starved adolescent without adequate interests who is most likely to plunge into experimentation with sex for the satisfaction which he has failed to find in ways more in keeping with his stage of development.

The Social Life of
the Adolescent

THERE is no phase in the individual's life in which friends count more than during the adolescent period. This stage of development in the child's life is characterized by intensity of feeling in combination with lack of experience to guide and direct these intense emotions with the wisdom of more mature years. There can be many substitutes for intimate friendships during childhood—brothers and sisters, parents, and the innumerable individuals whom the child meets in the daily routine; likewise in adulthood, one's family, business, and other interests, or one's philosophy of life may make intimate friendships unnecessary. It is extremely difficult, however, for the adolescent to accept anything in place of his chum, his pal, his buddy, or whatever else he may call that individual in whom he can confide with absolute assurance of receiving a sympathetic hearing and being understood.

ADOLESCENT FRIENDSHIPS ARE IMPORTANT

The need for intimate associations with those of one's own age is greater during this period, because adolescents are apt to entertain the idea that they are but little understood by the adult world. Thus the boy or girl who in the process of development has not acquired those personal characteristics which are essential to making friends is a pathetic figure. He represents one of the real catastrophes of life, and his situation is one of the most difficult to face, for although he appreciates his own needs he may fail entirely to understand why he does not measure up.

It is unfortunate indeed that those traits or lack of traits in one's personality make-up which are essential in building up the close personal contacts which we look upon as friendships are very often dependent upon environmental situations over which the individual has no control until the damage has been done. Yet, as one sees children during their early life, one may be easily aware of

636

the fact that there are also inherent traits which apparently allow one group of children to be responsive to attention and to react with pleasure, while the other group tends to withdraw, reject, and be offended by quite the same overtures. The fact that these responses to life are exaggerated by the environment—that is, that attention is invariably given where it is appreciated—is obvious to all who are concerned with the behavior of children.

Certain mental characteristics, or personality traits, are found sufficiently often, however, in these friendless, lonesome individuals to make it seem only fair to assume that these traits in themselves represent the barrier between the child and the social group with which he is brought in contact. There is, for example, the shy, diffident, reserved youngster who is inclined to be very introspective, who is extremely sensitive not only to the impressions that he makes upon the world but to the impressions that the world makes upon him. Everything seems to register, and everything that registers must necessarily be analyzed; it is in the process of examining and tearing these ordinary, everyday situations apart that the individual becomes more and more self-centered. Later in life he develops feelings of inferiority and inadequacy; he is prone to be unduly critical about himself, not infrequently setting his standards for himself so high that failure is inevitable.

The question arises: What are the environmental situations that are likely to produce this state of mind in the child when he is called upon to confront life during the adolescent period? As has been stated, the family may be substituted for friends during early life; but it is not uncommon for parents to put such a value on family life and to derive so much pleasure and satisfaction from their children that they very selfishly hold them too close to the family circle. Home life may be made so pleasant and attractive and in subtle ways so easy during the early years of life that there is little incentive for the child to reach out and make intimate contacts with the outside world.

Then, too, the child may be cut off from outside contact at a very important period in life because of some accident or illness which makes a temporary invalid of him, so that after recovery he may find it difficult to pick up the thread of social relations where it was dropped. The fact that parents move about and that the place of residence is frequently changed, or possibly changed at a rather critical time in the child's life, is another factor worthy of consideration. This important aspect of the child's life should always be kept in mind when a change of schools is under consideration. To be taken away at the age of eight or nine from the group with which he has played about for three or four years is a real calamity to one child, while another child will immediately make a place for himself in the new situation without any difficulty whatsoever.

Children Reflect Their Homes

In some homes neighborliness and intimate contacts are frowned upon. Parents do not encourage their children to visit other children or to bring other children home, fearing that such visiting may involve some social obligation to the parents of these other boys and girls. There is a lack of cordiality in such a home that cannot but affect certain children in their early relations with others. In other homes there is a critical attitude toward the neighbor's children and toward the neighbors themselves that is also restraining. For example, Johnny may be told that the children of one family are too dirty and rough or too indecent in their language to play with, other children are to be avoided because their families are economically or socially inferior, and another group may be undesirable because of racial or religious differences. Some families simply fall back on their old conclusion that John gets along so much better and causes so much less trouble if he keeps by himself; he either gets excited or uses bad words, or comes in all tired out or unpardonably dirty when he is allowed to participate in the activities of the group. These excuses are born of twisted, snobbish, arrogant, or intolerant attitudes on the part of certain parents, or are resorted to in an effort to make the job of rearing children as easy as possible. They are all, however, important factors in the development of certain traits that interfere with making friendships easily in later life.

TEEN-AGE "CRUSHES"

While some adolescents need help in learning to make friends at all, others need help in learning to maintain a sense of balance in their friendships. They must learn to keep their interest open in many people instead of centering all their attention, affection, admiration, and devotion in one person of their own sex.

Adolescent crushes are very common and can usually be looked upon as a normal phase of development. There are, however, a certain number of these intimate relations between individuals of the same sex that either because of their intensity or because of their duration require serious consideration. Parents and teachers ofttimes need to use great care and judgment in handling these situations in order that they may be most helpful to those who quite innocently become involved in some alliance which might become quite disastrous to the parties involved.

Crushes that continue are of significance not because of any undesirable activity but because of their interference with the natural, normal, healthy development of broad social contacts which are of special importance during this period in life. These intense emotional reactions between those of the same sex, more commonly seen in girls than in boys, are all-absorbing and in most cases leave no time or interest for other social contacts. At best, when one of those involved gets a more mature outlook on life and seeks a broader field for personal relations with boys and girls, the other is invariably hurt.

While the crush is on, any attempt to break it up or interfere in any way is met with open rebellion. Any criticism directed by friends or family is resented. The parties to the experience glory in their loyalty toward each other. Invariably they entertain the idea that this relation is something given to them alone, that no one has ever before experienced the joy of such a friendship, and that, therefore, no one else is capable of understanding it. Quite rightly they resent any intimation that there is anything wrong or bad about this relation. To those caught emotionally in this snare, it symbolizes all that is good and worth while. Helping these young people to get a proper perspective on this particular problem in relation to the entire life situation is therefore a delicate task.

Fortunately, when the fires burn so intensely, they do not last long, and most of these crush situations are self-eliminating. If managed wisely, they do no harm. It is not so much the crush itself that needs careful consideration as the individuals participating in it. When such a relation exists between individuals who because of their shyness, diffidence, and lack of confidence are unable to "put themselves across" in a normal way with the group, it requires all the skill and ingenuity of the adults who are trying to help them to find ways and means of developing new interests which may serve as a diversion while these young people are finding themselves.

The family must be tolerant and not give the impression by word or by deed that they are persecuting either party. They may judiciously introduce other young people of interest into the home life or arrange for a visit that would temporarily separate the two young people. Plans for a summer at camp might be considered, depending upon the situation and the extent to which the affair has developed. Whatever may be the plan, it will require nice judgment and much toleration and patience, but it will be worth the effort. The future happiness of these adolescents may depend upon establishing their lives on a more satisfactory basis than one which is narrow and emotional.

The teacher is often able to offer assistance in these situations because she may approach the subject with these young people in a perfectly natural and unemotional way by discussing the subject of friendships—the importance of first making broad general contacts which are interesting and profitable in an educational way and then of cultivating the more intimate relations upon which men and women place great value all through life. The disadvantages of cutting one's self off from the broad social contacts of the school, the community, or the camp for the sake of devoting one's time to any one individual can be made quite clear, and it is not difficult to explain how these emotional tie-ups between those of the same sex often lead away from a well-rounded life in the future. There may be particular reasons for going into the subject more deeply;

it may be brought out, for instance, that one may get in the habit of avoiding contact with those of the opposite sex because of the ease and satisfaction with which the present relation can be carried on, and that one may thus close the door to healthy contacts leading to normal mating, marriage, children, and a home.

These emotional situations must never be looked upon as occasions which necessitate trying to make young people good through fear of consequences. They represent just another opportunity for the parents and the child to get together and discuss the whole situation and all its implications in an unemotional way. The task of passing through that immature stage where autoerotic tendencies and crushes play an important part in life confronts every adolescent and is a difficult one for many of these young people. They fear to take the next step forward, oftentimes being filled with a feeling that they are unable to meet it adequately.

But they are very quick to grasp any real understanding which their elders may have of the problem and to reach out for help when they have reason to believe that it is available.

Many of the doubts and misgivings these young people have with reference to taking the next step in their social development are due to the fact that their early experiences in their own homes have prejudiced them against marriage. A mother whose marital life has been unhappy and whose dissatisfactions have been an ever-present example to her children, who presents marriage, particularly the sex aspect of it, as something to be avoided, is a tremendous obstacle to the normal, healthy development of her sons and daughters. Such childhood experiences are the most common factors leading to social immaturity in these unhappy children. The development of a normal, happy, well-adjusted sex life in young people is more dependent upon the examples they have before them than on all the instruction one can give.

BOY-AND-GIRL RELATIONS

With the introduction of coeducation and the discovery that taking part in athletics would not incapacitate girls for childbearing, a more normal and natural everyday relation between boys and girls began to prevail. Seeing each other under the prosaic circumstances of eight o'clock classes, playing at the same games, working side by side whether on class plays or on school annuals, studying the same subjects, boys and girls came to a clearer understanding of each other. Boys long ago discarded the Victorian conception of femininity and, instead of regarding girls as vague and mysterious combinations of physical frailty, intellectual stupidity, and frigid spirituality, accepted them as "pals," companions, and friends, while girls responded with a frankness bred of their own more honest recognition of boys.

This closer acquaintance between boys and girls has everything to recommend it. In the world of today men and women must work and play side by side. How will they learn to do this if they spend their entire youth carefully isolated from each other, fed on mysterious illusions of differences that may not exist? The element of romance with which young people wish to endow each other in their love relations, need not be lacking because of the better acquaintance between boys and girls; on the contrary, being adequately protected against endowing all girls or all boys with glamour, they should be better able to discriminate in their choice of the particular partner they seek.

Friendships between boy and girl, as between girl and girl, generally prove of greater value and greater happiness in the plural than in the singular during adolescence. It takes real ingenuity, however, to deal with fads of the moment, such as that demanding that each boy or girl have a "steady," and date only with that one person.

PETTING

We shall probably all agree that there is nothing particularly new about the practice of petting, excepting for the fact that it is now practiced more generally among those who are considered nice people, that it has become more of a pastime and perhaps less well defined as a step leading to matrimony, and finally that it is no longer a practice reserved for the subdued lights of the family parlor, the country wayside, or other secluded spots. In the automobile, on the beach, in the village green, in the city park, on the dance floor, on the public street, in cars and busses, and one might say wherever adolescents as a group can be seen, petting may be witnessed. There appears to be a casual indifference with many young people to what those about see or say regarding their activities in public. These observations can be made by anyone at any time, and almost anywhere.

It is difficult to account for what appears to be a decided change in the attitude of adolescents toward petting, and it is equally difficult to evaluate what it all means in terms of promiscuous sex activity. Certainly there is no reason to believe that the sex urge is more demanding at the present time than it has been in years past. Perhaps constant exposure to love-making in the movies has made such endearments appear more casual and commonplace. Probably time will reveal that more young people of all types are indulging in these activities and that they have not changed materially in degree and intensity. The fact that young people feel free to carry on petting in public is an indication of the less cramped and inhibited feelings about the whole subject of sex that are the result of widespread efforts toward revamping attitudes toward this part of life.

There has grown a more healthy comradeship among young people of both sexes, an effort to find in the one individual those varied satisfactions which it is but human to desire. This need not mean that actual sex relations are more commonly practiced. Petting is perhaps being utilized more and more as a sublimation.

The essential contribution that a parent has to make to this particular adolescent situation is that petting is very definitely a sex experience; that naturally and normally, under happy marital relations, it precedes sexual intercourse, which in the unmarried state is as dangerous in its social implications as it ever was, in loss of social approbation, mental conflict, venereal disease, and pregnancy.

Sex as one of the important factors of human development should be regarded and discussed by parents as they would approach health. The girl who overeats, who allows herself to get constipated, who fails to look after her skin, and who fails to follow other hygienic regulations gets fat and develops a poor complexion, never feels right, and is likely to become physically unattractive and soci‐ ally handicapped. The girl who permits promiscuous petting with unlimited privileges gets the reputation of being "easy" and "com‐ mon." As a social asset, she is less valuable and soon finds that she is left out of much that would contribute to her happiness. This may be a rather low level of adjustment from a purely moral point of view, but young people can and do understand when we talk to them about what type of conduct will actually work out to their advantage. We can tell young people that we understand all the urges that quite naturally prompt them to seek the thrills of life in this particular way, yet at the same time show them by the innumerable examples always available that it actually pays to postpone these gratifications, and help them find other emotional outlets.

It is well to keep before these young people the thought that the various activities which are generally covered by the term petting all too frequently fail to give the parties involved the satisfactions they are after. Frequently these experiences are difficult to digest. Even so, they may become habits after an appetite has been created for this particular type of emotional stimulation. The early indul‐ gences are often brought about by the desire to test out life, to try a new experience, to indulge in some new thrill. In the case of girls particularly, such behavior is often a sincere response to what seems a great need for demonstration of affection. A desire for popularity, attention, and the participation in social activity which they feel would otherwise be denied them is the motivating factor in many instances.

In dealing with this whole subject we need to remind ourselves that the high proportion of frigidity in women, and their failure ever to make a complete response in the sex relation, are almost surely the result of inhibitions and prohibitions set up early in life. That our cultural demands set up a great barrier to the development of normal sex attitudes should not be overlooked by parents.

These are all factors which should be discussed frankly with the adolescent, and, again, the discussion may well be carried on as a subject of interest and practical importance, rather than as a personal problem. It should be kept in mind that this problem of sex is but one aspect of life for the adolescent and that many conflicts may arise in his effort to solve this one particular problem. The adolescent will make his own adjustment to life adequately only when he does it without being harmful to others. The adult who is in a position to gain the confidence and respect of the adolescent holds the strategic position. This can come about only when the adolescent is sure that he is dealing with someone who has a clear idea of what youth's problems really are and a practical plan or philosophy of life that will meet his daily needs. The adult who deals with adolescents successfully will have an appreciation and understanding of adolescent problems in general as they exist today and also he should know well each individual whose conduct he is trying to affect.

How Bright Is Your Teen-Ager?

T HE physical growth of a child is self-evident in the actual gain in inches and pounds, but there are no such units and standards of measurement for determining his mental development. The parent may realize that the son or daughter has a more grown-up outlook on life; and the son and daughter may realize that they are able to do more advanced school work, but they would all find it more difficult to measure this growth in terms of mental inches or pounds.

Mind is thought of in terms of processes and activities, and it is naturally less easy to measure these than to measure body stature. Moreover, the various mental processes and activities become manifest at different times and in different degrees. It has been found that while many activities increase during adolescence, some remain about the same and some actually decrease. Mental development goes on unceasingly throughout life as the individual adds to his experience, knowledge, and insight.

Although the most important period of the individual's mental growth is past at adolescence, many parents first become interested in the mental development of their boys and girls at this time. Adolescents, too, begin to consider seriously their plans for the future. They begin to consider how far they can go in school and to what advantage; what they are best fitted to do vocationally; and, in general, what their special capacities and special disabilities are. Obviously these are questions that can be answered only after careful study of the individual boy or girl.

MEASURING INTELLIGENCE

Within the last thirty years a large number and variety of so-called tests for the measurement of various mental processes have been devised. There are tests of memory, perception, attention, motor co-ordination, comprehension, suggestibility, judgment, imagination, range of emotional response, learning ability, initiative, and so on. Some of these tests have proved unsatisfactory; they have been found to reveal acquired learning rather than native ability or to make insufficient allowance for environment factors or differences of personality. But through their continued use in large numbers of cases and through comparison of the resulting scores with such ordinary standards of judgment as school grades and personal impressions, a number of very useful tests have been developed. They are being used throughout the world for purposes of classifying children in schools, making vocational plans and recommendations, studying the special problems of individual children, and carrying on experiments in various fields of research. Essentially they do nothing more than sample the various intellectual processes; each sample is then scored, and the intelligence as a whole is estimated on the basis of the total score.

The individual's score may be rated in comparison with that of his fellow classmates, to give an estimate of his class rank, or it may be computed in terms of the ratio between his mental age, as determined in the test, and his chronological age in years and months, to give his intelligence quotient (I.Q.).

When the mental age is below the chronological age, the child may be said to be in varying degrees slow or retarded; when the two are equal, the child may be said to be average; when the mental age is above the chronological age, the child may be looked upon as accelerated or superior. To be sure, a range of ten points more or less must be allowed for possible error due to factors not under control. But, in a general way, the boy or girl can thus be classified in relation to the great numbers of boys and girls of the same age who have been similarly tested.

In order to be of any use, such intelligence testing must be done by well-trained people who have had wide experience with growing children under test conditions. Moreover the test results must be interpreted in the light of the norms established by tests in the past. *Even then no single test should be regarded as the last word and final verdict regarding the child.* It should also be noted that most tests given at school are group tests that tell us more about the child's relation to his group than about him as an individual. An intelligence test should be considered only as a point of departure to be supplemented by a child's medical history, consideration of his environmental limitations and opportunities, a history of his actual school achievement and his social adjustment, and further study of such particular aptitudes or handicaps as he may manifest.

It is of greatest importance that parents understand the nature of this type of intelligence test. The interesting publicity given to various kinds of mental testing has had the unfortunate effect of confusing and misleading lay readers regarding the purpose of psychological examination before they ever had a chance to understand what it was all about. It is perfectly true that psychologists and criminolgists have been working out tests for the purpose of discovering guilt reactions in individuals suspected of lying, stealing, and other delinquencies and offenses. It is also true that psychiatrists and psychologists have been working out tests for the purpose of discovering abnormal emotional reactions as an aid to establishing a diagnosis of insanity. But these tests are as distinct from the ordinary intelligence tests as laboratory tests for the presence of tuberculosis are distinct from the routine weighing and measuring done in the public schools. Parents sometimes ask whether the intelligence tests given to their children are not the same as those used to determine whether or not a child is feeble-minded. They forget that there is only one kind of scale for measuring weight, and that it is no disgrace to be found of normal weight on the same scale which showed someone else to be overweight or underweight.

So much for the nature of intelligence tests. Now let us consider their application.

THE SLOW MIND

In this chapter no attempt will be made to deal with the problems of the defective or severely retarded individual, first, because this discussion is limited to the problems of normal adolescents and, secondly, because the problems of the defective boy or girl must ordinarily be met and dealt with before the time of adolescence. The problems of the mentally slow child, on the other hand, are often not recognized until he reaches the upper grades.

There are three important principles to be observed by parents and teachers in planning for the boy or girl with a slow mind: (1) The necessity of giving frank and early recognition to whatever handicap he may have; (2) the importance of placing him properly in school so that he will not have to struggle beyond his capacity, or constantly experience a sense of discouragement and failure; (3) the wisdom of planning for the child's greatest satisfaction and happiness rather than for the fulfillment of parental ambition.

THE AVERAGE MIND

It would seem that the youngster with an average mind would be the last to require any special consideration and that life would present no special problems to him or to his parents, but it is the nature of many never to be content with their lot. Nor can it be denied that when the individual with an average mind is obliged to compete with a group of individuals having superior minds, he is at a great disadvantage.

"Average," like "inferior" and "superior," is but a relative term; and the individual who is average as compared to the general population or to the standard test scale is no longer average when compared to a selected group who, by reason of their superiority, are going on to special schools and colleges. Even within the family group, the individual with average ability may seem inferior.

The principles to be observed in guiding the adolescent with average ability are but variations of those to be observed in planning for the child with the slow mind: (1) The necessity of recognizing the child's ability for what it is; (2) the importance of placing him properly in school so that his powers will be developed to their maximum fulfillment and yet not subjected to competition that would lead only to failure; and (3) the wisdom of guiding the child toward his own satisfaction and happiness rather than toward the goal set by parental ambition.

THE SUPERIOR MIND

That the mentally superior child may perplex his parents and become a problem to himself is a not uncommon assumption. People have innumerable theories about the vagaries of children with superior endowment. They may be convinced that brilliant children are usually poor specimens so far as physical development is concerned; or that they are inclined to be introspective, absent-minded bookworms with no sense about practical matters; or that they are selfish, egocentric individuals who are ever greedy for more learning and more college degrees regardless of the economic cost to their parents or the necessary sacrifice of the aspirations of brothers and sisters; or that gifted children turn out to be dull adults; or that highly intellectual boys and girls make poor social adjustments and later become the crochety, cantankerous, neurotic, or psychotic members of society. Although everyone knows men and women whom the above descriptions would seem to fit perfectly, the conclusion that their maladjustments, their faults, and their failures are due to, or necessarily connected with, intellectual superiority is fallacious.

Thorough and long-continued studies of intellectually superior children all tend to show that true intellectual superiority is usually accompanied by superiority in other respects, as, for example, physical health and social adaptability. If certain of these boys and girls later turn out to be lopsided, topheavy, or otherwise unbalanced individuals, does the fault lie in their intellectual superiority in itself? Does it not rather lie in the fact that they have been encouraged by ambitious parents and eager teachers to spend all their time and energy in developing their intellects to the exclusion of their other faculties?

In some cases poverty may have made it necessary for them to be self-supporting while receiving their education, so that all the time not spent in class or at study has been spent at work, and little, if any, time was left for leisurely companionship with fellow students, or for participation in sports, in group activities, or in any other form of play and recreation. Others may have come from families whose social background was markedly inferior to that of their intellectual equals, so that they have always felt unable to enjoy the intimate companionship of the very people with whom they might otherwise have had most in common. All these factors, and more, have undoubtedly contributed to the maladjustments of some highly endowed individuals.

Modern American educators and psychologists seem to agree that it is far wiser to enrich the course of the superior child than to push him ahead. Some schools definitely plan for such extensions of their curricula, adding projects to be worked out in class providing adequate activity and stimulation for the bright boy and girl. Even when this is not provided by the school, parents can often guide and direct such pursuits. The increasing popularity of the junior high school which bridges the gap between the grade-school group and the mature high-school group contributes to the solution of such dilemmas. For, after all, the child with superior endowment often presents a dilemma.

The same three principles apply in dealing with the superior child: (1) The necessity for recognizing the superior ability for what it is, meanwhile taking stock of the physical development and personality traits that go with it; (2) the importance of placing the child properly in school, with reference not only to his mental age but also to his size and his general level of maturity; and (3) the wisdom of guiding the adolescent toward becoming a well-adjusted and happy individual rather than merely an efficient set of brain cells.

SPECIAL APTITUDES, TALENTS, AND DISABILITIES

Certain special abilities and disabilities, talents, and intellectual handicaps or defects occur not uncommonly. Examples of individuals remarkable for such special abilities and disabilities are known to everyone; there are individuals with extraordinary visual memories enabling them to visualize a printed page and thus recall to memory names and dates as if they were reading them; there are individuals with extraordinary auditory memories who can recite a poem or retain the tune of a song after hearing it but once; there are some individuals who earn a livelihood by showing off their ability as lightning calculators; and in contrast to all of these, there are the students who have "a wretched memory," "no ear for a tune," or "no head for figures."

Special abilities or disabilities may be a part of the intellectual equipment of the feeble-minded, the average, or the superior individual. It is, therefore, not sufficient to recognize the special ability or disability without also recognizing the general level of intelligence that goes with it. The father who said, "My son can draw well and could make a good cartoonist, but he has no ideas," showed good insight into the relation between a special ability and general intelligence, and also a good appreciation of his son's equipment. He realized that his son had superior ability in drawing but that his general level of intelligence was low.

This does not indicate that the special ability should be neglected or even that it should not be cultivated. The danger lies in building the young person's entire life around his one strong point regardless of his possible inability to bring the rest of his life up to this peak. One would not think of trying to make a tennis champion out of a boy merely because he had a good stroke and a good eye for the ball, without considering the condition of his heart and his general physical reaction to exercise; yet the mere fact that he is not up to the strenuous practice and the excitement of a professional tournament need not debar him from enoying amateur games.

It is even more disastrous, however, to build the young person's life around a disability and to say, for example, that there is no point in continuing his education because he can never learn to spell, or to classify him once and for all as stupid and dull because he has a poor visual memory or difficulty in reading. Reading disabilities, although they often go unrecognized, are relatively common and sometimes cause serious problems. In recent years much experimental work has been done in an effort to discover ways and means of helping individuals to overcome or compensate for such special disabilities. Special instruction, once a disability is recognized, will often help greatly in overcoming it. But even where it is not possible to provide such remedial assistance, it is still possible to prevent young people from looking upon a particular handicap as the stumbling block in the way of happiness regardless of the road pursued.

Naturally, the special ability has certain advantages over the disability, for it can often be capitalized with appreciable success. A good memory can be capitalized in dozens of ways and may completely conceal from the general public an otherwise inferior mind; but a poor memory—of what possible advantage can it be save to serve as a convenient excuse for failure?

Although the psychologists and their intelligence tests have contributed to an appreciative understanding of these deviations of the human mind, and although it may be necessary to turn to them for an expert opinion or a final word of advice when in doubt about the best plan for an individual child, there is no reason why parents and teachers should not be able to recognize some of these things from their own observation and take such steps as seem wise to overcome the handicap.

Some Teen-Age School Problems

OF all adolescent problems, those concerning educational progress are the most common. Practically every child, regardless of his mental or physical development and his social or economic status, is confronted with the task of acquiring knowledge of the world in which he lives. As he advances in years, competition becomes more keen and failures in academic work become more common.

These failures are due only to a very limited degree to actual intellectual inferiority. A child with an average mind—an intelligence quotient ranging from 95 to 105—may do very well in the lower grades but may not be able to survive the keen competition with children of superior intelligence as he advances to the higher grades and to high school. This underlines the failure of schools to provide subjects designed to interest the less academic-minded child. Children drop out of school for many other reasons than lack of ability to cope with school work. A large number are influenced by their desire to come to grips with something more meaningful to them than the classes they are attending.

Parents who fail to appreciate the increased intellectual demands that are made on children as they advance up this intellectual ladder may be quite unjust in their criticisms of those who fail. Many a parent complains that Johnny could do the work in high school if he only tried; that he never had any trouble in grammar school, where he worked hard and was interested. This may be true, but many of these children are carrying intellectual loads which are beyond their ability, and they just naturally lag behind and slacken in their efforts when nothing of real interest suited to their abilities is provided. It must be remembered, too, that on the physical side some have only a six-hour capacity for standardized work, while others can carry on for eight or ten hours unimpaired by fatigue.

It is not hard to understand why parents who are but little concerned about the emotional life of the child, perhaps being quite unaware of such personality traits as shyness, jealousy, or feelings of

653

inferiority, and those who are rather casual about physical growth and development, take this problem of school failure so seriously. They seem to feel that such failure indicates actual inferiority, and, either consciously or unconsciously, they blame themselves. Teachers are prone to view failure as a reflection upon their ability to teach, and they, too, frequently join with the parents in pushing and prodding and generally harassing this unfortunate group of children.

It is therefore important to keep in mind that there is a fairly large number of boys and girls well developed physically, capable of fitting into the varied social situations in life quite adequately, who require a broader type of instruction to meet their particular needs. In attempting to help them, one should think in terms of breadth, rather than height; that is, the boy or girl who reaches a mental age of thirteen or fourteen is intellectually capable of acquiring a more useful and practical grasp of those essentials pertaining to the social, economic, and industrial aspects of the world in which he lives than many students have at the end of a college course. It all depends upon the wisdom with which these individuals are guided and directed, and the degree to which schools are willing to accept their responsibility for providing wider opportunities.

There is another group of adolescents who run into scholastic difficulties, not on account of mediocre or relatively poor intellectual equipment, but rather on account of poor preparation. Many situations encountered by the child during the school years contribute to this particular difficulty. In some cities many children enter school before they are mentally ready to do first-grade work. Such children would do well to repeat the first grade; but in the natural course of events, there is a new line of children waiting and as the number of places in the first grade is limited, they must move on. Consequently, each year children are pushed ahead from grade to grade, unfitted by their previous experience to meet the task at hand. These children cannot be held back in any large numbers because actual space in the schoolroom is not available. But their inadequate preparation in early years, unless recognized and corrected, will obviously lead to serious difficulties later.

WHEN SCHOOLING IS INTERRUPTED

Children who are prevented from attending school regularly on account of illness or some chronic physical handicap must also be considered. They, too, are pushed along—sometimes at the instigation of an ambitious parent, sometimes because of misdirected sympathy on the part of a teacher, and then again to make a place for someone else.

There are also a certain number of students whose continuity in school work is interrupted, sometimes unavoidably, by having to change schools when their families move. It is no small portion of the population that must seek employment wherever it is available. This problem arises in various social and economic levels and may affect the minister or the teacher or the millworker. These periodic interruptions in school work may be definite factors contributing to failure.

Then there are those parents who build their lives entirely around their own pleasures with an utter disregard for the welfare of the child, so that children are taken out of school because parents want to travel, move to another neighborhood, or follow some other whim.

However, frequent removals are not necessarily a handicap. Some children develop an extraordinary ability to fit easily into different social situations and to make friends quickly, their adjustment being furthered by practice in adapting to change and new scenes. Such children speak volumes for the essential security their parents have been able to provide in spite of not being able to give them a permanent home.

WHY CHILDREN CANNOT CONCENTRATE

Inability to concentrate is often given as a cause of failure to acquire satisfactory passing marks. The ability to concentrate is a gradual acquisition, and parents should make an effort to see that they do not themselves interfere with its development by creating a program that is altogether too active. Extracurricular activities are of real educational value in giving the young boy or girl greater opportunity for finding out what life has to offer and what he can contribute, but such activities may be overdone. It may be that special interests for which the child shows some talent are permitted to assume an importance which they do not deserve. Too much parental interest can be demonstrated in building radios and airplanes, in sketching, in music and dancing lessons, to the discouragement of any concentrated effort on the school work to be done.

Too Many Diversions

Athletics, dramatics, and even the otherwise harmless associations with those of the opposite sex, may all become so diverting that the real purpose of school attendance is entirely overlooked. There are those individuals who seem to be capable of absorbing all these varied interests and still maintaining a satisfactory average in their school work. Most students, however, need considerable guidance lest they spread their interests and energies so thin that none of their activities receives adequate attention.

Lack of Interest

Occasionally one finds failure in academic work to be due to lack of interest in the subject matter. This being true, the adolescent will often seek for his intellectual satisfactions in outside reading or other diversions which may in themselves be educational but which do not contribute to his progress through the school. This may mean that a change in the curriculum is advisable; or, if the student has a definite objective, such as college entrance, it will necessitate his grasping the fact that certain subjects which he is required to learn in school must be studied because they are a means to an end, even though they hold no interest for him as an end in themselves.

On account of the lack of interest in the course of study, a student may develop the idea that the work is too hard, that it is over his head, and that, regardless of how much he might study, he would inevitably fail. Here one may do much to overcome this feeling of inferiority by arranging for him to have a psychological examination. It is reassuring to the student to know that he has a good set of mental tools with which to work, that the subject matter which he is tackling is well within his grasp, and that failure is due not to inferior intellectual equipment but to the way he happens to be using his equipment.

EMOTIONAL ATTITUDES MAY CAUSE FAILURE

Often emotional situations present obstacles to the child's ability to measure up to his group in school. Disturbed emotional attitudes toward life are probably far more common as a cause for failure than all other causes put together; and, although the situation may appear relatively unimportant in the beginning, the conflict over the failure itself complicates the emotional attitude toward the situation. Thus young people, who have never had an opportunity to grow up and actually become independent, may meet fairly well the situations to which they have been trained as a matter of routine but will find themselves totally at sea when it comes to utilizing their time and ability without strict supervision. This, again, is a matter of training.

Parents, in their eagerness to contribute to the happiness of their children and to protect them from even the minor hardships of life, are frequently inclined to believe that their own experiences, their own unhappiness and failures, can be utilized to save the child the pangs of humiliation that are brought about by failure and disappointment. They are always modifying the ordinary, everyday situations so that their children can meet them without even for the moment endangering their happiness. In other words, these parents never allow the child to meet life and all its complex problems, as it actually exists. They fail to appreciate that experience is the most trustworthy weapon and that knowledge is the best armor for those who are about to step out of the home and battle with the world.

Don't Set Impossible Standards

Overambitious parents must also be mentioned as a factor in creating emotional situations leading to school failures. In their desire to have children succeed and excel in their school work, they are likely to place too high a premium on marks and stress scholastic attainment to the exclusion of everything else. To desire success for one's children is laudable, but to demand scholastic honors of the child for the sake of gratifying personal pride is selfish.

The student himself may set his standard so high and become so concerned in competing for high marks that he misses much of the pleasure and satisfaction of school life. Friendships, athletics, dramatics, and the general welfare of the school are sometimes sacrificed in this keen competition; and if he fails to attain success in this scholastic striving, all is lost. This is an attitude that should not be encouraged either by teachers or by parents.

TRY TO UNDERSTAND YOUR CHILD

The emotional conflicts of youth often find their origin in many obscure experiences and situations to which the adolescent is subjected, and they can be understood only when one takes time to know intimately the personality make-up of the youth and the varied environmental situations which he has to combat. One must take into consideration the social, economic, and cultural conditions in which he has been reared; the moral codes, religious creeds, racial background of his family, and the peculiarities and eccentricities of the members of his family; what his parents demand of their children in the way of obligations and responsibilitites, and what they permit them in the way of privileges.

One must keep in mind that many of the individuals who fail to make a place for themselves in either school or college meet the more concrete and practical situations of life successfully. Many individuals who are not what is termed "intellectual" are very intelligent; and life in its everyday contacts is met successfully only with intelligence. The emotional conflicts which have been considered may lead to behavior that brings the individual into conflict not only with the family and society at large but with himself. These behavior problems are invariably the result of an environmental situation due to a multiplicity of conditions and circumstances; and the success of parents and teachers in handling these problems depends upon their ability to understand how these complex situations create emotional attitudes which affect the conduct of the adolescent.

Part Six

SPECIAL PROBLEMS
OF PARENTS AND CHILDREN

Aggressiveness in Children

To most of us the word aggression has a disagreeable ring. We think of the ruthless invasion of helpless countries, of the bully pushing people around. So when we see our ten-year-old son angrily clouting his younger brother, when we hear our little girl of four mutter that she hates us or wants to send the baby away forever, when we see a three-year-old, quite unprovoked, knock down a play-mate in the sandpile and take away his shovel, we become alarmed by such crude displays of aggressive feeling. What is this force, we ask ourselves, that makes ordinarily loving youngsters behave like little demons? How much of this is to be expected as a part of normal growing up? What should parents do about it?

WHAT IS AGGRESSIVENESS?

Aggressiveness is that force within us that gives strength and vitality to our actions. Aggressiveness isn't always evil and destructive; it can be good and useful and healthy. It spurs us on to overcome obstacles and to strike out against dangerous or unpleasant situa-tions. At its best, it makes for initiative, enterprise and healthy com-petitiveness. The scientist who seeks to conquer disease and the statesman who fights against poverty and injustice are aggressive in a socially useful way.

Aggressiveness propels children to grow and learn and master their environment. The newborn baby reaching out for food, the toddler tugging at the challenging electric cord, the little girl learning to skate, the schoolboy hitting a home run—all are dis-playing healthy aggressiveness. The young child, who pushes away the bowl of cereal when he wants no more of it, is also behaving in a normally aggressive way, even though to his parent, irritated by the whole procedure, this may seem like hostility.

Indeed, every step the child takes to free himself from his de-pendence on his parents and stand on his own feet is an expression of healthy and desirable aggressiveness.

But aggressiveness has another face—one that is hostile and destructive. We all know the harm it can do. Some people believe we are born with it, as with the sex drive. Others believe it is not inborn, but is the way people respond to frustration, disappointment and fear. Whatever its source, this undesirable side of aggressiveness (which we shall call hostile aggressiveness or hostility) naturally troubles parents. They want to know how to minimize or redirect it, so that they can help their children grow up to be socially responsible people, considerate of the rights of others and able to live peaceably with their fellow men.

HOW HOSTILITY BEGINS

The problem of aggressiveness is inevitably bound up with the child's early training. How these training procedures are managed may well determine whether normally aggressive impulses are turned one way or the other. In the management of these early training procedures, therefore, lies the key to prevention of many of the problems of aggressiveness.

We know that the infant is completely absorbed in his own appetites and desires, and wants them satisfied at once. Yet in the course of time, this self-centered creature must be transformed into a socially conforming individual, able to balance the demands of the group against his personal wishes. How does this come about?

It comes about through a gradual and rather complicated maturing process. At first the infant is a little king. Whatever he wants he gets; and it is right to treat him so. But gradually restrictions are placed on him. He must give up the nipple and drink from the cup; he must empty his bowels at a certain time and in a certain place. He must not hit; he must not bite; he must not throw things; he must not take things that belong to others. The world has become for him one big Must Not. In such a world he inevitably feels anger and resentment against the parents who impose these rules. Something within him rebels and makes him fight against such restrictions. But when he does, his mother frowns and calls him "naughty boy." She may even punish him or threaten to go away and leave him if he behaves that way. So he has angry thoughts about her and perhaps about his father too. If there is also a rival in the form of a new baby, one can be quite sure he feels angry about the intruder.

But this isn't the whole story. It's important to know that these very natural, hostile feelings are frightening to little children. Children seem to attribute almost magical powers to their own thoughts, and they tend to believe that just to *think* something is likely to make it happen. What's more, they expect to be punished in some unforeseen way just for thinking such "bad" thoughts. Imagine, then, the child's dilemma. He feels angry toward his parents, but at the same time he needs them desperately. Caught in this conflict, he becomes anxious and fearful that they will punish him or go away and abandon him for being so bad. If, then, his parents actually threaten to punish or to leave him, the child's fear is sharpened. Yet the hostile feelings are still there, are perhaps even increased.

The child is now in a difficult spot indeed. He wants to strike out when he feels angry, but he also wants his parents' love. Gradually, in order to keep his parents' love and approval, to feel that he is a good boy, he begins to accept restrictions and do what is expected. He adopts his parents' teachings. If you listen to a child of two or three, you can sometimes hear him scolding himself, "No, no! Johnny, don't touch," even while he's pulling the forbidden book off the shelf. He is developing a conscience, and trying to choose right instead of wrong.

In the beginning the child's deepest need is for love and protection. If this need is fully met by those around him, he can gradually develop the capacity to accept the rules. Feeling loved, he will be better able to love in return, and will gradually be willing to exchange the brief pleasure of getting what he wants immediately for the more lasting pleasure of keeping his parents' approval. In other words, he learns to give up his selfish aims through affection for people rather than through fear of them. In this way he escapes a burden of buried resentment.

But if in his babyhood a child feels insecure and unloved, this exchange cannot take place. If he feels cheated of the mothering and protection he craves, he will look upon the necessary restrictions as an attack—and his hostile aggressive feelings will surge up each time he is denied something.

Such a child's development may follow many patterns. Feeling that he has nothing to gain by giving up his selfish wishes, he may become an antisocial person. On the other hand, if his fear of punishment or loss of love is too great, he may deal with his resentment quite differently. For example, he may unconsciously bend over backward not to be hostile and become too gentle, timid, and passive. We are coming to recognize that passive goodness in a child is not necessarily a virtue. We know that it may cover up resentments and hatreds that sometimes break out in disguised form —in sly cruelties, in tormenting others who may be smaller or weaker, in barbed taunts against people of other color or religion. We have learned to be suspicious of too much goodness in a child— especially in a very young child.

There are still other ways in which a child's resentments may find expression. He may become generally discontented about every-thing—a chronic complainer. He may even take out his feelings on himself by becoming physically ill. Stomach disorders, headaches, and many other physical disturbances have in some cases been found to stem from dammed-up unconscious feelings of hostility.

CHILDREN WANT TO GROW UP

The notion that children must be pushed through strict training, begun as early as possible if they are ever to learn to behave properly, has been pretty well disproved. Actually most children want to grow up. But their growth toward well-balanced maturity depends on a feeling of understanding and genuine interest from those around them. This does not mean honeyed words. Children have an un-canny skill for seeing through—perhaps it is more correct to say feeling through—a grownup's words. No amount of endearing terms will convince a child he is loved if parents in fact are either bored with him or disappointed in him. On the other hand, occasional exasperation, even to the point of a slap, isn't likely to leave lasting damage if, deep down, the child is aware that his mother really understands and loves him.

Besides having warm and interested grownups in his life, the child should be physically and emotionally ready to accept the civilizing restrictions his parents must put upon him. Sometimes parents will push a child too fast because other children his age are, let us say, already trained; and it is understandable that they want their child to be just as advanced as the next. Just as some children talk or walk later than others, so some children take longer than others to grow up. One young child will push aside his mother's helping hand and insist upon holding the cup himself, while another of exactly the same age and intelligence will seem not at all interested in drinking from the cup.

Then, too, children differ in their constitutional makeup and in the strength of their inner drives. Besides, their life experiences, the emotional attitude of others toward them—all of the outside influences that play upon them—have a deep effect upon the way they respond to their environment and whether they are eager to go forward or inclined to hesitate.

Moreover, children don't grow in a straight line. Sometimes, under the stress of some special circumstance, they may fall back into earlier ways of behaving in which they found satisfaction. A six-year-old may consider himself an independent old fellow, who wouldn't think of allowing Mother to help him dress; but there will be occasions, particularly if he is ill or is feeling a bit low because of some defeat at school or on the playground, when he will want and need some babying by Mother to reassure him of her protection and make him feel that he has a place all his own.

On the other hand, we sometimes give children too much babying when they want none of it. Much as children want, in some ways, to cling to babyhood and its privileges, there is usually a healthy push from inside themselves that makes them wish even more to go ahead. They want approval and the satisfaction of achievement that comes with mature ways of behaving. They want to do things for themselves. Parents must be ready to help their children go forward, offering praise and encouragement for their efforts, exerting gentle pressure where necessary to help them try the next step.

It isn't easy, of course, to know how much to indulge a child's baby ways and how much to urge him to take next steps. Parents differ, too: some find it hard to be relaxed and to lead the child gradually to more mature ways of behaving; others find it hard to be firm even when firmness is called for. In either case, parents who keep in mind the fact that children need aid and encouragement—but resent being pushed—will go a long way in helping them toward healthy emotional growth.

BEHAVIOR HAS INNER MEANING

Growing up and becoming an independent cooperative member of society is never a smooth-flowing process. Each period in a child's life has its stumbling blocks for healthy emotional growth; and from time to time children will show strain through increased hostility or in other ways.

This does not mean that one should complacently brush off all of a child's difficulties as a phase he's passing through. If his troublesome behavior persists too long, or seems senseless, the wise parent seeks expert advice from a trained counselor, just as she would go to a doctor about persistent and unexplained physical symptoms. For example, a child who bites others should have stopped doing this before he is three or four years old. Most children become toilet trained before this age too. Senseless behavior is typified by the somewhat older child who, though he has an ample supply of toys or spending money, persistently steals; by the child who lies continuously when the truth would serve just as well; or by the child whose fears or other feelings are characteristically out of all proportion to the realities which arouse them.

Sometimes the source of a child's trouble may be found in his immediate life situation. A bullying youngster may have a domineering, overstrict father whom he fears and resents; being afraid to express his feelings against the parent directly, he takes it out on the neighborhood children. In another child, bullying may be traced to weak, overindulgent parents who give in to his every whim so that he comes to expect the same kind of subservience from playmates.

Sometimes the root of the trouble lies more deeply buried. For example, a youngster may bully other children because of hurt feelings left smoldering after some earlier experience when he felt himself deprived of his parents' affection. He may have been afraid to show his feelings at the time, and swallowed them instead. Now he takes out his buried grudge on smaller children without realizing what he is doing or why. This may be too deep a problem for parents to deal with themselves, and may require the help of a professional counselor.

It would certainly ease the task of parents, teachers, and others who come into close contact with children, if it were possible to prescribe a specific remedy for each and every behavior disturbance in children. But, as we have seen, the causes of children's behavior are both complex and highly individual. The same behavior may mean one thing in one case and something else in another. In one child, stealing money from his mother's purse may not be stealing at all. Not yet having learned the fine distinction between mine and thine, he takes the money, having seen his mother do so, to get something he wants. Another child, perhaps, deliberately steals because he wants to buy candy for the children in the neighborhood whose friendship he craves, and knows no other way of getting. Still another child, with money of his own in his pocket, may steal from his mother's purse as a symbolic way of taking from her the love he wants yet feels he doesn't get.

Helping children grow to wholesome maturity involves much more than applying formulas or rules. Helpful guidance can be given only when there is sensitive understanding of what a child may be saying in acts instead of words. Behavior has inner meaning. Children's actions, which to their parents often seem willful or naughty, are their way of responding to inner drives and outer pressures.

If parents understand what a child is trying to say by his behavior, they have taken the first step in helping him feel less hostile to the world. The child does not know why he acts as he does. All he knows, if he thinks about it at all, is that he feels tense or anxious or fearful or angry or hurt. If parents recognize and accept a child's feelings as natural, helping him at the same time to control his actions, he will make progress.

HURTING OTHERS

Some kinds of aggressive behavior in children seem to be especially distressing to parents. Perhaps the most common is hurting other children. As they take their first steps toward making friends, almost all children do some hitting. Actually, hitting is one of the ways in which children learn to get along together. If you watch a group of preschoolers, you will see two or three of them play briefly together, then quarrel, hit one another, go off to play by themselves for awhile, and then come together to play again. By the time they're in school, however, they've learned pretty well to control the impulse to strike, and to use arguments instead of fists. Of course there will also be some fighting during the school age, in order that a child may test out his strength and match it against others. Some of this will have to be tolerated by parents and teachers. If fighting goes too far, however, it will have to be curbed, not only for the sake of peace and safety, but because children need to learn other and better ways to settle disagreements.

Occasionally we find a child who seems bent on tormenting other children. Such a child may be expressing, in the only way he knows, his discontent and unhappiness in his relations with other children or with his parents. For his own sake, as well as for the safety of others, limits must be set to this sort of persistent cruelty. Such children want to be stopped. Though aggressive behavior may give the child some immediate relief for his pent-up anger, nevertheless he feels deep inside himself that he is bad when he continuously hurts others. This feeling becomes particularly acute when he strikes a parent for whose love he has so great a need. He wants to be helped to behave in a socially acceptable way, to have the approval of others. To accomplish this, a child needs parents and other grownups around him who, without being severe, are nevertheless squarely on the side of his own conscience. He has a right to count on them to control him when he cannot control himself.

How best to do this is no easy matter. Seeing one child hurt another, the grownup's first impulse is often to hit the aggressor in turn. While this may settle the crisis of the moment, it may also do more harm than good; for it may only serve to confirm the aggressive child's feeling that he is hoplessly bad. And besides, if a child sees his parent hitting, no matter what the reason, he may even feel that hitting must be right. At best, it will confuse him, since this is precisely what he has always been taught to be wrong.

If parents are sensitive to how a child is feeling at such times, then the means they find to stop him will not seem to him like a personal attack. Instead, he will know that his parents wish to help him. "I know you're mad at him," you may say, "but I can't let you hit Johnny." You may then want to relieve the situation by suggesting that you and he do something together. Success depends on the parents' skill. The child needs to feel that they will help him to be good because they like him.

There may be times when, to keep a child from hurting another, you may have to remove him, against his will if necessary, until he quiets down. You may want to stay with him for a while. You may want to see that he has something to keep him busy. The important thing is to make him feel that he is being helped to control himself rather than being punished.

Providing a child with such outlets as a hammer and nails, clay, or a punching bag is sometimes helpful. Activities give him a chance, not only to let off steam but also to express his aggressive feelings in a constructive way—a way that can win the sincere approval of his parents. The child may also need a chance to talk out his anger or frustration in words rather than in actions, secure in the knowledge that he won't be punished for saying honestly how he feels.

THE CHILD WHO ISN'T ASSERTIVE ENOUGH

So much has been said about the overly aggressive child, and so much parental agony is expended on him, that there is danger of ignoring the difficulties of the child who is apparently of the opposite type. This is the timid and passive youngster who often masks his inner conflicts behind gentleness and unselfishness. He refuses to stand up for himself; he may run away when other children hit him; he is a cry baby, too frightened to express his aggressiveness in a forthright manner. The discerning parent realizes that such a child may present an even more serious problem than does the overly aggressive child.

A timid child's insecurity with other children may stem, on the one hand, from having been crushed earlier by overdominating parents or, on the other, from having been so babied by overprotective ones that he could never call his soul his own. Such a child doesn't really lack the capacity for healthy aggressiveness or hostility, but has learned to be so afraid of his own aggressive feelings that he doesn't dare to let go at all.

It is always painful for a parent or teacher to see a child, who is constantly pushed around or hit, merely stand and cry. The natural inclination of the grownup is to urge him to hit back. In a young child, however, who hasn't had much contact with other children, what looks like timidity may only be inexperience. The child's world has its own code. Blows are among the things that most children must both give and take at some time. A child may not yet have learned how to defend himself, and needs time to find out. But he may also be held back by his feelings. In the first place, he may be afraid to hit back, afraid of the other child. But in addition, he senses that, in his parents' world, hitting is considered bad. How then is it possible for good grownups to encourage it in him? He is both anxious and confused.

This is a hard situation for any child, and one that can be met successfully only over a considerable period of time. A child so confused needs help in finding satisfactions through increased activity and the development of all sorts of technical skills. Since he fears competition, it may be better for him to work and play by himself for a while. If parents can help him acquire hobbies like drawing, clay modelling, or swimming, and perhaps do some of these things with him, he may gradually feel secure enough to try himself out with one or two other children. His mother or father may have to take the initiative for some time in getting such activities under way. But as he gains confidence, he will begin to feel more comfortable with other children. With this new-found confidence in the use of his intelligence and skills, he may become more constructively assertive and begin to hold his own in a group.

CHILDREN ARE INDIVIDUALS IN THEIR OWN RIGHT

What parents must finally learn is that their children aren't merely an extension of themselves but are individuals in their own right, separate personalities to be nurtured and respected. As parents, we are struggling to help our children to achieve the best possible lives. We are eager to see them avoid our own mistakes. As a result, we are apt to be in a hurry, or we may fail to take note of a child's own particular rate of growth. The athletic father urges his puny, timid son to be tough, and shames him for not fighting back when picked on, thus increasing the child's feelings of inadequacy and sense of failure, as well as his fear of his father. If a mother, in her own youth, was shy and lonely, she may unconsciously want to live out, through her daughter, her own dreams of popularity. So she nags her quiet, book-loving daughter to join clubs and go out more, as though by urging her to be popular she might actually make the girl change her personality.

In subtler ways and more insidiously, because parents rarely recognize it, fathers and mothers may unconsciously thwart their children's attempts to grow up because of their own need to keep them emotionally bound. A father, especially as his child approaches adolescence, may insist on directing his every move. A mother may get so much satisfaction out of her child's dependence that she actually fosters it. The overanxious mother may fuss unduly over her young child's health, fear to let him play with other children lest he catch something, encourage him to stay home from school when it rains, and thereby succeed in so thwarting the child's natural urge for independence that he becomes fearful of everything new, and is ready at all times to hide behind the protection of his mother's skirt. Or he may react to his mother's possessiveness by constant argument and defiance, or tear himself away completely, leaving her mourning his ungratefulness. Such parents are usually unaware of their own reluctance to let their children grow up, and they look upon attempts at independence as a kind of disloyalty. Unfortunately they too often succeed in making their children feel guilty for wanting independence. Yet this wish is an inevitable and necessary part of every child's struggle for maturity. If he is made to feel too guilty for resenting his parents' interference, he may suppress the normal feelings of rebellion, give up the struggle and remain bound to his parents long after he should be free.

PARENTS CARRY THEIR CHILDHOOD WITH THEM

There is no end to the subtlety of feeling that enters into parents' attitudes toward their children. These attitudes, of which they themselves are often unaware, are closely related to their own early development. They frequently stem from sources they have long forgotten or have pushed out of mind. A parent may punish a child severely for actions which stir up buried impulses for which he felt guilty in his own childhood. For example, if he was made to feel ashamed for being dirty and was forced to repress his childish interest in bladder and bowel matters, he may react with horror and disgust at seeing his child exhibiting similar interest.

Being human, all parents have hostile as well as loving feelings toward their children. Just as children try to deny their hostile feelings toward their parents by being too good, some parents cannot face their own hostile feelings toward their children and try to conceal these from themselves and others by being over-indulgent. They constantly find excuses for giving in, fail to exercise authority when it is called for, and leave the children to flounder about with no clear idea of what kind of behavior is expected of them.

The problem of aggressiveness in children is thus intimately bound at every turn to the parents' own development and character. It is a two-way problem in which success will depend on how well parents sense the child's need, on the one hand, and, on the other, how well they know themselves. To see our children with fresh eyes, as growing human beings apart from ourselves, and to come to terms with our own childhood conflicts which are constantly returning to plague the new relationship—these are the only possible ways to break these old patterns. Then, as parents, we can find satisfaction in our children's step-by-step progress toward an emotional maturity in which healthy aggressiveness plays an important part.

EDITH LESSER ATKIN, IN CONJUNCTION WITH
THE STAFF OF THE CHILD STUDY ASSOCIATION

GETTING ALONG WITH OTHERS

Wherever children gather in play, it is easy to detect which are well-adjusted and which are not. The trouble-maker who continually disrupts the harmony of group play often behaves this way because of some profound frustration. It must be traced to its root and corrected or he may grow into a hostile, unhappy adult.

U. S. Children's Bureau Photos
by Esther Bubley

LET YOUR CHILD PAINT

All children enjoy creative experiences. They take a special delight in producing something that bears the stamp of their personalities, and such self-expression enriches their emotional life. For this reason, no matter what a child's talent or ability, he should be encouraged to express himself artistically.

Above: New York City Board of Education Photo
Below: Play Schools Assn. Photo

Indoor Fun for Mother and Child

OR most mothers, keeping a child indoors because of bad weather or illness represents a real problem. The child will show interest in his toys for just so long. What is he to do when he gets bored, and you simply cannot think of a new activity that appeals to him? This section of Indoor Fun for Mother and Child has been planned to solve this dilemma for you. It provides ideas and directions for an ample variety of entertaining projects requiring only the simplest skills and inexpensive materials—paper, paste, cardboard, spools, and other things you are likely to have in your home. These easy projects will do more than give you and your child many hours of fun. They will also help develop his creative and manual abilities. Moreover, he will end up with attractive little objects he will enjoy all the more because he has made them himself, with your guidance.

NEWSPAPER ZOO

A Swan

How would you like to own a zoo? You can—a whole menagerie full of strange and wonderful animals. All you need is some newspapers, paste, tempera—and imagination.

A swan is very easy to make. Tear a sheet of newspaper into strips one inch wide by four inches long. Set them aside. Now crumple half a sheet of newspaper and roll it around between your hands until you have made a tight, egg-shaped ball. Roll the other half sheet lengthwise, loosely like a tube, and tie it around the paper ball—the long way. Make a small paper ball for the head. Attach it to the end of the paper tube with a paste-covered strip of newspaper. Paste paper strips over the whole thing. Add a cone-shaped piece of heavier paper for the beak. When the paste is dry, paint the whole swan white, the beak red, and the eyes black.

A Giraffe

It is just as easy to make an animal with legs—let's say a giraffe. Start this animal the same way you did the swan. Make the body, neck, and head. Now tie two smaller paper tubes around the body

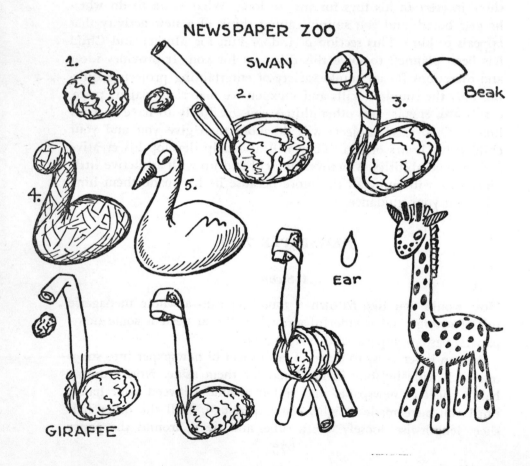

NEWSPAPER ZOO

SWAN

Beak

Ear

GIRAFFE

(the short way) to form the legs. Cover the whole animal with paper strips. Allow the paste to dry and paint the giraffe orange— or pink if you want! When this is dry, paint black or purple spots all over it—or green, or any color that suits you. Cut ears and tail of colored paper and paste in place. For the horns stick two short bits of match stick into the head—and you have a giraffe!

You can make all sorts of animals in this manner: short, fat ones —or long, lean ones. You can also create a remarkable bird by putting colored paper or feather wings on an animal with no legs.

Out of a cardboard box you can make a cage for the animals. Draw a line on the top of the lid, one half inch from the edge. Cut along this line and remove the piece of cardboard from the center. Paste strips of narrow tape or dark paper to the frame (the short way) to represent bars. Put the animals in the box and replace the lid.

SCISSORS PAINTING

Polish peasants have a charming custom. Every year at Easter time, they whitewash and decorate their homes. They paste colored paper cut-outs on the beams and walls of their rooms. They also decorate Easter eggs with cut-outs. The effect is beautiful and very gay. And all they do is to fold pieces of colored paper, and then, with a pair of sharp little scissors, they cut and snip—simple flowers, leaves, birds, roosters, animals, or just swirls and triangles. A little snipped off here and a little there—but when the folds are opened, the results are unexpected and lovely. Try it and see what happens!

All you need for scissors painting, besides the scissors, is a square of pinwheel paper or any other fairly thin colored paper. (Don't use tissue paper—it is too thin.) Cut a square, fold it as the diagram shows, and cut anything that strikes your fancy—a leaf here, a crescent there, a flower or a bird at the wide part. Cut away and have fun, but be sure to leave enough paper uncut to hold your design together, especially along the heavy fold. Mount it with paste on the thing you want to decorate. (If your design is very intricate it is always best to cover the object with paste, and then smooth

SCISSORS PAINTING

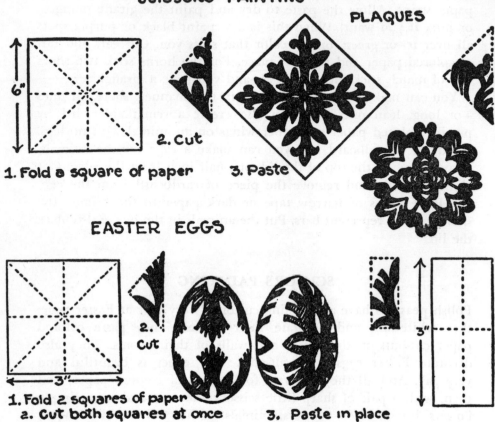

PLAQUES

1. Fold a square of paper   2. Cut   3. Paste

EASTER EGGS

1. Fold 2 squares of paper
2. Cut both squares at once   2. Cut   3. Paste in place

BOX DECORATED WITH CUT-OUTS

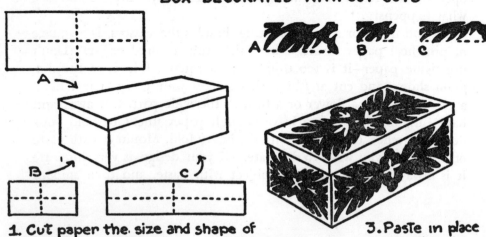

A   B   C

1. Cut paper the size and shape of
all the sides of the box   2. Cut designs

3. Paste in place
4. Shellac.

the cut-out down on it.) When the paste is dry, brush some clear shellac over the whole object, and a second coat of shellac when the first has dried.

Paper plates or squares of cardboard are easy to decorate and make lovely plaques for a playroom or kitchen. Scissors painting can make an ordinary cardboard box into a thing of beauty. Easter eggs decorated in this manner are different and quaint. Be sure the eggs are hard-boiled before you paste on the cut-outs!

GREETING CARDS

As you grow more skillful with the scissors, you can make unusual greeting cards. A piece of construction paper about five inches by eight, folded in half, for the body of your card, and a scissors-cut design from another color are all you need. White snow flakes on blue paper, yellow baby chicks with red beaks on purple paper, red holly berries and green leaves on gold paper—are just a few of the things you can use.

LUMINOUS GREETING CARDS AND ENVELOPES

There is another very effective way to make cut-out greeting cards. We call them luminous cards because they glisten and look like lovely little stained glass windows. To make one of these cards you need a piece of dark-colored construction paper, some colored cellophane or tissue paper (as many different colors as you can find), a piece of tin foil or silver paper, a light-colored crayon, a pencil, a safety-razor blade, and paste.

Fold a piece of dark construction paper (five inches by eight) in half, like a book, then open the fold. Lay the opened paper aside. On an ordinary piece of paper (four inches by five) draw your design. Any simple design—trees, stars, birds, a toy, Xmas candles. Rub the light-colored crayon all over the back of this piece of paper. Lay the drawing, right side up, on the front fold of the construction paper and trace the design. Tracing in this manner will leave thin crayon lines on your dark paper. With a razor blade, cut carefully along these lines until you have cut away all parts of the design. Paste different colored cellophane or tissue paper under each part

GREETING CARDS WITH CUT-OUTS

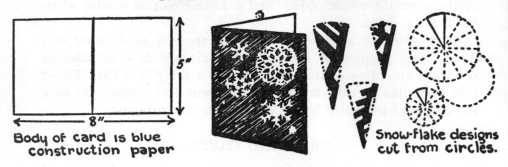

Body of card is blue
construction paper

Snow-flake designs
cut from circles.

LUMINOUS GREETING CARD

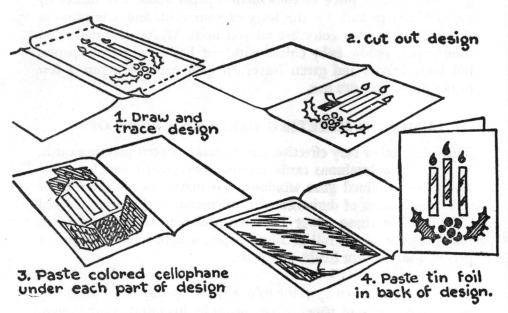

1. Draw and
trace design

2. Cut out design

3. Paste colored cellophane
under each part of design

4. Paste tin foil
in back of design.

HOW TO MAKE AN ENVELOPE

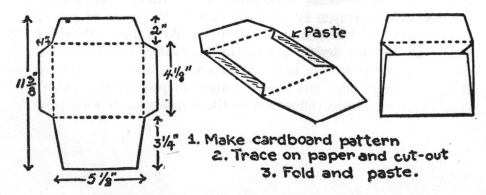

1. Make cardboard pattern
2. Trace on paper and cut-out
3. Fold and paste.

of the design. Now paste a sheet of tin foil or silver paper (three and a half inches by four and a half) under the whole picture, using a little paste on the four corners of the paper. This will make your design sparkle and look very gay. The diagram shows how to make the envelopes.

STORY PICTURES

It is always nice to own a picture of your favorite story, but to make one yourself and hang it in your room is twice as much fun. For

STORY PICTURES

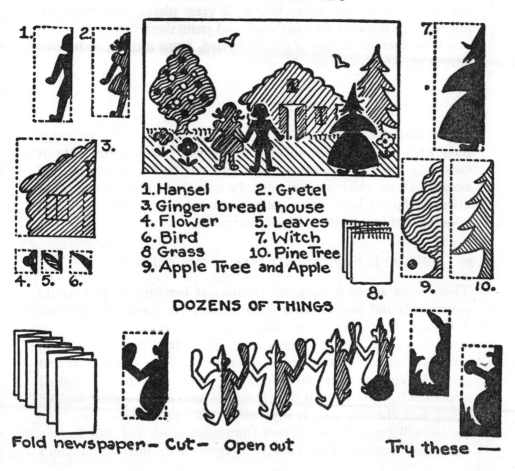

1. Hansel   2. Gretel
3. Ginger bread house
4. Flower   5. Leaves
6. Bird   7. Witch
8 Grass   10. Pine Tree
9. Apple Tree and Apple

DOZENS OF THINGS

Fold newspaper — Cut — Open out   Try these —

this kind of cut-out picture you will need a large piece of cardboard, scissors, paste, and as many bits of different colored paper as you can find.

Think of a story you would like to illustrate. Hansel and Gretel is a good one. We'll do that one now, but you can think of others just as nice. First make a list of all the things you want to put in your picture. For Hansel and Gretel we will need trees, birds, grass, flowers, a gingerbread house, Hansel and Gretel, of course, and, if we have room, the witch. Our next step is to decide which bit of paper will be best suited for each of our cut-outs. When you have decided, fold each piece of paper once and cut. The diagram shows you how to cut each piece. When all your pieces have been cut out, arrange them on the cardboard and paste them in place. Punch two little holes at the top of the cardboard. Draw a string or narrow ribbon through and hang the picture.

DOZENS OF THINGS

Some rainy day when you are entertaining younger cousins, cut a long strip of newspaper about four or five inches wide. Fold it back and forth in three-inch folds and cut half a figure, cutting through all the thicknesses at once. Be sure that there is some paper uncut at both edges! Open the paper carefully and you will find "dozens of things." (See illustration shown on page 679.)

WALL PAPER AND MAGAZINE CUT-OUTS

There is an art to cutting out pictures as carefully as you would paper dolls and pasting them together to form interesting designs.

For sedate and charming decoration, cut from wall paper or seed catalogues, flowers, birds, fruit, butterflies, etc. Paste them carefully to the object to be decorated in the form of nosegays and garlands. Your cut-outs may overlap, but be sure they are pasted smooth. After the paste is dry, brush on two coats of clear shellac, being sure the first coat is dry before you apply the second. The shellac will prevent the cut-outs from peeling off and will form a waterproof surface. This kind of decoration is fine for mother's

DECORATING WITH WALL PAPERS & MAGAZINE CUT-OUTS

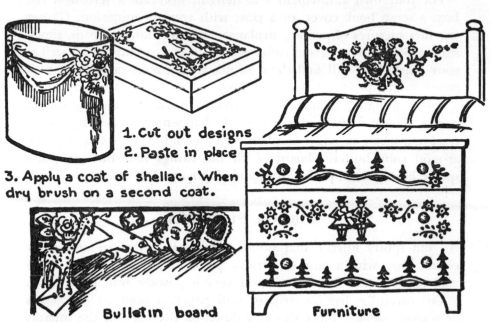

1. Cut out designs
2. Paste in place

3. Apply a coat of shellac. When dry brush on a second coat.

Bulletin board   Furniture

MIRROR PICTURE

1. Place cut-out face down on back of mirror. Mark outline with sharp tool.

2. Remove cut-out.
3. Scratch away mirror surface between lines

4. Paste cut-out in place.

waste paper basket or sister's vanity box. Even old furniture that looks woebegone will brighten up with an application of cut-outs.

For your own amusement and delight, decorate a screen, a hat box, a scrap book cover, or a tray, with your imagination. Gather together pictures of people, airplanes, animals, flowers, ships, shoes, sealing wax, cabbages, and roller skates—in fact anything that strikes your fancy. You will find them in magazines, seed catalogues, wall paper, circus programs, travel folders—everywhere. Cut and paste— a camel riding an airplane, your favorite movie star coming out of a rose. You can make the impossible happen; a bird can carry a tractor, a whole menagerie can ride on a cloud. Try making a frame around your bulletin board of all the things that interest you— sports, horses, dogs, pink gloves, and elephants.

MIRROR PICTURES

An old spotty mirror that nobody wants is a forlorn and sorry object. But, with a pair of scissors, paste, and a picture cut from wall paper it can be made into a very handsome wall decoration.

Cut carefully, from a strip of wall paper, a bouquet of flowers or a scenic design. Place this face down on the back of the mirror. Then with a short-pointed tool—a large darning-needle will do— scratch the outline of your cut-out into the back of the mirror. Remove the cut-out, and with a razor blade scratch away all the mirror surface inside the marked area. When this is done, wash the cleared space with a damp cloth so that no silvered particles remain. Dry the glass thoroughly. Apply paste to the right side of the cut-out, being sure there are no lumps in it. Paste the cut-out in place, smoothing it gently from the center out so that there are no air bubbles. Your picture will have a lovely silvery background.

PAPER DOILY DECORATIONS FOR A ST. VALENTINE'S DAY PARTY

All the decorations for your party can be made with white paper-lace doilies in various sizes, red construction paper, red, white, and green tissue paper, scissors and paste, and thin wire.

For a very effective invitation, cut a heart from red construction paper and paste it to a paper doily.

Nosegays make lovely party favors. For each bouquet, make five red and white flowers with green leaves, as in the diagram. Push the bouquet through the center of a small paper doily. Use green paper and paste to hold it in place. Attach a place card with a bit of red ribbon.

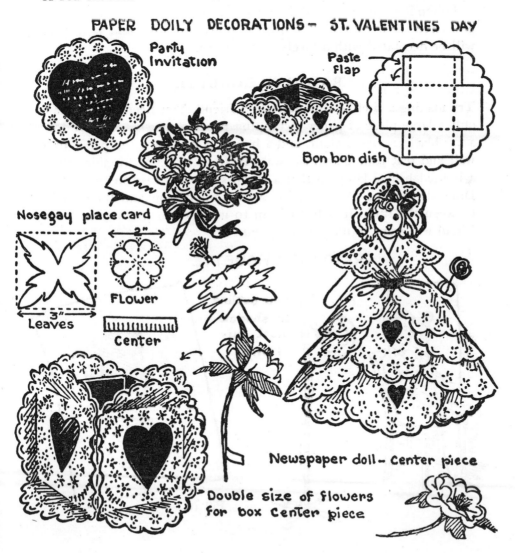

PAPER DOILY DECORATIONS — ST. VALENTINES DAY

Party Invitation

Paste Flap

Bon bon dish

Nosegay place card

ann

Leaves

Flower

Center

2"

3"

Newspaper doll — Center piece

Double size of flowers for box center piece

Follow the diagram for bon-bon dishes. All you need for these are red construction paper and small paper doilies.

To make the box centerpiece, paste four red-paper hearts mounted on paper doilies to a square cardboard box and fill it with large paper flowers. Or make a newspaper doll centerpiece. Dress her to suit your fancy. A red construction paper skirt covered with paper doilies and hearts is very charming.

To top it all off, place a doily on an unfrosted party cake. Sprinkle powdered sugar over it. Remove the doily carefully, and your cake will be decorated with a lovely lacy pattern.

CRAYON SILHOUETTES

Try making a lifelike silhouette of a friend. You need no camera—only a large piece of paper (wrapping paper or newspaper will do), a fat, black crayon, a chair, and a bridge lamp. Tack the paper to a wall and seat your friend sideways in front of it. At his side, place a lighted bridge lamp so that a sharp shadow is cast on the paper. Draw the outline of the shadow with your crayon and then fill in between the lines. It is lots of fun to make these silhouettes. Your friend will want to make one of you.

CRAYON SILHOUETTE

Draw outline of shadow cast by lamp.

Fill in

CIRCUS PEOPLE

Paper raffia or yarn dolls are easy to make. They can be large or small and can be dressed in many ways. The dolls' bodies are all made in the same way. You wrap strands of crepe-paper raffia or yarn around a piece of cardboard until it is nice and thick. Then fasten the strands at one end with a piece of wire. Cut the strands at the opposite end. The head, body, arms, and legs are made from this one bunch of strands. To make the head, place a little ball of paper between the strands and tie with a piece of string

CIRCUS PEOPLE

Pom pon

hat

ruffle

PETE
the clown

Hair

Skirt

ELLIE — The elegant
bareback rider

or wire. Separate the strands for arms and legs. Cut the arms the proper length. Braid or simply tie the ends.

Pete the clown has arms and legs, the ends of which are tied, a colored paper hat, paper raffia pompons, and crepe-paper ruffles. His eyes and mouth are bits of colored paper pasted in place. Use as many different colors for the body as you choose.

Ellie the Elegant is pink and has braided arms and legs. To make the skirt, wrap strands of a color other than pink around a narrow piece of cardboard. Then slip a piece of wire through the loops at one end. Cut the strands at the other end and tie the skirt around the waist. A strand of crepe paper makes the bodice. Crepe paper strands pulled gently over a knife will make the curls.

PECAN FUNNY FACES

Pecans make fine funny-faced lapel gadgets. With a scrap of cotton material, felt, india ink or tempera colors, scissors, household cement, a few bone rings, and three pecans, you can make all the lapel gadgets shown in this diagram.

For Carmen, paint the eyes and mouth with india ink or tempera

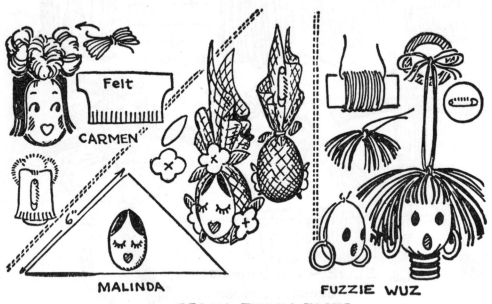

PECAN FUNNY FACES

colors, and then cut a piece of black felt, as indicated in the diagram, for the hair. Fringe the edge of the felt. Make three pompons of different colors of wool. Glue the felt hair in place and sew the pompons to it. Attach a safety pin to the back of the head.

Malinda's hair is painted on as well as her face. For her kerchief, cut a triangle of printed cotton fabric, and glue it to the back of the head as in the diagram. Make flowers and leaves of felt. Gather the ends of the fabric together on top of the head, sew securely, attach flowers to headdress. Sew on a safety pin.

For Fuzzie Wuz, after painting the face, tie two bone rings to a piece of black yarn and glue them in place on the head (see diagram). Make a pompon by wrapping black yarn around a piece of cardboard an inch and a half wide. Tie the strands together at one end with a double strand of bright-colored yarn. Cut the loops at the opposite end. Cover the back and top of the head with glue and stick the hair in place. Then cut out six little circles of two colors of felt and paste them one above the other, alternating the colors. This is the neck. Paste it to the bottom of the nut. Make two disks of felt, each a different color, one an inch wide and the other an inch and a half wide. Paste the two disks together and sew a safety pin to the back. Now make a bow at the end of the colored yarn that holds the strands of hair, and attach the bow to the front of the double disk.

HAZEL NUT JEWELRY

Hazel nuts can be made into buttons by putting little screw eyes into them. They may be decorated with enamels, shellacked, or left unadorned. Start by making a little hole with a nail or an awl. Then screw the screw eye into the hole.

For the bracelet and brooch, cut little flowers of colored felt. Thread a screw eye through a flower and then into a hazel nut. A cluster of these are sewn on a piece of felt to make the brooch. Sew a safety pin on the back. The bracelet is made by knotting the hazel nut flowers on a colored string, and is fastened with a loop that slips over the last nut. (See diagram.)

ALMOND BUDS

The shells of almonds are not very hard. It is easy to make holes in these shells with an awl. Punch a little hole at both sides of the shell, near the top. Paint or shellac the nut if you wish and allow it to dry. Meanwhile cut little leaves of colored felt, string a bit of thin wire through the holes in the almond, and push the leaves through the wire at each side of the nut. Fasten the leaves in place by twisting the wires. Then make a little loop on top. Combined with hazel nut flowers, these almond buds make interesting costume jewelry.

PINE CONE NOVELTIES

Small pine cones are soft enough to be strung with a needle and thread. Run the needle through the soft scales near the top. Gild the tips of the scales or paint them with tempera colors or enamel. Combine these with walnut flowers and almond buds.

HAZEL NUT, ALMOND and PINE CONE NOVELTIES

HAZEL NUTS — ALMONDS — PINE CONE — ACORN — BRACELET — BROOCH — DODO BIRD

Larger pine cones with painted tips make lovely tree ornaments. They can be hung by tying a string around the core, between the scales, or you can insert a small screw eye into the core at the top.

For a pine cone dodo bird, paint two eyes on an acorn. Glue the acorn to the top of a pine cone to make the head. The legs are two match sticks glued between the scales in the middle of the cone. Make two feet of plasteline and stick the match-stick legs into them. Glue a feather to the cap—and you have a dodo bird.

WATERMELON SEEDS

Watermelon seeds are fun to work with. Dried, they make interesting decoration when glued to boxes. First wash the seeds and spread them on a piece of paper to dry, then glue the seeds in place with household cement. When the glue is dry, paint the seeds with enamel.

WATERMELON SEEDS

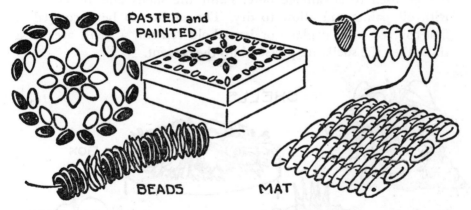

PASTED and PAINTED

BEADS   MAT

Watermelon seeds are easy to string with needle and thread, though they should be strung before they are dry and brittle. Combined with muskmelon seeds, they make fine necklaces and bracelets.

You can even make a small mat or coaster with watermelon seeds. String about forty seeds loosely on a strong thread, running the needle through the top of the seed on the flat side. Then push the needle through the last seed again, this time at the bottom of the seed. Now add a new seed, stringing through the top of the seed. Between each seed on the top row add a new one, as shown in the diagram. Be sure there are the same number of seeds in each row. Continue row after row until the mat is as large as you want it to be. String the bottom of each seed in the last row. Fasten, then shellac or paint with enamel.

SHELLS

If you have ever gathered beautiful shells and then wondered what to do with them, here are a few suggestions for next time.

Large scallop, clam, or oyster shells can be used as baking dishes or ash trays. Big coiled shells, conch or whelk, make fine flower-pots for small plants. Small shells are shown to best advantage when used as decoration for other objects.

Decorate boxes, brooches, and so on, with little painted or unpainted shells. Even the bits of broken shells washed up on the shore can be used to advantage here. Paint the shells and broken bits with oil paints and allow to dry. The surface to be decorated is first covered with airplane or household cement, a small area at a time; then the shells are pressed into the cement.

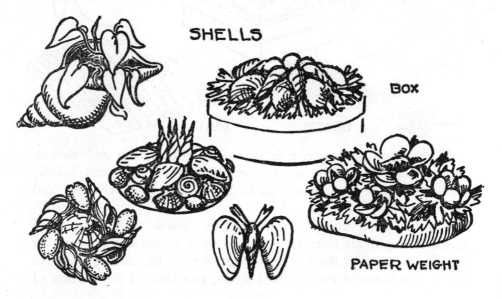

SHELLS

BOX

PAPER WEIGHT

Lovely flower forms and other interesting designs can be made this way. When making a flower arrangement it is best to start at the outer edge and work toward the center. Paste small bits of broken shell in natural or painted earth tones like brown, tan, or rust, and a few larger bits, painted green for leaves around the edge of the design. Then add a circle of small shells, overlapping like the petals of a flower. These need not be painted. The center can be a cluster of bright colored fragments or a little painted shell. A smooth, flat stone decorated in this manner makes a very handsome paper weight.

SPAGHETTI-NOODLE NOVELTIES

Spaghetti has a delightful habit of coming in various interesting shapes and sizes. Painted and shellacked, the smaller forms of

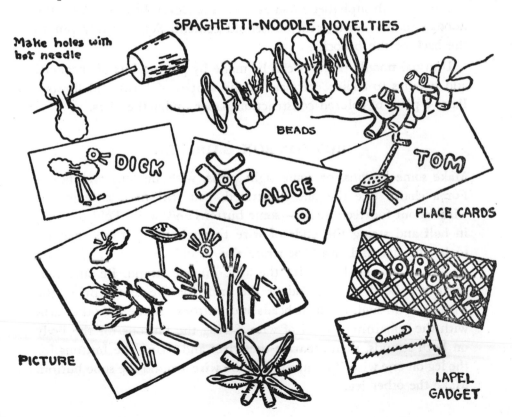

SPAGHETTI-NOODLE NOVELTIES

Make holes with hot needle

BEADS

DICK

ALICE

TOM

PLACE CARDS

PICTURE

DOROTHY

LAPEL GADGET

spaghetti can be made into beads and then strung, **or pasted to** plaques and boxes in interesting designs.

To string spaghetti (or noodles), force the eye end of a large needle into a cork. Holding the cork, heat the point of the needle over a flame and then with it burn holes into the spaghetti. Paint the spaghetti beads with tempera paint and allow to dry. Then shellac and string on heavy thread or thin elastic.

Or paste spaghetti and noodles to placques and boxes with household cement and paint after the paste is dry. Interesting place cards, too, are to be made with these noodles. Paste them to a piece of colored cardboard to form flowers and birds. Make the names with alphabet noodles. Paint with bright colors.

A small piece of cardboad covered with a bit of plaid fabric and decorated with alphabet noodles makes a clever brooch. Paste the noodles to the fabric with household cement. Sew a safety pin to the back of the brooch.

Unusual noodle pictures can be made by pasting bits of spaghetti and noodles to a piece of glass in the shapes of birds and flowers. Paste a piece of colored construction paper under the glass.

BUTTON-BOX GADGETS

Make some charms, or some light pulls, with buttons and beads. For a charm like the one illustrated, you will need a length of wire—about fourteen inches— some buttons and beads. Fold the wire in half and string the ends of wire through the buttons that are to be the hat and head. Separate the strands of wire, and string small buttons and beads, for the arm, on one strand. Be sure that there is a bead on the end of the arm, for the hand. Bring the wire back through the arm beads and buttons. Make the other arm with the remaining strand of wire. String the buttons for the body on both strands, then separate the wires and string the buttons for the leg on one wire. Tie the ends of the wire around the shoe button. Make the other leg.

A CORK GADGET

With a small cork, some small beads, a screw eye, a half a yard of wire, and some gilt, you can make a beautiful lapel gadget. Paint the cork with the gold or silver paint and let it dry. Make little flowers and leaves with the wire and beads, insert the screw eye into the top of the cork, and fasten the flowers to the screw eye. Attach a little safety pin to the end of the wire.

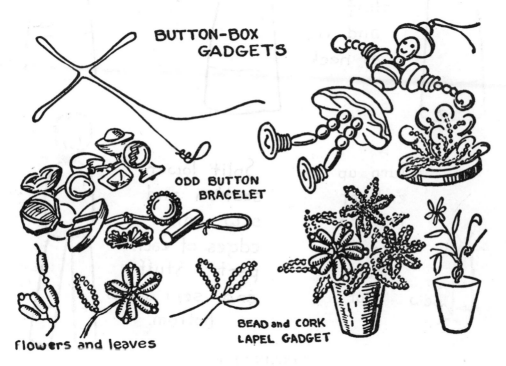

BUTTON-BOX GADGETS

ODD BUTTON BRACELET

flowers and leaves

BEAD and CORK LAPEL GADGET

JESSIE ROBINSON

Tie or sew cut end of stocking on wrong side

Turn stocking, stuff head and tie at neck

Stuff body and sew firmly across to make joint

Turn up end of leg and sew to make foot

sew

Split lower section and sew inner edges of each part. Stuff and sew across bottom.

STOCKING DOLL

1. Cut off the foot of stocking or sock and turn inside out. Gather by either sewing or tying up the cut end.
2. Turn right side out and stuff as far as desired for head. Use cotton for stuffing and stuff lightly.
3. At end of stuffed portion, tie for neck.
4. Stuff part of the remaining portion for the body. (About twice as much as for head.)
5. At the end of the stuffing, sew firmly across to make joint so that doll may sit.

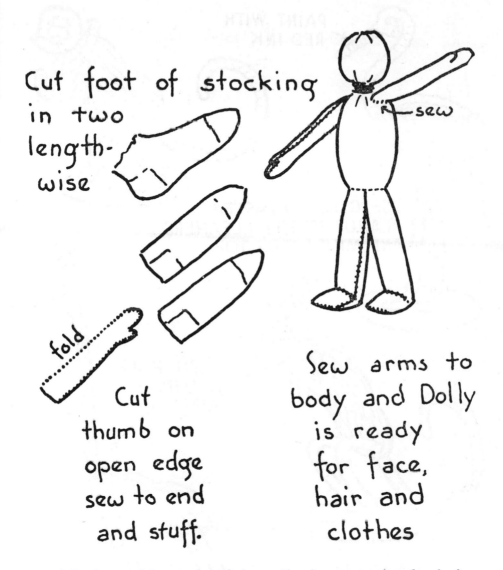

Cut foot of stocking in two length-wise

sew

fold

Cut thumb on open edge sew to end and stuff.

Sew arms to body and Dolly is ready for face, hair and clothes

6. Split the remaining portion of the stocking into two sections for the legs. Stuff each part and sew.

7. Take the foot of the stocking and cut into two lengthwise strips. Use these for arms. Stuff each and sew. Attach the arms to the body of doll at shoulder.

8. Draw, paint or sew in the features of the face.

9. Sew on the hair, using wool, cotton or silk floss.

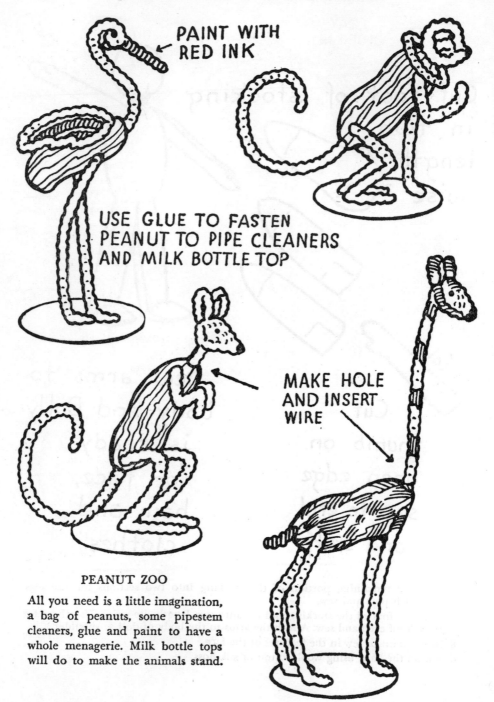

PAINT WITH
RED INK

USE GLUE TO FASTEN
PEANUT TO PIPE CLEANERS
AND MILK BOTTLE TOP

MAKE HOLE
AND INSERT
WIRE

PEANUT ZOO

All you need is a little imagination,
a bag of peanuts, some pipestem
cleaners, glue and paint to have a
whole menagerie. Milk bottle tops
will do to make the animals stand.

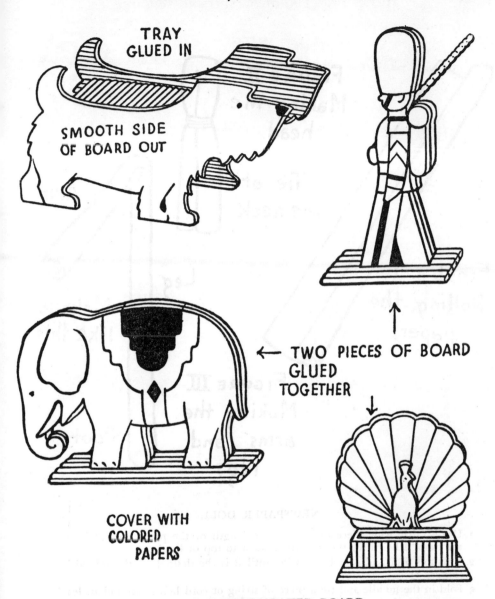

TRAY GLUED IN

SMOOTH SIDE OF BOARD OUT

← TWO PIECES OF BOARD GLUED TOGETHER

COVER WITH COLORED PAPERS

USING CORRUGATED BOARD

Save your corrugated boxes and corrugated paper wrappings, both lined and unlined. Here are only a few suggestions of what a little patience and imagination can do. Besides creating your own toys you can make such useful objects as **book ends**, waste baskets or fancy boxes.

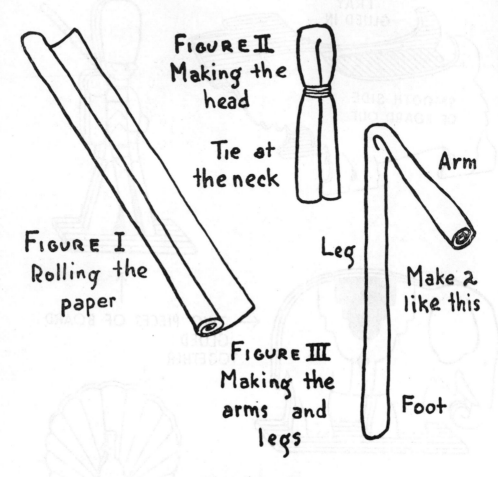

FIGURE II
Making the
head

Tie at
the neck

FIGURE I
Rolling the
paper

Leg

Arm

Make 2
like this

FIGURE III
Making the
arms and
legs

Foot

NEWSPAPER DOLL

1. Use a fairly wide piece of paper. The length of the paper should be twice the desired height of the doll from waist to top of head.
2. Roll this over and over lengthwise until it is the desired width and thickness *(Figure I)*.
3. Fold in the middle and tie a piece of string or cord lightly around it, leaving enough for the head *(Figure II)*.
4. Roll two pieces of paper the length of arm and leg combined, with enough added for the foot. Bend down enough for arms *(Figure III)*. Tie under arms *(Figure IV)* and again at waist.

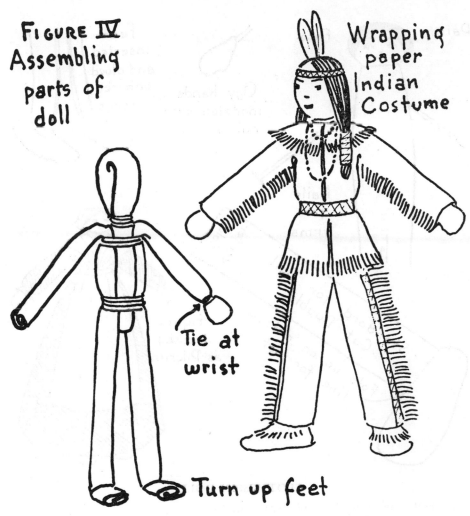

FIGURE IV
Assembling
parts of
doll

Wrapping
paper
Indian
Costume

Tie at
wrist

Turn up feet

5. Bend the two ends apart for legs and turn up the ends for feet.

6. If not thick enough, the head and body can be padded with cotton or paper.

7. Cover the head with a piece of stocking or cloth. Draw, paint or sew in the features. Wool, cotton or silk floss may be used for hair. Now make a costume for the doll.

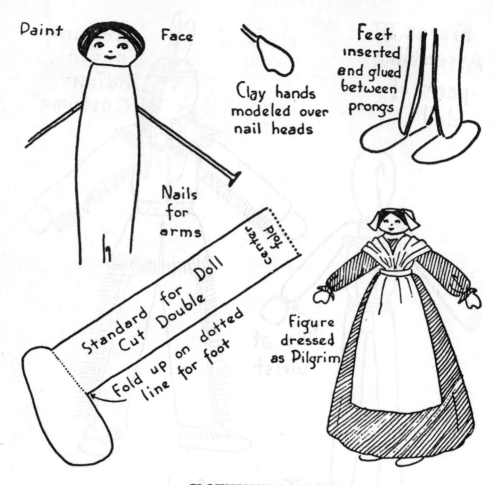

CLOTHESPIN DOLL

1. Use the top of the clothespin for the head.
2. Paint in the features and the hair.
3. Insert the two wire nails into the clothespin, at a slant, to serve for arms.
4. Mold upon the heads of the nails, lumps of clay to suggest the hands.
5. Insert between the prongs of the clothespin a folded piece of stiff paper with feet cut out.
6. Dress with paper or cloth.

Clothespin dolls are excellent for Indian and Pilgrim figures.

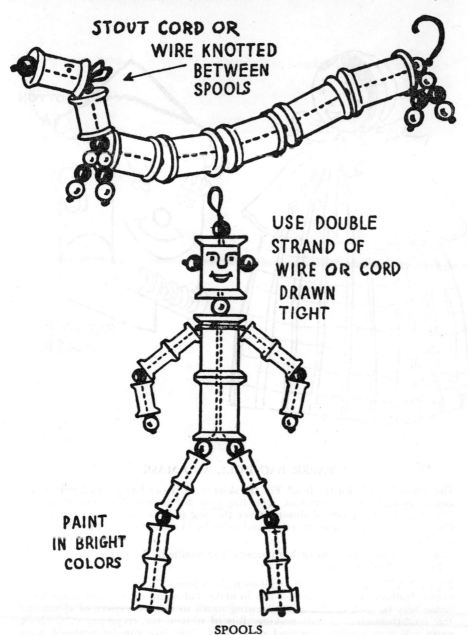

STOUT CORD OR
WIRE KNOTTED
BETWEEN
SPOOLS

USE DOUBLE
STRAND OF
WIRE OR CORD
DRAWN
TIGHT

PAINT
IN BRIGHT
COLORS

SPOOLS

Always keep a supply of spools on hand. In combination with beads, pipestem cleaners, wire, string or bits of cloth, many interesting things can be made.

COTTON

PAPER BAG
MASK

PAPER BAG DOLL AND MASK

Use a baby's rattle for the head. For the skirt use a paper bag painted with water colors, poster paint or crayons. The bag may be decorated in the style of a Scotch plaid or a flowered dimity. Over the bag place a smaller one for a cape. Cut open this bag, scallop the edges and color in an attractive color to blend with the dress.

Gather skirt and cape and tie both around the handle of the rattle. Tie with silk, velvet or cellophane ribbon.

PAPER BAG MASK. It is no trick at all to make a Santa Claus mask, such as shown above. Hallowe'en masks are also fun to make. Odds and ends found around the house may be used to add an interesting touch to a wide variety of characters that lend themselves to mask making. Bits of ribbon, fur, crepe paper, cloth or yarns will give special color and personality. The face can be outlined with crayons, colored inks or colored pencils. The eye holes and shoulder arches are cut out to fit the wearer.

COLOR BOTTLE

CUT OUT STENCIL DESIGN

**TIE STENCIL
IN PLACE**

**REMOVE STENCIL
WHEN PAINT IS DRY .**

**STENCIL STARS
ON FRUIT JAR . .
USE BRIGHT OIL COLOR**

STENCIL

PAINTED BOTTLES

Collect bottles and glass jars. Painted in bright show card or oil colors, with a simple design stencilled on after paint is dry, they make attractive vases. A twine hanger may be added to hold ivy or other vine plants *(bottom left)*.

A PIPESTEM CLEANER MONK

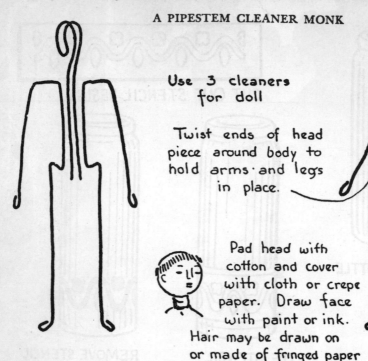

Use 3 cleaners
for doll

Twist ends of head
piece around body to
hold arms and legs
in place.

Pad head with
cotton and cover
with cloth or crepe
paper. Draw face
with paint or ink.
Hair may be drawn on
or made of fringed paper
Pad and wrap entire figure or
leave plain.

DESIGNS for MONK'S ROBE and HOOD

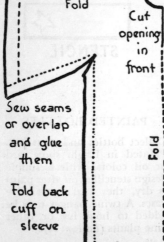

Fold

Cut
opening
in
front

Fold

Sew seams
or overlap
and glue
them

Fold back
cuff on
sleeve

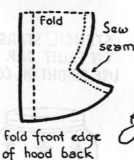

Fold

Sew
seam

Fold front edge
of hood back

PHONOGRAPH RECORDS ENRICH
A CHILD'S LIFE

"Participation records" bring out a child's creative instincts and provide physical and emotional outlets that release tensions. Here several children act out a railroad train song, while others give happy expression to their feelings through the rhythms of a dance.

Children's Record Guild

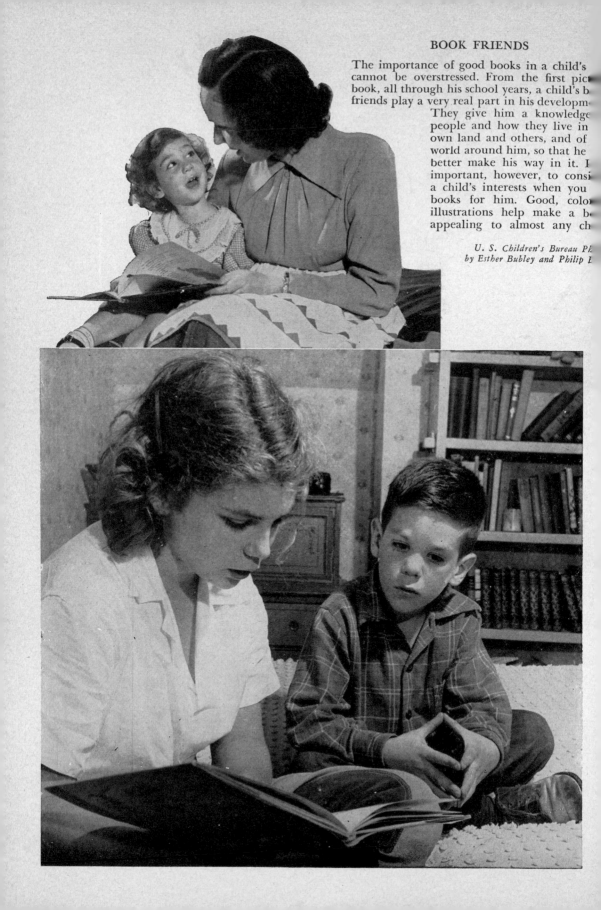

BOOK FRIENDS

The importance of good books in a child's
cannot be overstressed. From the first pict
book, all through his school years, a child's b
friends play a very real part in his developm

They give him a knowledge
people and how they live in
own land and others, and of
world around him, so that he
better make his way in it. I
important, however, to consi
a child's interests when you
books for him. Good, colo
illustrations help make a b
appealing to almost any ch

U. S. Children's Bureau PI
by Esther Bubley and Philip I

A Child's Bookshelf
in the Home

THE importance of good books and their place in a child's life cannot be overstressed. From the time the first picture book catches and holds his interest, and all through his school years, a child's book friends play a very real part in his life. Fortunate, indeed, are those boys and girls whose parents appreciate the value and need of good reading.

Books are more than fun to be shared by parent and child. Besides satisfying the child's insatiable curiosity, they are preparing him to take his place in the outside world. They are acquainting him with peoples, places and things, helping to establish rules of conduct, and building sound moral and ethical standards. All of this and much more awaits the child who acquires at an early age a love of good books and reading.

Giving books to children only on special occasions like birthdays and Christmas is a relic of the time when children's books were few. Nowadays we might well buy good books just as regularly as we do clothes, or anything else children require. It is hard to think of any other things belonging to childhood that are a more all-around permanently good investment.

Good books help to widen a child's horizon. They develop his sympathy and understanding and give him information on which his growingly thoughtful mind can go to work. From being a self-centered baby, he grows toward an understanding of himself as a part of the great world. He reaches out in wonder, grasping bit by bit at the fringes of knowledge about the universe in which he lives. He learns of his country's pioneers and of the world of today.

If he is a child who likes to dream, he will thrill to the tales of early man or ancient buried cities and begin to understand the world he lives in a little better.

No matter what a child's interests, there is always a book that seems to have been written just for him. There are animal stories for the child who is never content without some living creature to care for and books about the heavens for the one who is tantalized by what the winking stars seem to say to him. The lad who lives in a crowded city must take much of his adventure vicariously; but thrilling tales of narrow escapes, and the dangers of American pioneer life in his own country, will give him patterns of bravery as well as adventure.

We must acquaint our children with the peoples whose problems will be their problems in a common future. We must show them how like ourselves other peoples are, how differences in color or religion or food habits are unimportant as compared with the sameness of the blood—that identical stuff here or in Asia or the South Seas that makes people's hearts beat with fear or love or anger. Children will accept these truths as a matter of course if they are brought up on books about peoples elsewhere in the world.

ENCOURAGING READING ABILITY

An excellent reason for introducing a child early to good books is that the greater his reading experience, the more he is going to get from and contribute to his life in school. So much of a child's education must come through books that we should use every means to add to his chances of success in school adjustment by giving him skill in the tool of reading.

Many children struggle along through their school years, tremendously handicapped by their lack of ability to read with ease and comprehension. The farther they get in school, the more hopeless it all becomes; for their success depends more and more upon their reading rapidly and grasping what they read. Their hobbies and interests, whether music or boat building or electronics, will be furthered or hindered in accordance with whether or not they cut their eye teeth on books.

There are children for whom it has never become *fun* to read. Children to whom enjoyable, attractive, well-chosen books are supplied as food for their minds, just as good food is provided for their bodies, have an initial advantage over children whose first acquaintance with books comes at school. A child who already knows that books are a delight starts off on the right foot when he begins to learn to read.

CHOOSING THE RIGHT BOOKS

Now supplying books for children isn't a matter of buying just *any* books that appear in book stores. Of late, such a flood of books for children has poured onto the market that it is hard to know which books to buy.

It is not a question of price, for many excellent books are priced very reasonably. The average parent will feel safer if he relies on those who spend much time studying the books that are published and who take great pains to find out what children actually like. The help of librarians and of nursery-school, kindergarten, and other teachers is always freely given.

The best books are those that have such real quality that their appeal is very broad. The ideal child's book, in fact, is a "whole family" book—one that can be read with pleasure and absorption by grown-ups, too. Walter Edmonds puts it well, saying that a really good book for children should have "enough stuff, humor, reality, wisdom, excitement to be interesting to an adult mind." As proof of this we needn't go further than Kipling's *Just So Stories*. No father or mother ever thinks of it as a chore to read them aloud! Modern classics that parents enjoy as much as they did their own childhood favorites are not lacking.

The physical make-up of a book makes more difference to children than grown-ups would guess. Even the color of the cover matters! Blue, red, and yellow—the bright primary colors—are the very little child's favorites, inside a book or out. Not until children are older do they appreciate the softly tinted illustrations that appeal so much to adults. If a child is just beginning to read to himself, it is especially important that the type in his books be big and clear and not too different in style from that which he has been accustomed to in his beginning readers. Books should be stoutly put together; for although children can be trained to handle books carefully, anything that is going to be used as much as a well-liked book must be sturdy and durable.

GOOD ILLUSTRATIONS BRING ADDED ENJOYMENT

In illustrations, very little children want plenty of animals, children, and the other familiar things of their everyday life. They love many little details and want pictures to tell a story rather than to be fanciful and decorative. They are not yet ready at this age for the so-called "artistic" and intricately imaginative pictures that grown-ups like. They thoroughly enjoy humor in pictures as well as in words. And they like pictures on every page.

Little children enjoy variety in the size and shape of books as well as in their contents. They can be taught the care books deserve by learning to handle gently their large, beautiful picture books. They love to own and carry around very tiny books, too.

To be worth buying, a book should be of more than passing interest, one the child will enjoy listening to, looking at, or reading to himself over and over. A story may be very slight indeed, but its pictures may tell so much that a child will turn back to them often, always finding fresh enjoyment.

When buying books we must know what interests children have at certain ages. Is there a three-year-old who wouldn't listen with all his ears to a story about colts or kittens? Can you imagine a six-year-old who wouldn't be interested in the circus? Girls of ten rapturously read over and over again books about favorite heroines.

ENCOURAGING SPECIAL INTERESTS

Almost before we realize they are individuals with ideas of their own, children begin to have special interests that can be furthered by providing the right books. If they get in the habit of going to books for the answers to their questions, children will, by the time they are ten or so, be using a library as naturally as they turn on the radio.

This is our main object, is it not? That children shall come to have such friendly, natural attitudes toward books that they will seek them out when they want to learn something or when they want to spend some leisure in thorough enjoyment. If books have been their friends from their earliest years, they will always be a resource. When a moment's escape from reality is needed, when other forms of entertainment or companionship are not available, when hearing about a discovery in science or a famous name sets them wondering—these are the times when children should have books as readily accessible as water to drink.

And these books should be their very own. Books from the library are fine, but books of one's very own that can be picked up again and again, pored over, and reread whenever fancy demands, are even better. It is hard to estimate the value to a child of a library of his own, for the impressions made on his mind may lie too deep to be chattered about. A favorite character may, unknown to anyone but the child himself, serve as a stimulus to effort that is far beyond our ability to calculate. A good account of the life history of some bird or insect may be so exactly what a child needs to complement his own observations that he is given the initial impetus to serious study.

In selecting books, consider the interests of the child almost as much as his age. It is almost impossible to say of a book that it is for a child of five, or one of eight, for one child of three will like to hear the supposedly five-year-old story, and another of ten may not be mentally old enough for the eight-year-old book.

THE FAMILY READING HOUR

Children will listen with great enjoyment to a book that they are not yet capable of reading by themselves. Up to the age of nine or ten, most boys and girls are not reading full-length books; but a child is delighted to hear such stories as *Pinocchio* or *The Wind in the Willows* long before his reading ability is enough advanced to make it pleasurable for him to read them alone.

This advancement of a child's understanding beyond his reading skill shows how desirable (as well as pleasurable) it is for families to do much reading aloud. Even starting a story aloud sometimes whets the appetite of a child who hasn't yet become hungry enough for books, and needs a little anticipatory taste to get him started. A family that sets aside only twenty minues a day for reading aloud will have read more than 120 hours in a single year! Older children will be so eager to go on with the story that they can be counted on to "spell" mother and father in reading, turn-about fashion.

Keep in mind that many, many children who "don't like to read" feel that way because reading hasn't become fun. When that is the case, the reasons for the child's slow progress in reading should be sought, and help should be given where it is needed.

If this is done early enough, the teen-age years, during which leisure-time habits are being formed, will become a period when children eagerly feast on the wide variety of good things to be found in books. But no matter how well a child can read, he is unlikely to think of this as one of the very nicest ways of having a good time unless he is provided with books of his own and has parents who have enjoyed those books with him from the days when he began to listen to nursery rhymes.

Music's Place in the Child's Life

ALL children are musical. A baby will rock to the rhythm of music and can be taught to sing on pitch before he is a year old. A healthy and happy early experience with music can enrich the child's entire life. For the young child it can be the basis for creative play and a tool for learning.

Since so little of the music that comes over the air is presented for the pleasure of the small child, and it is almost impossible to control the selection of music attuned to his young ears, his early acquaintance with suitable music comes best from phonograph records.

THE PHONOGRAPH RECORD

With a well-selected collection of records to choose from, the record that best suits the child's mood or interest of the moment is always available. And it is there for him to play over and over as long as it pleases him to do so.

As all parents know, the single word that best describes two- to four-year-olds is the word "physical." At that age level his music, too, must be physical. The child must not only hear it with his ears, he must feel it in his muscles—it must become a part of him—he must *be* the music. If a song about a train is played, the words, rhythm and melody of the song must help the child to be the train. And, if the material is right for him, he will be. He will move across the floor to the rhythm of the music, he will ring his bell, chug like an engine. When he does all of those things he is having a complete musical experience.

And if we want the child to live the music to its fullest, then the subjects around which the music is written must be those that have meaning for him. That does not mean that we must necessarily limit ourselves to "here and now" material; there is certainly room for fantasy if it is treated at the right level. (The wrong kind of fantasy can frighten and confuse young children.) It does mean that everyday things like parks and policemen, trucks and teddy-bears, fire engines and cooking are good subjects upon which to base musical materials for two- to four-year-olds.

FREEDOM OF MOVEMENT

The child, as an important part of his musical experience, should be given the opportunity to bring his own creative instincts and ability to the music. That means he must have freedom of motion during his record music time. It's a good idea to set up the phono-graph near a floor area from which good furniture and expensive lamps and ashtrays have been removed. It's also a good idea to follow nursery school procedure and remove shoes. In such an atmosphere the average child is bound to have a wonderful time—if he receives the proper encouragement. And that's where the role of the parent comes in.

The first thing for parents to understand is that in musical devel-opment, just as in all child development, each child sets his own pattern and pace. It would be just as wrong to try to force him into some preconceived pattern set by an adult as it would be to deprive him altogether of the opportunity to enjoy healthy musical experiences. Rhoda W. Bacmeister, in her book *Growing Together,* puts it this way: "Expecting too much of a child, setting standards too high, is a frequent cause of nervousness, tensions and tantrums. Goals should be readily attainable so that the child's exertions will often be rewarded by success. He may go forward more slowly, but it will be with confidence. We shall not go far wrong if we provide appropriate material and interesting experiences—and then let the child take his own pace with them."

That's true. But, on the other hand, as Dr. Benjamin Spock says, "Your child will love to have you play with him if you are willing to play at his level. Let *him* show *you* how." Applied to musical activity material, that means that the parents' role is to help and encourage the child to express himself. One way to do that is through example. Parent and child can be bears, kangaroos and fire engines *together!*

But parents can do even more, by helping the child to enlarge upon the material presented and carry it over into many everyday activities. A train activity song on a record can show a parent how to create with the child songs about dressing or block-building activities as part of the regular routine of his day. Thus music can be made to assume its proper role—not as a specialized activity lim-ited to a particular time of the day in a particular place—but as an integrated part of the child's living.

Dramatic Play

As children grow older their ways of learning change. Certainly the physical element does not disappear, not even in adulthood—but the child constantly adds new techniques to his learning process. The technique that stands out in the five- to eight-year-old group is best described by the term educators use: dramatic play.

Dramatic play is the process by which children act out their knowledge and feelings about any aspect of life with which they come in contact. That covers a wide range—and so does the child's dramatic play. He learns about cowboys by being a cowboy—and he "plays out" his feelings, let's say, of jealousy about a new baby, by scolding his doll or teddy-bear.

Good children's records provide the child with facts and ideas for enlarging the scope of his dramatic play. That can be done through stories that are written at the proper age level, through song lyrics and through the music itself. A six-year-old who is a cowboy through most of his waking (and maybe sleeping) day, may spend his time shooting Indian after Indian. Give him a record like *Ride 'Em Cowboy* and you will soon find that he's doing more than make Redskins bite the dust. He stops a stampede, he eats chow at the camp fire, he rounds up the dogies. He does those things not only because of the new knowledge he gains from the ideas on the record, but also because he feels and lives the drama of the cowboy's life and the rhythm of his work, through the music.

That does not mean that every child who hears *Ride 'Em Cowboy* does all of those things at first—nor should parents try to get him to do so. In fact, the material he absorbs may come out in other ways and at other times.

In dramatic play records—just as in activity records—subjects with which the child is familiar—either through direct experience or through books, pictures and what he has heard—serve as good material. Does that mean we must rule out fantasy, like fairy tales? Especially for the five- to eight-year-old group, there is room for the fairy tale and similar material if such projects are presented at the child's level in concept, writing and music.

TOUCHSTONES FOR JUDGING A PHONOGRAPH RECORD

1. CONCEPTS.   It is obvious that a record cannot have real meaning for a child unless he understands what it's all about. A record based on geography—something about Mexico in song and story—could never be valid in the two- to four-year-old group because children of that age have no concept of geography. Similarly, a fairy tale based on emotions like love or greed, or on social relationships like slave or apprentice, can have little meaning for children that young.

There are concepts, though, that make sense for both age groups. Trains are a good example. A child at two will push a block across the floor and say "Choo-choo." At eight he is still fascinated by trains—but by then he speaks glibly of diesels and refrigeration cars. As Lucy Sprague Mitchell points out: to the child of two or three a steam engine is only a gigantic extension of his own energy and movement, while at six or seven it is a scientific example of the expansion of steam or of the desire of men to get rapidly from one place to another. In the case of each age group we can easily see that a different treatment of the material is required.

2. TREATMENT.   Here, to judge the value of a record for children of a particular age, we must think first of how the record is paced. It is hard to make a record that is paced *too* slowly for a two-year-old; it is easy to fall into the error of pacing it too fast. Narration, dialogue and lyrics of songs must be enunciated slowly and clearly. If activity on the child's part is desired, he must get lots of time to prepare for the movement and the rhythm must be slow enough for him to follow easily. Then he must be given time to stop and get ready for the next activity. For older children, we can increase the pace of story and music—but it is still very important to get words across with the utmost clarity.

The way sound is used on a record can give parents a good idea of how much the producer knows about children and their reactions. A fire-engine siren makes a fine and exciting sound for a young child to hear. But it can be very frightening if it isn't handled just right. Even the roar of a lion can be more or less friendly—if the record maker is conscious of the reactions of the children for whom the record is intended.

3. LANGUAGE. The choice of words on the record must, of course, be keyed to the child's understanding. But even more is involved in the proper use of language. May Hill Arbuthnot, writing in *Children and Books,* says: "Sometimes words induce a mood or feeling which cannot be wholly accounted for by their literal meanings but results from their sound, combined with their associative meaning." A good record script for young children recognizes the value of words that produce images and moods through their very sound. A cowboy's horse goes "loping along"—elephant's feet are "clomping"—"Smooth seals slip and slide."

Another aspect of the use of language is pattern. Here the outstanding element is repetition. A dog runs, sure—but a three-year-old will like the dog better if he runs and runs and runs and runs. (Incidentally, for the young child, if you say it slowly, the dog is running slowly—if you want the dog to run fast you have to indicate it by the way you read the line.) A word more on imagery: if you want to tell a young child that someone is bright, it's not a good idea to use an expression like "sharp as a tack." Because children have very literal minds, it's better to use a simile within their range of experience: for example, "smart as a daddy" for younger children—"smart as a teacher" for school-agers.

4. PRODUCTION. Many a good children's record script has been ruined by an over-elaborate production. Simplicity is one of the key touchstones by which to judge a good children's record. More solo voices than chorus parts, solo instruments and small groups, one sound effect at a time, keep away from the "colossal" production— are all basic rules of good children's record making. But, because a production is simple it doesn't follow that it should be anything less than the best possible production technically and musically. The very best singers and musicians, top narrators, expert engineers—

plus hours of work and loving care, it takes all of that **to produce a** good *simple* children's record!

5. MUSIC. It's difficult to translate one art form (music) into another (writing)—but here are a few simple touchstones for parents: For the child under two music should be chantlike—no big skips in the melody, simple and repetitive rhythms. For the two- to four-year-old group the melody, while retaining its simple and repetitive quality, can become more developed as a tune; rhythms can be more sharply accented to help body movement—such as songs for walking, rolling, swaying, chugging, etc. But the concentration is still on sound and rhythm rather than on content and meaning.

The five- to eight-year-old sings freely, is interested in learning the words to songs. So the melody must not be too complicated and difficult to recall—or he won't be able to sing the song. Music for this age group can have mood, contrast in tempo, intensity and instrumental color. The forty-minute symphony is not the five- to eight-year-old's dish. Nor need his head be filled with facts about fugues and sonatas. Music, however, should not become a secondary factor serving solely as a background to a story. It should rather be the other way around—the story should serve as a skeleton upon which the music is built.

6. THE PHYSICAL RECORD. Because children want to handle their own records, it is important that the physical record be as "child-proof" as possible. The material of which the record is made should be a tough plastic—the grooves should be cut deeply enough so a little scratch doesn't ruin the record. The record label is important, too—especially for non-reading children. Picture symbols help them to identify the records they want to hear—different colors for each side tell the child which side to play first. The packaging of the record should be colorful and appealing—for first impressions count with children, just as they do with adults.

7. FUN. Last, but very far from least, is the entertainment value of the total record. For, unless the child *likes* his record all the other values we have discussed are wasted.

How Can I Help My Child Be Musical?

THE time at which a child should start studying a musical instrument cannot be set at any particular age because children differ so widely in development and readiness. A child should never be forced to start before he is ready, and this is rarely the case before he is seven. The amount of musical background, his ability to sing, his sensitiveness to rhythm and melody, and his muscular coordination are all determining factors.

Although you may own a piano, this should not necessarily be his first instrument. The choice should be determined by the youngster's desire to play a certain instrument and his aptitude for it. Children often have a strong feeling about the tone and appearance, as well as the required techniques, for playing a particular instrument. If your young son or daughter wants to change instruments after a year's trial, be agreeable to the change and don't feel that the time has been wasted. Rest assured, the musical experience has been of value.

SELECTING A TEACHER

Assuming that a child has had all the background that is necessary for him to make a wise choice of instrument and to be prepared and ready for serious study, the first consideration is the choice of teacher. If there is a music school connected with the elementary school, this is less of a problem, although even then there may be a choice between two or three teachers in the same department. Your response to her as a person should influence your decision. More important than a conservatory degree is a fine personality—"distinctive, personal character." (Since she has chosen her profession as a music teacher, it is to be assumed that she knows enough about music to carry out her obligations.) By personality, I mean a mind and heart reflected by unflagging enthusiasm in her work, genuine love and respect for children, and keen interest in their over-all development. Such a teacher has no trouble winning trustful confidence. As has been said in these pages, children are quick to detect hypocrisy. By the same token, they recognize and respond to the warmth of true sincerity.

You may be able to find out something about a teacher's approach to teaching by visiting her studio, observing the equipment on hand for the children, discussing general policy with her, and possibly attending a recital. A good teacher will welcome your interest. If the atmosphere is the kind in which you, too, would like to share musical studies—if you sense an air of gaiety, and charm, together with well-being and dignity, it is a foregone conclusion that your child will feel relaxed and comfortable there.

Children are as sensitive as adults to pleasant surroundings. Whether or not they observe the details of furnishings, they nevertheless immediately sense the *spirit* of the room. The tools for musical learning should be invitingly displayed in the studio, so that the newcomer will be delighted at the opportunities afforded.

It is immeasurably better for a child to go to a teacher's studio than to have his lessons at home. The equipment she has gathered, such as extra teaching materials—a wide variety of music books, instruments, recordings, and possibly a recording machine—in itself a remarkable incentive to children, who eagerly look forward to making their own recordings—plus the professional atmosphere of such a workshop, encourages the desire for learning. Children, meeting friends for class lessons under such benign influences, actually come to look upon lesson day as a day of musical adventure, musical fun, and musical achievement.

As previously explained, class lessons are desirable before the serious study of an instrument begins. They are equally desirable *during* study. If both a class lesson and a private lesson can be managed, that is an ideal arrangement, both for stimulating interest and developing technique. But, if a private or a class lesson must be sacrificed, forego the private one. The advantages of class lessons are many: outstanding of them all is that they make music *sociable*. Children are accustomed to work and play with their classmates, and they actually need the challenge and stimulation which musical association provides for them. Also, ensemble playing with contemporaries is the most valuable experience an aspiring musician can have.

It is becoming accepted practice to teach beginners on any instrument together in groups. They must all cover the same material, be given the same instruction and reminders about technique, and the same advice about homework. It is a waste of a good teacher's time to repeat all this four individual times when she might more inspiringly present it to four children together.

Group lessons challenge not only the children but the teacher as well. And no teacher should be asked or expected to put into a private lesson the energy, ingenuity, and imagination she is called upon to exercise in group lessons. It is just and right that she should exert her greatest efforts for the greatest good of the greatest number of children.

Likewise, it is foolish for a parent to pay almost four times as much for instruction that can be *done better* at less cost. Do you send your child to school for his general education because you cannot afford to have him tutored at home—or because you know there are advantages in group learning? I am convinced that any normal parent, well able to provide home tutoring, would not for a moment hesitate to choose the group method.

Parents have no need to fear that a child will be idle or unoccupied in a class lesson. There are problems of theory to apply to the writing of music; accompaniments to be improvised to a classmate's melody (or vice versa); reading of ensemble music to be studied; a troublesome rhythmic pattern to be worked out on a drum; an elusive melody to be evoked from the marimba, with big arm movements rather than restricted finger exercises; an interpretation of a passage to be listened to critically in order to do it better oneself or to give constructive criticism to a classmate. And that isn't all! There will be playing by ear, playing by rote, playing by note; there will be creative exercises of harmonizing familiar melodies and improvising new ones; there will be some transposing of old pieces and some discovering of others through the printed page; there will be two-piano pieces or piano duets; there will be lots of singing, lots of sociability and lots of music!

Variety is the key word—variety of instruments to point up the chosen one; variety of material to play; a great variety in approaches toward making music. Such lessons are exciting adventures which any and every child enjoys. There's nothing humdrum or stereotyped or even repetitious in such lessons.

It is true that, after the second or third year, some children may very well need time by themselves, with the teacher giving her full attention to problems of technique or individual repertory. Even then, there is no reason to isolate this child from the others. A teacher can always manage to overlap lessons of advanced pupils so that each has some time alone and also some time in company with the next (or last) pupil.

Technique is an important part of every lesson, even for beginners, but it must always be introduced as a means to an end. The child himself must not only realize the objective but wish to obtain it. When a child tries to play a song he knows, he can be asked if it demands smooth, legato playing (wind in the sail), or does it hop and jump (as he has done himself) in a staccato way? If he knows what effect he wants, he will want to know how to get it with hands and arms and, what is more, his desire will instinctively help him to conquer the technical difficulties.

Children can familiarize themselves with the instrument of their choice by improvising freely for tonal effects without the restriction of scale patterns. One day, it may be a cowboy gallop; another day, a soldier's march. Each in its own way translates a childlike expression into sound. These experiments in sound, embracing rhythm predominantly, get a child over the keyboard without restraint, and they also emphasize the importance of dynamics. It is not the p (piano) or the f (forte) in the music which determines the softness or loudness, but the quality of the music itself.

Children who play the piano will certainly, at times, want to get closer to it than fingertips allow. Stroking the keyboard with elbows and forearms, they'll invent a rhapsody of colorful harmonies. Wise teachers and parents interpret these efforts as an attempt to achieve, with limited technique, effects which are pleasing to the child, rather than bang-bang evidence of frustration. At some later day, when a written piece demands the same shadowy feeling that was present in the "rhapsody," a parent can remind the child of that early rendition. This point of reference—to music the child himself has created—clarifies the reasons for interpretive expression. The child knows why *his* music had to be played in such a way; therefore he can understand why a composer would indicate how he wanted his work to be performed.

Techniques follow and refer back to these enjoyable, creative acts. They should be introduced sparingly—only as the child himself feels the need of them. Since reading is a mastery of a technique, the same rules apply. Playing by ear, improvising, harmonizing tunes, playing by rote, creating a melody—all these creative acts *lead to reading*. How? By *familiarizing* the child with music through the instrument. These elements are the stuff of which music is made; they make up the vocabulary of music. Until a child has such a vocabulary, there is no reason to show him notes which represent ideas in the language.

When he begins to understand the language of music, he will want material with which he can easily cope. His efforts should be attended with many successes until he is on sure enough footing to become adventuresome. It is better that he play *well* a simple piece—but necessarily interesting—than that he muddle through a more difficult one. However, the more difficult material can be introduced simultaneously for study *visually* rather than for performance. By this, I mean that he can look at a piece, beyond his ability to play, to see what phrases are repeated, what is the graphic outline of the melody, the general rhythmic pattern. This is the time to isolate the particular rhythmic or melodic passage which is difficult and allow him to study it separately before attempting to play the piece as a whole. Modern educators take "drills" from a piece the child is working on rather than have children practice special exercises to attain skill.

In this way, his study constantly presents a challenge but is always interesting and within the scope of his ability. If, after examining the *total* piece, he is sufficiently interested to cope with its difficulties, he will be willing to study the portion that stumps him so that he can perform the piece as music.

Thus, through a varied approach, a child will inch along, sometimes seeming to take great strides, another day seeming to drop far behind. The process of absorption takes time; progress cannot remain steady.

On the other side, however, some teachers err by waiting too long to utilize what children have learned. They fail to draw conclusions from a child's efforts, thus tending to allow children to think that performance at any level is an end in itself. This attitude lessens a child's interest and is responsible for the lowering of standards. Unless a youngster is challenged, his enthusiasm will quickly diminish.

PRACTICING

Parents can help in establishing good work habits by arranging *with the child* a practice time free from interruption, interference, and nagging. This time of day should be considered a peaceful, blessed time, set aside for private exploration into the art of music. Your belief in your child's integrity, your confidence in the depth of his feeling and breadth of his imagination (plus the inspiration given him by his teacher), these are the only outside influences that are necessary to establish his practice time as precious moments for personal fulfillment.

Questioning a child for the purpose of checking his procedures, which amounts to prying into his affairs, is an indication of lack of trust. A mother wants to know how a child spends his time mostly because she is afraid he will waste it—more accurately, waste the money she is spending for his lessons and instrument. Any child is sensitive enough to recognize the difference between this kind of question and genuine interest in his development.

In planning a practice time with your child, give it more consideration than you would a party. Make sure that together you arrive at an hour which can become as fixed a part of the day's routine as care of the teeth, sleeping, or eating. Never plan any other activity which might interfere with practicing—no activity for yourself that uses the room he practices in and no activity for your child that underestimates the importance of this unalterable appointment. Some families find that practicing just before the evening meal—after play and wash up—refreshes a young musician.

Others prefer different times, before school, during part of the lunch hour, or after the evening meal.

One noted teacher has been known to say that she wished the word "practice" wasn't in the dictionary. She always uses "play" instead because, she points out, she wishes her student to "play" the piano each day. Many teachers feel as she does and, instead of setting a certain amount of time for *practicing*, request that their students play each piece a certain number of times.

The amount of time devoted to study between lessons depends upon how much time the child needs to accomplish what he sets out to do and also, considering his other interests and activities, how much time he can allot to music. It may vary from fifteen minutes to an hour a day, but let your child decide what it shall be, for only he knows what he needs. There is, of course, no reason for you to watch the clock or to remind him that he "promised" to stick to it for half an hour when he has spent only twenty minutes. As a matter of fact, he should not be asked to make any promises. You are the one to promise him the privilege of a short span of time free from household interruption. Don't go back on your word and make this privilege a chore!

Your attitude about his practice time will affect *his* attitude. If you are convinced that he can be happy in his practicing—in spite of the fact that you may not have been as a child—you will convey this impression to him, not in words but in friendly co-operation and interest.

Often, when direct payments of money are involved, parents tend to overemphasize the fact that lessons and an instrument are an investment—which, of course, they are. There is a danger, however, in looking for results and accomplishments as a return on the investment. When these are not quickly perceivable, Mother starts pressuring her child. "You don't concentrate the way you should," she protests. "How do you expect to play well if you don't practice the way you should?" (Or "As long as you should." Et cetera.)

Eventually, if that's her tactless tactic, she'll be saying severely, "Those music lessons cost money—and what good are they doing?" She so wants her child to be accomplished, to prove his talent. But she doesn't know that every complaint, every reproach, makes him sink deeper into the quicksands of discouragement. All too soon, then, even the day of his music lesson, to which he once looked forward eagerly, is a nightmare because he is not "prepared." Even the most gifted teacher cannot cope with the frustration engendered by a mother's ignorance in not realizing that her child, like every other mother's child, must find his own pace for development and *in his own way.*

The only return you have a right to expect on your investment is that your child gain more and more freedom on the instrument of his choice; that he become more and more adventuresome in improvisations, playing by ear and harmonizing melodies he knows; that he be willing and eager to tackle new material through sight-reading; and that he have interest in all kinds of music—that which he himself makes at the instrument and away from it and all the music he hears around him. The drive to achieve these results is in the child; your role is one of understanding and co-operation.

REMEDIES FOR DISCOURAGEMENT

There are mainly two reasons for discouragement: a child's temperament and faculties may not be adaptable to the instrument he is studying, or he may be justifiably bored with his lessons. In either case, it is unnecessary to give up lessons at once. For one thing, it is unwise to stop lessons when a child is reacting unfavorably because of unsatisfactory accomplishments. In addition, it is usually possible to remedy the situation or at least improve it to a marked degree.

It is better to complete the term's work with the idea of changing to another instrument at the end of the time, studying another phase of music expression, or giving up study entirely. Whatever the plan is, there is no occasion for remonstrances or scolding on the part of the parent, because, with proper handling, the outcome can be different than you anticipate.

A parent must be patient at such a time, understanding and sympathizing with the child's point of view (there must be some justification for his attitude) and yet she must make it clear to him that a contract cannot be broken. The teacher's schedule has been set, his own routine established, and, if he is studying in a class, his group is dependent upon him. There is no reason to inconvenience other people, and deprive himself of the enjoyment that is known to exist in music, without the fair trial of a reasonable period of time.

When a child's discouragement is the result of a poor choice, he should be encouraged, nevertheless, to gain what he can from the experience, using it the while as a chance to gather his forces for more profitable studying later. He will, of course, learn something of music through the study of any instrument, and he will also have some pleasure in it if he feels free to use this time in an experimental way. Removing pressure, demanding nothing in the way of measurable accomplishment, while the lesson and practice times are maintained, often wins back a child's interest under wise guidance.

Usually, it turns out that, when a child thinks he doesn't like the instrument he chose to study, the teacher or the parent is at fault rather than the child. Perhaps the physical demands made upon him are too great; he may not be ready to cope with difficulties involved in producing results satisfying even to himself. He must then be introduced to devices by which he can achieve results more easily. Such devices are known to teachers of all instruments. They can be practiced even in class work, where each child progresses at an individual pace, so that all may work toward a common end.

On the other hand, perhaps he has not had enough background in music; he has had too little experience upon which he can now draw. So much has already been said on this subject that it is not necessary to repeat it here, but let me point out that lack of sufficient musical play before lessons is ample reason for discouragement when they begin. While your child continues his study of an instrument, it would be well to give him as much fun in music as you can at home to make up for this inadequacy.

If a child is studying alone, instead of in a group, this, too, will account for waning interest. The isolation from his companions, the distraction of knowing that they are engaged in other activities while he is having a lesson or practicing, and the plain loneliness of his study are factors which play an enormous part in his reactions to an instrument. He will blame the instrument for keeping him from his friends. If it is too late to change lesson arrangements at this date, at least give him the opportunity for playing informally with his friends. You might also try to enroll him in a class, unrelated to the study of an instrument, where he can enjoy music with his classmates.

Suppose, however, that the ground has been well prepared for his study of an instrument, that he is studying in class, and still is not content. Then you must see his teacher—alone. Let her know that your child is going to continue long enough to give the lessons a fair trial. Discuss the possibilities of working together to make his study more enjoyable, more challenging, more satisfying. Some children are discouraged when they have not had enough success on an instrument. They need many simple pieces which require little work to master so that they can enjoy them quickly. And they need many books for wide and free choice of pieces. They need to be encouraged to play familiar songs by ear, to play an effective piece by rote. They want appreciation from adults when they are able to transfer to an instrument some of their impressions—however crudely they may be expressed.

Playing in the next recital often gives reason and purpose to the preparation of a favorite piece and wins the approval which will further encourage a child. A more immediate spur is the chance to record a song which he can play and sing or a piece he himself has made up. If such a recording can be given to a member of the family as a surprise present, it will have a great effect in increasing his ambition.

Less criticism and watchfulness, more friendly interest in simple accomplishments and in music in general, are the essentials which parents can contribute to the remedy for discouragement. Teachers can supply a great variety of materials, suggest a limitless number of ways to use them. Then a child goes forth—secure in the self-confidence engendered by the confidence shown in him by his elders.

MUSIC RECITALS

Recitals in friendly, informal surroundings can be fun, and stimulating also—if no false standards are set up. Both beginners and advanced students should play at such a time, each to the best of his ability, without fear of comparison. Even the simplest pieces, well played, add to general enjoyment, while more difficult ones offer musical treats for less accomplished players.

This is not a time for printed programs or formal order. Children who prepare music with the idea of sharing it with their friends will be glad to play—solo or ensemble—at any point in the program. A teacher might say for everyone to hear, "Mary, would you play 'Loch Lommond' once through to remind us all of the tune, and then we'll sing it along with you as you play it again."

Another beginner will welcome the chance to play an original composition or to add an easy part of a more complicated ensemble.

A variety of instruments heightens interest and also helps to lessen comparisons. An intricate rhythm on a drum, a delicate melody on a marimba, a lilting tune on a recorder—any student would be proud to perform these alone or as part of group playing. Furthermore, instrument teachers should join in giving recitals so that their pupils have an opportunity to play together. Rather than upset a schedule to arrange previous rehearsals, they can take this recital time to put together what each has prepared alone.

Such a workmanlike demonstration not only relieves tensions in its informality and cuts out the possibility of an individual's showing off, but it gives both parents and students a chance to hear other instruments and realize the problems and satisfactions that others have in playing them.

WHERE WILL IT LEAD?

There is some kind of musical adventure for every child which he will understand and enjoy. Be aware, yourself, of the possibilities and help your child find the one in which he wants to participate at the level proper to him. His satisfaction will be in making music, himself, on the instrument of his choice. He may not choose the instrument you had hoped he'd choose and, what's more, he may even change his mind after further investigation and want to study a different one. This is a sign of growth. He is not losing time but gaining experience.

When he grows up, he may be a basso in a quartet or a saxophone player in a jazz band. Does it matter, as long as he finds in music his own channel for expression?

You may come to congratulate him, and yourself, on his musical ability, even though he never plays any instrument, as long as he enjoys music and learns to listen with a hearing ear. You may find that his real talent is not less but more than you are asking—less in technique, more in the harmony of living. He may grow up not to wriggle or doze at a concert because he associates music with misery—*but to find in music a satisfaction actual and lasting.*

BEATRICE LANDECK

Start Your Child's Creative Art Experiences Early

Answers to Questions Parents Most Often Ask About Their Children's Art Work

1. Does my child need talent to benefit from art experiences?

The notion that a child must be talented to enjoy or profit from an art experience has probably deprived more children of much-needed creative satisfaction than can ever be estimated. All children, regardless of ability, need creative experience just as they need vitamins, fresh air, and exercise. Art is as important to the child's emotional and spiritual security as food is to his body. Parents often fail to recognize this need because the effects of being deprived of art experiences are sometimes subtle.

2. Who is responsible for a child's art development?

Parents are most responsible for children's creative development because parents are actually a child's first art teachers. What a father and mother do to encourage or discourage a young child may form an indelible pattern. A child of two or three does not yet know how to distinguish between the expert and the amateur. Because of his love for his parents and dependence on them, he looks on them as authorities on all matters. "My daddy is the strongest man in the world" applies also to his aesthetic stature.

3. When should a child's art education begin in earnest?

As soon as a child begins to scribble or look at pictures, play with blocks, or make mud pies. Creative experiences start at birth as a child reacts to the world about him. His parents and his home environment make an important and lasting impression. When a child begins to handle both toys and tools, to choose and arrange them, he has started his active creative career. In most cases this happens at about the age of three.

4. What are the best materials for my young child? Do you recommend finger paints?

We find that finger painting is limited in usefulness, but it may serve to free a child and make him ready for painting. Poster paint and clay are among the materials most generally appealing to children. In the children's classes at the Museum of Modern Art we start the three-year-olds with only five colors—black, white, red, yellow, and blue—because we want them to learn how to mix other colors for themselves. Later we add green and other often-used mixed colors to save time and to stimulate the children to mix more subtle colors.

Glass furniture coasters, one for each color, hold the paint to be used. In addition, a low flat aluminum tray about 10 inches wide by 15 inches long by 1/2 inch deep is used for mixing colors. The coasters are arranged along the back of the tray to leave room for mixing. The paint supply can be stored in half-pint-size syrup dispensers so that the child can help himself. This method avoids the likelihood of ruining the paint by accidentally dipping a soiled brush into the whole supply.

Three flat short-bristle brushes called "brights" (3/4 inch, 1/2 inch, and 1/4 inch wide at the ends) are recommended. We first give the young child only the 3/4- and 1/2-inch brushes, but as soon as he wants to make smaller lines, we add the 1/4-inch size. A pointed soft-hair camel's-hair brush (about 1/4 inch in diameter) should be added when the child wants to paint in finer lines and details. This may happen when he is about ten years old. A cellulose sponge for drying the brushes and a pan of water complete the equipment. White 18 x 24-inch drawing paper is desirable for all painting purposes.

Moist clay should be used exclusively for modeling or other plastic work. Modeling wax or the self-hardening commercial clays are not recommended because they lack the necessary pliability and are often unpleasant to touch. Let the child use clay freely, working with his fingers or a clay tool. The tool can easily be made by cutting off an end of a tongue depressor at an angle. Children enjoy modeling animals, people, and just forms. When the pieces have dried, they can be painted with poster colors. Clay can be used again and again if it is kept moist by covering it with a damp cloth and putting in under an inverted can, in a tightly covered glass jar, in a plastic bag, or in aluminum foil. Keeping the clay moist is especially necessary if the piece is to be worked on by the child from time to time.

5. Are there any other desirable materials besides paint and clay?

Making collages and constructions offers a vast and exciting field of enjoyment and exploration to children. These are expressions, invented and developed by modern artists, that have been introduced into education with great success. A collage is made by pasting pieces of different materials—colored decorative papers, cloth, gelatins, strings, feathers, sticks, or any other material—to a background of paper or cardboard. Constructions are imaginative designs in three dimensions; they stand free in space like sculpture and they are likely to be abstract. These are made on a base of wood or clay; sticks or dowels or wire are nailed to the base or stuck in the clay, and materials are hung from them. Sometimes the construction may have parts that turn or swing, or the whole design may hang from a wire to be moved by the breeze. It is then called a "mobile." Once given the idea and supplied with the materials to make collages and constructions, children don't need a great deal of instruction. An enterprising child and his parents together can find a wealth of material around the house, such as Christmas and party wrappings, colored string and ribbon, canceled stamps, wire, feathers, cloth, scraps, buttons, and balls.

6. Creative materials may be good for the child, but aren't they hard on the house?

Of course, paint and clay may tend to mess up the house a bit, but with wise planning they can be controlled. Part of a child's room can be devoted to art work, or the game room or rumpus room can offer space. In a city apartment a child can have his corner.

A simple easel can be made by tacking a piece of building board to the wall or by hanging it on wires from the molding. A large piece of oilcloth hung behind the board and extended out onto the floor will protect both wall and floor. Clay work can be done on the kitchen table or on any small worktable.

7. I bought my child picture books to color. Is this a wise thing to do?

Color books usually damage a child, because they deprive him of the opportunity to create in his own way, and they make him depend on a ready-made picture or design. Often the child shows this colored picture to a relative who says, "How nicely you draw rabbits." The child has not drawn a rabbit, only colored it. After that, he may try to copy the book design so that he can get the praise for himself.

8. Friends and relatives say that my son has talent. Should I send him to an art school?

Friends and relatives mean well, but they are not always the most reliable guides. It is hard to tell whether a child is talented, because children change so much as they grow. Often a child who seems talented at an early age loses his special interest later on, whereas a child with only average interest turns out superior work and may eventually become an artist. A child should not be sent to an art school where he competes with mature art students. He should attend a children's class where no distinction is made between the average and talented child, where his ability will be encouraged in a natural way.

9. How can I help my child's creative growth if I don't know any-thing about art?

You don't have to know a great deal about art to help your

child. If you are sympathetic and encouraging and seem interested without being eager or ambitious for him, you will be a great help. As soon as possible, get your youngster the proper tools with which to work, put him under the direction of a well-trained teacher, and show real interest in what he does at home.

10. My young daughter goes to art class, but there is no instruction given. She just does what she likes. Shouldn't she have lessons in drawing or perspective?

This is a common complaint from parents who remember traditional art teaching and the exercises that were given to children. In the best schools today instruction is given casually and individually, as the child needs it. Often the child thinks the teacher is making only an interested comment like "Did you mix the red or did you use it directly from the jar?" Actually the teacher is saying, "You know, you can mix red for yourself by adding another color. You need not depend on the color the way it comes." Of course, a child's best motivation comes from himself when he does what he likes and when he chooses the paints or the subject matter, but the teacher helps him to discover and invent and to discipline his thinking and seeing.

11. My son's art teacher visited our home recently and implied tactfully that the pictures on the walls were not in good taste and might be a disadvantage to my son's creative development. If I change the pictures in his room, can't I have what I like in the rest of the house? After all, haven't I a right to my own opinion?

I am not sure that your son's art teacher was tactful, but she was right to this extent: Because your son loves you, he will be influenced by everything you do and say. The pictures you hang on the wall are likely to be the most beautiful pictures in the world to him. His whole environment will affect him, so, while you do have a right to your own opinion, you are not completely free, because what you do sets an example for your child.

12. The teacher raves about the meaningless scrawls and splashes of color my young child makes, but I want him to draw and paint things that look real. Am I right?

A child's idea of realism is different from that of an adult. Children tend to express their ideas through feelings, and this means they emphasize and exaggerate forms and colors. Adults tend to see things literally. There is a big difference between the two. If you insist on your child's doing things literally, as you see them, you deprive him of his own individual way of expressing himself.

13. What about copying? My boy makes good copies of comic characters and magazine covers. Is that all right—if he enjoys it?

Copying is deceptive. It gives the child the notion that he is creating the thing he copies when actually he is only following blindly. Later, perhaps too late, he will realize that it is a form of counterfeiting and that he can do none of the things—draw or use color—that he thought he could. The discouragement may be too great for him to start learning all over again, and he may give up for good. A parent who encourages a child to copy is only helping the child to deceive himself.

14. I have been told that a child's emotional difficulties show up in his art work. Can you recommend a book that will help me recognize the symbols so I can be on guard?

Some of a child's emotional difficulties can sometimes be determined from his art work, but it takes a trained psychiatrist to do so. A psychiatrist takes the child's whole behavior into account and does not rely on his art work alone. I think books that try to make amateur psychiatrists out of parents present a danger and cause parents undue concern. If you have a doubt about your child's emotional security, consult a psychiatrist, just as you would a doctor if you felt your child was ill.

15. What are the qualities a good art teacher should have?

Generally speaking, a good art teacher is one who respects the child's own creative power, who understands children, who doesn't impose his or her own methods, and who is more concerned with the child's growth than with the finished product. A good teacher is sensitive to the child's feelings and respects what the child does for what it means to him.

16. What would you think of a television program that would teach children to draw?

Television programs on how to draw are likely to be dangerous because they encourage children to copy. This is an undesirable way of getting results.

17. What about books on making drawing easy? Are they good for children's home use?

All most of these books offer are tricks, and parents should avoid them. There's no easy way to learn to draw or paint. Drawing and painting require effort, insight, and experience. Under the right direction a child will be willing to work, and his creative expression will grow in scope as he does.

VICTOR D'AMICO

A FEW PRACTICAL SUGGESTIONS FOR THE YOUNG PAINTER

Large sheets of inexpensive newsprint or a roll of brown wrapping paper cut into large sheets is also excellent for children's painting. Large-sized jars of poster paints are more economical than small jars. Some of each color can be transferred into smaller containers, such as pint-size, wide-mouthed mayonnaise jars. If jars are too small and full they are apt to tip over or the paint may spatter about, unless the child has an easel. Such easels are inexpensive to buy or are easy to make. Get brushes with stiff bristles (not camel's hair). Cover the floor with newspapers or oilcloth to protect the floor or rugs. Large crayons and sheets of drawing paper should also be part of the home art supply. You can buy crayons that are "washable"— that is, you can wash off any marks made with them on walls or furniture.

Finger Paints

As the name indicates—the child uses his fingers, or his whole hand (and usually his whole body), to spread the colors and to form designs. Finger paints are very exciting to the small child and require some supervision. If you let him use these paints when he is alone, there will probably be some smears on nearby areas. Newspaper may be necessary to protect table and floor, and an apron or smock will be needed to protect the child's clothing. But the paints wash off easily and there will be no permanent stain where color "spills over."

The finger paints you buy have rolls of smooth paper included in the box, and spatulas for lifting out the thick paint. Finger paints are messy, so be prepared for them—but don't let their messiness dismay you, because they are so fascinating that you'll want to get right in and paint too.

Getting Along with In-Laws and Grandparents

WHY do we so often take it for granted that one's in-laws are hard to get along with? All of us have seen examples of the greatest understanding and enjoyment between individuals whose ties were made by marriage only; but we are apt to remember the unhappy examples the same way the one marriage which breaks up strikes us more than the five or six marriages that do not.

We often forget that there is a basis for mother-in-law jokes, going down into the roots of our behavior. It helps, sometimes, to recognize the origins of conflict.

While deep, strong attachment to one's mother (and father) seems to be related to the ability to make a happy marriage, too strong an attachment may lead to unhappiness. A boy who thinks his mother is just about perfect, and who expects to find the same traits in his wife that he admired in his mother may hurt his wife. He compares her with his mother or tends to follow his mother's advice too slavishly. The shoe is on the other foot when a girl has admired her father so much that she expects her husband to measure up to him.

The results, to either partner, are sometimes irksome. The more we understand such harkings-back to our parents, the more we will be able to throw them off, realizing that they should long ago have been outgrown.

Not only will family relations be happier and more relaxed if we can look at these remnants of our childhood loyalty and dependence with some humor, but we will avoid creating made-to-order sources of antagonism for our children to contend with when they are married.

Grandparents are often a source of inspiration to children, in addition to being the best-loved of all their family connections.

The presence of several generations in a household works out successfully only in proportion to the good emotional balance of those concerned. If any one member of the group is unstable and demanding, he or she can make it so unpleasant for the rest that they may be forced into appeasement. As with other dictators, the more an individual is given in to, the greater becomes the pressure of his demands.

Children are often the victims when the ideas of two generations clash. The mother who is exasperated at the way *her* mother interferes with the handling of her children, sometimes snaps at the children rather than at the older person.

When differences can't be harmoniously settled, parents have to decide whether the risk to the child's mental health is great enough to warrant hurting the older person's feelings. As children become mentally mature enough to appreciate some of the problems involved (which will vary greatly with different children) they can be taken into their parents' confidence. They are likely to be very fond of their grandparents, despite his or her peculiarities, and they will be in a position to learn some good lessons in politeness, self-control, and gentleness. Younger children need to be protected from the confusion resulting when methods switch with the person who is in control at the moment.

On the other hand, having grandparents to visit, whose whole-souled and unselfish love gives children a backlog of faith and respect, can be a great asset. Nowadays, grandparents are so familiar with the new knowledge about raising children that they very often are helpful in aiding and abetting parents' methods of guidance.

First Aid and Home Emergencies

FIRST aid is immediate assistance rendered to the injured or suddenly ill person in the absence of adequate medical care or before it arrives. This treatment is based on principles of medicine and surgery that may be applied by persons not professionally trained in these subjects.

When an accident or sudden illness strikes a home, it is well for someone to be able to cope with the emergency. It is not expected that he usurp the role of the physician, and his work ceases when the patient is turned over to the doctor.

Any intelligent individual having a certain knowledge of emergency first aid treatment can avoid confusion and alarm, alleviate suffering, prevent the development of serious complications, boost morale by inspiring confidence, and occasionally be instrumental in saving a life.

FIRST AID SUPPLIES AND EQUIPMENT

First aid materials for home use are frequently scattered all over the medicine chest or on several bathroom shelves. For this reason these supplies are often misplaced and become unclean. It is desirable to have a kit large enough to contain all the supplies with the contents so arranged that the desired package can be found without unpacking. Bandages and supplies should be wrapped in cellophane or paper so that unused materials will not become dirty through handling. If the medicine cabinet is used, a definite part should be set aside for first aid equipment and kept clean, neat, and orderly.

A good first aid kit contains the following articles:

12 sterile gauze squares on adhesive, individual wrappers ("Bandaids")

Assorted sterile bandage compresses in individual packages

4 ounces sterile cotton

Adhesive tape (2 inches by 5 yards), may be cut to suit all purposes

3 two-inch gauze roller bandages

12 applicators

6 tongue blades

A clinical thermometer (Fahrenheit)

1 ounce tincture of iodine (2 per cent)—antiseptic for application on cuts and skin wounds

1 pint alcohol—used externally as a mild antiseptic for wounds. Also used as a liniment. Use pure or diluted with 1-3 parts of water

2 ounces aromatic spirits of ammonia. Used as a stimulant for shock. Dose: ½-1 teaspoonful in water every ½ hour until three doses are taken

4-ounce box boric acid powder. A concentrated solution makes a mild antiseptic. One-half teaspoonful dissolved in a glass of water may be used as wash for eyes and ears

8 ounces hydrogen peroxide. Diluted 1-2 times with water, it makes a good cleansing wash for wounds. As a gargle, dilute 1-3 times with water

4 ounces bicarbonate of soda. It may be used as a gargle or for sour stomach or heartburn. Dose: ½-1 teaspoonful in ½ glass of water. Repeat in ½ hour if necessary

Aspirin—for the relief of pain. Dose: 1-2 five-grain tablets. May be repeated after three hours

Burn ointment such as 5 per cent tannic acid jelly, 5 per cent sulfathiozol ointment, or "Unguentine"

Vaseline—as protective dressing for burns, chafing

Mineral or sweet oil—for use in eyes or ears. This should be sterile, and can be made so by boiling a bottle of oil in a pan of water for 15 minutes

Zinc oxide ointment or 5 per cent ammoniated mercury ointment—as an antiseptic ointment

Scissors—these should always be kept available

An ice bag and a hot-water bottle (rubber) or heating pad
   should be available

These supplies can be purchased or replenished at any reliable
drugstore. The liquids will keep satisfactorily in bottles with tight
rubber stoppers. Make sure all bottles and packages are clearly
labeled—particularly poisons. Keep the medicine chest well out of
reach of children. Never remove bottles or take medicines in the
dark. A wise individual will check over the medical supplies every
few months and renew and replace the necssary articles. It may
be well to have the family doctor check the first aid supplies and
offer advice as to any other materials he feels are essential.

BE ACCIDENT-CONSCIOUS—TAKE NO CHANCES

Prevention of accidental injuries is largely a problem of education.
Every member of the family must be accident-conscious. It is a
well-known fact that there is a lower accident rate, and accidents
which do occur are less serious, in homes where families are educated. Factors which may lead to injuries should be eliminated.
Parents should train their children to be careful. A high percentage of accidents can be avoided and an untold amount of suffering
and misery prevented by proper guidance. Commonsense is the
basis for accident prevention teaching. An accident to the wage-
earner in the average family may be very serious. Do not take
chances. When working in a potentially dangerous place, never
relax and allow yourself to become careless. Safety demands constant vigilance.

All wounds should be properly cared for immediately. Even a
wound the size of a pinpoint provides an entrance for hundreds of
bacteria. Many wounds can be avoided if ordinary precautions are
taken. Some hints for safety are:

(1) Train children to report any cut or abrasion at once—most
cases of infection and blood poisoning start from very small wounds.
(2) Instruct children how to use sharp knives and tools. (3) Always
exercise caution whenever using a knife or sharp instrument. If
cutting with a knife, never cut toward the body. (4) Never let
children *run* with knives, forks, scissors, sticks, or any sharp plaything in their hands. (5) Be careful when chopping with an ax.

It may glance off and strike your foot or ankle. (6) Be especially careful not to fall against a plate glass window, or while carrying dishes or glasses. (7) Do not attempt to catch a falling glass or dish. (8) Do not walk with bare feet where glass has been broken or where there is metal scrap or nails which might cut your feet. (9) Do not put sharp knives in the dishpan with other dishes, and do not throw razor blades in waste or work baskets. (10) Be careful not to cut yourself on the edges of papers and boxes. (11) Use caution in opening cans and disposing of the empty cans. (12) Do not leave straight pins or open safety pins in clothing, as one can receive a serious scratch from these.

Electrical Accidents

Electrical accidents are apt to be fatal under certain conditions, so observe these rules in connection with electrical equipment. (1) Never use electrical appliances while taking a bath, as an electrical shock while standing in a tub of water may result in death. (2) Never touch loose wires—they may be crossed with a live wire. (3) Purchase only a good grade of electrical equipment. (4) Have worn wiring replaced by an electrician immediately. (5) Never put pennies or conductors in fuse boxes to replace burned-out fuses. A "short" may cause a fire. (6) Never use electrical wiring in which the insulation is broken or frayed. Have it repaired or replaced. (7) Never replace electrical connections yourself. (8) Do not have wires running under carpets where they will be walked upon. This may result in a "short" and a serious fire.

Gas Poisoning

Carbon monoxide poisoning is a serious killer in regions where natural gas is burned. It is particularly dangerous because it is odorless. If headaches occur while working in an atmosphere where carbon monoxide may be found, have your doctor check you. You may be unusually sensitive to carbon monoxide and may need to change your job.

Every automobile driver must observe a set of safety commandments to avoid the menace of waste gas. First of all, you should not run an automobile in a garage with the door closed, unless the exhaust is piped to the outside. Nor should you sit in a parked car for more than a few minutes with the motor running—the hot exhaust gases rise and may leak through openings in the floor. Finally, if you are stopped in a tunnel for any length of time, shut off the motor.

In the home, the housewife should not think that the worst that can happen if liquids boil over on the gas stove is a messy range. The liquids may put out the flames and allow gas to escape.

Never ignore the smell of illuminating gas escaping. This is an ever-present menace, and may be due to the fact that your gas heaters are connected with rubber tubing which has deteriorated, permitting the gas to leak through a crack. Only the highest grade flexible tubing should be used, and this ought to be inspected frequently. Or, again, the flues of your gas burners may not be adequate to carry off waste gases. In case you smell gas, do not look for its point of origin with a lighted match. A flashlight is a much safer device. If you cannot discover where the gas is escaping from, ventilate the home and call for the advice of the gas company.

One caution that cannot be repeated too often is that you should never leave a gas flame burning low in a room where people are sleeping. Every year many deaths are due to this cause, and only thoughtlessness is responsible.

Falls

Aside from the human factor of carelessness, mechanical factors are often to be blamed for falls. Loose carpeting on stairways is dangerous, and little effort is required to fasten it down. Inadequate lighting is bad anywhere—it is a positive menace in halls and on stairways. The top or bottom of a flight of stairs is not the place for a small rug, nor should you allow any object to lie on the stairs, or anywhere on your floors, sidewalk, or porch, for that matter, where someone may trip over it.

Slippery surfaces, covered either with ice or wax, are a frequent cause of falls. Clear ice and snow from steps and sidewalks immediately. If the ice is so solid that it cannot be removed, cover it with sand, ashes, sawdust, or salt. When waxing floors, do not do it to such a degree that they become slippery.

Climbing up on chairs, boxes, barrels, or crates is frequently unsafe—use a ladder instead. With a straight ladder, block the base before mounting it. If at all possible, have someone support your ladder while you are on it.

With small children in the house, special care is called for. You should employ gates and barriers to prevent them from falling downstairs. Never allow open windows to be unscreened, and make certain that porch railings are of adequate height and are secure.

Burns and Scalds

Containers of hot liquids should be regarded as a potential source of burns and scalds, and treated with the proper care. Contrary to the proverb, a watched kettle does indeed boil, but it is less likely to boil over and cause injury. The edge of a stove, sink, or table is not a safe place for a kettle containing a hot liquid.

If you employ gasoline or naphtha to clean clothing, avoid using it in a closed room. Do it outside. Fireproof cleaners are available, and these are far preferable.

A screen placed before an open grate or a fireplace is not merely ornamental—it is a highly recommended safety measure, and will keep hot ashes or other burning matter from setting fire to your rug. A metal sheet beneath a stove provides protection for the floor.

When grease catches fire in a pan, water will not put it out. Sand, salt, or soda are the effective means with which to fight this type of fire. Pour it over the flames and cover with a lid.

Oil-soaked rags, piles of old newspapers, and magazines are a constant fire hazard. Inflammable material of this type should be disposed of, not allowed to accumulate in basements, attics, stairways, outbuildings, etc.

Newspaper headlines on the day after Christmas and the Fourth of July invariably proclaim tragic accidents due to carelessness and neglect on these holidays. To celebrate a safe Christmas, make certain that the electrical wiring for your tree is safe. If you use lighted candles, the tree should be set up in a place where curtains or draperies will not blow against them. On the Fourth of July, keep fireworks out of the hands of your children. Nowadays, many cities are making fireworks illegal and substituting plays, pageants, and exhibits of fireworks by expert showmen.

WOUNDS

A wound is a break, opening, or puncture in the skin or an internal surface, caused by violence. Therefore, wounds may vary in size from pin pricks to severe injuries tearing into body cavities. The chief dangers from wounds are infection and severe bleeding. Wounds may be of various types, each receiving a slightly different treatment.

Abrasions are superficial wounds caused by the scraping off of skin. This type occurs when the knees are skinned in falling or the elbows scraped against a rough wall. The floor burns (which are not really burns) are also wounds of this type. These injuries become infected very easily, and they must be treated with great care.

Cleansing the Wound

Bacteria which may be harmless on the skin surface can cause serious infection if allowed to enter a wound. Proper first aid treatment prevents this. Soap and water washing should be avoided because of the danger of contaminating a wound. Always keep a wound clean. Often it is only necessary to cover with sterile gauze or a clean cloth. If it is necessary to cleanse a wound, do so with gauze soaked with rubbing alcohol. Always wash away from center of wound toward outside. Tincture of green soap or one-half strength hydrogen peroxide may also be used for this cleansing.

Remove dirt and foreign materials with sterile applicators. Grease and oil may be removed by ether, naphtha, or oil of turpentine. The wound then should be painted with some antiseptic solution—the best of these being a 2 per cent solution of tincture of iodine, merthiolate, or metaphen. Use a cotton applicator and paint from the center of the wound outward for a distance of one inch around the wound. A sterile gauze dressing large enough to cover the wound is spread with boric acid or zinc oxide ointment.

Apply snugly and hold in place with tape or bandage. This prevents germs or dirt from entering the wound. Do not let a dressing slip, as it becomes contaminated by the germs on the adjacent skin.

Care should be taken to avoid getting iodine in the eyes. Never use more than one applicator of iodine, as too much iodine will burn the tissues and delay healing. Iodine should always be allowed to dry before applying a dressing. This prevents blistering. If you apply adhesive tape directly over iodine, this may cause severe burns.

In taking care of any wound, you should not only be sure that your hands are clean, but also try to avoid touching the wound with the hands. If the wound is very extensive and a physician is available, it is better to allow him to do the cleaning. If the wound occurred in the street or in any area where it is apt to be contaminated by germs which breed in manure, it is necessary to consult a physician so that this patient may receive tetanus antitoxin to prevent the development of lockjaw.

Lockjaw or Tetanus

Lockjaw or tetanus is a dangerous disease caused by certain germs that grow best without air. They are frequently found in garden soil, manure, street dust, or on dirty clothing. They can enter even the tiniest wound. Tetanus is easy to prevent but difficult to treat once it develops. It is fatal in nearly 90 per cent of the cases. The symptoms are stiffness of the neck, spasms of the body, and a locking of the lower jaw. The use of tetanus antitoxin is an effective preventative, and a physician will administer it whenever he feels there is any danger of the disease. Never wait until lockjaw develops. So serious is the disease that most city health departments furnish free antitoxin to make certain that cases of lockjaw do not develop.

Exploding firecrackers, blank pistols, and toy cannons formerly caused deaths of hundreds of people celebrating the Fourth of July. The chief danger from these agents is the many puncture wounds caused by small bits of powder or wadding penetrating the skin. These are apt to carry in tetanus germs from dirty skin or clothing. Never fail to take these cases to the doctor.

INFECTION OF WOUNDS

Infection is one of the most serious complications of any wound. Most little cuts and scratches, whether treated or not, heal without difficulty. Still, whenever the skin is broken, no matter how small the wound may be, germs enter the wound. Occasionally small wounds and more often the larger ones become infected. When germs grow in the tissues a throbbing pain, tenderness, swelling, redness, heat, and the formation of pus result. Infection may arise in any wound regardless of how carefully it is cleaned and dressed.

What To Do Before the Doctor Comes

When infection develops, a doctor should always be called, as this is a wound complication which can well lead to a fatality. Before the doctor arrives, apply hot applications of salt, boric acid, or epsom salts. Prepare the salt solution by adding two teaspoonfuls of table or epsom salt to one pint of boiled water. Apply as hot as can be comfortably stood. Wrap the arm or leg well above the point of injury with a towel or several thicknesses of gauze soaked with the solution. Change them as often as necessary to keep them hot.

BLEEDING

Bleeding is the second serious complication of wounds. The blood is pumped through the body by the heart. The blood that leaves the heart is carried by arteries which branch to finer and finer vessels until they form the tiny network called capillaries. These capillaries nourish all parts of the body. The blood flows from capillaries into small veins and then to larger veins until it is finally returned to the heart. Depending upon which type of vessel is injured, three types of bleeding may occur.

Most often the capillaries are damaged. The bleeding is bright red and flows steadily for a few moments, slows, and finally ceases spontaneously as the body's clotting mechanism begans to function. The slight bleeding is usually beneficial as it washes bacteria out of the wound. If the bleeding does not cease spontaneously, apply pressure with a pad of sterile gauze or bandage it tightly. Elevate the limb if the wound is on an arm or leg. Avoid giving stimulants, since these make the heart beat faster, increasing bleeding. The use of styptics, turpentine, cobwebs, etc., is undesirable to control bleeding.

BLEEDING FROM VEINS. When a vein has been cut, the blood wells up and is dark red to black in color. The blood loss may be large. This bleeding should be treated in the same way as capillary bleeding. Avoid using a tourniquet in these cases, for if it is placed between the wound and the heart, bleeding will be increased. Tight clothing, such as garters or collars, should be removed.

ARTERIAL BLEEDING AND PRESSURE POINTS. If the bleeding is arterial, it is bright red and comes in spurts. The bleeding of small arteries can be controlled by pressure. There are several pressure points where arterial bleeding can be arrested. (1) For bleeding from the temple, pressure applied just in front of the ear will usually control the flow. (2) For bleeding from face wounds below the eye level, apply pressure along the jaw bone. (3) If the neck is cut, place the fingers against the side of the windpipe and compress the cut vessel against the spinal column. (4) Bleeding in the upper arm, shoulder, or armpit can be controlled by pressure applied in the hollow behind the inner third of the collar bone. (5) To control arm or hand bleeding, grasp the upper arm halfway from the shoulder to the elbow with the fingers inside. The fingers press the artery against the bone. (6) For severe bleeding of the thigh, leg, or foot, press the heel of the hand in the middle of the groin, pressing the artery against the pelvis.

APPLYING A TOURNIQUET. Arterial bleeding of the extremities is also well controlled by applying a tourniquet. A handkerchief, a necktie, towel, belt, or any piece of material which can be knotted about the limb can be used. Never use a rope, wire, or sash cord. A pad of gauze should be placed over the vessel to avoid injuring it. The two most convenient places for correctly applying a tourniquet to the arms and legs are: (1) about the upper arm a hand's breadth below the armpit or (2) about the thigh the same distance below the groin. A tourniquet is a dangerous instrument. Never use one unless the hemorrhage cannot be controlled by any other means. Tighten the tourniquet just enough to stop the bleeding. Loosen every fifteen minutes. If left on too long, gangrene may set in. Never apply a tourniquet under a blanket or clothing; in the excitement it may be forgotten. Always tell the doctor if you have applied one.

POISONING

Food Poisoning

Food poisoning (more commonly called ptomaine) is an acute illness due to some injurious property in partly decayed food or improperly cared-for milk. More people seem to be afflicted during the summer months. Not all gastro-intestinal upsets are due to food poisoning, but largely to indigestion, dietary indiscretions, and eating when fatigued. Therefore, it is important to call a physician for any gastro-intestinal disturbance.

The usual offending foods are milk or meat—especially mixtures prepared several hours before eating and not refrigerated or home preserved. Sea food, chicken, and potatoes are also offenders. Some foods are natural poisons, examples being so-called "toadstools," certain berries and roots. One may be the victim of accidental poisoning from eating fruits and vegetables sprayed with an insecticide containing arsenic. Wash thoroughly fresh fruits and vegetables before eating. Rarely, the gastro-intestinal upset may be due to an allergic hypersensitivity to certain foods.

SIGNS OF FOOD POISONING.   The common symptoms are discomfort in the upper abdomen, pain, cramps, nausea, vomiting, diarrhea, fever, prostration, and weakness. The symptoms may come on soon after eating or be delayed several hours. A characteristic of food poisoning is that the weakness often remains several weeks.

Food intoxication is usually due to the consumption of poorly preserved home foods. Usually several persons who have eaten the same food become ill at the same time. This illness has a high death rate. It is characterized by weakness or paralysis of the muscles, constipation, and absence of fever and gastro-intestinal symptoms. The treatment of choice is an antitoxin which must be administered by a physician.

How to Treat Food Poison Cases.   In treating any food poisoning, if vomiting has not occurred, promptly give an emetic of a tablespoonful of mustard in one-half glass of warm water. The stomach should be washed out if possible. A soap suds enema should be given to empty the bowel. The patient should be treated for shock and made to abstain from food for twenty-four hours—however, adequate fluid intake should be maintained.

Chemical Poisoning

The treatment of poisoning demands immediate action. If the poison can be removed from the stomach before it is absorbed, the patient is seldom harmed. Once the poison is absorbed there is little even a physician can do.

Children are particularly likely to take poisons accidentally. Proper preventive measures would entirely eliminate this cause of home accidents. The poisons most commonly taken are: (1) phenol or carbolic acid, (2) tincture of iodine, (3) mercuric chloride, (4) hydrochloric, nitric, acetic, or sulfuric acids, (5) lye, (6) belladonna, (7) morphine and codein (pain-relieving drugs), (8) sleeping potions or barbiturates (nembutal, phenobarbital, seconal), (9) kerosene, (10) arsenic, (11) wood alcohol, (12) strychnine, (13) phosphorus (matches), (14) cyanide, and (15) lead.

The symptoms vary with the poison taken. Most poisons produce pain in the stomach, nausea, cramps, vomiting, diarrhea, and collapse. Overdosage of sedatives causes severe drowsiness, sleep, and unconsciousness. The corrosive poisons burn or stain the mouth and tongue. Some poisons bring on convulsions or spasms.

Discovering the Nature of the Poison.   If poisoning is suspected, call a physician. Be calm. Do not waste valuable time rushing the patient to a hospital or awaiting the arrival of a doctor— during this time the poison is being absorbed. Endeavor to discover the nature of the poison. If no information can be obtained from the patient, search the surroundings for an empty poison bottle, look for clothing stains, smell the patient's breath, and look in his mouth for burns or stains. Check if any of the household poison containers have been opened recently. If the poison can be determined, give the antidote when available. Most products containing poison give the antidote on the label. The antidote combines with the poison and renders it harmless.

How to Treat Chemical Poisoning Cases. If the antidote is unknown, give white of eggs, milk, or strong tea. They are harmless and will be antagonistic to many of the common poisons. A poison diluted with large amounts of fluid is never as rapidly absorbed as when concentrated. Vomiting can be more easily induced if the stomach is full. After the antidote has been administered, the stomach should be emptied as quickly as possible. Induce vomiting by tickling the back of the throat after administering an emetic. Any of the following are satisfactory emetics: (1) soapsuds, (2) salt or mustard water (a heaping teaspoonful to a cupful of lukewarm water), (3) soda water using ordinary baking soda, (4) lukewarm water, (5) egg white or (6) milk. Give four to seven glassfuls if vomiting has not occurred sooner. Cause the patient to vomit several times and have him drink freely of lukewarm water in the intervals. Do not waste time looking for an antidote.

Give a large dose of epsom salts after the stomach is emptied as it is good treatment for any poison. If the poison was a corrosive, in addition to the above treatment give soothing drinks of milk, or milk and eggs beaten together.

After emptying the stomach, treat the various symptoms which arise. Keep patient warm and treat for shock. If breathing stops, give stimulants such as hot coffee or one-half teaspoonful of aromatic spirits of ammonia. Stimulants should not be given in strychnine poisoning, and the patient should be kept quiet. If one of the sleep-producing drugs has been taken, keep the patient awake with strong hot coffee. As long as the patient is awake, he will continue to breathe. Avoid making the patient exercise and overtiring him. Make every effort to obtain an inhalator to treat these cases.

FOREIGN BODIES—SPLINTERS

Splinters of wood, small pieces of glass, and metal shavings are the most frequent foreign bodies found in wounds. If the foreign body is near the surface, it can be picked out. Sterilize the skin with tincture of iodine. Sterilize an instrument such as a knife point, needle, or tweezer by passing it through a flame. If the splinter is large, insert a knife blade under the end, grasp it between the thumbnail and blade, and remove. After removal, the wound is made to bleed. Iodine is then applied to the wound and a sterile dressing applied.

Splinters under the nail which are broken off are removed by scraping the nail thin, cutting out a small V-shaped piece over the splinter, and removing it as above. Deep splinters or large foreign objects are best treated by a physician.

Foreign Bodies in the Ear

Solid objects such as a bean, pea, or button are often introduced into the ear and may be the source of considerable discomfort and pain. Many of these swell when wet and are difficult to remove. Never use pins or pieces of wire to remove them, as there is a great danger of seriously injuring the ear drum. Small objects may be removed by gentle syringing with warm water. Take these cases to a doctor as he has the proper instruments to remove these foreign objects.

Insects frequently crawl into the external ear and are very unpleasant. An insect can be removed by turning the head to one side and pouring sweet or olive oil in the affected ear. The warm oil suffocates the insect, and it may be floated out with warm water. In syringing the ear, spray the water against the side of the canal rather than directly against the drum.

Foreign Bodies in the Eye

Particles of dirt, dust, sand, cinders, glass, coal, and fine specks of metal frequently get into the eyes. They either lodge under the eyelids or become firmly adherent to the clear part of the eyeball.

Usually they do not make a wound. A foreign body in the eye is very annoying and leads to pain, interference with vision, and a profuse flow of tears.

How to Remove Foreign Bodies from the Eye.   No one should attempt to remove a foreign substance from the surface of the eyeball without special training. Place a small pad of wet gauze over the eye to restrain the motion of the eye while awaiting expert care. Put a couple of drops of clear olive oil, mineral oil, or castor oil in the eye before applying the compresses. With a little experience, it is not difficult to remove foreign bodies from beneath the lids. If the object is under the lower lid, pull the lower lid down and have the patient look up. If the speck is seen, it can be removed with a corner of a clean wet handkerchief or a cotton applicator. If the object is under the upper lid, grasp the lashes of the upper lid and pull down and out over the lower lid. The tears will wash the foreign body to the inside corner of the eye, from which it can easily be lifted out.

Small foreign bodies can often be washed out of the eye with a boric acid solution (a full teaspoonful in a pint of cool boiled water). Use an eye dropper or a small eye syringe. Never wash the liquid directly against the eye. Gently spread the lids and flush the eye thoroughly. Many eye specialists advise against using the eye cup.

If these methods are still unsuccessful, one should try to turn the upper lid. Wash the hands first. Grasp the eyelashes and have the patient look down. Lay a matchstick or toothpick across the lid and turn the lid upside down by pulling the eyelashes over the stick. Holding the lid in this way, a foreign body can usually be removed.

Foreign Bodies in the Nose

Children may slip beans and other similar objects in the nose, or insects may become lodged in the nose. If the individual can be made to snort or sneeze by tickling the nose with a feather, the foreign body often can be blown out. If the object can be seen, it may be hooked with a blunt end of a hairpin. Should these simple devices fail, use a few drops of olive oil or mineral oil to relieve the irritation and to prevent swelling. There is no immediate danger. More harm is done by attempting to dislodge a foreign body with improper instruments than by leaving it in place until competent advice is available. Take the patient to a physician.

Foreign Bodies in the Throat

Young children are especially likely to put small objects in their mouths. If they try to swallow them, they may block the windpipe. When a child chokes, there is no time to call a doctor, so you should try to remove the foreign body immediately. If large, it can be felt and removed by hooking the index finger behind it. Be careful not to scratch with the fingernail or push the object further down. Frequently a sharp slap between the shoulders will dislodge objects and allow them to be coughed out. Invert children and encourage them to cough. Adults should lie crosswise on the bed and hang the head and shoulders over the side.

If the patient is unable to breathe, give artificial respiration. Sometimes even though the air passage is not totally obstructed, the throat may be thrown into a spasm and severe symptoms of suffocation may result. The patient may get livid, gasp for breath, and be thrown into violent coughing fits.

If pieces of food, fish bones, coins, false teeth, or other objects lodge in the throat, windpipe, or gullet, one must be taken to a specialist. He has "scopes" of all types with lights and forceps or hooks for removing these objects.

Foreign Bodies in the Stomach

If a child swallows a tack, safety pin, coin, or a bone, feed him mashed potatoes and thoroughly chewed bread. These aid the passage of the object to the stomach. Never give a violent laxative. Always seek medical advice. By the use of the X-ray, metal objects can be located and a decision then made as to the best method of removal. In most instances a foreign substance that is swallowed will pass from the body by the way of the bowel without harm.

The Handicapped, Exceptional
or "Different Child"

EVERY community numbers among its children those who differ physically, mentally, or emotionally from so-called normal children.

Some of these differences are so outstanding that they can be recognized without difficulty, some are discovered only after careful examination, and others may go completely unnoticed for a long time by both parents and teachers.

Children with defective speech, the crippled, the blind and partially seeing, the deaf and hard of hearing, the delicate, the emotionally maladjusted, the mentally retarded and those with superior ability—these are the children who may vary widely from the normal and for whom the home and the school may need to provide treatment and/or a special type of training in order to help them develop as well adjusted and useful citizens in the future.

Because these children are different in a variety of ways from those who have no handicaps they are termed exceptional children by educators today. Perhaps you have always thought of exceptional children as those who were especially gifted in some way or of very superior mentality. The term exceptional, however, means unusual or different from the average and consequently fits all children who vary from the normal in physical, mental, or emotional characteristics.

753

We must remember that exceptional children *are like all other children in many more ways than they are different from them.* They want the same things that other childen want; they react to love and kindness, to scolding and nagging, to pampering, overindulgence and overprotection, to firm but fair treatment, to injustice, and so on, much as we would expect any other children to react.

Too often parents of exceptional children fail to realize that many other parents have problems similar to theirs. Count the children in your own school and community and even in your own home who are handicapped in some way. Accidents and illness that will result in handicapping conditions can come to any child, for no family is immune.

To find the exceptional children, to meet their fundamental needs, to develop their capacities to the fullest extent, and to give them equal opportunities with all other children is the obligation of all of us in the home, the school, and the community.

What Are the Needs of Exceptional Children?

Their needs are like those of all children for they have the same traits and desires as their normal brothers and sisters. They need good physical care and they need the security that comes from a feeling of being a loved member of a family group and having a part in its work and play. Above all they must have an opportunity to achieve success in the things they are able to do, both at home and at school.

It is true that the methods we use in meeting the individual needs of our exceptional children must often differ from those used with normal children but if we keep in mind continually that they are just children, even though handicapped, our own understanding of their additional needs will be increased.

How Can We Find the Exceptional Children?

It is not always easy to identify exceptional children. Johnny has had an attack of infantile paralysis which has visibly crippled him so much that he needs not only physical care but also placement in a special school for crippled children where treatments, special equipment, rest periods, etc., are made available for him. There is no question in anyone's mind as to his crippling condition and what is needed to help him.

But what about Jean? She does very poor school work, she is listless and inattentive, she daydreams and frequently fails to answer when spoken to. She is often quite disobedient in school and at home. No one seems to understand why she adjusts so poorly and is such a poor student when she really seems like a bright little girl. But Jean is hard of hearing, which no one has yet discovered. Because she cannot hear what the teacher or the children are saying in the classroom, she has little interest in classroom activities. To avoid complete boredom, she finds other ways to occupy her time, some of which are not acceptable to the teacher or the group.

If we are to give our exceptional children the greatest possible help it is important that we identify their problems or capabilities as early as possible. Your doctor will tell you how important from the standpoint of a cure is the early diagnosis of a disease—that frequently the visible signs of the disease appear only when it is too late to help the patient. This is just as true when we are dealing with exceptional children of any type. We need to be alert to symtoms that indicate a deviation from the normal in any way, both physical and mental. With children who are physically and mentally different, help will be more effective if given early.

We need to know also that many of the symptoms of one handicap are the same as those of another. Poor school work, defective speech, inattention, disobedience, day dreaming—these traits and habits may indicate either mental retardation or poor hearing. Some of these same symptoms are noticeable in the child who has poor eyesight. Every type of physically handicapped child displays some of the characteristics of a slow learner. It is never safe to make a decision as to the nature of a child's handicap until a thorough physical and mental check up has been made.

THE PRESCHOOL EXCEPTIONAL CHILD

The doctor, the psychologist, and the educator are trained to note differences in children. Unfortunately, they rarely have the opportunity to observe the exceptional child and note his handicap until he is in school. Then it is too late. It is vital that parents recognize in the home, early in the child's life, some of the differences in children. If discovered in time, many physical handicaps can be remedied and other serious conditions prevented.

Children learn most rapidly during their first five years of life. Then, during their preschool years, their education really begins. The training and experiences of their early home life must be such as to help them adjust happily to the people and situations they are going to meet as they grow older.

This isn't easy for parents to manage, particularly for the exceptional child. Whatever the type or degree of disability, it often seriously disturbs the emotional life of both the youngster and his family, causing anxieties, stresses, and strains. The result is a perplexing problem day in and day out for anxious parents.

Most parents earnestly try to *do* the job they know must be done, but they do not always know *how* to do it. To know how and what to do for the exceptional child, one must know something about the growth and needs of the normal child. The exceptional child has the fundamental needs of all children. The difference is that he also has some special needs.

These Make Him Exceptional

POOR VISION. The child who squints, who seems always to be falling over things may have poor vision. Disease, infection, or injury may have affected his eyesight. Prompt medical care may mean the difference between a permanent disability and near normal vision. Take him to an ophthalmologist (eye doctor) immediately to determine the nature and extent of his disability. Children can now wear glasses much earlier than they could a generation ago. Too, present medical science can do more to correct defective vision.

Some children are blind from birth. The blind child during infancy and childhood is better off at home, where he can receive love and security, than he would be in an institution. To lessen his confusion he needs a daily routine, a regular time for eating and going to bed. It is important never to do anything for him that he can do for himself; though he may stumble and grope, it is best for him to have the thrill of success in finding his blocks, rattle, or other simple toys. His clothes and the things he uses each day should be placed in a certain place where he can reach them without groping. Remember to encourage and teach him to do some of the things babies who are not blind do by themselves. It is essential to his feeling of achievement.

No matter how bright he is, he will be limited in his achievement, slow in walking and talking, for normal preschool children learn by seeing, hearing, and imitating. You may have to teach him to pull himself up and lower himself, to hold up his head. Almost surely you will have to teach him to creep and walk, because he has no sense of space and no urge to move from one place to another. As he begins to learn to walk, support him gently by holding his hands. This will encourage him to move about and explore. His sense of touch will help him. Keep the furniture always in the same place to prevent unnecessary bumps; remove unnecessary articles and breakable objects. You will, of course, have to teach him to run and skip, and he will need plenty of space so he can do it without fear.

Read to him from books that tell him about things as they are, that help him imagine the things he cannot see. Talking with him helps to increase his vocabulary and widens his horizons.

He will need training in eating and dressing. Teach him to use a cup or glass and spoon and fork by placing his hands on them and helping him raise them to his mouth. Help him with the feeding motions over and over again until they become simple to him. He can be taught to dress through his sense of touch. As you guide his hands, describe each article of clothing in simple words explaining the order in which it can be put on.

Help him to help himself, always letting him feel the joy of accomplishment. Take him to places that would be suitable for any child, explaining beforehand what he is going to visit; explain it again as he views it through your eyes. In planning his schooling, get the advice of your local board of education or the state board for the blind to help you prepare him for going away when the time comes.

POOR HEARING.   It is often difficult to know when a child's hearing is poor. Parents may wonder why their child does not respond and imagine all sorts of reasons for it. Children with defective hearing early in life do not speak because they have not had the opportunity to hear sounds and words. Where some speech has developed, it may be far from perfect. If hearing difficulty is suspected, consult a reputable otologist (ear doctor), who can diagnose and measure the hearing capacity of your child.

Skills have been developed in teaching a deaf child to speak through the senses of touch, sight, and sound. Using the voice pitch the child can hear best, speak clearly and distinctly, assuming always that he will understand. The more you talk to him, the more he will want to respond. Avoid correcting him too often. Get his attention before you speak to him; face him directly with a pleasant, animated expression. If a hearing aid will improve his hearing and your otologist has advised it, by all means see that your child has one and that he is guided in the use of it. This will require a long period of gradual and delicate adjustment.

INABILITY TO SPEAK.   When a preschool child's inability to speak seems out of line with normal development (the average age of beginning speech is fifteen months) take him to a pediatrician for a thorough physical examination. Poor general health may be the cause. It often is. A hearing defect can be an indirect cause of delayed or faulty speech. Emotional problems, illness, birth injuries, organic conditions—any one of these can affect speech ability. In many cases today, treatment can help correct the defect. Remember, a child does not speak well because he has not *learned* to speak well.

Stuttering is a common speech problem. No two cases are exactly alike. There are a number of theories as to the cause of stuttering. We know that strain and tension aggravate it. Harmony in the home, time for quiet play, activities and materials which he can manipulate successfully will help the stuttering preschool child. At no time should you make a point of his speech defect or call undue attention to it. If the child has cerebral palsy, his speech may be greatly delayed and is often slow, jerky, and labored, hard to understand.

RHEUMATIC FEVER.   This is a disease which usually occurs among children at about seven or eight years of age, later than the preschool age. It varies in severity, appears in different ways, and is often difficult for doctors to diagnose. The illness itself lasts for weeks or months: convalescence is often a matter of months and perhaps years. It is important for the parent to cooperate in a program of physical hygiene outlined by the doctor and hospital staff. A medical social worker can give counsel and help with important decisions as to whether the child should go to a convalescent home or convalesce at home. If the child is kept at home, give him the praise he deserves for cooperating with you in his daily health habits.

EPILEPSY.   It is comforting to know that epilepsy is now better understood; new medications, in most cases, can either completely eliminate or reduce the seizures. Seizures arise from various causes and are evidence that something is out of order physiologically. They are not an indication of a mental or personality disorder. Although the child's handicap is not constant and though seizures may occur only rarely, it is important to get medical diagnosis and attention immediately.

It is a mistake to treat the child as an invalid or even as a semi-invalid. The fuller, more active life he can lead, the fewer seizures he is likely to have. He should be allowed to play freely, be given a good nutritious diet and the usual amount of sleep for a normal child of his age.

In some children, seizures appear early in life; other children go through the normal infancy before the first one occurs. Seizures are not in themselves fatal. When the convulsion occurs, there is little a parent can do about it except to make the child comfortable. He is in no pain because he is unconscious. Sleep usually follows and is good for him. The importance of proper diagnosis and medical care, however, cannot be overemphasized.

CEREBRAL PALSY.   Cerebral palsy is caused by damage to the area of the brain that controls motor development. Sometimes involving speech, hearing, vision and use of hands and legs, cerebral palsy demands diagnosis by a team of medical specialists. It is now possible to help cerebral palsied children to improve their speech, and the use of hands and lower limbs.

Many agencies are cooperating to make training and treatment services available for cerebral palsied children. From them parents may receive the help and guidance of specialists to begin the long, consistent program of training essential to progress. It is not the child's age but his muscular condition that will determine what can be expected of him. With the cerebral palsied child, as with all crippled children, the most common mistake is in doing too much for him rather than encouraging him to do everything for himself that he possibly can.

THE BRIGHT CHILD. The bright child needs the same consistent program desirable for all children—good physical care, playmates and play materials that will give him an opportunity to explore and experiment constructively. A good nursery school will recognize and provide for his individual abilities. The parent and the nursery school teacher together should be able to plan a balanced program for best development of the child's talents.

THE SLOW-LEARNING CHILD. The slow-learning child needs what every child needs to become a well-adjusted person. Training must be geared to his ability and given more slowly than it would be to a normal child. Do not be too concerned about the preschool child's lag in accomplishing one or two of the things that other children his age are doing. A child who has been babied or overprotected and not given the opportunity to develop his growing body and mind may be slow because of his limited environment and activities. Where a parent has serious doubts of his ability to estimate his child's true capabilities, it is essential to get the help of a competent psychologist or psychiatrist to estimate the child's capacity to learn and to help in planning future care and education for him.

What the child can or cannot do depends chiefly upon the degree of his mental handicap. You will want to instill good habits in him. Before habit is formed, you will have to repeat directions over and over again, giving only one direction at a time. Do not depend upon him to work out the best way of doing something. Show it to him yourself in detail. Even though he may be slow, once he has mastered the process of dressing, you should expect him to keep it up if clothes are of a simple self-help type.

Help him to establish routines where one act becomes associated with another, praising him and recognizing his accomplishment when he deserves it. Discipline will be as important for him as for any child but should never mean bodily punishment. Ordinarily a retarded child does not present many serious discipline problems, for he does not have the initiative or imagination to be guilty of deliberate wrong doings. However, he cannot help being slow and forgetful and may have a number of irritating ways.

Contact your local schools and other agencies to find out about special classes or home training for your child. If he is so retarded that he will probably always need care and protection, you can work out a plan with some of your community agencies that will be most beneficial to him when he reaches school age. While they are still very young, the large majority of slow-learning children can live comfortably and securely in the home where there are many opportunities for friendly, interesting activities that they can enjoy and participate in at their own rate of development.

Things You Can Do

There are many things you can do to help your child live with his handicap and yet be able to live happily with the world in which he will grow up. Let him live in a home where there are mother and father, harmony, respect and love. If he is a part of a happy family, he will be happy. He should *feel* a *part* of the family, and no matter what his handicap he should have responsibilities according to his age and ability. To have a job, even a small one, will give him a sense of security, of belonging, of helping.

He needs attractive, nourishing food served in small portions in a pleasant, leisurely atmosphere. All preschool children need ten to twelve hours of sleep with an afternoon nap in a bed and room where they can relax and feel secure. You can help your child by providing simple, self-help garments with front openings, large buttons or zippers and elastic waist bands that he can pull down himself. Low hooks for his clothes, his towel and a large shelf within reach for his books and playthings will help him develop constructive play habits.

He needs friends of his own age who will include him in their play even though he cannot actively take part. A "play hour" where he has some special toy will bring little friends who will eventually accept him as one of them. He needs a mother and father who somehow manage to find time to refresh themselves, to gain courage, to make friends, to have some outside interest, to gain perspective and to bring him wholesome and interesting parents to face each day.

VERNA S. CARLISLE

Sterility — the Childless Marriage

STERILITY means that one is unable to produce a living child. Some women never conceive; others conceive, but are unable to carry the child to an age where life after birth may be expected. Still others who have given birth to a child cease to be fruitful. Sterility is considered primary when the woman has never been pregnant. It is considered secondary when she has borne a child and then becomes sterile. Temporary sterility generally occurs during the milk-producing period, and as a result of serious illnesses. The term infertility is often used to denote the inability on the part of a woman to give birth to a child capable of living outside the womb.

FERTILITY

Fertility is dependent on the deposit of healthy spermatozoa, or male sperm cells, in a normal vagina. The mouth of the womb and the womb itself must be in a state favorable for the transmission of spermatozoa, and the lining of the womb must be in a suitable condition for embedding the ovum or egg. The ovaries must produce healthy ova and function normally, and the Fallopian tubes must offer no obstruction to the passage of healthy ova. There must also be normal secretions in both the man and the woman, with biochemical reactions which are not incompatible. A failing in any of these factors may result in sterility, and in an effort to solve the question, they must all be tested methodically.

The period of fertility is commonly measured by the length of menstrual life, but there are exceptions on record where women long past the menopause have borne children. Menstruation is not absolutely essential to conception, for many women conceive while suckling a child, even though menstruation has not begun again since its birth.

CAUSES OF STERILITY

It has been estimated that some 12 per cent of marriages are involuntarily childless. The causes of sterility include physical defects, prolonged use of contraceptives, venereal diseases, and the various psychological stresses of modern life.

Formerly, the investigation and treatment of sterility centered almost solely on the wife. Lately, it has become increasingly obvious that in one-third to one-half of barren unions the husband is responsible for the state of affairs. The woman usually accepts the suggestion that she is at fault and is willing to submit to everything to remove the stigma, if stigma it is. Frequently the man refuses to listen to the suggestion that the responsibility may possibly be his. Often he refuses to submit himself for examination.

A great proportion of women who are sterile have defects in development. These are total or partial absence of genital organs; imperfect development of the ovaries; arrested development of the tubes or womb, or both; bent or displaced womb; and closure of the mouth of the womb. Acquired defects which prevent conception are usually the result of inflammation in the pelvis, which may close or distort the tubes. There are in addition many other causes, some of which have already been suggested.

Another little-known cause of sterility in women is increased acidity of the vaginal secretion. Spermatozoa are quickly killed in an acid medium. Therefore the chemical reaction of the vaginal secretion must be determined. The treatment for this is douching with lime water before intercourse.

Meaning of Sterility in Men

Physiologic impotence, or sterility, may occur at widely varying ages in different individuals. No average age can be given. A man may be perfectly normal in every respect except that he is unable to produce healthy sperm, or the process may be reduced. This man is said to be sterile. Congenital sterility of the male is uncommon. Sperm production, of course, changes with age, but here we are concerned only with an abnormal condition.

There must be a clear understanding of the difference between the ability to produce children and the ability to have satisfactory intercourse. They are two separate and distinct activities. A man may be capable of having intercourse and yet not have normal semen. The opposite may also be true.

TREATMENT OF STERILITY IN MEN

The first requirement is the examination of a fresh specimen of semen. This should reach the physician not more than an hour after discharged. Chilled sperm soon lose their motility. If there is a reduction in the number of sperm to less than one half, or deformities of the sperm, or inactivity of the sperm, or a total absence, then we have found the source of the sterility.

The next procedure is to have a complete physical examination, paying special attention to the blood examination to see if there is any anemia, and to rule out the possibility of a latent syphilis. There should be an investigation of the other hormone glands by means of a basal metabolism test.

Sometimes impotence is psychological in origin. A good psychiatrist can accomplish wonders with a disorder of this type.

If all other possible conditions are ruled out, the conclusion is that the testicles are at fault. For this condition hormones are given by muscular injections.

EXAMINING THE WIFE FOR STERILITY

The special tests for the wife include an examination after intercourse to demonstrate that the vaginal secretions are not harmful to the sperm, and also an examination by the injection of air or special oils to demonstrate the patency (openness) of her Fallopian tubes. She should also have one of the various tests to demonstrate that she is actually producing egg cells. These are the tests which are directed specifically at the genital apparatus and its functions, but there are other tests which should be performed. A basal metabolism test, for instance, is the most useful single test to demonstrate the normality of the endocrine glands. These glands have an important bearing on the bodily functions, including fertility; where they are functioning abnormally, this derangement may well be the cause of the failure to become pregnant. Injections of glandular extracts are often helpful in such cases.

There are many intangibles to the investigation which are recognized but which cannot in any way be measured. It has been shown, for instance, in investigations on animals, that dietary deficiencies may be of importance, and the three dietary factors which are found to be most important are proteins, calcium and butter fat.

We do not know very much about the necessity for the various vitamins with the exception of vitamin E. It has been demonstrated that this is important in animals in starting a pregnancy and maintaining it during its early stages, and it is assumed to be equally important in humans although we have no actual proof of this in terms of human experiments. It is a common practice for the doctor to prescribe vitamin E for patients who have had difficulty in becoming pregnant because it is the general belief that it is effective and there have been no reported instances of its being harmful.

HOW YOUR PHYSICAL AND EMOTIONAL STATES INFLUENCE FERTILITY

Good physical condition is another important element in fertility, and this must be maintained, of course, by adequate diet, sufficient sleep and a satisfactory amount of exercise and recreation. Besides this, we know that emotional states have an influence on fertility. It has been demonstrated during times of emotional stress that men's fertility may be lowered temporarily in terms of the sperm count, and although we have no comparable test to use for a woman's fertility, it is supposed that her fertility may be affected in the same way.

SOLUTIONS FOR THE CHILDLESS COUPLE

Adoption

In cases where pregnancy is impossible for a couple, the most common and obvious possibility is the adoption of a child. Adoptions now in many states are supervised by the appropriate state authorities, who make every effort to see that the child is healthy and normal and that the parents can offer the child a satisfactory home, with a good education and start in life. In some states the babies are put into the foster home for a trial period before the final adoption papers are given out, and the home is visited by representatives of the state board from time to time to see that the home surroundings come up to standard, that the child is flourishing and happy, and the parents are satisfied. (See page 768.)

Artificial Insemination

Another alternative, which is less practiced than adoption but is preferred by some mothers, is artificial insemination. The reports of various doctors vary considerably as to the efficacy of this procedure. Some doctors are enthusiastic about it and report a high percentage of success, while others have not been so fortunate.

THE WOMAN MUST BE CAPABLE OF PREGNANCY. Before undertaking artificial insemination, the woman must be carefully gone over to demonstrate so far as possible that she is capable of becoming pregnant. It must be remembered that with all the tests for fertility we can never give a positive and final answer in the affirmative. We can frequently demonstrate that pregnancy cannot take place in a given couple because of a failure of spermatogenesis (production of sperm) or the closure of some of the passageways which prevents the union of the sperm and egg cell, but the furthest we can go in the affirmative direction is to demonstrate that the couple are physically normal and that there is no demonstrable reason why pregnancy should not occur.

SELECTING THE DONOR. Having demonstrated normality in the woman, it is then the doctor's concern to find a suitable donor to supply sperm to be injected into the uterus. It is his responsibility to see that the donor is physically sound and comes of sound stock, to have him carefully examined and tested to rule out venereal or other diseases, and to have a sperm examination which will prove his capacity to furnish sperm in normal numbers, of normal development, and of normal vitality. Here again, neither the donor nor the patient should ever be allowed to know who the other is, to prevent any future claims on the patient or on the patient's baby if she becomes pregnant and delivers a child.

It is the usual procedure for the doctor to secure the semen immediately before the artificial insemination, and to return as soon as possible to the office, where the semen is injected into the patient's uterus. Many women prefer this procedure to the idea of adopting a baby because in this case the baby is theirs, although the husband is in no way concerned.

Cases in Which Artifical Insemination Is Not Resorted To

It is needless to say that artificial insemination cannot be resorted to when the cause of the sterility lies in the wife and not in the husband. In case the husband's sperm is normal and pregnancy has not occurred under the ordinary circumstances of intercourse, there is little point in resorting to artificial insemination from the husband to the wife. This is rarely as effective as intercourse. The only exceptions to this statement would be the cases where the husband's sperm are normal but for some reason he could not secure an erection and could not, therefore, have intercourse. Under these circumstances it may be advisable to transfer the sperm artificially into the vagina.

The Facts About Adoption

A COUPLE may take years to make up their minds that they want to adopt a baby. But when they come to the point of deciding, they want action, and they want it now. If a legitimate agency goes through a lot of what looks like impressive folderol, they are going to be sorely tempted to take a short cut. Why shouldn't they go to a doctor, or a minister, or an unlicensed agency, and get immediate action?

It takes but a moment's thought to make any sensible person realize that there is much more to an adoption than the mere placing of a homeless child with doting parents. As a matter of fact, in every adoption there are three factors to be considered.

These are (1) the baby for whom a home is being sought; (2) his natural or "biologic" parents, of whom frequently only the mother is known, and (3) the couple who want to adopt a baby.

The welfare department or licensed professional adoption society is charged with the duty of insuring the best interests of all three, whereas the unlicensed agency is under no such obligation. Skill, training, adequate facilities and above all a certain amount of time are needed to look into the background and history of each party, if the best sort of adjustment is to be obtained for each. The baby broker who is concerned only with his paying clients, the physician or clergyman who sees only a bewildered mother struggling to escape what society considers the shameful burden of an unwanted baby—these can obviously do a quick job with no questions asked and no waiting. But how permanent will it be? And how advantageous for all concerned?

Each of the following case histories is illustrative of a large number of actual instances familiar to any welfare worker.

The Johnson's friends couldn't say enough in praise of the little dark-eyed beauty their minister was able to obtain for them from a pastor in a neighboring city. They did not take it too seriously when little Gladys made no effort to sit up until she was a year old. But when she did not even attempt to stand until she was eighteen

768

months, they forced themselves to face facts, do as their doctor advised, and have a psychologist examine her.

Now they know to their sorrow that their beautiful little girl will never learn to read more than a few of the simplest words, or add more than a few digits. She won't be able to get through even the first grade of primary school. She is hopelessly retarded mentally— a condition that the welfare department's routine medical examination might have indicated, and that would have been obvious long before the probationary year had passed.

It never occurred to the Goodwins to make sure that their lovely little fellow's mother had gone through the legal formality of giving him up. It was no one's business to tell them how necessary this is, and no one did. It was a complete and most unwelcome surprise when one day, long after they had come to love him as their very own but before they got round to adopting him, they received a letter on legal stationery informing them that the baby's mother had changed her mind, and would vigorously oppose them when they applied for adoption papers. Of course, if they were to offer her a substantial pecuniary consideration to change her mind . . .

A shyster lawyer's trick? Of course. But that made no difference. Any court would be obliged, no matter how regretfully, to sustain a mother's claim to her child if she had never legally given him up. The Goodwins' ignorance was no excuse under the law. They'll have to pay, and pay heavily, to insure their happiness, or they'll lose it. But what does a shyster care, or a mercenary parent?

The welfare department knows all about such dangers, and would never have allowed such a slip-up. But this was one of those short-circuit adoptions. There was no opportunity for experienced management and the avoidance of legal pitfalls. It's too late now.

The Carpenters were more fortunate in this respect. They were tipped off by friends and made sure that they had a copper-riveted release properly executed by their baby's biologic parents. But they made just as serious a mistake when they let the baby's natural mother and her parents, the baby's grandfather and grandmother, know who had taken her child. It was no time at all before they were insisting on visiting him, taking him presents and interfering with the Carpenters' management of him. The result, and the endless complications involved, can only be imagined—no one but the Carpenters will ever know what they have gone through, and what the future will bring.

This would have been quite impossible in a professionally managed adoption. The welfare department sees to it that all records concerning the baby are sealed and deposited at the state capital. There they can never be seen except on court order, granted only to parties who have a right to see them—if anyone has. Parents who have renounced their parenthood have no such right.

None of these dangers attending adoption through unlicensed agencies apply to getting news of a baby to be adopted, through any means or sources that may present themselves. The doctor, the minister, relatives or acquaintances of unmarried mothers, even maternity homes or unlicensed adoption agencies, are often able to give information about where there is a baby in need of a home.

There is no earthly reason why couples who wish to adopt a baby should not avail themselves of any information, regardless of its source. This is especially true now that professional agencies are swamped with far more requests for adoption than they can fill. It should always be borne in mind, however, that agencies or persons offering babies for adoption at a price are by that very fact open to suspicion.

In any state, even those in which it is not required by law—and many states are deplorably backward in this respect—the actual adoption proceedings should be carried through by a professional agency, such as the city or county welfare department. For they are alert, as no nonprofessional agency can be, to all the mistakes that can be made. Here are some mistakes most likely to cause trouble:

Neglect to secure waiver of parental rights by the biologic parents.

Failure to keep the adoptive and the biologic parents' identity from each other. Unimportant as this point seems, its neglect almost always causes endless difficulty and unhappiness.

Incomplete study of the histories of both pairs of parents as well as of the child's whole background. This calls for laborious questioning that requires skill and experience few lay people possess.

Carelessness or ignorance about placing brilliant children with mediocre parents, or (quite as disastrous) the reverse. When cultured parents find that their adopted child cannot take a college education, or when a brilliant child grows up in a home with mentally limited parents, tragedy is likely to ensue.

"Matching" child and adoptive parents in intelligence, descent, religion and physical characteristics is a highly technical job.

Is all this long drawn-out business of carefully engineered adoption through proper channels too much to ask of prospective parents? People whose babies come to them via a more conventional route do not find their task any too easy. Ask any new parent!

No, there seems to be no way in which parents can safely sidestep the annoyances and delays incident to having a baby, no matter what way is selected. If it has to be adoption, it's wise to play the game and make it the safest way for all concerned, rather than what looks like the shortest and easiest. There is no royal road to parenthood—even to parenthood by adoption.

FRANK HOWARD RICHARDSON, M.D.

Home Problems of a Special Nature

THE ADOPTED CHILD

To take a child when he is a baby means that parents have a freer hand in his care and guidance, and the child does not have the insecurity that often comes from having had to adjust to a number of different homes. The younger a child is when he is adopted, the more years of sheer pleasure his parents have as they watch him develop.

But parents who adopt an infant or a very young child have a special obligation for the very reason that he does not remember any other home. That is, to make him familiar with the fact of his adoption as he grows, and so protect him from the shock of injury of learning it later from somewhere outside.

Why tell him at all? Because experience has shown that not doing so, instead of being a kindness, can lead to tragic results. Over and over again parents who have tried to keep from their child the fact that he was not their own have had the sharp sting of having the child learn it suddenly or even cruelly from outsiders. It is impossible to be sure that this won't happen if he is not informed of his adoption by his parents.

Such an experience is totally unnecessary. A child who gradually becomes aware of his special place in the family adjusts to it bit by bit, in keeping with his increased understanding of its meaning. At six, he is aware only of the superficial differences between being an own and an adopted child. He is content with a very simple explanation, provided his parents give it in a casual way, without becoming emotional.

A child who knows that he was a "chosen" baby, picked to fill an empty place, has a warm sense of being wanted in a very special way.

Adoptive parents stand in special need of reassurance. They sometimes feel that their friends and neighbors are looking at their child with critical eyes, and judging them accordingly. Actually, adoptive parents themselves are the ones who are most critical of their methods and the "results." Uncertain as to just what they may expect of their child, they sometimes watch him more closely than they would one born to them. Of course the behavior and abilities of an own child would be just as unpredictable, but it is hard for them to realize this.

It is not only useless, but dangerous, to worry about the material with which we work when we bring up an adopted child. Our job is to be sure that the influences with which we surround that child will bring out all the best that is in him. An adopted child will bring out a lot in his parents, too, that they didn't know was there. As he takes hold of his parents' emotions, he plays an important role in shaping their attitudes. They grow as much as the child they adopt does.

The tragedies that sometimes result when children are placed in homes that are either above or below their general mental ability can be avoided by very careful study, both of children and prospective homes, before placement. The importance of going to adoption agencies of high repute is obvious.

At the same time, adoptive parents, like any others, need to watch themselves to see that they are not too ambitious, or ambitious along wrong lines, for their children. The fear that many people who adopt children have that they will not "turn out right" sometimes leads to pressures and overanxiety that actually help to create problems. Adoptive parents should value highly, and strive to achieve, the relaxed fear-free attitudes that help to insure happy family life.

PROBLEMS OF THE STEPPARENT

What kind of problems do stepparents have that own parents don't? For one thing, they often have to compete with a memory about which a child has strong feelings. Even though he may not actually remember his own father or mother, he may have had the absent parent built up to heroic proportions, if no longer living, or heard him spoken of with contempt or hatred if there has been a divorce.

A stepmother, being more closely associated with the children, has to adapt in more ways, probably, than a stepfather. Too, she takes the place of the children's first and most intimate love objects. A woman is lucky if she takes on stepmotherhood while children are very young. In this case they have neither formed such long-time attachments for their own mother, nor have they—in case of her early removal—been under the care of a number of different people, as is often the case with older children.

The first thing a newcomer in a home needs to do is to prepare herself for liking the children. This doesn't mean that she should immediately begin to be demonstrative with them, or expect them to call her mother, for love is a matter of slow growth. Until a stepmother can really *care* about them, she must make up her mind to accept them. If she thinks of the children as "spoiled" or "naughty" or sees many disagreeable things about them she will probably have trouble. But if she thinks of them as victims of unfortunate circumstances, who look to her to make their situation happier, unpleasant behavior will not seem so bad.

If a child's own mother needs to understand what children are like, and how they differ from one another, such understanding is even more vital to a person coming in without knowledge of all that has gone before. Jack's smarty, pert manner, Jill's utter indifference to the looks of her room, the habit both children have of trying to dodge tasks and errands would be baffling to anyone. But how much more baffling they are to the new mother who has no idea how to arouse their interest and cooperation. This means she must take things very slowly. To rush in and expect the children to fall in love with her as their father has would be a bad move. In fact, their father's interest in her may be an extra hurdle. They may resent her at first because she takes away some of his attention.

Such a ticklish situation demands a period of watchful waiting. It means developing great insensitivity to things that would hurt her if she let them.

One stepmother made a very clever move by immediately arranging for her twelve-year-old stepdaughter to have a permanent wave, showing her sensitiveness to the little girl's despair over straight hair. Another sided with the boy (after discussing the matter privately with her husband) in his pleas that he was old enough to have a bicycle.

Own children place ability to cook high on the list of "important" things about a mother. Surely taking a little extra trouble to find out what children's favorite dishes are isn't too obvious an approach to lifting oneself in their esteem. Being helpful about a child's school work, sensitive to his hurts, and jubilant over his joys are short cuts to understanding.

Turning a blind eye to a child's shortcomings is something even own mothers could afford to do oftener. New mothers will find a useful technique with a child who has a chip on his shoulder is not to see the chip!

The new parent may need to bring about some changes of habits. Children may have poor eating habits, or a generally haphazard way of living. The new mother is almost bound to want to introduce her own ideas into the family living pattern. We can't expect change overnight. We often defeat our own ends by being impatient, by not realizing that it takes a long time, even under the best conditions, to substitute new ways for old ingrained habits. If Bobby has "gotten by" for years without eating cereal, or without hanging up his pajamas, we may have to go the long way 'round in getting him to change. (We may have to become acquainted with the radio characters who eat cereal to such good effect!)

As with own parents, things will have an enormously greater chance of going smoothly if the mother and father agree on the general guidance of the child. Seeing eye to eye on every issue is too much to expect; but if both parents have the same approach, and realize that they will need to meet on a common ground of compromise many times, they will be able to work things out.

DIVORCE—PROTECTING CHILDREN OF BROKEN HOMES

Even though parents may try to persuade themselves that divorce is not going to harm their children, they are shutting their eyes to the truth. To the best knowledge of some of our most experienced mental health specialists, divorce is always harmful to children. It may be more harmful, or less harmful, they say, but it always harms them. It hurts the parents, too. They are bound to grieve and be unhappy over not being able to provide the normal home life they expected to share with their children.

Parents who have after careful consideration come to the conclusion that a broken home will be less damaging than the conditions resulting from their trying to live together, are bent on finding ways of making children suffer as little as possible. What are some of the ways in which they can protect their children?

The parent who has custody over the children can try to see that the life lived by the children is as stable as possible. While we cannot say that security is any more necessary at one time than another in a child's life, the young child, who cannot grasp the reasons for sudden, upsetting changes, is in especial need of protection. He depends to a greater extent upon the physical security of the same walls, the same familiar faces and the same voices than the child who can express his questions and feelings, and to some degree understand what is told him.

Children need two parents. A father and mother each have something special to contribute, and there is no substitute for a home that has them both in it. But it has to be assumed when parents have decided upon separation that what each supplies the children involved may be more desirably given as an individual. The pulling and hauling that goes on while they are living together may be more disastrous than the broken home.

That children are more usually given over to the custody of the mother is in large part the result of the mother's traditional role as homemaker. The law is slow to recognize changing situations in our culture, one of which is the frequency with which mothers now spend as much time away from home, either at work or at play, as fathers do. In such instances, the care given by a mother may be no better either in quality or quantity than the care given by the father. With the increased understanding of the importance of the father-child relationship, the question may be asked as to whether a mother is any more important to a child than a father.

Because most of us are easily fooled into believing what we want to believe about ourselves, divorced parents should watch their attitudes toward the other parent. A woman may think she is being very careful not to infect her children with her feelings about her former husband and yet, in subtle ways, poison their minds against him. "No, you can't have a new coat this year. Your father hasn't sent enough money for me to buy you any decent clothes!" is the kind of insinuating remark that puts the blame on the father, though he may really be quite blameless.

The man who feels bitter toward his wife may unthinkingly show the children, when they are in his care, that he doesn't care a rap about their mother's ideas or practices. Or he may actually, and vindictively, encourage their acting counter to what he knows would be her wishes. Either parent, or both, may in their disillusionment, impart feelings of pessimism and gloom, and may, without being aware, set up distrust of the opposite sex.

While the relief that comes to a man and woman through divorce may be great, failure to have made a success of a venture of which great things were expected is often such a painful experience as to make many parents turn to their children for solace. This over-dependence on the children may not be very wholesome for either the children or the adults.

The very fact of divorce suggests that at least one parent, and possibly both, were unable to make the personality adjustments necessary to successful marriage. Young people need to understand more about the ingredients that must go into marriage to make it turn out right, such as the possession of common interests, attitudes, friendships, and associations, with emotional balance to leaven the whole relationship.

Knowledge of the personality factors that seem to be associated with happiness in marriage may help parents to try to surround their children with influences that encourage such qualities.

Some things turn up over and over again in the background of people who are happily married. They are lack of conflict with parents, and strong attachment to both mother and father; early discipline that was firm but not harsh, with mild and infrequent punishment; and parents' frankness about matters of sex. When these background factors, pointing to a happy childhood, are present in a child's life, they apparently strengthen his or her chances of being able to create a successful marriage partnership.

Teaching Your Child About Sex

THE child's total world and all its works begin with an interest in the functions of his arms and legs and eyes. His interest extends from these to all other matters outside his body. Probably, all of the very complex explanations of things in the material world take on meaning for him in the light of his observation and knowledge of the way his body works. And even the vocabularies used to designate body function are employed in his talk about—or to—these externals.

Unfortunately, the poorest and most inadequate type of education parents give is usually that which refers to body function in general, and particularly to the nature of the sexual organs and their role in reproduction. Therefore, first and foremost in importance in the education of the child in matters of bodily function and sex is the preparation or education of the mother (and the father, too) to the end that they themselves may become qualified teachers of these topics.

But this whole body of knowledge, as one generation transmits it to the next by word of mouth, is clouded with taboos and dogmatic "don'ts." It is surrounded with feelings of shame and notions of "dirtiness," and the parents themselves, in their attempt to educate their children, are many times the victims of their own inadequate training and their own distorted point of view. Thus, generation after generation, mothers and fathers have failed in this important and, we might say, central theme in the child's preparation for life.

The real aim of all education in sex—and we emphasize here the ultimate or final aim—is the necessity of eventually disclosing the method and features of sexual intercourse, of sexual union of male and female. The need someday to divulge this information looms in the backgrounds of all mothers' minds the very first time the child asks for information about the structure or use of his sexual organs, and because of the social restrictions and prohibitions regarding the sexual act at the time of maturity, mothers fear to talk about any aspect of it with their children.

Now the fact that the mother does have this eventual training in mind is not altogether undesirable. It is well for her to view the child's present questions in the light of the total information that she will have to give in due time. Such a viewpoint aids her in planning her instruction in an informal way. The difficulty arises, however, in her assumption that all—or even most—of the questions that her child will ask are a reaching out for information regarding the sex act itself.

HOW MOTHERS VIEW IT

The actual act of intercourse is that bit of information which is
needed least of all by the younger children. In their very early years
they are probably least interested in it; in truth, it is the last link
which has to be given the youngster to complete his knowledge.
The great majority of children of preschool age ask other questions
much more important to them before they inquire about the role
of the father in the actual creation of the baby. We are stressing here
the point that the mother is prone to *think* that such a question is
imminent or lurking in the background of the child's mind even in
connection with its earliest questions, and she becomes quite terri-
fied at the prospect of telling such a young child this bit of highly
emotionally toned knowledge.

The mother fears, of course, that the child will disgrace her by
divulging his knowledge in the neighborhood, by telling other children what he knows, hence bringing condemnation on the parent,
and that his playmates may be forbidden to associate with him.
Perhaps she is even afraid that her five- or six-year-old child will
attempt such behavior with young relatives or children in the
neighborhood. At any rate, this presumption by the mother may
definitely block or interfere with her sincere desire to give the child
information regarding sex. As will be pointed out as we go along,
it need not be seriously considered as the bit of information which
the child most desires. There is much more to be taught the child
before the mother is called upon to describe in any detail the act
of sexual intercourse.

A COMMON PROBLEM

An equally important hindrance to the mother's fulfillment of her
role as an educator in sex matters is her own background training—
she may too closely associate things sexual with elimination of
waste products from the body. It is actually an "accident," but nonetheless a very important physiological fact, that the two excretory
systems—the intestinal system and the urinary system—are anatomically closely related to the system (genital tract) which has to

do with intercourse and the birth of the young. Now the need for proper control of bowels and bladder is responsible for one of the earliest and most stringent set of prohibitions taught and impressed upon each individual; therefore it is not strange that the "dirtiness" thought of in connection with these functions, the prohibitions demanding "cleanliness" and even the "unspeakability" associated with them should be associated closely with the external portions of the genital tract, the penis and vagina.

This fact is significant not only because of its background importance in the mother's attempts to talk about sexual matters with her children, but also because the child being educated has already been imbued in his earlier months of life with a feeling of disgust for the "messiness" and "naughtiness" of all things having to do with those body structures. Consequently, the child should be made to see the distinction between the structures and functions of intestinal, urinary, and sexual organs. To this end, it is essential that the mother, if she is to assume the role of the teacher, must, as best she can, free herself from these age-old feelings of disgust based on this unfortunate association.

To be sure, all this is a very difficult feat for the mother to accomplish, because her associations are riveted so early in life, and they are strengthened by such powerful prohibitions that they almost take on the power of an inborn aversion to talking about such matters. However, in this introductory education of the mother as teacher, we wish to emphasize the fact that such feelings of disgust are not inborn, and hence they are subject to change in the mother. But, more important, because they are instinctive, the child himself will not "by nature" be imbued with any such unfortunate associated feelings; thus it is possible to prevent the child from ever having them if the mother's attitude toward this subject is entirely devoid of disgust or loathing.

HOW TO TELL YOUR CHILD ABOUT SEX

There are certain general rules or policies that can be followed by the mother in the sex education of the child and which can be applied to the solution of any questions related to it, regardless of their type or content. These general rules are explained in detail below.

Use Scientific Terms

Always use the correct scientific words to designate the anatomical areas of parts you are discussing with the child.

It is our experience that children—even very young children—can learn the correct words for the sex organs and parts of the gastro-intestinal and urinary systems, just as easily as they can learn any silly substitutes that parents may feel it necessary to tell them because they themselves have prohibitions against the use of the scientific terms.

Children should learn the proper anatomical vocabulary *from the beginning,* regardless of how they may temporarily stumble on a word. Giving a child the words penis, vagina, bowels, urethra, urine, feces, testicles, as well as a knowledge of their exact anatomical location, is the first and important step to all later discussions and all later teaching and learning about the functions of these parts. By using such words, the mother herself can be—or at least can feel herself to be—more objective in her discussions with the child, as such terms are freed to a large extent of the naughtiness that accompanied the "bad" words she herself picked up as a child from other children.

By following this rule, you will make it easier for the child to come to you with questions, because he will be able to use the correct terms and will not feel forced to resort to the obscene or dirty words that he has picked up from his playmates, words which he knows to be bad and naughty. Many times, the extension of the child's knowledge beyond even the most rudimentary (and perhaps distorted) knowledge has been blocked because the child is afraid to ask for information, since he lacks the terminology necessary to express his questions. He will not allow himself to come in from the playground to get a correct interpretation of some added bit of knowledge that perhaps does not agree with that which his mother has already told him, if he must shock his mother by "swear words" and risk a possible punishment at her hands.

Finally, an understanding of correct terms will serve as an adequate basis for helpful reading on the part of the child later on, when his sex education is to be completed. And if the mother herself is not acquainted with these terms, she should definitely make it a part of her own parental training to acquire this simple but nonetheless scientific vocabulary.

Avoid an Emotional Tone

Be as unemotional and matter-of-fact as you can in presenting sex information.

Many times it is not so important what you tell the child as *how* you tell the child. By this we mean that from the beginning the young mother should know that questions regarding the human body and the process of reproduction are going to be asked, and she must not assume an air of being shocked or the role of the stern puritan, but should as best she can become the giver of information and the teller of facts. As suggested above, sex education really begins with the proper type of education and the proper methods of training used in bowel and bladder control. If the mother has been objective and unemotional in these earlier "lessons," it will be much easier for her to be unemotional as regards the genital system and its function. So the popular phrase, "It isn't what you say but how you say it," is certainly applicable here.

Be Truthful

What you tell the child about sex should be the truth and nothing but the truth.

There are many parents who are unable to answer children's questions truthfully, and hence resort to some subterfuge in the form of childhood fantasies or fairy-tale expressions, not so much to help the child as to aid the parent to cover up her own embarrassment. These tales in themselves may not be harmful, but they do make it necessary for the child later to relearn the facts. One great "harm" which can come from this lack of truth in sex education, however, is that a child thus misinformed may feel that he cannot fully rely upon his parents to give him correct answers to any questions about his world.

Evasions in reply may do the child another significant harm—they may suggest to him for the first time that all matters having to do with the sexual organs are "bad" things, that they have something intrinsically naughty or evil about them. This in turn will tend to make the child even more reticent about coming to his parents for further information, and will throw him more and more upon the only other source of knowledge that he has in these matters, his acquaintances beyond the home.

THE HARD METHOD THE BEST. In the field of professional education, it is an accepted fact that learning the proper way to do something or the giving of the proper information *at the very beginning* is by far the most valuable method, even though it may be more difficult at first. When, for the sake of simplicity, untruths and incorrect methods are taught at the outset, these can be corrected later, but there is always a danger that the individual will revert to his previous improper information and cling to it, finding it difficult to completely supplant these untruths. This seems to be particularly true when we are dealing with such emotionally toned items as the contents of sex education. Children, despite repeated instructions to the contrary, will again and again revert to a faith in the myths taught them earlier.

The reasons why children insist so desperately on the truth of these incorrect teachings can, of course, be many and varied, but the association of the mother as the instructor and the added associations of 'badness" in the truth indicate some of the origins of this later (and needless) resistance to the truth. Thus it would seem an unnecessary and educationally expensive procedure to load the education of the child with stories of storks and fairies and heaven-sent brothers, sisters, cousins, etc. The "big blooming confusion" which William James used to say is the world of the very young child is certainly not clarified by such additional teachings in this more circumscribed area of sex education.

Don't Tell More Than You Need To

Even though the truth and only the truth should be told to children in answer to their questions, you do not have to give the child the whole truth about sex matters at any one time.

If you study the child's questions very carefully, inevitably you will see that they are aimed at a definite phase or aspect of sex— for example, anatomical differences or the place where babies were living before they were born—and not at the complete story of reproduction. Therefore, note very carefully first what the child is asking you, and particularly the limitations set by the question, in order that you will not go beyond them in your answers.

DON'T CONFUSE THE CHILD.   If you extend your answers beyond the interest that the child has at the moment, he will undoubtedly fail to have his own question answered or will think that it is unanswered, or he will not understand the added material which you have felt it necessary to give him.

There are certain very definite steps and phases in the child's understanding of the growth of the body or the change of the seasons, or the occurrence of certain holidays, or the father's or mother's daily routine of work and recreation. Of all these things, though repeated day after day after day, he takes unto himself but certain aspects of each routine; gradually, as he matures, he works them into relationships in time, and relationships with all the other events going on about him. With sex education, too, the child does not grasp the total meaning of all bits of related information at any one time—to try to give him the whole story of sex would be as fruitless and unsuccessful as to attempt to give him the total story of growth, of holidays, or the complex reasons for Daddy's being at the office day after day.

You will remember that the ultimate end of sex education is felt to be the story of sexual intercourse and reproduction. The mother, believing that this is in the child's mind, may attempt to give him too much long before he is ready for it. This should be avoided. Above all, it's a safe assumption that the first question the child asks about sex is but a tiny fragment arising from some observation of the moment or from some need, or, possibly, *anxiety*, aroused by some observation of the moment and the primary object of your education at that moment is to allay the anxiety, to eliminate the fear, and to satisfy the curiosity that may surround the particular item.

His Friends Teach Him Too

It must not be assumed that the child is going to go through the primary and grammar school grades (or even his preschool years) without finding some answers to his questions in the conversations of his schoolmates and friends.

Not only will the child pick up information about sex outside the home, but we should not feel that it is altogether bad that he does so, or that everything he picks up will necessarily be evil or untrue. Children a year or so older than one's own will tend to educate the younger ones in such matters, and may even satisfy their own curiosity and the curiosity of the child trainee by exhibiting themselves or investigating the sex organs of younger children. Should such demonstrations take place, the mother must not immediately assume that either the words or the deeds are motivated by sexual impulses in the adult sense, or that they are going to lead to an overemphasis on or overinterest in sex in the child so exposed, or whose curiosity is so early satisfied in part.

It is noted by all workers in child guidance that when a child learns about sex outside the home, his previous training and relationships to his mother will be of such a nature that he will immediately bring home anything alarming, upsetting, or threatening, for proper evaluation by the understanding parent. It is at such times that the previously assumed unemotional attitudes regarding anatomy and physiology of the body, and the previously taught, accurately descriptive words will stand the parent and the child in good stead. The words which the child brings home and the descriptions which are elaborated for him by his companions can then be modified and tempered aand rephrased in the more "polite" and the more accurate information and terms that the parent is able to give him. And even though the child perhaps does have his curiosity first stimulated by association with other children, this does not have to be thoroughly bad if the stage has been properly set for the handling of such information.

WHY THE MOTHER NEED NOT FEAR.   It is not unusual for shy or reticent or lonely, isolated or only children to be totally unsophisticated in such matters until their attention is turned to them by their youthful friends—and part of the educational value of the social process of one child with another resides in just this area of need for knowledge. This situation is also present in the family where all children are of the same sex. As to the fear that the information which the mother has already given the child at home will be spread throughout the neighborhood and thus bring condemnation of the neighbors upon her—the mother need have little fear if she has given truthful explanations in the proper scientific manner. In fact, in some respects many parents are known to have been very much relieved that other people's children have taken upon themselves the burden of educating their children in these matters, a task which they themselves deliberately shunned or sidestepped with evasive answers.

Avoid "Birds and Bees" Approach

Do not use the sex life of animals and plants as a means of conveying information regarding human anatomy and physiology to the young child.

The use of animals and "birds and bees" is probably not nearly so valuable in giving information to children as was once supposed, and very likely is but a carryover of our reticence and feelings of shame regarding these matters. To be sure, such material may be valuable as *supplements* for the child to *read* in the years immediately preceding puberty, but we should not at all favor it as the primary information with younger children. The great anatomical differences and the differences in physiology of sex and birth are such that they can lead the child to as many false conclusions as they can to right ones, or even more. In other words, the material just does not lend itself to the formulation of an adequate and consistent educational technic in these matters.

Not only do the differences in anatomy, length of pregnancy, and methods of birth through eggs within and without the body lead to confusion on the part of the child, but such answers or such examples do not really answer the child's question. It is about human beings that the child wishes to talk, and it is concerning himself and other human beings that he wishes his information—such deviations will rarely meet his demands. As associated learning, it is interesting and important, but as sex information it is merely a substitute of no particular significance to the child. If children are old enough to understand animal reproduction, they are old enough to understand reproduction in human beings. Of course, if the child asks questions regarding the birth and development of certain species of animals or birds, one should answer the questions as fully as possible, but as a method of imparting information concerning humans the "birds and bees" approach is unreliable.

INSTILLING THE VALUES OF MARRIAGE. The use of facts from the sexual life of lower animals has yet another drawback, and a very serious one—it tends to destroy many of those cultural and social values in marriage that you hope to instill as you go along in the child's education. For instance, even though you do stress the fact that there are always a mother cow and a father cow or a mother bird and a father bird, you are definitely hard put to it to satisfy the child's curiosity or feelings of insecurity that may arise from the observation that the "father cow" and the "father bird" are rarely if ever present to take care of the immature young.

Following the Rules

The general rules or policies outlined for the mother to follow in answering sex questions her children may ask her are obviously not to be followed religiously. Individual children will demand deviations from these answer policies, and we emphasize again the general nature of them.

Two Types of Sex Questions

Of the most specific types of questions asked by children, there are two definite groups which must be answered by the mother, and it is very important for her to determine as best she can into which category each question falls. We refer to the fact that most children's questions regarding "sex" are either (1) questions aimed to educate them in the field of human *anatomy,* or (2) questions aimed at satisfying their curiosity regarding sexual *function*—sexual practices as they relate to the creation of a "new baby." It will be noted that the object and aim of the questions are quite different in these two instances, and it is very necessary that the mother answer *only in relation to the advice or information desired.* Much of the confusion, much of the poor learning, and much of the relearning that we find it necessary to do in early adolescence, it seems, comes about because of a misunderstanding (plus confusion) of information relative to these two factors.

Child's Age and Sex Questions

If one evaluates the many questions asked by the children, one discovers there is an age difference in relation to the type of questions asked. For example, the first questions of the young child—say at the ages of three, four, five up to nine or ten—will be those that have to do with the differences in sex and the anatomy of the genitourinary system in each sex.

On the other hand, from the age of ten or eleven on, the questions concerning anatomy will be somewhat modified or even completely replaced by questions regarding the operation or function of these organs, with the desire for complete information regarding the sexual act coming more and more to the fore. We do not by any means wish to maintain that there is an absolute age difference in the type of question asked, for it not unusual, of course, for children of four or five or even younger to have received some inkling, either by direct observation or through conversation, that such an act as sexual intercourse takes place between male and female; moreover, it is not uncommon for considerable anxiety to be aroused by such partial or incomplete observations or information. If the mother suspects this to be the case, she should provide the child with at least enough education to allay his fear that something cruel, sadistic or bad has taken place between the parents. With young children, however, it is safer to confine one's attention to remarks regarding anatomy.

In considering the standard questions in the two areas of sex anatomy and function, we shall point out the modifications in answers that are desirable for boys as opposed to girls. Also, we shall point out in what respect the mother should anticipate the parallel misinformation or even frightening information that the child at that particular age may be getting from others within the family group or outside in the playground.

DIFFERENCES BETWEEN THE SEXES

The Little Girl's Question

The first question usually asked by girls in the preschool or kindergarten years is "Why do I not have a penis like John or like Brother?" The reason for this question is probably direct observation of the sexual organs of boy members of the family or boys outside the home who expose themselves deliberately or unwittingly and—less usual, perhaps—hearing conversation regarding these differences. The answer to such a question is, of course, "Because you are a girl, and girls do not have them," but this is unsatisfying unless it is followed by definite emphasis on the fact that there are two sexes in the world, boys and girls, men and women, differences which the child herself probably has already noted.

However, this should not be considered *enough* of an explanation to satisfy the girl. Two other points should be made to allay probable anxieties already existing, or to prevent possible anxieties that may arise later. First, it is necessary to emphasize with the girl that this is a completely "normal" state of affairs, and particularly that she, being a girl, *never did* have a penis; that is, the situation is not that she once had a penis like Brother or her male playmate and lost it, or was deprived of it in some way. This secondary answer is aimed at the elimination of the notion that the girl, because she has no penis, is a partially finished or unfinished individual, and hence in some way less complete than the boy. Possible feelings of inferiority thereby may arise within the girl because of a sense of anatomical inadequacy, and these should not be allowed to take root in her thinking.

As a further attempt to eliminate this feeling, the girl should be told that not only did she never have a penis, because she is a girl, but that she also never will grow one and cannot expect one to appear—again, because she is a girl. Every precaution should be taken to reassure the child that she has sustained no loss, and that her prestige as an individual is by no means lessened due to this difference in bodily make-up.

The Little Boy's Question

The boy's question regarding observable external differences in sexual apparatus is usually framed in the same fashion with the question, "Why does not my sister have a penis?" This is a more usual question than the boy's asking, "Why do I have a penis?" because he has already assumed that everyone else is anatomically similar to himself. It is only after his observation of some girl in the house or play yard that he comes to the mother with questions regarding these differences. Here again the answer is aimed at establishing firmly in the child's mind the fact of an existing and permanent difference in the two sexes, and the answer, "Because she is a girl," is followed by the emphasis on universal sex difference already indicated.

But here again this information is not complete enough to allay possible present fears or to prevent the occurrence later of anxieties regarding the penis. As in the case of the girl who first wonders about these sex differences, it is the associated information given by the mother that is probably far more important than the actual matter-of-fact answer regarding sex differences. For example, you will note that the boy first perceived that certain individuals, namely girls, do not have a penis. This observation can in itself be a very frightening or even terrifying thing, because the boy, assuming that everyone is constructed alike, now adds to this the logical conclusion that the girl once had a penis and lost it, and that he himself may be in danger of such a loss.

Preventing Future Anxiety

The mental processes of the young boy of the preschool, kindergarten, and primary school, which are here outlined, are not merely conjectures on the part of psychiatrists and psychoanalysts, but are the daily bases of anxieties presented to the trained worker as he attempts to help boys and girls brought to him because of their fears, anxieties, and worries. Also, the bases of many neuroticisms in later life are found, upon an intensive analysis of the patients, to reside in just such early anxieties of their childhood as we are now emphasizing. Hence, in the interests of preventive mental hygiene, it is necessary for the mother at this very early age to stress, first, that girls never have had a penis and subsequently lost it through any injury or illness, but that they never had one because of the very fact that they are girls, and girls *are from the beginning* made differently. Secondly, it is equally as important to emphasize with the boy that he will never lose his penis and nothing will harm it, and that his actions or thoughts will not lead to any disease or injury of this part.

This expansion of the mother's answer to this question is a very simple, but nevertheless very important bit of associated reassuring information that should be given to the boy at the instance of his very first questions. It is needed also as an antidote to present or later fears that may be inspired by misguided family members or by boys beyond the home in relation to activities of a sexual nature. Specifically, he may be frightened by the myth that resorting to or indulging in pleasurable sensations from this organ (masturbatory activities) then or later in childhood will result in permanent injury to the part or in an illness.

The Castration Anxiety

All of these fears and worries are included under the psychiatrist's or the psychoanalyst's phrase of "castration anxiety"; though this has actually little or nothing to do with castration in a technical sense, it does refer to the great fears of injury to or loss of the penis that present themselves at various times to the minds of preadolescent boys. In turn such fears can be generalized in this "complex" to include or to become a prototype for all other physical injuries to parts of the body, actual or imagined. This being the case, it is not necessary to emphasize how very important is the mother's role in the prevention of future emotional upsets or deviations through her adequate answers to these anatomical questions and by her correct *assumption* that fears of injury or loss may be in the background of the boy's mind.

It should be noted also that the mother will be again and again confronted by this question regarding the presence of the penis in the boy and the absence of the penis in the girl by both the boys and girls in her family, and each time the same sort of reassurance regarding fundamental anatomic sex differences *existing from the beginning,* plus the total absence of any injury or disease having resulted (or being possible as a future event), will have to be patiently reemphasized.

Questions about the Breasts

An anatomical question of perhaps lesser importance, but always asked by both sexes, concerns the presence or absence of breasts. Here again is an opportunity to stress fundamental sex differences and to point out to the girl that she will eventually have breasts like her mother's, and to emphasize with the boy that this is an anatomical variation that he will not have. This question, as contrasted with the previous anatomical questions, is usually couched in terms of function—that is, "What are they for?"—and their use in the feeding of the new-born baby should be adequately explained to both.

This reply usually leads to another question, such as "Did I get milk from the breast, too?" With the answer "yes," the child's curiosity regarding the breasts is taken care of.

Girls approaching puberty (ages nine to eleven) often feel considerable anxiety in the case of non-appearance of, or the lack of growth of, the breasts, taking this as an indication that they are not going to grow up to be women or that, if they do, they will never be able to have babies. With the proper background information, these transitory fears can be adequately handled by the mother. In this situation the girl should be reassured that, although she is eleven or perhaps twelve years of age, she has not yet reached that period of a year or a year and a half when maximum growth and change from childhood to adolescence takes place; that when she reaches that rapid-growth stage, the development of the breasts will take place in the course of a few months, and she therefore can definitely look forward to being like other girls in this respect.

THE ORIGINS OF LIFE

"Where Do Babies Come From?"

The second important group of questions asked by children from six years onward are those having to do with the origins of life. Specifically, the questions are usually, "Where do babies come from?" or "Where did I come from?" or "Where was I before I was here?" In line with the general principles for presenting explanations outlined above, the answer most usually given by mothers is, "You were inside mother's stomach." This reply, as will be seen in a moment, should be, "You were inside of mother," without particular reference to "stomach," but should later be elaborated to include the fact that the child grew in a special place inside the mother which was there for that single purpose. It is necessary also at this point to emphasize again the differences in the sexes, in order that the child will know that the girl has a uterus and that the boy does not, and also to add the technical term "uterus," which will be used for the first time.

"How Did I Get There?"

The question, "How did I get there?" or "How did I grow there?" will be answered with an explanation of the origin of the child from an egg, the fact that the mother has these eggs, and from time to time they become ready to grow into a baby inside the mother. This in turn, of course, leads to the giving of information regarding the gland (ovary) that holds these eggs until they are ready to go into the uterus to grow into a baby.

Any mother can attest that all of these questions will probably not be asked at one and the same sitting, but the chain of questions started by the principal or primary one—"Where do babies come from?"—will be somewhat after the order followed above. The young child will be content with a mere factual and even matter-of-fact answer to the sex question. In the process of absorbing this information, other questions will be formulated in the child's mind.

"How Does the Baby Get Out?"

It is very rare that the child will accept the answer of growth in the uterus without following it immediately with the question, "How does the baby get *out* of the mother's body?" The necessary answer, of course, is that the baby, when old enough to live in the outside world, comes out of the mother's body by a special opening which the mother has for this purpose. If the previous education of the child in anatomy has been adequate to give information regarding the birth canal—the opening of the uterus into the vagina which allows the baby to come out—it will not be too difficult for the child to grasp.

Preventing Harmful Ideas

Now, as emphasized many times previously, it usually is not this factual knowledge itself that is difficult for the child to understand, nor does it in itself create many problems. The "problems"—that is, the anxieties and worries, if they arise—may come from incomplete understanding or misunderstandings which the child harbors in association (seemingly remote) with the whole process. For example, it is extremely important with both boys and girls —but it is especially important in the case of girls—to stress again and again at the time these questions are asked, and frequently thereafter, the exact distinction between the intestinal tract, the urinary tract, and the genital tract. Otherwise, children, when told that the baby grows for a period of nine months "inside the mother's stomach," frequently assume at once that the child is growing somewhere within the *intestinal* tract. Such a notion leads to fantastic and even disgusting associations of the close relationship of the baby within the mother and the contents of the intestinal tract (feces) .

This whole mistaken impression, in turn, may be so strengthened by the mother's statement that the baby is fed from the "mother's food," that the child immediately assumes that the food eaten by the mother is in part, or later, eaten by the baby. Finally, on the basis of all these impressions, the child herself finds the answer to the question of how a baby "starts" in the notion that the mother eats something and therefore becomes pregnant.

Anxieties That May Arise

Now it is not merely that these ideas are untrue that we call them to the attention of the mother, with the hope that she by proper education will avoid them. The fact of the matter is that not only are they untrue, but they very inevitably and very soon become the bases of severe anxieties and fears on the part of the child. Such fears have to do with fear or disgust at eating, fears and worries regarding bowel movements, worries and resistance concerning a child's own role as a mother, and obsessive thoughts in relation to cleanliness and training routines. It is wise for the mother to *assume* that children will tend to confuse the intestinal tract in all its dirtiness with the genital tract, regardless of how careful she may be at the outset to point out the distinction between them. Knowing this, every mother should proceed to make the anatomical distinctions as clear and as emphatic as possible. This is particularly essential with young girls.

FEAR OF PAIN OF CHILDBIRTH. There are other anxieties and worries that may need to be allayed. The first is fear of the pain and injury which are associated with the birth of the baby. These must be minimized. More specifically, the mother should be careful to point out that the mother is not operated on, or her stomach opened up by the doctor and the baby taken out; she should emphasize the normal readiness of the genital tract to open large enough to allow the baby to come out when it is old enough to live outside.

THE DOCTOR. The mother may explain to the child the usual presence of the doctor at the birth of babies or the mother's stay in the hospital by stating that certain medicine can be given under the doctor's direction to aid in the easy birth of the baby; furthermore, that although no operation is performed on the mother, she is usually tired after childbirth and needs a rest from the usual routine of the home.

The fact may also be emphasized that although babies can very easily be born at home, and can be born without a doctor, it is best that one be present either in the home or at the hospital, lest the baby's size or lack of strength not permit it to come out into the world easily. In whatever is explained in this area, it is vital that notions of injury, trauma, and operations be minimized.

"Is a Baby Growing in Me Now?"

Either in answer to direct questions or through anticipation, the mother should carefully explain to the girl child, in the course of supplying this information, that babies are not "growing in 'her' now." The power to have them later is naturally dwelt upon, but with it the children are assured of the need to grow up before they are able to actually *form* babies. Inasmuch as children are always comparing themselves in some way with older children, it usually suffices to say to the girl, "You have to be at least as big as a high school girl before the eggs are able to grow into babies." At this point, one should explain about a girl's being married and having a home of her own in which to take care of the babies.

"Do I Have to Be Married to Have Babies?"

It goes without saying that all girl children will ask sooner or later, "Do I have to be married to have babies?" and to this the truthful answer should be, "No, you don't *have* to be, but it is best in order that the child may have both a mother and a father to help bring him up."

Questions about the Father's Role

At some time, usually late in the series of questions which the child asks, there will be questions pointed directly at the role of the father; in reply, the facts of sexual intercourse for the purpose of fertilizing the egg within the uterus should be presented. Again the mother should see to it that she gives the child the truth in the matter, couching it in medically acceptable terms, such as "sperm," "fertilization," "insertion of the penis," etc. Fortunately, these specific questions usually follow those already outlined, and if previously stated questions are answered correctly, the child probably will have little difficulty in accepting these later facts given to him by a person whose education he by this time trusts.

RESISTING THE MOTHER'S INFORMATION. The mother should not be alarmed, however, at what may seem to be unnecessary resistances on the part of the boy or girl to the acceptance of such information. "Extra" information of a not too "scientific" and probably not too "clean" nature has probably already been given to the child by his companions; moreover, it is not unusual for children to cling desperately to the non-sexual nature of impregnation and growth of babies, occasionally reverting to hopeful belief in the story of the stork or other non-personal agencies. Thus it is generally necessary to repeat the information regarding the role of the father and to take care to emphasize the lack of evil or sinfulness surrounding this act. The relation of this to the founding of a home, and hence the making possible all of the joys and values of home life for children and adults, can very easily be stressed in association with the plainer and more startling facts of anatomy and physiology—though the latter should never be used in order to avoid one's own confusion, lest this lead to confusion in the mind of the child.

SHOULD SOMEONE ELSE TELL THE CHILD?

Finally, you may wonder, "Is it better for the mother and father to give this information to the child, or should he be referred to some other interested family member or to the family physician?"

It seems to us that the main bulk of sex education will continue to be given by the mother, and only secondarily by the father. This will continue to be true because, on the whole, the most important questions, or at least the important basic questions, will be asked of the mother when the child is very young, and presumably in settings where the mother, and not the father, is taking care of him. Questions need to be answered when they are asked —if you refuse to answer or refer the child to his father or to anyone else, he feels this to be an artificial, unsatisfactory, and even threatening response. If a question is put to another member of the family, it ought to be referred to the mother.

OTHER HELPS IN SEX EDUCATION

Questions in adolescence, or further information or reassurance regarding problems concerning menstruation or masturbation, can perhaps be best and most objectively supplied by the family physician—though here again the secure child will probably be able to get adequate information from one or the other of the parents. In relation to books for children in this area, it is often best that they be used as supplementary material; they can hardly begin to take the place of the parent, and particularly the mother, as a purveyor of these important facts. To educate the child in matters of sex and all other functions of its body is not only a duty of the mother—it is a marvelous opportunity to cement a worthwhile and lasting relationship of confidence between her and her children in all matters.

THE MOTHER'S APPROACH

We have attempted to outline some of the particular and specialized questions that children will ask their mothers regarding sex, and have mentioned some of the ways in which the mother can meet these questions. No one, of course, can anticipate what the questions of the *individual* child in a particular family will be, nor can one outline with any degree of exactness the order in the series of questions which we have mentioned above. We have endeavored particularly to show here some of the dangers of a lack of information or of misinformation in regard to some of the basic facts about sex. Always the approach used by the mothers should be the "hygienic approach"—an approach that, insofar as possible, will prevent the creation of anxiety, fear or shame in her children regarding the expression of this fundamental instinctive drive.

GEORGE E. GARDNER, M.D., PH.D.

Diseases of Childhood

INFLAMMATION OF THE BREASTS IN THE NEWBORN

SYMPTOMS. This condition is not uncommon. The breasts of either girl or boy babies become swollen and tender, and a few drops of thin milk may exude from them. Ordinarily, the child's temperature is not above normal, nor is the appetite disturbed, and the condition subsides without causing any trouble.

TREATMENT. The breasts should be gently yet thoroughly, washed with soap and warm water, and then covered with a few layers of cheesecloth, which has been wet in a warm solution of boric acid (a teaspoonful in half a pint of water). Then cover with oil silk and a flannel band about the chest, with shoulder straps to keep it in place. A fresh, wet application should be applied each day.

ABSCESS OF THE BREAST. Rarely, abscess of the breast results, with increasing inflammation and redness, formation of "matter" (pus) and fever, loss of appetite, and general disturbance. Such a case, of course, must be referred to the surgeon at the earliest moment for incision.

RETENTION AND PAINFUL PASSAGE OF URINE

WHEN THE CHILD DOES NOT PASS URINE. The baby may pass no urine for twenty-four hours after it is born, and yet there may be no cause for worry. If no urine is passed in the first twelve hours, it is well to put the baby in a warm bath. If this does not lead to a passage of urine a physician should be consulted, as there may be some deformity or obstruction.

After a bad attack of colic in some instances, no urine is passed for many hours, but this condition may be relieved by the warm bath.

PAINFUL URINATION. Pain during the passage of urine may be observed when the urine is too concentrated and stains the diaper with a reddish or yellowish substance. Giving the baby an abundance of water to drink will relieve this condition.

BOWEL DEFORMITY. Very rarely there is no opening for escape of excrement from the bowels. A surgeon must be summoned at once to remedy this condition.

SMALL OPENING IN THE FORESKIN

SYMPTOMS. This is seen in the newborn boy baby as a natural condition. The opening is not only small as a pinhole, but the foreskin cannot be drawn back so as to expose the head of the penis.

This state changes naturally as the child grows. However, if it does not, and if the foreskin remains attached to the parts beneath so that it cannot be moved freely over the penis, and if the opening for the passage of urine is very small, several complications are apt to follow.

COMPLICATIONS. The end of the penis is likely to become sore, red, and swollen, and the passage of urine painful. Some discharge may occur. The irritation leads to rubbing of the parts, and the habit of masturbation often begins in this way. Bed-wetting is a common consequence of the irritation. Prolapse (falling down) of the bowel, or rupture, may be caused by straining to pass water. Various nervous disorders may owe their beginning to a tight foreskin.

TREATMENT. This consists of circumcision. The operation is done by a surgeon. Parents should consult a physician when there is any suggestion of trouble such as has been described.

BLEEDING OF THE CORD AND SORENESS
OF THE NAVEL IN THE NEWBORN

TREATMENT OF BLEEDING. Bleeding of the cord occurring soon after birth must be stopped immediately by tying a soft string tightly about it as far from the belly as the string will hold without slipping off. Slight oozing after the cord has dropped off is usually of no consequence. Sometimes the cord becomes soft and offensive, and when it comes away leaves a large sore behind it. There may be a little pea-shapd swelling in the sore which discharges "matter."

TREATMENT OF SORE. In the absence of a physician, the sore should be washed three times daily with boric-acid solution (one teaspoonful to half a pint of warm water) and clean absorbent cotton. Then dust it with dry boric acid or aristol powder, and cover it with clean gauze or soft cotton. With such treatment it usually heals. ·

PROLAPSE (FALLING DOWN) OF THE BOWEL

CAUSES. This condition is brought about by great or constant straining caused by diarrhea, constipation, a narrow foreskin with difficult urination, worms, whooping cough, overeating that results in too frequent large movements of the bowels, etc.

SYMPTOMS. There is to be seen a protrusion of the bowel, from one-half inch to several inches long. Ordinarily it presents the appearance of a dark-red or purplish, puckered ring at the point of opening of the bowel. It goes back or can be pushed back into place. It reappears, however, whenever there is much straining, as during a passage from the bowels.

There is usually little pain associated with the prolapse, unless it is large, when—if it remains out for a considerable time—it becomes very painful and inflamed, and may ultimately cause the death of the patient.

TREATMENT. Treatment consists in removing the causes, if possible. Keeping the feces soft, prevention of constipation, avoidance of straining, and discouraging the spending of too much time on the toilet are the best curative measures.

EMERGENCY TREATMENT. The first thing to do is to place the child flat on his face, cleanse the protrusion with warm water, grease it with vaseline, and gently push it back. The injection of a little ice water into the bowel (a cupful three times daily) will have a most beneficial effect.

To prevent a return of the trouble, the child should be required to have a movement while lying on its back on a diaper. A baby must not be allowed to sit on a vessel more than five minutes at a time; there is no more pernicious habit for causing prolapse of the bowels than long sessions of this kind. An operation is necessary to cure chronic or large protrusions of the bowel.

WASTING (MARASMUS)

CAUSES. Wasting is an extreme state of malnutrition. It may arise from incomplete starvation, protracted malnutrition, persistent intestinal indigestion, and repeated attacks of inflammation of the bowel.

SYMPTOMS. The body is extremely wasted, and the infant appears aged. The face shows wrinkles, the features are drawn, eyes sunken, temples hollow, and cheeks flat. The skin is dry and inelastic, and hangs in wrinkles and folds over the bones. The joints are prominent. The abdomen may be flat or distended. The temperature is subnormal, and the cry and activity of the infant are extremely weak.

TREATMENT. Human milk should be secured and given in increased quantities. The processed milks (fermented milk, powdered half-skimmed milk, evaporated milk) should be used when human milk cannot be obtained. Vitamins A and B are helpful.

FEVER

SOME GENERAL FACTS. Fever is only a symptom of many diseases, but until the cause is known the same general treatment may be pursued in all instances. The first thing to do is to take the temperature with a thermometer. This is the only way to be sure of either the presence or degree of fever; no other signs are certain. For an infant, a temperature of less than 101°F. might be called a slight fever; between that point and 103°, a moderate fever; over 103°, a considerable fever; and over 104°, high fever. High fevers are much more common in children, and are not of as serious import as in adults, unless they are continued. A temperature of 100° or over always means some sort of a physical disorder; no single test is as reliable in determining whether a child is sick or not as taking the temperature.

Fevers lasting for a few days are not as harmful as commonly believed, unless the temperature is high. Fever is nature's method of combatting the cause, in most conditions, and moderate fever, unless it continues for many days, need not cause anxiety, as far as the increased temperature itself is concerned. High fever—especially in children—should be reduced, since headache, delirium, and, in infants, convulsions are common. A child with fever should be immediately isolated in a room by himself, and other children should be kept away until it is known that the disease is not contagious. The eruptive diseases of childhood, tonsillitis, grippe, and diphtheria are often first brought to attention through fever.

TREATMENT. When fever is high, cold applications should be kept on the head. This is best done by applying a rubber cap containing cracked ice. If this cannot be obtained, a single thickness of soft cotton wrung out of ice water should be placed on the forehead and frequently moistened with ice water as it evaporates. The cloth or ice cap ought to be applied as long as the fever remains high. In addition, the entire surface of the body may be sponged with tepid water.

It is not necessary to reduce the temperature below 102°, in most instances. The application of a cold pack, under your physician's direction, when there is fever with restlessness and sleeplessness, is frequently useful in place of sponging.

DIET AND GENERAL CARE. In most fevers the diet must be liquid. Infants on milk should have the mixture diluted a third to a half with water. Milk, broths, albumin water, and thin cereals generally make up the best diet. An abundance of cool water may be allowed in fevers, but the rule is to give a little at a time, and frequently.

Rest in bed is imperative. Moving the bowels is also a good practice; milk of magnesia or a cleansing enema is often advisable. If vomiting is present, avoid giving any food for twelve to twenty-four hours. Never give a laxative without consulting a physician if there is vomiting and/or the child complains of abdominal pain.

INFLAMMATION OF THE GLANDS

CAUSES. Glands are a natural part of the structure of the body. They are, however, not usually noticeable unless they become enlarged through inflammation. This inflammation is simply an extension of an infection from other parts of the body, since glands are a part of a system of vessels (lymphatic system) which drain the tissues all over the body, and empty finally into the general blood stream. The glands may be regarded as acting like traps in a drainage system, to catch the germs, or poisons which the germs produce, and so protect the whole body from invasion, although the glands may themselves become invaded. Germs gain entrance to glands through wounds, sores, abrasions, and inflammation in various parts of the body.

Enlarged glands are commoner in the neck than elsewhere, because inflammation about the throat and mouth is so frequent. Enlarged glands are seen and felt as movable lumps under the skin. They may be more or less tender. In the neck they may be found below or behind the jaw, along the sides, and below the scalp at the back of the neck. Enlarged glands in the armpits arise from extension of inflammation in the hands, arms, or chest; enlarged glands in the groins, where the upper and inner part of the thighs join the body, occur from inflammation in any part of the foot or leg or external sexual organs.

In the neck, enlarged glands at the angle of the jaw and upper part of the sides of the neck are caused by inflammation of the tonsils, by sore mouth and tongue (enlarged glands beneath the jaw), by abscess of the ear (enlarged glands below and behind the ear), or by eczema or lice of the scalp (enlarged glands at the back of the neck). Sore throat from any cause, particularly tonsillitis and the type common to many of the germ diseases, including measles,

German measles, scarlatina, diphtheria; adenoids; decayed and loose teeth; cracked lips; and sore tongue and mouth—these are frequent origins of enlarged glands of the neck.

The enlargement of these glands is brought down by treating the underlying cause.

Tuberculous Glands

CAUSES. Enlarged glands of the neck are more often seen in children under ten, and the most serious and important form is that caused by the entrance of the germ of consumption or tuberculosis. This germ may enter the healthy gland. More often it attacks the gland already enlarged and inflamed from the causes enumerated above. The gland attacked by the germ of tuberculosis is called a tuberculous or scrofulous gland, or the disease is spoken of as scrofula—an antiquated term.

SYMPTOMS. Tuberculous glands develop very slowly; one or more lumps appear in the neck; they are not very tender, but persist and tend to increase gradually in size and number. Finally, after weeks or months, they often become red and sore, soften, and form abscesses. The enlarged glands which are not tuberculous usually vanish spontaneously after a time. These are exceedingly common in children, and differ from the tuberculous glands in that they arise suddenly—usually after a sore throat—and although they may be quite tender at first they rarely go on to abscess, but slowly disappear. If they do form abscesses, they do so in a short time after their appearance. But tuberculous glands, after persisting for a long time, may likewise disappear without further trouble.

TREATMENT. As in other forms of tuberculosis, dietetic and hygiene measures should receive first consideration. Enforced rest is necessary during the most severe period of the infection. Ultraviolet rays, applied generally and locally, are extremely effective. During the summer, sunlight treatment can be used. Certain drugs, like streptomycin, given under the directions of a physician, are valuable curative agents. (See Tuberculosis, page 866.)

RICKETS

CAUSES. Rickets is a nutritional disorder of infancy marked by insufficient amounts of calcium phosphate in the bones. The disease causes softening of the bones, which consequently bend easily and produce deformities of the head, neck, chest, and legs. The abdomen is enlarged. The milk teeth are late in coming through the gums.

Rickets is a preventable disease. It is common especially among the poor. It usually occurs in infants from three months to three years old. Almost invariably it begins during the winter and early spring months. Premature infants are more liable to have rickets than full-term infants. If unchecked, the disease results in severe anemia.

SYMPTOMS. The disease begins with restlessness at night on the part of the child, profuse sweating of the head and neck, and increased skin pallor. The muscles become flabby. Soft spots appear in the bones of the skull. There is also swelling of the joints, beading of the ribs, enlargement of certain finger joints and evidence of acquired deformity. (Beading consists of a row of nodules, or knoblike structures, which are found at the junctions of the ribs with their cartilages.) Constipation is common.

PREVENTION. Inadequate diet is the chief factor in the production of rickets. The essential dietary factor is vitamin D. This vitamin occurs in milk, cream, butter, egg yolk, and some animal fats. In the strongest concentration, it is found in the oil extracted from the liver of certain fishes (cod-liver oil, halibut-liver oil, salmon-liver oil, etc.). Vitamin D is also manufactured, and in that form is known as viosterol. Cod-liver oil or viosterol, or a combination of these, should be given from the time the infant is two weeks old, and continued through the years of childhood.

Sunlight is a protection against rickets. (Ordinary window glass interferes with the passage of ultra-violet rays. The child must therefore be placed out-of-doors to obtain the beneficial effects of the sun's rays.)

TREATMENT. Cure and prevention are alike in many respects. The diet should include ample amounts of vitamin-D-enriched milk, egg yolk, butter, and cream. It should be rich in anti-rachitic foods (that is, foods valuable in fighting rickets), which should contain an abundance of calcium phosphate—as is to be found in cheese, nuts, cabbage, and milk—in addition to vitamin D. Dicalcium phosphate may also be given, and daily sun baths are suggested. The various bone deformities should be treated by an orthopedist. Under treatment, most children recover.

PELLAGRA

CAUSES. This is a nutritional disorder of subtropical areas. It is widespread in the southern United States. Pellagra mainly affects persons living chiefly on maize. It is caused by absence of niacin, and may be accompanied by lesions due to lack of vitamins B_1 and B_2. The disorder is rare in infants but it often affects young children. It has a tendency to recur in the spring.

SYMPTOMS. The disease begins gradually, without striking symptoms. In a poorly nourished child, or an adult, repeated attacks of redness of the skin suggest the presence of pellagra, especially if associated with a tendency to diarrhea or constipation. The redness which encircles the neck is often more intense.

The skin becomes thickened, rough, scaly and dry. A sign of importance for diagnosis, after the redness has subsided, is the brownish pigmentation of the skin. There are nausea and anemia, and sometimes mental symptoms—dementia in the severe forms.

TREATMENT. The principal treatment is dietetic. Fresh meat, milk and eggs are given. Extract from the germ of wheat or yeast should be given daily to supply the deficiency in vitamin B. Niacin (nicotinic acid) tablets given two or three times a day seem to have a definite effect in improving the condition.

CHOREA (ST. VITUS'S DANCE)

CAUSES. This disorder is a nervous manifestation of rheumatism. The disease occurs most frequently in later childhood and puberty. It is rare before the age of five. Females are much more susceptible than males. Like rheumatism, it often follows some acute respiratory infection, such as tonsillitis and pharyngitis. The psychic factor is sometimes evident—sudden fright, great grief, or other emotional causes, such as a bad relationship between the parents.

SYMPTOMS.   As a rule the beginning is gradual. In the mild conditions there may be nothing more than restlessness and inability to sit still. Some slight twitchings of the face and a tendency to involuntary facial grimacing are noted. The irregular movements are exaggerated when the child tries to carry out some normal act, such as handling objects or feeding himself. Sometimes the unexplained dropping of a plate or spoon first draws the attention of the parents to the child's condition.

In moderate conditions, the child shows emotional disturbance—cries over nothing and indulges in queer laughing spells. The characteristic jerking movements are most obvious in the neck and upper extremities. As a rule the movements cease during sleep.

In severe forms of the disease, the movements are greatly exaggerated, so that the child can neither feed nor dress himself. In such conditions, the irregular movements are constantly present. The speech also is affected.

TREATMENT.   A physician's care is important. The child must be kept quiet and must avoid excitement. In severe conditions, absolute rest in bed is essential, and the child should receive three or four doses daily of aspirin. A high caloric diet is necessary.

Fever treatment seems to be helpful, and is carried out in most hospitals. Fever brought on by the hypodermic injection of typhoid-paratyphoid bacillus often shortens the course of the disease to a marked degree. This is a drastic procedure, which should be resorted to only after careful consideration.

The heart is often affected, and should also be treated by a physician.

After recovery, great care must be taken of a child's general nutrition and health in order to prevent relapses. If the child's tonsils are infected, they must be removed. It is important for the child to be in a happy home atmosphere.

CONVULSIONS IN CHILDREN

CAUSES. A convulsion (fit) in a child is not a disease, but a symptom. It may be a sign of some digestive disturbance or of epilepsy. It is sometimes occasioned by incorrect feeding, or by food to which the child reacts abnormally.

SYMPTOMS. Convulsions may begin with squinting of the eyes, restlessness, starting or crying out in sleep, grinding the teeth, bending the thumbs, or slight twitching of the muscles of the face or limbs. Such signs should serve as a warning, particularly if the child is feverish. The patient should be bathed immediately with cool water as described further along.

The fit may begin with a choking sound. The body stiffens and is arched forward, while the head and neck are bent rigidly backward; the eyes are fixed, staring, squinting, and rolling, but sightless; the child neither sees, feels, nor hears—is wholly unconscious. The face becomes blue, the hands are clenched, and then the body and limbs begin to jerk and twitch, the arms and legs being alternately bent and straightened. The breathing is rapid and noisy; there is grinding of the teeth, and frothing at the mouth; sometimes the tongue is bitten.

The whole attack may last but a moment, and there may be no more; on the other hand, the attack may last for several minutes. Rarely, it may last for hours, or there may be frequently repeated attacks.

If the immediate cause, fever, for example, can be removed at once, there is little probability of a return of the fits. The child, after the convulsions, acts bewildered, begins to cry, and returns to consciousness; or he may fall asleep, or into a stupor.

TREATMENT. Call the physician. Undress the child and give him an alcohol rub. If this is not effective, place him in a hot bath at once, keeping a cold cloth to his head. The temperature of the water should be 100° to 103° F. One-half cupful of powdered mustard may be dissolved in each gallon of water. Be careful later to rinse all mustard from the folds of the child's skin.

A better procedure is to use a hot pack made by wrapping the naked child in a blanket or in heavy towels wrung out of water at the same temperature used for the bath. Use either the bath or the pack up to thirty minutes, if necessary.

POTT'S DISEASE (ANGULAR CURVATURE OF THE SPINE)

CAUSES. This disease is caused by softening and destruction of a part of the vertebrae (bones of the spine) by the germs of tuberculosis. It is a tuberculosis of bone. It begins usually in children between the ages of three and five, although at other periods as well. If it goes on without early treatment, it eventually causes death in about one-fifth of all patients, or leads to deformity of the spine or humpback, and many other conditions, such as abscesses in the groins and back, paralysis, etc. If, on the other hand, treatment is begun early, before there is any, or but slight, deformity, the disease is frequently cured completely. It is of the greatest importance, then, for parents to recognize spinal disease at the earliest moment.

The seat of the disease is more often in the upper two-thirds of the back. The exciting cause in many instances is a blow or fall received a long time before the spinal disease became evident.

SYMPTOMS. The disease begins slowly. Before any definite symptoms present themselves, the child appears fretful, lies on the floor, is loath to stand or play, and often has a cough or pain in the abdomen.

The chief symptoms are pain, stiffness of the back, awkwardness in moving, weakness, and deformity. Pain is not usually felt in the back except when jarred, although at night the child often cries out in his sleep, owing to his unconscious movements, which cause pain. Tenderness on pressing the spine is not common, but pain is felt more often in the belly, as stomach-ache and colic.

Stiffness of the back is a very important sign. The child does not bend his back freely, but carries himself stiffly, and, when he stoops to pick up anything, squats down by bending the legs at the knees and hips. Weakness is shown by the child's dislike of standing or walking. He tries to hold on to something for support, totters about on his toes, and falls frequently.

Deformity is usually the first sign which calls attention to the real nature of the disease, unless the parents are alert to the possibility of the disease and consult a physician before the disease is advanced.

The deformity is seen as a knuckle-like projection in some part of the back, and is made much more noticeable by bending the back. Occasionally there is a curvature of the back caused by rickets. In this case the spine is bent outward through a great part of its length, and there are other signs of rickets, such as enlargement of the wrists and beadlike swellings on the ribs. If the spine in the neck is diseased, the shoulders are apt to be held high and there is often a chronic stiff neck. If the disease is in the lower part of the back, the child is apt to lean forward with the hands resting on the thighs.

The temperature in Pott's disease or tuberculosis of the spine is apt to range about 99.5 to 100° F.

The diagnosis is made certain if there is spasm of the spinal muscles and a consequent rigidity of the spine in testing its mobility by passive and active motion. The tuberculin test is positive, and X-ray examination shows more or less destruction of one or more vertebrae.

TREATMENT. This consists mainly of complete immobilization of the spinal column by an orthopedic surgeon. In addition, dietetic and physical treatment for tuberculosis should be prescribed, with plenty of rest and sunshine.

LATERAL CURVATURE OF THE SPINE

CAUSES. This disorder differs entirely from Pott's disease. Lateral curvature of the spine is a deformity of the body caused by a permanent bending of the spine to one side, so that instead of being straight it assumes somewhat the shape of the letter S. Not only is the spine bent to one side, but it is turned, to some extent, on its axis. In the beginning this distortion of the spinal column is not usually brought about by disease of the spine itself, although sometimes, in children with rickets, the softer bone makes the child liable to favor the deformity. It arises from causes which tend to pull the spine out of line more or less constantly. Since it occurs at an early age, when the spine structures are very pliable, permanent distortion results, with gradual changes in the structure of the bones of the spine (vertebrae).

It is very important, then, that this condition should be discovered before actual structural changes occur, because the disease may be overcome, and in this way incurable and lasting deformity can be prevented.

Among the predisposing causes are all sorts of circumstances leading to faulty positions of the body, such as improper arrangement of school desks; carrying of heavy weights constantly in one hand or one arm, as when children carry books; certain occupations; effects of clothing; difficulties, such as faulty sight, requiring bending of the head and body to see. Other causes are paralysis of muscles on one side of the body, loss of one arm, rapid growth, rickets, etc.

Symptoms. Lateral curvature is much more frequent in girls than boys; but it may be seen in robust boys who practice special exercises. While the deformity often begins in young children, it does not commonly become obvious until a later period (from eight to fifteen years of age), when growth is rapid. The bending in the upper part of the spine is usually to the right, while the left shoulder is lowered and the left hip is raised as compared with these areas on the right side of the body. The condition can best be observed by marking the line along the bony projections of the spine down the back.

There are frequently no unpleasant symptoms. Sometimes, however, there are fatigue from slight causes, general irritability, and pain on the left side, if the bending of the spine is toward the right. More often no pain is produced. Occasionally the disease may closely resemble angular curvature, already described, but the fever, pain on movement, and stiffness of the back are absent.

Treatment. In children, this deformity of the spine may sometimes be corrected by properly selected exercises or by orthopedic apparatus. Special knowledge and skill are required for this purpose, so that the physician should be informed as soon as any evidence is found of lateral deformity.

HIP-JOINT DISEASE (HIP DISEASE)

CAUSES. The disease of children commonly called hip disease is usually an inflammation of the hip joint, caused by the germ of tuberculosis. It begins slowly, lasts from several months to many years, and sometimes may apparently be traced to an injury, such as a fall or blow.

SYMPTOMS. The first symptom which attracts attention to the disease in the child is usually a slight limp and stiffness of the affected limb in the morning. This stiffness may pass off after a while when the child is playing. Sometimes there may be periods of weeks when this disappears, only to return in a worse form. More often, however, it is constantly present and grows worse.

Along with the lameness, or a little later, pain appears. But the pain at first is not as a rule in the diseased hip joint, but in the toe, calf of the leg, or knee. This is naturally apt to mislead parents into thinking the condition is due to the misnamed "growing pains," to rheumatism, or to weakness in the knee. This error must be avoided. At night the child often cries out in pain.

The position in which the child holds the affected leg is often typical. The lameness increases in severity, and the weight is chiefly borne on the sound limb, while the diseased limb is bent slightly at the thigh, and the toes and limb are turned outward. At the same time the crease, naturally present under the buttocks, is less noticeable on the leg of the affected side.

TREATMENT. The constitutional treatment is that of tuberculosis elsewhere in the body. The local treatment consists in the provision of complete rest for the joint by means of special orthopedic measures, such as traction, braces, plaster of Paris cast, and sometimes surgery.

If the physician's attention is drawn to it in the beginning, almost every case can be cured by rest in bed, splints, and apparatus of various kinds. If neglected till late, abscess about the joint, years of suffering, permanent crippling and lameness, loss of the limb, or even death may result.

MALFORMATIONS IN CHILDREN

Any deformity that a child has should be corrected as soon as possible. A club-foot, for example, can be corrected if treated early enough, whereas if the condition is neglected the child may be lame for life.

To neglect physical defects during the first year in the hope that the child will outgrow them is unwise. During this year of rapid growth, defects grow rapidly worse.

CLEFT PALATE. In a newborn infant with a cleft palate, for example, the objective of greatest importance is to maintain the child in a condition of good nutrition. The difficulty arises from the fact that the infant cannot grasp the nipple. This makes a cleft palate a far more serious condition for the infant than for the child later on. The condition is remediable by plastic surgery.

BOWLEGS AND KNOCK-KNEES. These deformities are usually caused by rickets, but a hereditary factor must be assumed in some patients. Bowlegs are relatively rare, but knock-knees are seen daily in spite of the use of anti-rachitic (anti-rickets) remedies. Overweight is a cause. To prevent knock-knees, the heavy child should lose weight and receive large doses of concentrated cod-liver oil. It is important that he wear shoes that fit properly. Severe cases of the disease require orthopedic treatment, but if the deformity is recognized early, prescribing a proper diet or ordering the proper shoes may be curative.

BOWEL DISTURBANCE (ACID DYSPEPSIA)

CAUSES. This disorder often begins about two or three weeks after birth. The cause is unknown, but the disorder may be due to milk too rich in fat or to infection of the intestinal tract.

SYMPTOMS. The baby cries—sometimes continuously—and does not sleep. Severe attacks of colic occur soon after nursing. The infant may stop nursing. His abdomen is distended. The stools are frequently thin, watery, containing much mucus and often full of bubbles.

TREATMENT. The main objective is to try to maintain maternal nursing. When the infant is on artificial food, the disorder may be cured by withholding all food, except weak tea, for twenty-four hours. An ounce of barley water is given before feeding, and a mixture of paregoric and atropine, prescribed by the doctor.

DIARRHEA

CAUSES. Diarrhea is only a symptom. The causes are many. They are usually classified as mechanical, toxic, chemical, nervous, metabolic, and infectious. There are various kinds of diarrhea. In fermentative diarrhea, there are frequent, offensive and sour-smelling stools. Specific diarrhea of infants may occur in newborn infants who often have a looseness of the bowels even when breast-fed. Giving too much sugar water during the first milk period may cause intestinal fermentation. Artificial feeding sometimes starts the episode, when the food is too concentrated or fed in large quantities. There is also summer diarrhea, a condition which may be caused by bacterial toxins in the milk—food poisoning. It arises principally from contaminated and decomposed cow's milk.

SYMPTOMS. The symptoms sometimes begin with fever and vomiting. Convulsions may occur. Thirst is a prominent symptom. The stools are fecal (formed) at first, but soon become watery and have an offensive acid odor. There are small curds and mucus in them. Greenish or slightly yellowish stools are noted. The infant may have as many as fifteen to twenty bowel movements a day.

TREATMENT. It is advisable to consult a physician. For mild diarrheas (three or four movements daily) solid foods should be omitted and the quantity of milk reduced to half by the addition of water or barley water.

To prevent this disorder it is important to purchase the freshest and cleanest milk obtainable and to boil it during the summer *even if it has previously been pasteurized.* The bottles and nipples must also be kept scrupulously clean.

During an attack, the milk should be excluded from the feeding. Plenty of sweetened and salted barley water should be given—at least a quart daily. The infant is kept in the coolest part of the house and sponged a few times during the day with alcohol and water.

DYSENTERY

Causes. This disease usually appears in the summer months, mainly in infants and older children. It is caused by a group of bacilli.

Symptoms. There are vomiting and high fever, abdominal pain, and diarrhea. There are quick loss of weight and even early prostration. Convulsions are common at the beginning. The stools are full of pus cells.

The mortality is high during hot weather.

Treatment. The purity of the milk and water must be safeguarded.

The child or infant is kept in a cool room. No adult who is suffering from any kind of intestinal trouble should be permitted to come near the patient. In the summer, mosquito netting should be used over the child's crib, because the germ may be carried by flies.

The milk must be discontinued for a number of days. To infants, sweetened and salted cereals, boiled until they are soft, should be freely given. Plenty of water, sugar, and some salt will prevent a severe loss of fluids from the body. Every effort should be made to maintain a normal balance in the body fluid.

Vitamin C is added to the feeding in the form of orange or lemon juice as soon as possible. Vitamin B is included by giving some juice of vegetables. Milk is gradually added to the diet in the form of whole buttermilk or powdered protein milk. In some instances one to three pounds of ripe, peeled, and grated apples are given daily. Another form of treatment consists in giving fruit juices early, and banana pulp.

Sulfathiazole or sulfaguanidine is used on the physician's prescription as an intestinal antiseptic in all examples of infectious inflammation of the intestine.

Sulfaguanidine is used especially for the treatment of dysentery caused by bacilli, for ulcerative colitis (in adults), and for stomach and intestinal disturbances in children.

To control the diarrhea, irrigation of the bowels with normal salt solution is sometimes necessary. Bismuth, kaolin, and charcoal powders diminish the intestinal fermentation, but should be given only on a doctor's prescription.

CONSTIPATION

As a rule the infant is considered constipated if he does not have at least one bowel movement a day. The term is also used when the stools are firm and dry.

The disorder often occurs in breast-fed infants.

TREATMENT. A mild soap or glycerin suppository can be used at first. In bottle-fed infants the constipation can be overcome by adding a fermentable carbohydrate to the milk. The most effective are sorghum molasses and honey. Corn syrup also has a laxative effect.

In severe constipation, a teaspoonful of milk of magnesia may be added to a single bottle.

The pulpy fruits, stewed, such as prunes, pears, apples and peaches, may be prescribed even for young infants—one tablespoonful daily, an amount which can be increased. The addition of an ounce of prune juice to the diet may prove effective. Enemas—not too frequently—may sometimes be given.

In older children it is best to diminish the quantity of milk and increase the pulpy fruits and vegetables in the diet. Sorghum molasses should be substituted for the sugar. Malt extract in tablespoonful doses, two or three times a day, has a laxative effect. Whole-grain cereals (Wheatena, for example) are useful in the relief of constipation in infants over three months old.

TEARS AT THE ANUS (FISSURES)

A single tear at the anus may be caused by the passage of a constipated stool or laceration by some foreign body. There is sharp, stab-
bing pain in the anal region during and after moving the bowels.
It is often so acute that the act is deliberately postponed, with consequent constipation. The condition should be treated by a physician.

INFANTILE SCURVY

CAUSES.   In general, infants and older children who have been
inadequately fed are likely to develop scurvy or rickets, or both. The
child getting the disease is usually about eight months old, and is
rarely a breast-fed infant. The cause of scurvy is an inadequate
amount of citrus fruit juices—vitamin C—in the diet.

SYMPTOMS.   There are collections of fluid in the body cavities
and swellings in the tissues beneath the skin.

Restlessness at night and increasing pallor are the first general
symptoms. The earliest symptom noted, as a rule, is that the infant
cries when diapered. It becomes obvious that the pain is caused by
certain movements, especially of the lower extremities. The gums
show a characteristic change. A bluish spongy swelling appears
around the upper central incisor teeth, if they are present. A swelling along the bones is found usually above the knee or the ankle,
which is tender to pressure. Occasionally a bleeding tendency is
noted in the urine and in the substance that has been vomited.

There is a "beading" of the ribs (appearance of nodules where
the ribs join the cartilage).

It is often thought mistakenly that the infant suffers from "rheumatism."

TREATMENT.   The infant should be put on a diet of fresh milk
and meat juice. Orange juice or grapefruit juice should be given, at
least one ounce daily. An older child should receive two or three
ounces daily.

If tomato juice is substituted for orange juice, twice the quantity
must be given, because tomato juice contains less vitamin C. Tomato

juice or canned tomatoes are less expensive than orange juice. (The juice poured off from canned tomatoes should be used rather than canned tomato juice; the latter contains condiments and other substances that may sometimes upset an infant's digestion.)

Pure vitamin C tablets can be purchased at drug stores.

When an infant is on a mixed diet and receives other raw fruit (apples, peaches, cantaloupe) the amount of orange juice may be reduced. During the summer, the fruits which a child is fed should be varied to include: raspberries, strawberries, tomatoes, peaches and apples. (Raw cabbage is a good source of vitamin C, and can be given to older infants.) When tomato juice or orange juice is not tolerated on account of vomiting or diarrhea, banana pulp, scraped apple, or fresh peach juice may be given.

Dry cereals and legumes (peas, beans, etc.) of all varieties contain no vitamin C. Butter, eggs and cheese contain no vitamin C. Bread and most of the prepared infant foods do not contain vitamin C. The exclusive use of these foods for several months almost invariably results in latent or obvious scurvy, unless the necessary vitamin is supplied by an accessory diet of fruit juice.

Milk is the most nearly perfect food and the food one can least do without. Even so, the vitamin C content of commercial milk, raw or pasteurized, is not dependable and should never be relied upon to supply the requirements. Loss of vitamin C, owing to pasteurization, aging, reheating and diluting, such as usually occurs in preparing a formula for babies, results in a formula extremely low in scurvy-prevention value.

MEASLES

CAUSES. Measles is an acute, contagious disease marked, over a period of a few days, by a slowly rising fever, symptoms of a "cold," and a rash which appears about the fourth day. The disease is caused by a filterable virus. It is one of the most contagious diseases known.

SYMPTOMS. The child appears to have a "cold." His eyes are congested; he sneezes, and a cough develops. By the fourth day there is high fever—104° F. or more—and a dry "barking" cough. An eruption appears in the mouth. The rash develops first behind the ears, on the forehead and on the neck. It soon spreads all over the body and becomes profuse on the face and neck. The fever now declines unless there are complications.

Complications are frequent in infants and young children; of these the most serious are broncho-pneumonia and ear infections.

During an epidemic, practically all susceptible children who have been exposed get measles after an incubation period of ten or eleven days.

TREATMENT. The child should be isolated, and kept in bed in a darkened room, since there is usually great sensitiveness to light. The bowels must be kept open, and there should be a bland diet till temperature goes down. Give copiously of fluids—water, fruit juices, and milk.

There is no specific drug for measles, but lung and other complications, owing to secondary bacterial invasion, must be dealt with by the appropriate antibiotics and sulfonamides. Where the sulfonamides are used, some secondary infections may be held in check.

SCARLET FEVER (SCARLATINA)

CAUSES. Scarlet fever is an acute, eruptive, contagious disease caused by the streptococcus scarlatinae. Formerly, the disease was usually a serious one, but of late years it seems to have lost much of its severity, and the grave form of the disease is now exceptional.

SYMPTOMS. Scarlet fever begins suddenly with high fever, vomiting, and sore throat. The eruption usually appears within twenty-four to forty-eight hours as a red flush, first upon the neck and chest. It then spreads rapidly. The rash consists of minute red points closely packed together. Fine brown scales form after a time. The cheeks are flushed, and a pale circle of skin is noted around the mouth and nose. The eruption lasts for two or three days.

No disease of childhood produces so many and such serious after-effects as scarlet fever. Of these, involvement of the neck glands, ears, and kidneys are the most common.

IMMUNITY TO SCARLET FEVER. A physician can determine whether a child is susceptible to the disease by the use of what is known as the Dick test. If the child is found susceptible, he can be made immune to the disease.

Immunity (resistance to development of the disease) may be conferred by injecting increasing doses of the Dick toxin. However, the reaction is sometimes so severe that the method has not been widely adopted. The danger of a severe reaction may, however, be avoided by using a smaller dose, and increasing the number of injections from five to eight. Normal human or convalescent serum may also be used to increase the resistance of children who are susceptible. Sulfonamides may aid in preventing the disease when given for five to seven days after exposure.

TREATMENT. Prompt isolation is extremely important. The quarantine should be rigidly enforced for three weeks in mild conditions and for six to seven weeks in severe ones.

In the severe form of the disease, scarlet-fever antitoxin should be promptly injected and the injection repeated in twenty-four hours.

In the treatment of the gravely ill infant, immune serum from an adult may be used.

In mild conditions, the serum may be omitted and the disease controlled by sulfadiazine. Penicillin has been found effective in preventing complications.

In scarlet fever the throat needs special attention. An ice-collar may be worn part of the day if the neck glands are enlarged and tender.

In some instances the patient continues, even after recovery, to harbor hemolytic (blood-destroying) streptococci in the nose and throat. Penicillin is then more efficient than antitoxin in reducing the number of disease carriers as well as in preventing complications. The urine should be carefully watched for several weeks after convalescence. There is danger of a chronic Bright's disease coming on later.

GERMAN MEASLES (RUBELLA)

CAUSES. This disease is an acute, contagious disorder which is marked chiefly by enlarged neck glands and a rash. (German measles has no relation whatsoever to measles.) It is caused by a virus.

SYMPTOMS.   The rash appears first on the face and neck, and then spreads over the body in twenty-four hours. It consists of rose-red macules or discolored spots on the skin, which are not elevated above the surface.

There are mild catarrhal symptoms of the upper respiratory tract during the stage when the spots come out.

TREATMENT.   The treatment is directed at the symptoms. The patient stays in bed, away from others who may contract the disease. The diet should be bland.

CHICKENPOX (VARICELLA)

CAUSES AND SYMPTOMS.   Chickenpox is an acute infectious disease in which an eruption appears, marked by successive crops of tiny blisters. These later dry, to form scabs that are brownish in color. General bodily symptoms may be entirely absent, but they are usually moderate. There is an irregular fever which persists for a few days. The disease is produced by a virus.

TREATMENT.   Bed rest and isolation are important until all the minute crusts have fallen off. Bathing should be discontinued for a week or ten days. Carbolated ointment, or a 1 per cent ointment of thymol iodide, may be used effectively on the small open sores. Scratching should be avoided to prevent secondary infection and permanent scarring.

WHOOPING COUGH

CAUSES.   This is an acute, contagious disease of the respiratory tract, caused by the pertussis bacillus, which is found in the sputum. The disease is characterized by violent fits of coughing with apparent strangling, ending in a whoop. The infection is most rapidly spread in the first stage before severe coughing has begun. An attack confers lifelong immunity to the disease.

No age is exempt, but most cases occur in children under five. Whooping cough causes more deaths in children under two years of age than any other acute infection, except pneumonia and the diarrheas.

SYMPTOMS. The time from exposure to the development of symptoms (incubation period) is estimated variably from three to fifteen days. The beginning stage (catarrhal stage) resembles an ordinary cold. Sneezing, redness of the eyes, and slight fever are present. A short, dry, irritating cough arises and persists. The first phase ordinarily lasts two weeks before the secondary symptoms of more severe coughing develop.

THE COUGH IN WHOOPING COUGH. The occurrence of a characteristic cough reveals the transition to the second stage. The paroxysm of coughing is often brought on by some act, such as swallowing, crying, or gagging. The child gives a series of short, explosive coughs without stopping to take a breath. His color, first red, changes to blue; his eyes water and become congested. Saliva dribbles, his tongue protrudes, and the veins of his neck are distended. When at last the cough stops, the child takes a long breath, with the characteristic whoop, and temporarily holds his breath. The process is sometimes repeated a number of times; when the paroxysms finally end, a small pellet of sticky mucus is expelled.

The spells occur at irregular intervals, sometimes in rapid succession, and sometimes at several-hour intervals. Vomiting usually follows immediately after the coughing spell, particularly if food has been recently taken. The disease may last from six to eight weeks. Ordinarily, after a few weeks, the intensity and frequency of the spells gradually subside, and only a slight cough remains.

DIAGNOSIS. Whooping cough in the second stage can hardly be mistaken for any other illness. The diagnosis is made by hearing the characteristic cough. In the early stage the bacillus responsible for the infection may be grown from special culture plates exposed to the patient's cough.

TREATMENT. In the early stage and until the more severe coughing spells have abated, rest is important. Later the child does better in the open air, but he should be kept from other children to prevent spread of the disease. Sedatives and codeine mixtures are useful in decreasing the number and severity of the coughing paroxysms. Steam inhalations may be prescribed. If secondary pneumonia develops, penicillin is frequently given with good results, but penicillin has no direct effect on the pertussis bacillus. Recently encouraging results have been published suggesting that aureomycin may shorten the course and severity of whooping cough.

PREVENTION.   Effective artificial immunity can now be produced by pertussis vaccine. It is usually given by the pediatrician sometime in the first year of life in a series of injections. Most often it is combined with diphtheria vaccine, and tetanus toxoid. Booster doses are given yearly for the first few years by many physicians. Widespread immunization in the infant has greatly reduced the incidence of the disease and mortality from it.

DIPHTHERIA

CAUSES.   This throat infection is most prevalent from the second to the twelfth year of life. It is most dangerous in late infancy and early childhood. Predisposing causes are chronic tonsillitis and other inflammatory conditions of mouth and throat. Diphtheria occurs the year round; but is most frequent in autumn and winter, when nose and throat infections make persons more susceptible to the disease.

SYMPTOMS.   The incubation period is usually two to four days. The disease sets in, often quite suddenly, with a mild sense of illness, sore throat, and fever (100° to 102° F.), with a disproportionate degree of prostration and illness. The pulse is usually rapid. A membrane gradually forms on the tonsils, which are swollen and inflamed. By the third day the membrane may cover the tonsils and uvula, the fleshy lobe hanging down in the middle of the back of the soft palate. This membrane varies in extent and is greenish or grayish. The glands of the neck are swollen. The membrane may grow down the throat, cover the tonsils completely, enter the nose, larynx and trachea, and bring about death by suffocation.

COMPLICATIONS.   Bronchopneumonia is a common and dangerous complication of diphtheria, and a frequent cause of death. Heart failure and paralysis are apt to occur in the second or third week of convalescence.

IMMUNIZATION AGAINST DIPHTHERIA.   The average child under eight is susceptible to diphtheria, and all children should be immunized. The Schick test is a specific skin reaction for the purpose of finding out whether and how much a person is susceptible to diphtheria. Another test, the Moloney, determines susceptibility to the toxoid (the injected substance capable of producing antibodies). If this test is positive, it is an indication that the injections of diphtheria toxoid should be given gradually.

In epidemics, Shick-positive or susceptible people, i.e., those who give a local skin reaction to injection of the diluted toxin directly *into* the skin, should be immunized by three weekly injections of a substance called diphtheria prophylactic toxoid antitoxin. In epidemics, and in persistent sore throats, cultures of the throat and nose should be taken, since it is the mild, unknown infections that spread the disease.

INFANT VACCINATION. Vaccination of infants at six months generally makes them immune during the months when they would be most susceptible and the disease most dangerous. There are a number of methods of immunization against diphtheria. The most satisfactory, apparently, is to immunize infants against diphtheria, tetanus, and whooping cough all at the same time.

TREATMENT. The patient suffering from diphtheria must remain in bed in a well-ventilated room. He must be isolated for four to six weeks, until he has had three successive negative throat swab reports on alternate days after the disease has "died out." He must be kept in bed for at least three weeks after the throat has cleared. Then gradually he may be permitted to sit up and finally to walk. The diet must be liquid.

Every doubtful condition must be treated as diphtheria, until it has been disproved. A culture of the nose and throat must be taken at the earliest possible opportunity.

GIVING ANTITOXIN. By far the most important factor in the success of antitoxin treatment is the time factor. The amount of antitoxin needed varies according to how severe the infection is and how long it is since it began.

Therefore, antitoxin must be given as early as possible. The earlier it is injected, the greater the prospect of a quick recovery. Usually the dose is given under the skin or in the muscles, and repeated in twenty-four hours, and again, if necessary. A rash frequently appears soon after the injection, but soon disappears. In severe forms of the disease, half of the dose is given in the muscles and the other half by way of a vein.

USE OF DRUGS. The administration of vitamin C is valuable. The sulfa drugs have no curative effect on the disease, but penicillin seems to be of value in shortening its duration. For the average patient, antitoxin alone is adequate, but for the gravely ill the use of penicillin is vitally important. When antitoxin and penicillin are both given, the results are often miraculously effective.

TRUE CROUP (LARYNGEAL DIPHTHERIA)

CROUP AND DIPHTHERIA. True croup is a different disease from that ordinarily referred to as croup. The latter is a form of catarrhal laryngitis, whereas true croup is a form of diphtheria. Its cause is the diphtheria bacillus. It is most likely to occur in children under two years of age. Children at birth, and most adults, are immune. Formerly the disease had a high mortality, but nowadays it is readily controlled. It is most common in the autumn and winter.

SYMPTOMS. The disease may affect the larynx primarily, or it may be secondary to a similar involvement of the nose or pharynx, or both. It begins with only a slight temperature, cough, and moderate hoarseness. The cough is croupy (hoarse and ringing). Loss of voice, as time goes on, is accompanied by shortness of breath and a bluish tinge to the skin. Later, breathing becomes harsher, with increasing evidence of obstruction in the larynx. This obstruction may be mechanical, caused by the presence of a membrane (see Diphtheria); or it may be reflex, the result of spasm of the larynx caused by inflammation of the muscles of the larynx.

TREATMENT. The treatment is, in general, the same as for diphtheria. The sooner the disease is treated, the less danger. If diphtheria antitoxin is given promptly, the patient recovers. The membrane loosens, small pieces are coughed up, and respiration becomes easier and finally normal. The condition is sometimes so severe that a tube is inserted in the larynx to enable the child to breathe. If the proper instruments for this are not available, the trachea may have to be opened from the outside for the same purpose.

It is best to hospitalize a child suffering from true croup.

NASAL DIPHTHERIA

SYMPTOMS. This condition occurs mostly in children. Its beginning is similar to that of the common cold, with little or no fever, but a sense of illness. A more or less chronic nasal discharge, on one or both sides of the nose, soon becomes bloody and irritates the upper lip. Nasal bleeding may be severe and frequent.

TREATMENT. A culture of the nasal discharge should be taken. It will reveal the nature of the condition. The specific antitoxin must be administered.

TETANUS

CAUSES. This is a disease caused by the tetanus bacillus, which occurs especially in the earth. Accordingly, tetanus is liable to follow wounds contaminated with ground dirt. Of these, puncture wounds are the most dangerous.

SYMPTOMS. The incubation period is about ten days, as a rule. The disease sets in with stiffness of the neck and jaws, which eventually enter into a state of lockjaw. Gradually the spasm invades the whole body.

PREVENTION. Immunization should be carried out at about the sixth month of life. This should be repeated every two or three years, and additionally a booster dose of toxoid should be given if the child receives an injury which is contaminated with dust, soil, animal excretion, or other materials which are likely to contain the germ.

TREATMENT. If the disease becomes evident, tetanus antitoxin is given. If there are convulsions, the physician also uses avertin.

MUMPS

CAUSES. Mumps is an acute infectious disease, caused by a virus which occurs in the saliva during the first six days of illness. Severe swelling of one or more of the salivary glands occurs. There is a tendency for other glands to be involved, particularly the testes or ovaries in adults.

The condition is rare in children under four. It occurs chiefly between the ages of five and fifteen. Although not highly communicable, mumps may occur in epidemic form, when large groups of susceptible persons are living in close association, as in army barracks.

SYMPTOMS. The average incubation period is eighteen days, with extreme limits of eight and thirty days. The disease sets in with headache, chilly sensations, loss of appetite, and tenderness of the affected glands. Several glands may be involved in succession, the first to enlarge usually being one or both parotids (glands in front of and below the ears). The temperature ranges between 100° and 104° F., with a relatively slow pulse.

Mumps in itself, while painful, is not fatal, both fever and glandular swelling subsiding in a few days. However, complications, chiefly in the years after adolescence, may be serious. Atrophy of the testicles occurs in about 6 per cent of hospitalized boys and young men, though it is extremely rare in childhood.

TREATMENT. The treatment is directed toward the symptoms. Adults must have absolute rest in bed.

SMALLPOX (VARIOLA)

CAUSES. Smallpox is an acute infectious disease occurring in epidemics. It attacks people of all ages. Infection is carried by the excretions and exhalations, and particularly by the dried scales which occur on the skin of convalescent patients.

Three varieties of the disease are found: discrete smallpox, confluent smallpox and hemorrhagic smallpox.

SYMPTOMS. The discrete variety sets in acutely, with chills, severe headache, acute pain in the back, and vomiting. The pulse is rapid. The temperature rises quickly to 103° or 104° F. The rash appears on the third day as small, red shotlike papules (slight elevations) on the forehead at the hair margin, and on the wrists; later it spreads to the face and limbs. On the sixth day the papules become blisters. On the eighth day they contain pus.

The initial symptoms in the confluent variety are more severe. The rash appears earlier and is more thickly set. The pustules combine and form superficial abscesses. The temperature may rise to 105°.

In hemorrhagic smallpox the symptoms are extremely severe. As the term denotes, hemorrhages occur in the skin.

PREVENTION. Smallpox vaccine virus should be administered at the sixth month of life or shortly thereafter. This should be repeated at six and twelve years. Revaccination is carried out when the child is likely to be, or to have been, exposed to the infection.

TREATMENT. The patient must be isolated, and most careful disinfection of all things used or touched by him should be carried out. The nursing must be extremely careful. Complete bed rest is required.

The skin should be kept clean with mild antiseptics. Local itching should be controlled with soothing lotions. The light in the sickroom should be subdued. Boric acid solution should be used for the conjunctivitis (inflammation of the eyelids) that occurs. Medicine for relief of headache and backache should be given. The maintenance of fluid balance and general nutrition, plus a vitamin supplement, is recommended.

Vaccination of all persons in the immediate vicinity is essential.

Drug treatment is useless against the virus. However, penicillin for three or four days appears to be of great value in the pustular stage, resulting in improvement in the general condition, rapid drying of the pustules, and a minimum of pockmarking. Aureomycin may be substituted for penicillin.

CEREBROSPINAL MENINGITIS

CAUSES. This disease occurs in epidemics and also in isolated cases, and is commoner in the later winter months than in spring. It is caused by a germ, the diplococcus intracellularis. The source of the infection is obscure, as a rule. We know, however, that many persons may harbor the germ in the nose and throat. It is believed that these germ carriers are the principal source of the infection and that dissemination takes place by contact. Contrary to general belief, the disease is rarely spread in schools.

SYMPTOMS. The incubation period is one to five days. There is an abrupt beginning, with headache, vomiting, fever, and frequently convulsion. There is general irritability and stiffness of the neck; the head is bent backward and cannot be moved forward. There is also sensitiveness to light, noise, or passive motion. A general muscular rigidity is often detected.

In examining patients showing suggestive signs and symptoms (convulsions, stupor, retracted neck, general hypersensitiveness), the physician looks for two signs of cerebrospinal meningitis which are obtained by passive movement: the inability to extend the leg when the thigh is bent on the abdomen and involuntary bending of the thighs when the head is bent forward. These signs confirm other signs.

The diagnosis rests on the fever, headache, vomiting, stupor, rigidity of the limbs, and the position of the head. When the spinal fluid is examined, it is found to be turbid and to contain white blood cells, as well as the germs.

TREATMENT. The treatment by administering sulfonamides and antibiotics (penicillin) is regarded as the best. As soon as the diagnosis is complete, the physician makes injections into the spinal canal.

INFANTILE PARALYSIS (POLIO)

PREVENTION. In its brochure entitled "Doctor, What Can I Do About Infantile Paralysis?" The National Foundation for Infantile Paralysis states:

"Since there is no specific means of warding off the disease, such as medical science has provided for diphtheria, typhoid fever, smallpox, and many of the other communicable illnesses, prevention, for the present, depends on avoidance of exposure. This is exceedingly difficult, if not even impossible, in most cases. During an epidemic many carriers and persons with the mild undiagnosable forms of poliomyelitis infection unintentionally and unknowingly spread the virus.

"There is yet no practical way to detect these carriers. All that can be done is to prevent unnecessary contact with others. During epidemics, avoid having children come in contact with new groups of people. Since this disease comes from other infected persons, the less the number of contacts, the less the chance of being infected. Even rigid confinement of a child to his home, however, will not always prevent the disease from being carried to him.

"See that children—and all other members of the household—take nothing into their mouths that could have been soiled by the discharge from the bodies of others.

"Screening of the house against flies may be an important preventive measure as this insect may be capable of carrying the virus from known cases or undetected carriers. . . .

"Hard and fast rules cannot be formulated relative to attendance at schools. In most communities, this and similar problems will be carefully considered by the health officer. In cities, the child actually makes fewer new and intimate contacts in school than out of school. In cities, children are drawn from a relatively small area. In the country, the reverse may at times be true, for here the children may travel long distances, and to them the school may add new hazards and new exposures.

"Swimming may be an important factor during an epidemic. Swimming itself is not thought to be harmful, but if the water is contaminated by sewage and human pollution a definite danger is introduced. If the child meets new people and is exposed to new crowds, swimming may be a menace even though the water itself is safe. Chilling and fatigue are to be avoided.

"All children with fever should be isolated in bed pending diagnosis. Avoid undue fatigue and exertion during the polio season. Avoid unnecessary travel and visiting in areas where polio is known to be prevalent. Nose, throat and dental operations, unless required as an emergency, should *not* be done in the presence of an increased incidence of the disease in the community."

All patients and those with symptoms suggestive of infantile paralysis should be promptly reported to the local health officer.

TABLE OF COMMUNICABLE DISEASES

Disease	How long from exposure to onset (incubation period)?	How long communicable (isolation period)?	How serious?	Can it be prevented by inoculation? If so, at what age?	Is there specific treatment?
CHICKENPOX	2 to 3 weeks	Not more than 10 days after appearance of rash	Not serious but very contagious	No	No
DIPHTHERIA	2 to 5 days	Until germs have disappeared from discharges and nose and throat	Very serious	Yes. Diphtheria toxoid. At 9 months	Antitoxin
DYSENTERY (BACILLARY)	2 to 7 days	Until germs have disappeared from stools	Moderate to very serious	No	Serum may be tried
GERMAN MEASLES	2 to 3 weeks	Not more than 7 days from onset of first symptoms	Not serious but very contagious	No	No
HOOKWORM	3 weeks to several months	As long as infested	Moderately serious	No	Tetrachlorethylene
INFLUENZA	24 to 72 hours	Unknown. Probably while fever lasts	Serious	Not yet. In experimental stages	No
MALARIA	Usually 14 days	As long as the blood contains enough parasites to infect mosquitoes	Serious	No	Quinine; atabrine
MEASLES	8 to 14 days	Usually 5 days after appearance of rash. Until discharges have stopped	Serious, especially in child under 3 years of age	May be prevented or made milder by use of convalescent serum, as soon as exposed. Consult physician	No

	Incubation period	Isolation period	Seriousness	Vaccine	Treatment
MENINGOCOCCIC MENINGITIS	2 to 10 days	Until germs have disappeared from nose and throat	Very serious	No	Sulfa drugs; serum
MUMPS	12 to 26 days	Probably until swelling has disappeared	Not very serious	No	No
PNEUMONIA (LOBAR)	Variable. Probably 1 to 3 days	Probably until recovery is complete	Very serious	No	Sulfa drugs, penicillin; serum
POLIOMYELITIS	7 to 14 days	Not known. Probably at least 2 weeks after beginning	Very serious	No	No
SCARLET FEVER	2 to 7 days	3 weeks from beginning and until all discharges have stopped	Serious	Yes. Dick toxin. Not advised for all children. Consult physician. No special age	Antitoxin; sulfa drugs
SMALLPOX	8 to 21 days	From first symptoms to disappearance of all scabs and crusts	Very serious	Yes. Smallpox vaccine. At 3 months and every 5 years	No
TETANUS	4 to 21 days	Not infectious	Very serious	Yes. Tetanus toxoid and antitoxin. At 9 months	Antitoxin
TYPHOID FEVER	3 to 38 days	Until repeated examination shows germs have disappeared from urine and stools	Very serious	Yes. Typhoid vaccine. No special age. Consult physician	No
WHOOPING COUGH	5 to 14 days	Most catching in early stages and for about 3 weeks of whooping period	Serious, especially in child under 3 years of age	Yes. Whooping-cough vaccine. At 7 months	No

SYMPTOMS.   These depend upon the severity of the infection, and vary in different patients. The mild variety may start with very slight symptoms such as irritability of the child, some redness of the throat, and maybe nausea or vomiting. The temperature may be only 100° to 101° F. These findings, at the bedtime hour, may be all there are. By morning, the temperature, instead of being lower, has risen to 103° to 104° F. Then there is definite soreness of the muscles of the back and legs, and, of special importance, "stiffness" of the neck. This symptom, together with the others mentioned, is almost a sure sign of the disease.

The other type, or malignant form, of the disease is violent in its beginning. There are nausea, vomiting, sudden rise in fever to 105° to 106° F., bending backward of the head, extreme tenderness of all the muscles, marked prostration. Within six or eight hours, paralysis has set in. This may be confined to the legs or also the breathing apparatus.

If during an epidemic any of these symptoms develop in a child, be prompt in calling your doctor. A few hours' delay may mean the difference between life and death or crippling for life.

TREATMENT.   In the acute stage, there is little that can help. A serum is used, but it is not specific, since the exact cause of the disease is not known. Care is thus directed mainly toward the symptoms.

If there is paralysis, various orthopedic measures are carried out to prevent shrinking of the muscles, regardless of how mild the condition may be, because weakened backs and limbs, if not supervised, may result in permanent injury.

Moist heat, massage, and early gentle exercises are the only means of restoring potential polio cripples to normal life and of helping the stricken to adjust themselves to their handicaps.

USE OF ARTIFICIAL RESPIRATION.   In severe attacks of polio it is sometimes urgent to give artificial respiration. This is done by what is termed an "iron-lung." Another machine about the size of a portable radio is used where the "iron-lung" proves ineffective and cumbersome. It is also cheaper than the iron-lung.

The respirator induces rhythmic controlled breathing by means of an electric current carried into the phrenic nerve at the base of the neck. This is the nerve that causes the diaphragm to contract and draw the air into the lungs. The electric charge is controlled by a timing device that decreases the current automatically from time to time, thus causing the diaphragm to relax and force out the air.

INTESTINAL WORMS

Cleanliness of person is the first requisite in the avoidance of parasites. Children are more apt to be attacked by worms, as they are much less clean in their habits than adults.

CAUSES AND PREVENTION. Children suck their fingers, and handle dogs and cats from which they may acquire the eggs of the worms. They are also apt to scratch themselves about the exit of the bowel. In this way, if they are suffering from worms, the eggs may again be returned to the bowels, through the child's fingers and mouth. As many as three thousand worm eggs have been counted in a piece of excrement as large as a single grain of wheat. Worms are often conveyed, too, in the form of eggs, in drinking water contaminated with human excrement. Uncooked vegetables may also be infected, in backward and undeveloped areas, by human or other manure.

The common varieties of tapeworm are acquired by human beings through eating raw or imperfectly cooked beef, pork, or sausage. Dogs may contract tapeworm from eating the offal of slaughtered sheep and cattle.

The greatest care must be taken to destroy tapeworms and other parasites by fire, and to keep the rectum clean. In the case of pinworms, after their removal by treatment, the bedclothes should be boiled, children's toys burned, carpets cleaned, and floor and furniture washed, in order to avert a return of the disease through eggs which may be attached to these objects.

SYMPTOMS. To hear the opinions of many mothers, it might be supposed that worms are among the most common causes of disease in children, and that, together with teething, they account for the chief part of infantile illness. Both are enormously over rated as sources of trouble. The only proof of the presence of worms in the body is their appearance in the excrement, or in vomited matter, or in or about the patient.

All symptoms are very indefinite and uncertain, even to the physician, as, with the exception of pinworms, they often produce no trouble whatever. There are a great number of possible symptoms of worms in children. They include weakness, peevishness, nervousness as shown by fidgets, twitching, crying out or grinding the teeth when asleep. Also, picking the nose, fever, convulsions, uncertain—sometimes ravenous—appetite without gaining weight, pain and uneasiness about the navel, foul breath, vomiting, constipation, and diarrhea. These symptoms, however, are often merely the result of debility and have no connection with worms.

In the presence of pinworms, there is almost always great itching about the bowel, in the early night especially. The worms may indeed often be seen about these parts. In girls the worms may wander into the vagina, causing inflammation with swelling and discharge from the sexual organs. The local irritation of the pinworms in the lower bowel may also lead to bed-wetting, masturbation, fainting, and sleeplessness in children.

Tapeworms in adults also produce very indefinite symptoms, such as nausea, diarrhea, discomfort in the bowels, pallor or anemia, and, in nervous persons, sometimes melancholy.

TREATMENT.   In this condition tablets of methylrosaniline chloride, which can be procured on a physician's prescription, bring about a cure. Two tablets are to be taken immediately before meals three times a day for eight days. After an interval of a week, the medication is repeated. If a child suffers from pinworms, the entire family should be treated at the same time.

Another drug, which should be used with great caution and only under strict instructions of a physician, is remarkably and quickly effective in the cure, without the necessity of a few days' abstention from the drug. It is oil of chenopodium. For a child, as many drops of the oil are given on a piece of lump sugar as the child is years old. The dose is repeated in two hours, followed by the use of castor oil.

Round Worms

These are from four to ten inches long, pointed at the ends like earthworms, but of a yellow-white color or tinged with red. They naturally inhabit the upper parts of the bowels, but wander about and often are vomited from the stomach. They may thus be found in the nose or throat. They are ordinarily seen in the excrement, and a white, mucous discharge from the bowels is occasionally mistaken for them.

TREATMENT. Santonin is one of the most ancient drugs used for the cure of round worms. It is tasteless and non-irritant, and easily administered to children. It is the most effective remedy. It is also used for the removal of pinworms. It is prescribed by the physician with calomel. For children the small crystals can be used with sugar.

Tapeworms

The common tapeworms are of two varieties: beef and pork tapeworms, caused by the eating of the raw or imperfectly cooked meats. If raw beef is very finely minced, or if the juice is squeezed out of raw beef and strained, the danger of tapeworm is averted. There is great danger of children with tapeworm conveying some of the eggs from the parts about the rectum to their mouths, through sucking their fingers. In this event the immature tapeworms enter the body and attack other organs, thus endangering the life of the patient. The ordinary tapeworm is from twenty to fifty feet long, made up of white, flattened joints or segments. The head is the size of a pinhead, and the neck is not much thicker than a thread, but the middle and lower part of the body is from a quarter to half an inch wide. The presence of the worm is recognized by the escape of pieces of it in the excrement every few days.

TREATMENT. The treatment should be given only by a physician. He administers a drug which has a specific action on the tapeworm.

SCABIES (THE ITCH)

The most frequent infectious and contagious skin disease is known as scabies, or "the itch," and causes intense itching and burning. The disease is spread by contact with an infected person, his bed, or his personal clothing or belongings.

CAUSES AND SYMPTOMS.   There is a single cause—a parasite which burrows its way into and out of the skin. The itching is worse at night. The burrows made by the parasite are found between the fingers and along the wrists, along the front of the armpits, on the lower abdomen, buttocks and genitals. The face usually escapes attack. In infants the palms and soles are frequently infested.

TREATMENT.   The most reliable treatment for scabies consists of the application, from the neck down, of 10 per cent precipitated sulphur and 10 per cent balsam of Peru in equal parts of petrolatum and lanolin. Four ounces of the ointment are used, one third of which is applied at night after a hot soap bath. On the next day, without bathing, one third is applied in the morning and the remainder at night. On the following morning, a hot soap bath is followed by spreading a generous amount of talcum powder over the entire body. Fresh underclothing and bedding must be used and all infested members of the family must be treated to prevent reinfestation.

For a child of five to twelve years, the strength of sulphur and balsam of Peru is reduced to 5 per cent. For younger children it is reduced to 2½ per cent and the amount of the ointment is cut in half.

LICE INFESTATIONS (PEDICULOSIS)

When there are head lice, the hair should be soaked in a mixture of half-and-half kerosene and vinegar. This treatment should be given several times, and the hair combed with a fine comb frequently soon afterward. Tincture of larkspur is also used.

Pubic lice—lice in the pubic hair—are treated with ammoniated mercury, under the supervision of a doctor.

If there are body lice, all you need do is remove them and sterilize the clothing, in which they live.

CHAFING AND CHAPPING

CAUSES.   Chafing occurs when two opposing skin surfaces rub together and are irritated by sweat, as in the armpits, under the breasts, between the thighs and buttocks, and beneath overlapping parts of the abdomen of obese people. The same result follows irritation brought on by discharges touching the skin, as is seen in infants from the presence of urine and bowel discharges. The irritation caused by saliva when the lips are frequently licked is commonly called chapping, but it is proper to consider chafing and chapping together, since the treatment is the same for both.

Chafing occurs more often in hot weather and after violent exercise, and is aggravated by the friction of clothing or of tight shoes. It may, on the other hand, appear in children who sit a great deal.

Symptoms. The parts affected are hot, red, and tender, and emit a disagreeable odor when secretions are retained. The skin becomes soaked with retained sweat, and may crack and bleed. The same kind of redness and tenderness is seen in the chapping of the face and lips, or other skin surfaces.

Treatment. In chafing, the first requisite is to avoid soap and water. Calamine liniment is helpful. Infants' diapers should be boiled thoroughly and dried in the sun.

PRICKLY HEAT (MILIARIA)

This is a common eruption which afflicts adults in hot weather. It frequently attacks children. It consists of a fine, pointed red rash or tiny blisters, and occurs on parts of the body covered by clothing, frequently on the chest.

Causes and Symptoms. The eruption is caused by much sweating, which leads to congestion and swelling of the sweat glands. Burning, stinging, and itching accompany the disorder, which must be distinguished from contagious skin eruptions. The latter conditions are accompanied by fever, sore throat, backache, headache, and general sickness; in prickly heat there is no general disturbance. There is no fever, unless the eruption comes out in the course of a fever, and then it is of significance only as one of the indications of fever.

Treatment. The treatment of this hot-weather complaint consists of avoiding heat as much as possible, and sponging the body with cold water, then dusting it with some simple powder—starch or flour, or better, borated talcum. An effective measure to relieve itching is sponging with lime water or a saturated solution of baking soda (as much as will dissolve) in water. Bran baths, made by tying one pound of bran in a towel, which is allowed to soak in the bath, are helpful, as is calamine liniment.

HIVES OR NETTLERASH (URTICARIA)

CAUSES. Hives is an allergy that may result from many different causes. Certain unusual foods may be a provocative factor; on the other hand, some simple article of diet, such as eggs or berries, may be the principal cause. Food hives or urticaria is usually discovered in childhood.

An attack may be brought on by physical agents, such as light, heat, and cold, or by scratching. Some injected foreign proteins, especially serums and bacterial products, produce hives in susceptible persons. Hives may also result from the inhalation of pollen, from insect bites, from the fur or saliva of domestic animals, or the taking of various drugs, including aspirin, morphine, codeine, barbiturates, iodides, bromides, quinine, atropine, belladonna, sulfa drugs, and phenolphthalein.

Chronic urticaria is sometimes caused by certain foods, by focal infection, or by animal parasites, but is usually caused by nervous exhaustion.

The allergy may be of obscure origin, and in some cases many factors may be involved.

SYMPTOMS. Hives is characterized by the sudden appearance of hard round or oval lumps in the skin, varying in size from a pea to a silver dollar. They are pinkish-white, or white in the center, and often surrounded by a red blush. The rash is accompanied by itching, burning or tingling, especially at night when the clothing is removed.

The eruption may affect any part of the body, but the lumps do not run together. Scratching the skin often brings out lumps in a few minutes. The swellings may last a few minutes or hours; they may suddenly disappear, to reappear in some other place. The whole trouble usually continues only a few days, although at times it becomes a chronic disorder.

TREATMENT. The treatment of hives requires the services of a physician. Chronic recurrent urticaria is not easily treated, and search should be made for the cause. Relief is sometimes sudden, following extraction of a decayed tooth. Histamine desensitization is sometimes of benefit. Histaminase may be taken by mouth in coated capsules, if the physician prescribes it. The condition is also frequently alleviated by the use of benadryl or pyribenzamine in tablet form.

For itching, the following substances are used with varying degrees of relief: sodium bicarbonate baths; starch baths; calamine and zinc lotion containing 1 per cent carbolic acid; cold applications; applications of heat; anti-itching ointments; adrenalin, injected under the skin by a physician; or ephedrine by mouth. In severe cases of the disease, calcium lactate, calcium gluconate, or calcium chloride may be given in the veins.

Usually in urticaria attacks a saline cathartic is necessary.

ACNE (PIMPLES AND BLACKHEADS)

CAUSES. Pimples and blackheads are both caused by inflammation around the glands of the skin, which secrete oily material. The mouths of the glands become plugged, thus retaining the oily secretion and causing the blackheads. If these glands are then invaded by germs producing pus, a pimple results. Constipation and indigestion favor the occurrence of pimples and blackheads; also a poor state of the blood, or anemia.

SYMPTOMS. Acne appears chiefly on the face, but often also on the ear, the back, shoulders, and chest. It is a disorder which is seen mostly in young people of both sexes at about the age of puberty. "Blackheads" appear as slightly elevated black points, sometimes having a yellowish tint, from which a little, thin, wormlike mass can be pressed. Conical elevations of the skin, from a pin head to a pea in size, form an eruption which is often reddened and tender on pressure, and with a tendency to form matter or pus, as shown by a yellow spot in the center of the pimple. After three to ten days this matter is discharged, but red elevations remain, which later become brown and disappear without scarring, except in rare cases.

TREATMENT. The bowels must be moved daily. The blackheads should be squeezed out with an instrument made for the purpose, not with fingernails. Pimples containing matter should receive an application of iodine or rubbing alcohol, then be emptied after being pricked with a sterilized needle.

Do not use complexion brushes and creams. If there is redness of the skin and irritation associated with pimples, bathe the skin with very hot water and green soap three times daily, and apply calamine lotion or lotio alba at night. When the skin is not sensitive, and zinc or mercury has not been used, a treatment with sulphur soap and hot water at bedtime (allowing the suds to dry and remain on the face during the night) is recommended. An ointment consisting of one-half teaspoonful of precipitated sulphur with one-half ounce each of powdered starch and vaseline applied each night, and hot water used on the face three times daily, are also effective.

A highly successful technique in the treatment of acne consists of the use of what is known as a polysulphide. Vaccine therapy and injections of vitamin B are occasionally beneficial.

The various sulphur products have been combined with neutra-color (a mixture of betonite and oxide of iron powder) to produce a lotion closely resembling the color of the skin. It can be filled at the drug store.

Shake and apply to the face after treatment with sulfated oil.

DIET FOR ACNE. The diet should consist principally of vegetables, fruit, milk, eggs in moderation, and meats (only once a day, unless engaged in active physical exercise). Drink at least six to eight large glasses of water daily.

Omit—pastries, pies, cakes, ice cream, soda fountain drinks, jam, jellies, fried foods, gravies, alcoholic drinks, iodized salt, peanut butter, nuts, chocolate, cocoa, sugar, potatoes, rice, macaroni, noodles, spaghetti.

Limit—fats, meats, bread, cheese.

Cereals—cereals, hot or cold, may be eaten with milk (or cream) and a *limited* amount of sugar, two or three times a week.

Eggs—poached, soft boiled, scrambled, or in omelet. Not more than once a day.

Soups—all soups or broths. Avoid overseasoning.

Meats—all meats except pork and veal. Meats may be boiled, broiled, or stewed, but not fried.

Vegetables—all vegetables, fresh or canned, cooked or raw, except potatoes.

Bread—whole-wheat and graham bread, preferably toasted; hard rolls, corn and bran muffins.

Desserts—fruits only, preferably stewed.

Beverages—tea, coffee, milk, buttermilk.

COLD SORES (FEVER BLISTERS)

CAUSES. Cold sores are caused by a certain virus infection. They often occur in the course of fever, including the common cold, influenza, pneumonia, malaria, and meningitis. Windburn or sunburn are often responsible for them, and indigestion is a common predisposing factor.

SYMPTOMS. The sores, usually a few in one place, form on the face, generally around the mouth. The inner surfaces of the lips are sometimes affected. The sores contain a watery fluid.

TREATMENT. Picking and scratching are very harmful, and cigar or pipe smoking must be stopped. Painting the sore with collodion, by means of a camel's hair brush, as is often done, is poor treatment in the early stages. In the earlier stages it is better to use spirits of camphor, and afterwards, if there is much itching or burning, to dab the eruption with calamine liniment to relieve the discomfort. A 5 per cent solution of silver nitrate, applied lightly once a day, will help in the healing process.

In a patient with fever the mouth must be kept as clean as possible. Clean it before and after eating. Lubricate the tongue and lips with equal parts of lemon juice and glycerin, using cotton-tipped swabs.

SHINGLES (HERPES ZOSTER)

CAUSES.　This is an acute inflammatory skin disease. Its typical sign is the appearance of small blisters along the course of some superficial sensory nerve. Evidence seems to show that it is essentially an acute inflammation of the posterior spinal ganglia, and is caused by a virus, at times that of chickenpox.

SYMPTOMS.　The disease attacks all ages, and is common in those who are overworked or ill. It appears, as a rule, only on one side of the body, with a discharge of serum and formation of blisters. There is intense pain.

TREATMENT.　It is important to keep the blisters dry in order to prevent reinfection, because the virus of zoster is present in the blister-fluid. Locally, calamine liniment is a useful dressing.

Among the remedies the physician uses which often work miraculously are injections of pituitrin (surgical), cobra venom, ethyl chloide spray, dry heat, and thiamin chloride. Injection of sodium iodide into a vein on the first, third, fifth and seventh day diminishes the pain and hastens healing. Other pain-killers are also used.

RINGWORM

CAUSES AND SYMPTOMS.　Ringworm is an infection of the skin, hair, or nails, caused by various fungi. On the body it attacks the neck, face and hands. It appears first as small, red, scaly spots which may spread into a circular patch as large as a dollar, with a red ring of small, scaly pimples on the outside. The center may exhibit healthy skin, or may be red and thickened. There may be several patches of ringworm near each other, and they may run together, or there may be only one patch.

TREATMENT.　Any one of the following ingredients, when applied in a base, is usually curative: thymol (0.5 per cent); sulphur (2 to 15 per cent); sodium thiosulphate and salicylic acid (of each, 2 to 10 per cent); resorcinol (1 per cent); ammoniated mercury (5 to 10 per cent). If the condition is persistent, it requires a physician's attention.

Ringworm of the Scalp

This is a disease usually confined to children and is difficult to cure. It is contagious and may be acquired from children with the disease, or from fondling and handling cats and dogs who have ringworm. Preventive care is necessary when there is an epidemic. The hair should be closely clipped, and the scalp should be washed with non-medicated soap and water once a day, or once in two days. A child suffering from ringworm of the scalp should wear a skull cap, and have brush, comb, towels and wash cloths carefully reserved for his personal use.

The following solution may be used for washing the scalp in ringworm of the scalp, or for ringworm of the body proper. It is dispensed by the druggist.

Precipitated sulphur .... 1 drachm
Betanaphthol .... 20 grains
Medicinal soft soap .... 1 ounce

Use like soap in cleansing the scalp.

The condition is sometimes helped by applying compresses of hot boric acid solution to the affected areas for fifteen to twenty minutes several times a day. Following each application, a 5 per cent salicylanilid ointment should be thoroughly rubbed into the affected areas. In ringworm of the scalp caused by a human type of fungus, temporary removal of the hair by X-rays is sometimes necessary.

Athlete's Foot (Ringworm of the Feet)

This is the most common variety of ringworm. The feet should be washed with soap and water each night, rinsed well, and scaly accumulations wiped away. The toes should be dried carefully after bathing. A preparation of boic acid, tannic acid and zinc oxide in equal parts is then used.

Blisters should be opened with a sterilized needle, and the area painted with a 10 per cent watery solution of silver nitrate.

The feet should be soaked in some antiseptic foot bath, such at 1:8000 potassium permanganate or 1:10,000 bichloride of mercury, either of which can be had at a drug store. The soaking should last at least ten minutes, from two to eight times a day, using lukewarm water. Sulphur-salicylic acid ointment is helpful.

IMPETIGO CONTAGIOSA

CAUSES.   Impetigo is one of the most common skin diseases of children and is caused by germs, the streptococci or staphylococci. It is spread by direct contact or through the use of infected towels, and is often acquired in barber shops.

SYMPTOMS.   Impetigo usually occurs on the face and scalp and rarely on the limbs or body proper. Blisters form. When they break, they produce yellow "stuck-on" crusts. The fresh crusts are yellow but later turn brown; when mixed with blood they may turn black. Itching is severe.

TREATMENT.   Treatment by a physician soon clears up this condition. The crusts are removed with forceps by the physician and the residual base is touched with an appropriate antiseptic. Bacitracin or aureomycin is applied in ointment form. In mild varieties of the disease ammoniated mercury ointment is prescribed.

BOILS

CAUSES.   Boils are the result of an inflammation which has its beginning in an infection of a hair-sac. A pustule surrounds the shaft of the hair, and the pus-infected boil develops. Boils are usually found on the neck, armpits, face, buttocks, and legs, although no area of the body is exempt. The basic infection is caused by staphylococci, which are germs.

TREATMENT.   Formation of a boil can sometimes be prevented by the early application of tincture of iodine or mercurial plaster. If this fails, you can bring the boil "to a head" with the aid of dry heat.

Mild antiseptics may be applied. A good plan is to paint the boil once daily with diluted tincture of iodine or 1 per cent gentian violet in alcohol; then apply a large gauze pack (hot) moistened with half-and-half glycerol and alcohol. Physicians often prescribe bacitracin or aureomycin ointment.

It is unwise for anyone but a physician to cut into a boil, and it is seldom necessary. Infected hairs should never be pulled out. Also, the boil should never be squeezed out.

IVY POISONING

CAUSES. Poison ivy, like poison sumach and poison oak, causes inflammation of the skin in certain persons who touch it. In some cases, even approaching within a short distance of the plants sets up the inflammation. The plants contain a poisonous oil, and the pollen blown from them by the wind may convey enough of this oil to poison susceptible persons. Signs and symptoms may appear within four to five hours, or in as many days after exposure to the plant.

There is a common belief that ivy poisoning recurs at about the same time each year. This belief has no foundation in fact.

SYMPTOMS. The skin of the hands or other affected parts becomes red, swollen, painful, and itchy. Soon little blisters form, and scratching breaks them open so that the parts are moist and then become covered with crusts. The poison is conveyed by the hands to the face and other parts of the body and, in men, to the sexual organs, so that these areas soon partake of the same trouble. The face and head may become so swollen that the patient is almost unrecognizable.

TREATMENT. Ten per cent sodium perborate in a protective ointment base protects successfully if applied to exposed parts of the body before contact with poison ivy. Clothes and equipment must be decontaminated after exposure.

If you touch poison ivy, take a hot bath and rub the body thoroughly with soap. In mild ivy poisoning, some relief is obtained from swabbing the parts with 2 per cent potassium permanganate solution and carbolized calamine lotion. Burow's solution (aluminum acetate) may be tried as a healing, wetting agent. This may be made up with prepared tablets. Keep the solution in a bottle labeled "For Poison Ivy." Use it as a wet dressing for not more than ten minutes; after that, daub on a little if the itching returns, and let it dry.

The affected parts may also be bathed for a few minutes at a time in water just hot enough to be uncomfortable—paradoxically giving comfort. Dry heat is just as good.

An effective formula for poison ivy treatment consists of the following medical ingredients in the proportions given. It can be made up by the druggist, and is applied locally, as a lotion.

Castor oil	21.5
Olive oil	21.5
Lanolin (without water)	21.5
Diglycol stearate	12.9
Paraffin, refined	8.6
Boric acid	2.0
Sodium perborate	10.0
Duponol W. A. Pure	2.0

ECZEMA

Eczema is an inflammation of the skin, of uncertain cause, marked by blisters, watery discharge, and the formation of scales and crusts. Fluid is concealed beneath the surface or appears on the surface after the skin has been irritated. There are many varieties, and they are classified according to whether they are of internal origin or of external origin, caused by occupation, climate, or by certain glands of the skin.

ECZEMA OF INTERNAL ORIGIN. This form of the disease almost invariably appears on both sides of the body at once, as for example, on both cheeks, or both arms, or both thighs. Its border shades into the surrounding skin; it is dotted with papules (or heads) filled with fluid, and its surface is clean and not greasy. Exhaustion plays a prominent role in causing it. Among the drugs producing it is cod-liver oil.

ECZEMA OF EXTERNAL ORIGIN. Occupational eczema occurs first on exposed parts—the hands, arms, face and neck—of those who handle irritant dyes, sugar, formalin, etc.

Climatic eczema includes the "winter itch" common in the north temperate zone. It appears on wrists and ankles in the form of clean, scaly patches, often ringed.

The seborrheic variety caused by the oil glands of the skin spreads from the scalp to the folds of the skin. Its borders are sharply defined, its crusts and scales yellowish and greasy. It spreads from a center in all directions at once.

How to Treat Eczema. The treatment of eczema is puzzling to the physician. As a rule, only specialists in skin diseases are able to diagnose easily the subacute or chronic forms. It may appear different and require different treatment, almost from day to day; consequently only general suggestions can be made for home management of the disease. However, the outlook is always good; and even in the case of weak patients, there is excellent chance of cure. Soap must be religiously avoided. Where there are pustules, a 2 per cent watery solution of gentian violet is of value. The germ-killer, bacitracin solution or ointment, is often effective in the treatment of pustular eczema. Eczema with secondary infection is improved by local treatment with this drug.

If itching is pronounced, remove crusts and scabs after soaking with olive oil, and dust borax, finely powdered, on the surface. If the itching is not controlled in twenty minutes, wipe off the borax with a cloth moistened with olive oil.

The following three eczema prescriptions are often helpful:

Powder for Eczema

Boric acid	2 drachms
Zinc oxide	1 ounces
Purified talc	4 ounces

For Pustular Eczema

Boric acid	10 grains
Bismuth subnitrate	1 drachm
Pine tar	20 grains
Rose water ointment	add to 1 ounce

Apply to the pustules.

Ointment for Chronic Eczema

Salicylic acid	1 drachm
Pine tar	1 ounce
Vaseline	4 ounces

After removing all crusts in the affected areas, apply this ointment freely once a day.

WARTS

Warts are flattened or rounded outgrowths from the outer and middle layers of the skin, varying in size from a pinhead to one-half inch in diameter. Warts most commonly appear on the hands of children, but they may be present on any part of the body and at all ages. They may disappear quickly or remain indefinitely and are not communicable from one person to another. There are several varieties, among which the following are common:

SEED WARTS.   These have numerous, little fleshy projections over their surface, which are enlarged normal structures (papillae) of the middle layer of the skin, together with the thickened, outer, horny layer.

THREADLIKE WARTS.   These are found along the edge of the nails, on the face, neck, eyelids, and ears. They are formed by the great prolongation and growth of the projections, or papillae, of the middle layer of the skin.

FLAT WARTS.   These warts are raised but slightly above the surface. They are more common in young people.

MOIST WARTS.   These are present when softened by secretions of the body, as in the region of the external sexual organs (in connection with their diseases), and about the anus, or natural opening of the bowel. They are white, pink, or red, and consist of numerous, little fleshy projections, usually covered with an ill-smelling secretion.

TREATMENT.   Many warts disappear by themselves in time. Warts can sometimes be removed by painting them frequently with acetic acid, or with tincture of iodine. These remedies are harmless, but somewhat slow and not always effective. Application, morning and evening, of a saturated solution of "washing soda" (impure bicarbonate of potash) will often remove a wart.

Warts are readily removed by physicians, who may use caustics, surgery, or other methods. The administration by mouth of 100,000 units of vitamin A daily for from two to three months will cure many warts.

THE COMMON COLD

Someone has labeled the common cold "Public Malady No. 1." The common cold is indeed the commonest of all diseases of the respiratory system. It is an acute inflammation of the nasal mucous membranes, marked by signs and symptoms throughout the body. It frequently has temporary or lasting complications.

Popularly, any infection and acute inflammation of the upper respiratory system is called a cold. It must be kept in mind, however, that almost all of the communicable diseases of infancy and childhood—for example, measles, scarlet fever, whooping cough, diphtheria, and tonsillitis—may at first show symptoms suggestive of a cold. Everyone knows that sneezing spells may usher in a cold in the head, hay fever, or infectious childhood diseases. Sinus infections, particularly during their flare-ups, are likely to be referred to as colds. Allergy to foods and to various inhalants may produce the symptoms of a cold because of changed tension of the blood vessels of the nose.

THE COLD VIRUS. The common cold is primarily caused by what is known as a filterable virus. This agent of infectious disease, chemical or living, is so small that it cannot be discovered by ordinary microscopic means. Since it can pass through certain filters it is called filterable. The virus is highly contagious and is spread by coughing, sneezing or kissing.

When a cold virus infects the lining of the nose it weakens the natural defenses by interfering with the activity of the cilia and the secretion of mucus. Bacteria then have a favorable environment. They induce sneezing, nasal obstruction, nasal discharge, headache, temperature, and a sense of fatigue. The nasal infection sometimes spreads. It may spread up into the sinuses or downward into the throat or lungs, or both. While the common cold *per se* is rarely a cause of death it may bring on such serious infections as pneumonia.

Conditions Favoring the Common Cold. Infections of the respiratory system are more common in winter than in summer. This is perhaps due to the fact that people are more likely to stay indoors during cold weather and are therefore in closer contact with each other. This favors the distribution of disease germs.

Almost every susceptible person who is in immediate contact with an infected person will contract the disease. The immunity gained is ordinarily of short duration; consequently it is possible for one individual to have a number of attacks of the infection each year. Another reason why the common cold is so prevalent is its relative mildness. The disease as a rule is so mild that infected persons often continue at their usual occupations, thus spreading the infection to others.

Chills and Drafts. Colds are usually attributed to a chill because they are frequently ushered in by a sensation of being chilly. Actually, there is no scientific proof that exposure to chills and drafts causes colds in healthy persons who have not been exposed to infection. It is known, for example, that those exposed to arctic conditions, such as sailors and fishermen, do not readily catch colds and pneumonia.

Epidemics of colds are most common when atmospheric humidity is great, and the temperature is cool but variable; when the weather is raw, with thawing snow and sleet; or winds blow with cold rain, and the ground is wet and cold. However, cold dry weather and strong dry winds do not provide favorable conditions for epidemics of infections of the upper respiratory system.

Bad Ventilation. Bad ventilation is a common predisposing cause. It produces lowered resistance in the nasal and respiratory membranes, which is not so likely to occur in persons living open-air lives. Bad weather, as previously stated, drives or keeps people indoors. Windows are kept shut, and infection is thus spread. People in passing suddenly from overheated rooms into cold air put a strain on the functions of the respiratory mucous membranes.

In general the predisposing factors in the case of the common cold are physical fatigue, damp clothing, sudden changes in atmospheric pressure, poor ventilation, nasal obstruction, susceptibility, and certain occupations.

COLD SYMPTOMS IN CHILDREN. Infections of the nose and throat, or those of the rest of the upper respiratory tract, are extremely common during childhood. They are a common factor in the production of many of the minor, and some of the major, diseases of infancy and childhood. Infants incubating the common cold are fretful and sleepy. An initial vomiting is often alarming to the mother or nurse. There is fever, accompanied by headache and loss of appetite. Older children complain of pain in the throat and in the chest. Nose breathing is obstructed. There is a profuse, watery discharge at the nostrils, and at first a dry cough.

COLD PREVENTION. The best method of prevention is to avoid contact with infected persons and to stay away from crowded places. Surgical removal or correction of conditions which predispose to acute respiratory disease is frequently helpful. These include infected tonsils, infected sinuses, enlarged adenoids, and the various causes of nasal obstruction, such as deformities, deflected septums, enlarged turbinates, spurs and polyps.

COLD TREATMENT. There is actually no sure way to cure a cold. The principal treatment consists of relieving the local discomfort. Aspirins are helpful, and the bowels should be moved regularly. Rest plays an important part in raising the resistance, and so does a well-balanced diet. Fruit juices and water should be drunk in abundance. When the larynx is involved, absolute rest of the voice is essential.

If an infant or older child has a cold, he should be put to bed. The room should be warm, and hot baths and hot drinks, as well as alkalis, are helpful.

ANTIHISTAMINE DRUGS FOR COLDS. Many people assert that the use of antihistamine drugs—as for example, benadryl, pyribenzamine, and chlortrimeton—in small doses for a short period of time is effective in the treatment of colds. It is declared that the cold can be avoided or controlled if a few doses are taken beginning within an hour or two after the appearance of the first symptoms. However, this is still an unsettled subject, and it must be remembered that some persons experience ill effects from taking the antihistamine drugs.

NASAL ALLERGY (ALLERGIC RHINITIS)

CAUSES. Of the many factors which are responsible for nasal allergy, the following are the most common: drugs, food, pollens, cosmetics, linens, silks, dust, dander from horses and dogs, furs, feathers and hair, local irritation, heat stimuli, deficiency of blood calcium, intestinal toxemia, glandular disturbances, certain phenomena of climate, and any other agents which produce allergies.

As a cause of respiratory allergy, ordinary house dust is generally of basic importance. Next are such specific factors as may be present in feathers, cotton, wool, kapok, etc. Of secondary influence are certain occupational and environmental dusts, such as the dust in grain elevators and stables. Some authorities consider dusts to be the cause of respiratory allergy in 90 per cent of patients.

Among foods that cause attacks of nasal allergy, melons, for example, and strawberries, raspberries, cucumbers, and cherries are commonly responsible. Often the same variety of reaction occurs from eating crab, lobster, or other shellfish; and sometimes from pork, as well as from a number of common foods which are not well tolerated.

How ALLERGIES ARE CLASSIFIED. Stated simply, nasal allergy or allergic rhinitis may be divided into three varieties: (1) seasonal; (2) perennial, with positive skin tests; (3) perennial, with negative skin tests.

In seasonal allergic rhinitis, symptoms are caused by the breathing in of pollen. They are limited to the seasons when the specific plant to which the patient is sensitive pollinates.

In perennial allergic rhinitis, a person shows all the signs and symptoms common to the seasonal variety, but these are felt all year round, constantly or in repeated attacks, and are brought on by sensitivity to a number of substances in the air or in food. The group of people afflicted throughout the year usually give positive skin tests, showing that an allergy is present.

The perennial allergic rhinitis group that give negative skin tests possess a definite immunity. In a large proportion of cases, those in the first two groups give clear evidence of a hereditary tendency and reveal other signs and symptoms of allergy (asthma, for instance); those in the third group generally present only nasal symptoms.

SYMPTOMS. The person who suffers from this variety of rhinitis appears to have a constant head cold. Spells of sneezing on arising in the morning are followed by a profuse watery nasal discharge. There is obstruction to nasal breathing, a dull headache, and a feeling in the ears as though the ear canals were blocked with cotton wool. Speech is nasal, as if uttered through the nose. The condition is often associated with asthma. These symptoms vary considerably in different persons, both in degree and duration.

The common cold is always present as a possibility, and may temporarily hide the signs and symptoms of allergy. Repeated observations may therefore be necessary to determine the precise nature of the infection. For an accurate diagnosis, the following factors must be kept in mind: (1) the nasal, sinus, and bronchial symptoms; (2) conditions discovered on examination of the nose; (3) composition of nasal and bronchial secretions; (4) information obtained by X-ray examination; (5) bacteriologic data; and (6) skin tests. Nasal allergy is common in children, and the attacks of sneezing and nasal obstruction may lead to the diagnosis of an infectious cold. It must be remembered, however, that infection and allergy may occur at the same time.

TREATMENT. In general, the treatment is the same as for hay fever, which follows.

HAY FEVER

This is a condition, not purely nasal, in which a person shows excessive sensitiveness to the pollen or germ cells of the male plant of certain flowers and trees, and especially to grasses. Hay fever is primarily a seasonal (summer or fall) disease, which occurs most often in young adults and children. It may be associated with a neurotic tendency. Heredity appears to play a part. It is often considered a form of nasal allergy. In hay fever victims, the mucous membrane lining of the nose and upper respiratory system has a particularly high degree of sensitivity.

VARIETIES OF HAY FEVER. There are two common varieties of hay fever: that of early summer, brought about by an allergy to June grass and timothy; and the more frequent autumnal form produced by sensitiveness to ragweed, or a combination of ragweed and other pollens.

In the eastern part of the United States, three varieties of seasonal hay fever occur. (1) The spring form begins at the end of March or early in April and extends to the end of May. It is caused almost exclusively by pollens from trees, especially oak, hickory, maple, birch, and elm. (2) The second, or summer, variety beginning at the end of May and extending to the middle of July, is ordinarily caused by the pollen of grasses. The important pollens in this group are redtop, timothy, June grass, orchard grass, sweet vernal, and plantain. (3) The third, or fall, variety begins in the middle of August and continues until frost. The pollen of the ragweed is mainly responsible for this group.

RESULTS OF HAY FEVER. Children and adults who have suffered from perennial nasal allergy during early childhood often show nasal depressions which make the nose unduly prominent, a V-shaped palate, and marked overriding of the teeth. A child with nasal allergy frequently becomes a nose-rubber or a nose-wrinkler, or both, because of uncomfortable itching of the nasal mucous membrane. If such a habit begins in early life and continues over a period of years the result is often a distorted nose. This effect upon the features, however, is quite different from that caused by adenoids, with the characteristic pinched appearance of the nose, the prominence of the upper incisor teeth, and the abnormal mouth and lower jaw.

TREATMENT. Treatment includes: elimination of the cause or causes, and desensitization. If the particular substances causing the allergy can be discovered, they should be avoided, whenever possible.

A change of residence to a pollen-free area, filtered-air rooms, air-conditioned living quarters, and an ocean voyage are all helpful for the relief of symptoms. If this is not practical, the process called desensitization should be carried out. There are two plans of treatment: the preseasonal and the perennial or all-year-round plan. In both, small doses of the sensitizing agents are injected.

A number of drugs (especially benadryl and pyribenzamine, both of which may be taken internally in tablet form) have been found effective in many allergic conditions. However, these drugs are not panaceas, and frequently cause unpleasant after-effects, such as marked dizziness and grogginess. A single application of pyribenzamine nasal solution from a fine-spray atomizer often brings quick relief from allergic nasal congestion. Relief is obtained for a number of hours or days but the effect is not lasting.

THRUSH

SYMPTOMS. This is a fungus infection of the mouth, found in children. It appears as if patches of milk are left stuck to the cheeks, tongue and roof of the mouth, and these patches are not easily removed. The mouth is sore. Want of cleanliness in feeding children is the chief cause.

TREATMENT. If the patient is a nursing infant, the mother's nipple must be kept clean. The areas in the mouth should be touched twice daily with a 1 per cent solution of gentian violet, with absorbent cotton wound tightly on a toothpick. The mouth should be cleansed several times a day, especially after feeding. For the child that is old enough to use a mouth wash, a good one can be made up by the druggist, consisting of boroglycerin, and sodium sulphite, one drachm to one ounce of water. Cod-liver oil should be given. For a child of six months, give one-half teaspoonful once or twice daily.

TONSILLITIS

CAUSES. Tonsillitis is an inflammation of the tonsils which can be caused by many different germs. There are two forms of the disease, acute and chronic. In severe cases, tonsillitis can have serious results. It may lead to rheumatic fever, pneumonia, arthritis, ear infection, or other disorders.

Lowered resistance favors an infection of the tonsils.

SYMPTOMS. Enlarged tonsils are not in themselves a symptom of tonsillitis. However, in tonsillitis, there is swelling of the tonsils and a sore throat, making it hard to swallow. White spots appear on the tonsils. The lymphatic glands are enlarged. Mild fever, restlessness, and general discomfort are present. There is an increase in the pulse rate. If a gray or greenish membrane appears in the throat and on the tonsils, this is a symptom of diphtheria, and urgent action is called for.

TREATMENT. Rest in bed is required. Ice bags may be applied to the throat. Gargling with a mild warm salt water or baking soda solution is helpful. The diet should be light, with ample liquids. The physician will prescribe medicines to aid in controlling the infection. However, if the condition is a chronic one, removal of the tonsils is essential.

The operation is avoided when the patient is very young, and, indeed, is rarely necessary in children under three years of age. It should be avoided, too, during epidemics of contagious or infectious diseases; in the presence of serious blood and lung diseases, especially tuberculosis; when there is a throat abscess; and in cases of diabetes or thyroid gland disease.

ADENOIDS

CAUSES. Children are not born with adenoids although some authorities claim they are. These enlargements of lymphoid tissue begin to form early in life, and are a common trouble in childhood. In most children, some degree of enlargement is always present. Excessive enlargement, sufficient to induce symptoms, frequently follows one of the acute infectious fevers—for example, scarlet fever, measles, or diphtheria. Serious adenoid trouble is rare before the third year.

Adenoid enlargement is relatively uncommon in adults. Climate is an important factor; adenoid enlargement occurs more often in a cold, damp atmosphere than in a hot, dry climate.

SYMPTOMS. The symptoms vary according to the degree of adenoid enlargement. In severe examples, a characteristic picture —the adenoid face—is noted. This is the result of persistent mouth-breathing caused by nasal obstruction, a condition which gives a child a dull facial expression, an open mouth, a pinched nose, and a deep toneless voice. The child with adenoids sleeps restlessly and snores. He is tired and listless in the morning, and is an indifferent student at school. His appetite is poor and he remains undernourished.

In some children the chief symptoms are ear complications. In many, deafness is the result of enlarged adenoids. The condition varies somewhat with the weather, and is worse when the child is suffering from a cold. Nose bleeding is common in children with enlarged adenoids. A chain of small glands can nearly always be felt in the neck.

The most common effect is a tendency to repeated colds. The mouth breathing is responsible for laryngitis and bronchitis. The nasal obstruction causes a chain of symptoms including headache, mental depression, and a listless state. Some children, unable to breathe with food in the mouth, swallow food hurriedly; others, having difficulty in chewing, take only small mouthfuls.

TREATMENT. Adenoids should be surgically removed. Such operations are often remarkably beneficial. Even after well-performed adenoid removals, however, there is a definite tendency to recurrences in some children. When this lymphoid tissue becomes re-infected (as it usually does), it often causes repeated, and later, chronic, inflammations of the respiratory tract.

INFLUENZA

CAUSES. Influenza is an acute, often highly contagious disease caused by a filterable virus. It has occurred in world-wide epidemics, periodically. The last one of severity was that of 1918. It occurs sporadically during the winter months in minor forms.

SYMPTOMS. The incubation period is about two days. The disease begins suddenly. A chill or a sense of chilliness is experienced. Fever rises usually to 101 or 102°F. Prostration is marked. There is aching, sometimes severe, of the muscles, especially in the back and legs. In about twenty-four hours, sneezing and irritation of the eyes and throat develop. Later there are hoarseness and some cough and sputum. As a rule, fever and symptoms subside in four or five days. Weakness and fatigue may be present for a week or more.

In the severe type which occurred in the great epidemics such as in 1918 death was frequent, due to a peculiar type of bronchopneumonia.

TREATMENT. Treatment is only to relieve the symptoms. The sulfa drugs and the antibiotics such as penicillin and aureomycin are ineffective in this disease. Bedrest and abundant liquids are important. Aspirin and codeine are used most frequently for the aching. Whether the new drugs would be effective in the complicating bronchopneumonia remains undetermined since the severe epidemic form has not occurred since their discovery.

PREVENTION. Temporary immunity may be produced by the injection of influenzal virus A and B. There are probably other types not isolated, so that complete protection is not afforded. Immunization must be repeated yearly.

RHEUMATIC FEVER (INFLAMMATORY OR ACUTE RHEUMATISM)

Rheumatic fever is also known as inflammatory or acute rheumatism. Its exact cause has not been established. In general, it attacks young adults and children. However, extremely young children are usually exempt.

Rheumatic fever is a disease of late winter and early spring; it is also a disease of the slums. It is more prevalent in cities than in rural areas, and the greatest number of cases appeear where persons are subjected to the most crowding. Conditions favorable to its development are dampness, cold, and tonsillitis. Poor diet also favors it, as well as lack of warm clothes, and poor heating in homes.

The greatest damage in rheumatic fever occurs in the heart and arteries. The fever for which the disease is named may play only a minor part in its course.

The disease involves every part of the heart, as a rule—cover (pericardium), muscle, and lining of the heart and valves. The more severe the rheumatic infection in early youth, the more extensive, as a rule, is the damage to the heart. When, as frequently happens, all parts of the heart are involved, the term "pancarditis" is used by physicians to describe the condition.

RHEUMATIC HEART DISEASE. Rheumatic heart disease is the most serious aspect of rheumatic fever. It may include acute, subacute, or chronic involvement of the heart. There are several varieties of rheumatic heart disease: mild, where the heart symptoms are the least severe; ordinary grade, where the child is ill, pale and thin, the pulse rate is raised, the respiratory rate is somewhat raised, and fever up to 102°F. is present; and severe inflammation of the heart, where the child is extremely ill, the heart functions badly, and the child is pale. In this variety, the lips tend to be bluish, there is shortness of breath, especially at night; the pulse is rapid and feeble, the temperature is between 102° and 104° F.; there is also pain over the heart; and vomiting may be troublesome.

Rheumatic heart lesions are described as active or inactive, depending on whether inflammation is present, or there is merely scar tissue resulting from previous inflammations. An extremely serious variety noted in childhood results in death from cardiac (heart) failure.

SIGNS AND SYMPTOMS OF RHEUMATIC FEVER. The attacks may vary greatly, depending on how severe the general symptoms are, and the extent of involvement of the joints. The disease usually follows acute tonsillitis or an acute upper respiratory infection, and there is ordinarily a quiescent period of from ten to twenty-one days. The beginning is sudden, with moderate fever and sometimes a chill. The patient complains of severe pains in one or more joints.

An important indication of the disease is the increased heart rate, but it may not rise in proportion to the rise in fever. There may be pain and palpitation in the heart area. When the infection is severe there may be shortness of breath, and a heart murmur, which is discovered by the physician. Rheumatic nodules (lumps under the skin) indicate a severe infection. The electrocardiogram (graphic record of heart action) shows various indications that suggest the disease.

In childhood, acquired heart disease virtually means rheumatic inflammation of the heart. The rheumatic state in childhood, as previously mentioned, is almost unknown under two years of age, and rarely under three, but becomes more common from then on up to fifteen years. The pulse rate is very important. Records are kept of the pulse in the waking and sleeping state. In the early acute conditions the pulse rate is usually rapid.

IMMUNITY.   An attack of rheumatic fever gives no immunity. Indeed the opposite is actually true: each recurrence tends to inflict further damage on various structures of the heart.

How the Disease Affects Children

In children, infection of the joints is usually slight and may be absent, but the heart is frequently attacked. The only obvious evidence of an active rheumatic infection may be so-called "growing pains," tonsillitis, or St. Vitus's dance. The doctor, stethoscope, and electrocardiogram are necessary to detect the heart disease.

In dealing with the symptoms of rheumatic inflammation of the heart in children, two points are of fundamental importance. First, with the exception of pain caused by friction of the heart-cover, all the heart symptoms are the result of involvement of the heart muscle. As the heart muscle becomes more and more diseased, it fails to maintain the blood circulation sufficiently—at first during exertion, but later even when the child is at rest. Second, the beginning of heart symptoms in a rheumatic child always denotes fresh, active inflammation of the heart.

It must be borne in mind that irregular beating of the heart is definite evidence of disease of the muscle part of the heart.

As a rule, the symptoms are only moderately severe. Pain over the heart, palpitation, rapid heart action, and shortness of breath are present. Among the signs of active change in rheumatic fever, showing that the disease is still smouldering, are the following: fever, aches and pains in the joints and limbs, weakness, rheumatic nodules, and frequent, spontaneous nose bleeds. There are also vanishing skin eruptions, failure to gain weight. There is persistent increase in the white blood cells. Changes in the heart action are shown by the electrocardiogram tracings.

Difference Between Rheumatic Fever in Children and in Adults

Rheumatic fever is liable to be overlooked in childhood. It may, as Dr. Osler once said, "lick the joints, but bite the heart." It is important to bear the following distinctions in mind: in adult life, arthritis is the chief way in which rheumatic infection appears. It is considered to be the characteristic attack, and the heart involvement is regarded as a complication. In children, on the other hand, arthritis is often only slightly in evidence. It may even be entirely absent. Infection of other parts is more frequent and overshadows the remaining features of the disease. For example, the disease is sometimes limited to the tendons or the fascia (sheets of tissue which surround and connect the muscles) or to the joints (synovial membranes).

Another point is that while inflammation of the heart may occur in an acute form in children, it more often appears in a subacute form. Often there is a complete absence of symptoms felt by the person involved, or if they are present, they are masked by other signs and symptoms of rheumatic fever. Weakness, pallor, fatigue, loss of appetite and irritability are the usual symptoms.

It therefore becomes obvious that when there is even the suspicion of rheumatic infection in a child, *that child should be put to bed at once* and the most thorough examination of the heart made daily, including electrocardiograms.

In the absence of complications, the fever and acute symptoms subside in about ten days. In the subacute form the duration may be long. Relapses are frequent. In children, rheumatism tends to attack all the parts that make up the heart; in adults, the heart cover often escapes damage. For this reason rheumatic heart involvement in children has a much more serious outlook than in adults.

Complications of Rheumatic Heart Disease

The three most important complications of rheumatic heart disease are: congestive heart failure (overfulness of blood vessels) ; inflammation of the inner lining of the heart; and changes in the upper chambers of the heart (auricles). Inflammation of the heart muscle is present to a greater or lesser extent in the majority of children who are affected. Inflammation of the cover of the heart (pericardium) occurs in 10 per cent of afflicted persons. It may affect the lungs, their blood vessels and covering (pleura).

Treatment

Medical management has a number of aims: First, to arrest the progression of the active rheumatic process, and to prevent recurrent attacks and heart damage, as far as possible; second, to prevent psychic disturbances resulting from chronic, prolonged illness. The treatment varies with the stage of the disease. The care of the acutely ill child can usually be given best in a hospital, though in special circumstances the child may be adequately treated at home. The final decision must, however, rest with the physician.

There are a number of suggestions that may prevent serious impairment of the heart during an attack of rheumatic fever. These should be followed under a competent physician's direction. The child should be confined to bed until the heart rate is normal and all signs of fatigue are gone. Later all foci (centers) of infection should be removed; and adequate doses of salicylates should be administered. The affected joints, if any, should be wrapped in absorbent cotton soaked in oil of wintergreen. The limbs should be "cradled" under a frame made to support the weight of bedclothes and keep them from pressing on the joints.

DRUGS.   There is no known successful specific remedy in the treatment of rheumatic fever. Drugs are of value only in certain phases. During the active stage of the disease, salicylates are the most important drugs. They help to reduce fever, swelling of the joints, muscle pains, and other symptoms. For example, sodium salicylate or aspirin is given. In correct doses these give much relief from the pain.

CORTISONE TREATMENT FOR RHEUMATIC HEART DISEASE. Cortisone is a hormone (internal secretion) from the adrenal gland near the kidney. It holds considerable promise of effectiveness in rheumatic fever, as in rheumatism in general. On account of the scarcity of the drug, its use has been limited to institutions with adequate facilities for investigation and clinical control.

The giving of cortisone has certain disadvantages. Whenever a new drug with astonishing effects is discovered and tried out by the medical profession, conservative physicians give considerable thought to the question of whether the benefits that follow its use may not be associated with harmful effects that are worse than the original affliction itself. After cortisone administration, symptoms appear that suggest overdosage or intolerance.

The major importance of cortisone treatment in acute rheumatic fever is the fact that it throws a blanket, as it were, around the patient, between him and the disease, and thus protects him from some of its ravages. This pertains especially to the changes in the heart muscles and heart valves. The cortisone helps to defend the heart while the infectious process is running its course. The evidence so far is that the largest share of patients treated with cortisone have their hearts spared when the attacks have passed over.

DIET FOR RHEUMATIC FEVER. The diet should be based on the following principles: The food should be simple, well-cooked and easily digested. Moreover, the total quantity should be small and served three times a day, with the largest meal at noon. A light evening meal should be served early enough to insure complete digestion before retiring. If food is insufficient, light "snacks" in mid-morning or mid-afternoon should be given; fluids should be restricted to a quart or 1 1/5 quarts in twenty-four hours.

To be avoided in the diet are: foods that are bulky, or fried, those causing fermentation, highly seasoned foods, pastries, elaborate desserts, condiments and relishes. Above all, the sick person should avoid overeating, especially at night.

Convalescence

When a physician decides that it is safe for the patient to get up, it must be done gradually, starting with a short period each day out of bed in a chair, and later, more and more frequently, walking about and taking mild exercises. There is a strong indication that removal of a patient to a tropical or subtropical climate affects the condition favorably.

Prevention of Rheumatic Fever

There is general agreement that preventive measures must continue as long as relapses are likely—that is, until adolescence. Preventive treatment is not begun until the acute attack of rheumatic fever has subsided; it is, however, necessary to wait until certain tests are made. In the hope of preventing throat infections, particularly those caused by streptococci, tonsillectomy has been carried out extensively, after attacks in rheumatic patients. Reports as to results have been conflicting. There should be avoidance of damp or chill and avoidance of dietary deficiency, notably in protein, iron, calcium and vitamin A. Progress has been made in prevention of rheumatic fever. There has been administration, every winter for a period of several years, of hemolytic streptococcal filtrates to patients known to have had rheumatic fever. This has reduced the number of attacks of the disease.

Living conditions should be the best that circumstances permit. When feasible, change of residence to a warm, equable climate is desirable, either permanently or at least during winter and spring.

TUBERCULOSIS

Tuberculosis in childhood may affect almost any part of the body. It may affect the lungs, but it most commonly affects the glands—especially those inside the chest and abdomen—and the joints and bones. Tuberculosis may also cause inflammation of the lining of the chest (pleurisy), the covering of the brain (meningitis), the lining of the abdomen (peritonitis), the membranes of the eye (conjunctivitis), and the skin.

CAUSES. Tuberculosis is acquired most often by contact with someone who has it, by drinking raw milk from tuberculous cows, or by eating milk products made from such raw milk.

SYMPTOMS. Some of the symptoms common to all types of tuberculosis are: Loss in weight or failure to gain weight, unexplained fever, enlarged glands, pallor, and fatigue. Unlike adults, children with tuberculosis rarely have a cough as a symptom of the disease.

PREVENTION. A child should never live in the same household with anyone who has tuberculosis. All children who have come in contact with such a person should be examined by a doctor and have a tuberculin test. Those with positive tuberculin reactions should also have an X-ray of the chest; those with negative reactions should have the test repeated every year. If this is not possible, tests every three years beginning at the age of three and continued to the age of eighteen are advisable.

EARLY DIAGNOSIS IMPORTANT. Young children who get tuberculosis have a good chance for recovery, provided the diagnosis of the disease is made early. For this reason, if a child has any of the symptoms of tuberculosis listed or if he has been in contact with a person known or suspected to have tuberculosis, he should be taken to a doctor at once for thorough examination, X-rays, and testing.

ANEMIA

CAUSES AND SYMPTOMS. Anemia is a condition in which the child's blood has less red coloring matter than it has under normal conditions. If a child looks pale, the doctor should be consulted; he will probably make a test of the blood to find out whether the child has anemia.

There are several reasons why a child may have anemia.

1. He may have had a severe illness in which some of his blood was used up. A general building up after the illness will cure this type of anemia.

2. He may have had a wound that bled a great deal. If the loss has been very great, it may be necessary to give him a transfusion of someone else's blood. If the loss has not been too great, he will recover from the anemia without a transfusion.

3. He may have a serious disease which is destroying the blood. Such a disease, however, is rare among children.

4. His diet may be lacking in iron. Iron is necessary to make the red coloring matter of blood. Foods that supply iron are red meat, especially liver, kidney, and heart, egg yolk, green, leafy vegetables, whole-grain cereals, and molasses.

TREATMENT. A balanced diet, in which the foods just indicated play an important role, forms a vital part of any treatment. Liver extract and iron preparations are given, as prescribed by the physician.

NERVOUSNESS

Most people think of nerves as causing and controlling feeling, so that when a child shows an unusual amount of feeling or emotion his parents usually call him "nervous." Then, too, if a child is unduly restless or overactive, he is likely to be considered "nervous."

CAUSES. Most parents are inclined to think of "nervousness" as being caused chiefly by physical conditions such as malnutrition, fatigue, or inherited make-up. It is true that any of these can affect a child's way of feeling and behaving. We all know that we are more grouchy when we are tired or hungry. On the other hand, one frequent cause of "nervousness" is often overlooked, and that is—fear. A child can be afraid without showing it in an obvious way.

All children have fears and worries, many of which may seem silly to us but are very real to them. Probably the most common single important fear children have is fear of not being loved by their parents. Parents—some intentionally, others unintentionally—teach children to believe that they are "bad" if they do not always behave "nicely," think only "good" thoughts, and have only "kindly" feelings toward others, particularly toward their parents and brothers and sisters, although it is often more difficult to have only kindly thoughts about the people one associates with closely than about strangers.

Little children develop a great many feelings about the grownups who live with them and train them. In order to help children learn to cope with the many difficult and unpleasant things that are expected of them, we must give them time, patience, and reassuring affection. Without these, children cannot feel secure in their parents' love for them and safe in the strange, changing world about them.

Children who are brought up too strictly and are made to feel that they have failed or are "bad," cannot help feeling resentment. That is natural. Yet we often make them feel ashamed of this natural feeling.

The parent who understands the natural wishes and abilities of small children will not expect too much of them nor make them feel too guilty for their small misdeeds. Of course, some children are more quick to feel guilty or to get their feelings hurt than others are, some show anger more quickly, some more easily become restless and overactive.

TREATMENT. Finding the cause of "nervousness" sometimes requires considerable study. A persistently nervous child should certainly have a careful medical examination. If your physician thinks the child's condition cannot be accounted for on a purely physical basis, ask his advice about consulting a child-guidance clinic, if one is available. Specialists in child-guidance clinics study and treat nervous children. These clinics exist in most large cities and some state health or welfare departments supply such service through traveling clinics. If you are unable to locate a child-guidance clinic, write to your state health department or the Children's Bureau, Washington, D. C., for information as to the service nearest you.

TWITCHING AND OTHER HABIT SPASMS

CAUSES AND SYMPTOMS. Twitching of the face, blinking of the eyes, making faces, and other odd repeated movements are called habit spasms or tics. They may be signs of general fatigue or, occasionally, of some physical irritation, but more frequently they indicate the inability of the child to adjust himself to some emotional or nervous strain of which neither child nor parent is aware. Stuttering and stammering are habit spasms, occasionally due to imitation but usually to some nervous strain.

TREATMENT. When a child shows symptoms of this type, he should be taken to a doctor. If the underlying cause is to be found, it is important to discuss with the doctor the problems of the family life as well as the child's routine.

KIDNEY DISEASE

Kidney disease in children may take several forms. The two most common of these are acute nephritis and pyelitis.

ACUTE NEPHRITIS. This is an inflamation of the kidneys, which may follow a sore throat, scarlet fever, or other infection. Occasionally, however, acute nephritis may appear in a child who previously has seemed well. The urine is usually scanty and dark-colored and it may be slightly or even quite bloody. The child may not seem very sick; but as the disease can be serious, a doctor should be called if a child shows these symptoms.

PYELITIS. This is an infection of the kidneys in which pus is present in the urine. The symptoms of this disease are often vague. The child may have fever or headache and seem sick but complain of no pain, or he may have to urinate frequently and complain of pain on urination. Pyelitis is more common among little girls than among little boys.

Since neither of these diseases can be diagnosed without examination of the child's urine, the mother should always save a sample for the doctor whenever a child is sick.

TREATMENT. The doctor may try sulfa drugs in treating these diseases, as they have been of benefit in many cases.

DIABETES MELLITUS

CAUSES. Children, as well as adults, may suffer from diabetes mellitus. In this disease the body is unable to use the sugars and starches of the diet, and sugar is excreted in the urine. Formerly it was almost always fatal in childhood.

SYMPTOMS. If a child begins to drink unusually large amounts of water, urinates frequently in very large amounts, or has a very hearty appetite and yet loses weight, take him to the doctor at once, as these may be the early symptoms of diabetes. **Carry a specimen of urine with you for examination.**

TREATMENT. With the use of insulin and diets carefully prescribed by a doctor, the disease may be so controlled that a child can continue to grow and live a normal and happy life.

APPENDICITIS

Acute appendicitis is not especially common in children under six, but it can occur at any age.

If appendicitis is diagnosed promptly and operation is performed early, complete recovery is the rule. It is only when the condition is not diagnosed early enough and operation is delayed that appendicitis becomes dangerous.

SYMPTOMS. The early symptoms of appendicitis are nausea, fever, which may be only slight, pain in the abdomen, and sometimes vomiting. The pain may seem to be in the region of the stomach or it may be in the right side (rarely the left side). A child with these symptoms should be seen by a doctor immediately. Any child with persistent abdominal pain which lasts more than a short time, even in the absence of other symptoms, should be seen by a doctor. A laxative should never be given to a child with abdominal pain.

EAR DISORDERS

An earache or a running ear usually develops during a cold or some other illness. Never try to treat a painful or discharging ear without a doctor's advice. Warm, wet compresses or a well-wrapped hot-water bag may relieve the pain.

Deafness, mastoiditis (inflammation of the mastoid bone), or even meningitis may result from neglected ear infections.

Mastoiditis, which used to be common following ear infections, seldom is seen now if such infections are treated with the newer drugs.

EYE DISORDERS

INFLAMED EYES. Red or inflamed eyes with watery discharge may be due to inflammation or irritation, to a cinder or dust, or to hay fever.

It is a safe temporary measure for the mother to apply either warm or cold wet compresses in order to relieve swelling and discomfort.

CINDER IN THE EYE. Any speck of dirt that is not washed out soon by the watering of the eye should be removed by a doctor. Any injury of the delicate membranes of the eye is a serious matter.

PUS. Discharge of pus from the eyes is a sign of infection, which may be very contagious. Eye infections, if neglected, may lead to permanent injury and blindness. Painful or discharging eyes should be treated by a doctor.

EYESTRAIN. Eyestrain may show itself by redness of the eyelids, by blinking, or by general irritability. Even very young children occasionally need to be fitted with glasses. Poor sight may be unnoticed by parents, and some children who are thought to be dull or clumsy may have serious eye defects. The possibility of poor vision should be considered if a child has these symptoms.

STIES. A stye or pimple on the edge of the eyelid is caused by an infection entering at the base of an eyelash. The infection is usually introduced by rubbing the eyes, and when a stye forms, the irritation makes a child even more likely to put his hand to his eye. Placing a hot, moist compress on the eye several times a day may help him to keep from rubbing it. Another stye is likely to follow if the infection is spread by rubbing.

PINKEYE. In pinkeye, inflammation makes the eyes look red and runny. It is very contagious, and therefore easily spread among school children. It looks more serious than it is. Moist, hot applications, and sponging the eyes with boric acid solution may help to relieve the irritation. It is highly important for the towels and washcloths used by a child suffering from pinkeye to be kept separate from those in use by other members of the family.

HERMAN POMERANZ, M.D., IRVIN S. KOLL, M.D., AND OTHERS

COMPLETE
READY-REFERENCE INDEX

Index

875

• G •

• T •

• U •

• V •

• W •